Instrumental Methods of Experimental Biology

Instrumental Methods of Experimental Biology

EDITED BY

DAVID W. NEWMAN
Department of Botany, Miami University, Oxford, Ohio

ILLUSTRATIONS: T. J. COBBE

The Macmillan Company, New York
Collier-Macmillan Limited, London

Fourth Printing, 1967

Library of Congress catalog card number: 64-23513

THE MACMILLAN COMPANY, NEW YORK

COLLIER-MACMILLAN CANADA, LTD., TORONTO, ONTARIO

Printed in the United States of America

DESIGNED BY ANDREW P. ZUTIS

Preface

THIS VOLUME is intended to serve both as a text and as a reference book for the experimental biologist. It has been prepared so that courses dealing with methods, techniques, and instrumentation in the biological sciences may use it as a single text. Included are discussions of separation techniques in addition to discussions of instrument components, possible sources of instrument and technique error, the physical and chemical properties of matter which are measured, and examples of uses. These examples, for the most part, may be adapted for laboratory exercises by integrating the information with details concerning the operation of specific instruments being used. The book has been organized so that separation techniques and other preparative procedures are discussed first followed by discussions of analytical tools and systems. Finally, somewhat detailed discussions of input and output transducers are included since it is around these systems that the remaining components are built.

The contributors have, in addition, added sufficient information so that many of the chapters may serve in reference. Some chapters contain significantly more reference information than others, since this information would require considerable time to recover from the literature. Parts of two of the chapters, centrifugation and input transducers, contain some mathematical relationships which may be omitted by the reader and yet he should be able to obtain a suitable understanding of the instrumental methods discussed. However, a greater understanding of these relationships will permit the operator a wider choice and a greater ease of handling these systems.

Since a primary effort of the Editor is to provide a single volume covering the topics, some topics such as electron microscopy, etc., were necessarily omitted. It was felt that these topics were better treated in the more extensive treatise.

Special recognition is due Prof. Hans H. Jaffé and Dr. Martin Isaks at the University of Cincinnati, the late Dr. Richard J. Block formerly at the Boyce Thompson Institute for Plant Research, Prof. E. A. Jones at Vanderbilt University, and Mr. G. Douglas Winget for their review of various sections of the book. In addition the Editor wishes to extend his appreciation to each contributor, to Dr. Thomas J. Cobbe who prepared most of the illustrations, and to Mr. David Wykes for his help in preparation of the manuscript.

DAVID W. NEWMAN

Oxford, Ohio
Sept. 1963

List of Contributors

Contents

Introduction

Howard A. Strobel

Physical Methods in Biology

In experimental biology instrumental or physical methods are indispensable. Such studies as the investigation of the structure and chemistry of cells or the elucidation of the kinetics and mechanisms of basic physiological systems are not possible without them. Indeed, so great is the complexity of many biological systems that physical methods and instrumentation are generally involved both in resolving mixtures and in determining the identities and amounts of the separated constituents.

The range of physical methods is nearly as broad as the range of physical properties that substances exhibit. For example, solubility, infrared absorption, magnetic susceptibility, molecular weight, mobility in solution, and many others are the bases of physical methods. The properties are fundamental both to separation procedures such as paper chromatography, electrophoresis, centrifugation, and gas-liquid chromatography, and to determinative techniques such as infrared spectroscopy and potentiometry.

For a particular biological system the choice of the methods of separation and analysis will require a consideration as to whether a specific property permitting direct identification and quantitative measurement is available. With simpler mixtures, for example, infrared absorption may serve in this capacity. More often, however, small differences in properties such as in solubility or electrical mobility must first be taken advantage of to achieve a separation; then the pure substances may be determined by standard direct techniques.

Many of the procedures of biology thus involve physical as well as chemical factors. An understanding of the majority of these techniques requires an emphasis upon the principles of instrumentation and of measurement.

Physical Measurement

Basic to a physical or instrumental method is the process of measurement. In general, several steps are involved. These may be identified as (*a*) separation from interfering substances; (*b*) generation of

1

signal and exposure to it; (*c*) detection and transducing of an altered signal; (*d*) amplification; (*e*) computation; and (*f*) presentation or read out of the desired results. Where possible, one or more steps are eliminated for greater simplicity. For example, computation can be omitted if a property of a sample is not to be compared with that of a standard or reference. Simplicity and efficiency also determine whether each step is to be associated with a separate component, or process, or whether a single component may perform two or more of the above functions. The application of steps (*b*) through (*f*) to a representative analytical technique is illustrated in Table 1.

TABLE 1

STEPS IN AN INFRARED ABSORPTION SPECTROSCOPIC MEASUREMENT

Measurement Step	IR Absorption Spectroscopy Step
Generation of signal	Electrically heated glower emits IR, which passes through sample (and reference) cell(s), and is separated (dispersed) into wavelengths of interest.
Detection and transducing	Thermocouple detects transmitted IR and transduces it to an electrical voltage.
Amplification	Small voltage from thermocouple amplified.
Computation	Ratio of amplified signals from sample and reference taken electrically.
Read out	Pen traces absorption curve for sample as a function of wavelength.

While the steps appropriate to each technique discussed in this volume will be treated in the subsequent chapters, a few of them deserve additional comment here.

GENERATION OF SIGNAL

Physical properties in general are determined as a response of a substance to an imposed electrical, optical, or other type of signal. For example, the infrared absorption spectrum of a sample is its response to infrared radiation just as the conductance of a solution sample is its response to an imposed electrical voltage. By contrast the pH of a solution brings about the generation of a signal—a voltage difference between a glass electrode, usually, and a reference electrode. A signal, influenced by the sample, is the basis for a measurement in any case.

DETECTION AND TRANSDUCING

Once the signal has been altered, or generated, by the sample, it must be sensed or detected and, if necessary, translated into electrical or other usable form. Ordinarily, a single component is both detector and transducer and is termed an *input transducer*. For example, a phototube not only senses the light transmitted by a sample but also transduces or transforms it to an electrical current.

COMPUTATION

Very commonly after the signal has been amplified, it is compared with the signal from a reference sample or otherwise manipulated to obtain direct information on percentage composition. A potentiometer or ratio device may be introduced to perform this function.

SELECTION OF METHOD

It is important to appreciate that factors other than those inherent in the process of making a measurement, however, will determine the selection of the method to be employed, the most favorable design of any instrumentation, the selection of components for the instrumentation, and the devising of the best procedure for the measurement. These factors will include (*a*) the amount of sample available, (*b*) the complexity of the sample: the types of constituents present and their concentrations, (*c*) the precision of measurement required, (*d*) interferences present, and (*e*) any time restrictions on the measurement. The user of instrumental methods is as concerned with these requirements as is the designer of instrumentation. Naturally, the user, if he is to be able to select the appropriate instrumentation for separation and measurement and to employ it effectively, must understand the considerations involved in reaching design and procedure decisions.

The Control of Variables

In establishing a measurement procedure or examining different instruments it is essential that all factors which will influence projected determinations be explicitly considered. What variables, such as temperature, humidity, pH, or pressure, will affect (*a*) the separations to be made, (*b*) the property to be observed or its measurement, or (*c*) the reliable functioning of the instrumentation? Somehow all of the variables that influence either the physical procedure or the property of interest must be allowed for or regulated during the measurement. Thus, allowance in measurements may be made for variations in pressure while regulation by the use of a buffer may be used to control the pH of a solution. It may be assumed that many of these factors have been considered in the design of instrumentation, but an explicit review is desirable. Indeed, to ignore even a seemingly unlikely parameter without checking the range over which it may vary in the system under study, and the effect produced by such changes, is hazardous. Many a strange seasonal variation in determinations, for example, has been traced to fluctuations in humidity or temperature.

Not all variables may be easily allowed for by regulation or even by appropriate instrument design. For example, changes in the purity of chemicals or drift in the functioning of apparatus must be handled differently.

Before such sources of determinable or determinate error can be controlled, they must be brought to light. Both the use of standard samples and of an independent method of measurement are helpful in this regard. Then errors should be minimized by suitable adjustments in the apparatus or by modification of the method. Whenever these means are inconvenient, however, there are other established methods available to reduce the effect of these sources of inaccuracy in data. The methods are *calibration*, the use of *blanks*, and the use of *controls*. One or more is required for all precise work.

Calibrations are periodic standardizations of equipment and instruments. They may be made by checking the response of the instrumentation when a standard sample is used. Any calibration curves or corrections derived by such testing can then be applied to measurements on samples. In this manner chemical impurities, irregular scale graduations on apparatus such as burets and pipets, changes in balance weights, and inaccurate responses of instrumentation in general can be corrected for as measurements are made.

On the other hand *blanks* will frequently be effective in reducing errors introduced by the method of bringing a sample under observation or arising from slow changes in the response of instruments with time. The blank or reference is a sample identical in make-up with the unknown except that the constituent of interest is omitted. It must be treated in the same way as the unknown during the separation and measurement procedures. Then, if the blank and the sample are affected similarly by drift or other systematic errors, the comparison of the response secured from the two should produce data free from error. The use of a solution blank in spectrophotometry is a particularly good example. In this case the reference is used to cancel intensity losses caused by reflection from the faces of the sample cell, absorption by its walls, and certain other errors as well as to eliminate the effect of drift in source intensity and phototube response of the instrument itself.

Finally, the use of *controls* is common where all variables cannot conveniently be held constant, as in flame photometry. Such controls are samples as much like the unknown as possible, but of known concentration in the sought constituent. They are subjected to the same procedures as the unknown and provide a "running" calibration of the instrumentation or method. In general, the more empirical the procedure, the greater the need for controls. Two well-known examples are the use of controls in the study of enzymes and in the clinical testing of drugs.

Instrument Design Patterns

The general type of design chosen for an instrument also has an important bearing on the quality of the determinations which can be made. In pursuing this point it is helpful initially to view a measurement system as a structure. It consists of various components that are coupled in a manner which will ensure that the signal entering the sample progresses without interference from stage to stage and produces the desired response in the read-out device. There must be a faithful reproduction of the impact of the signal in one component after another. Actually, each stage may be designed as a detachable unit or module if desired as long as suitable coupling is provided.

In developing the general aspects of instrumentation it must be noted that probably the most important criterion in design is that of simplicity. Ordinarily, the simplest instrumentation that yields the desired sensitivity, accuracy, and operating features will be the best choice. Its operation will be less involved; there will be fewer components to give trouble; erroneous results will be more easily noted and traced to their source; maintenance will be reduced, and usually the cost will be less.

In terms of pattern, instrumentation may be laid out either as (a) single-channel, direct or null-balance read out, or (b) double-channel, direct or null-balance read out. The first consideration is which of these basic designs is more suitable.

SINGLE CHANNEL INSTRUMENTATION

Most instrumentation is of the single channel type. Colorimeters and many spectrophotometers, pH meters, gas chromatographs, balances, radioactivity counters, and many other types of instruments fall into this category. In these devices the information contained in the signal moves from the detector to the output along a single path. As a result, the instrument may be designed with considerable simplicity and ruggedness. The degree of reliability of measurement will depend chiefly upon whether quality components are selected, well coupled, and operated at a fraction of their rated values, and whether the instrument is calibrated at appropriate intervals. If these criteria are followed, it will be possible to minimize unpredictable fluctuations and to reduce the drift in output with time.

The accuracy of an instrument is, of course, finally limited by its read out device. Options are therefore provided. The least expensive is probably an "output" meter, and it will be reliable, at most, to about ±1% of full-scale deflection. Regardless of how accurately the rest of the components function, the data furnished by the instrument will be uncertain by at least ±1%. For the usual needle deflections amounting

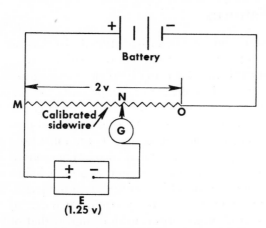

Fig. 1. Schematic diagram of a crude potentiometer. Unknown voltage E is to be measured. Galvanometer G is used to determine the position N along slidewire at which a voltage is "tapped" off which matches voltage E. At this value N the galvanometer will show no deflection, i.e., no current will be drawn from E. Voltage E is then equal to MN/MO × 2 = 1.25 v.

to appreciably less than full scale, the error will be substantially larger. If a steadily fluctuating output is obtained, time-average readings may be substituted for instantaneous ones with only modest loss of reliability.

Where higher accuracy is desired, a null-balance type of output can be substituted. It is necessary to introduce a potentiometer, a null device in which the output signal is balanced against a known potential as shown in Fig. 1. The critical reading is that of the position of the tap on the slidewire, and this location can be determined to ±0.01%. In such null devices the galvanometer or other current meter is used only to find the point of balance and is not read.

A self-balancing potentiometer, with chart drive attached, is used where automatic recording, and a permanent record of the output, is desired; one can expect accuracy of about ±0.5% from a good recorder. These devices usually furnish data as pen tracings on charts. For example, in ultraviolet spectrophotometry a recorder would draw a curve of per cent transmittance, or absorbance, of a sample as a function of wavelength or wavenumber.

DOUBLE CHANNEL DESIGN

While most measurements may be satisfactorily performed by arranging the appropriate steps in sequence, i.e., in single channel fashion, there are valid reasons for going to the complexity and expense of a double channel arrangement. It may be noted that in a sense, a second channel is incorporated whenever a procedure calls

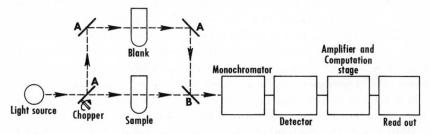

Fig. 2. A schematic diagram of a double-channel spectrophotometer. Mirrors A are front-silvered. Mirror B is half-silvered and both reflects and transmits light. One half of the rotating chopper is cut away; the other half has a front-surface mirror.

for the use of a blank. In such instances the instrumentation is used twice to obtain a single datum. The measurement on the blank in effect constitutes a calibration, because the response of the instrument to it is adjusted to a standard value.

The double channel arrangement incorporates such reference samples, blanks, in the added channel, which is used for standardizing the instrument. An example of such design is shown schematically in Fig. 2.

Ordinarily a double channel arrangement is more attractive than a single channel design when there are many variables to be controlled, and it is found that (*a*) either they are only under partial control, i.e., vary somewhat more rapidly than can be allowed for by a procedure using blanks, or (*b*) the variables are under control but automatic operation and recording are desired. In either of these instances, the double channel arrangement provides accuracy and sensitivity unobtainable in other ways.

A substantial amount of redesigning is required before most instruments can control their own operation according to given instructions. Energy, usually in an electrical form, must be tapped off at appropriate stages to run the motors which adjust the components. For example, in one type of automatic spectrophotometer one motor slowly rotates the prism or diffraction grating to vary the wavelength and another motor either drives an absorbing wedge into or pulls it out of the reference channel beam to keep the power in that beam at the same level as the power in the sample beam. This device operates on an optical null principle.

Sensitivity and Noise

In modern research there is a need for high sensitivity in measurement that is met by careful selection of method, very good signal detection, and high amplification. The degree of sensitivity incorporated into instrumentation, for example, depends on whether a substance can be detected in the presence of interfering components with properties differing only very slightly from those of the substance. If a direct determination is possible, a preliminary separation and some loss of accuracy can be avoided. High sensitivity is also needed when a trace constituent is to be measured or when a very precise analysis of a macro component is to be undertaken.

With a powerful method of measurement, careful work, and precise instrumentation, sensitivity reduces to a matter of coping with the noise produced along with any signal. *Noise* consists simply of the random electrical fluctuations that are generated by the unavoidable thermal "oscillations" of electrons. It is generated in transistors, electron tubes, resistors, and other components such as detectors. Since it provides a background of voltage fluctuation it may easily obscure a faint signal. Thus, the ultimate level of detectability of a substance depends upon the ratio of the amplitude of the signal to the noise.

Several stratagems are available to raise the signal-to-noise ratio. (*a*) Though not widely used, the detector and certain other parts of an instrument may be operated at very low temperatures, i.e., at liquid-air temperatures. The level of noise rises as the temperature increases because of its thermal origin. (*b*) Selective amplification of a signal can be used. If the signal from the detector is an alternating current, its frequencies will ordinarily be different from the frequency of most of the noise. Noise characteristically consists of all frequencies — it is completely random. Thus, amplification of only a narrow band of frequencies that are centered about those frequencies characteristic of the signal will enhance the signal and reject most of the noise. (*c*) A difference in frequency may be deliberately introduced into the signal. Since most instrumentation produces dc signals, the stratagem of converting such an output to a particular frequency of ac before amplifying is widely used. The conversion can be readily made by closing and opening the instrument channel at a steady rate. In an optical instrument such as a spectrophotometer, for example, the beam of radiation falling on the detector may be chopped, i.e., periodically interrupted. Often a rotating shutter or sector mirror is used. With electrical inputs as from a pH meter, a vibrating reed electrometer, i.e., a dynamic capacitor, will suffice. Rapid mechanical switching devices are also widely used to convert to ac. Following any type of chopping or modulation selective ac amplification is used as above. In this case the slim band of frequencies amplified center about that of chopping.

Regardless of the stratagem, however, some noise cannot be excluded, and indeed, some will be generated in the amplifier. As a result, the meaningful amplification of very faint signals and the very great amplification of ordinary signals will be impossible.

Reliability and Precision

The experimental scientist is faced constantly with the need to estimate the reliability of the results of measurements. Data are of value to the degree that their uncertainty is known, i.e., to the extent that their accuracy and precision have been ascertained. *Accuracy* is a measure of the closeness of a result to the "true" or accepted value; *precision* is a measure of the degree of reproducibility of a measurement. A related responsibility of the experimenter is a decision as to the level of error which can be tolerated in his own results. He can generally make such an estimate by examining the use to which the data are to be put. Ordinarily a compromise between accuracy of a high order and the effort which is necessary to secure such results must be made. An advance estimate of the precision needed often allows a considerable saving of time and work, especially if greater precision is found necessary later. Modifying a procedure which yields ±5% accuracy to give ±1% accuracy may involve developing elaborate instrumentation or spending a great deal of time to refine the control of variables. A thoughtful analysis at the outset would have suggested these difficulties and allowed the consideration of alternative methods more easily capable of accuracy.

The two aspects of reliability, accuracy and precision, must now be examined. Once a method of sufficient sensitivity has been selected, the probable error in the data it yields can be considered. Consistent or systematic errors will affect all results and lessen accuracy. For that very reason they can be identified. These *determinate errors* have been explored in discussing the control of variables in the section on THE CONTROL OF VARIABLES and are allowed for by periodic calibrations and the use of blanks or controls.

While further refinements of techniques and instrumentation will improve the accuracy of a measurement, they, of course, will not eliminate all scatter in the results. This residual, random fluctuation, attributable to the accumulation of many small errors, is designated *indeterminate error*, for its origin is ill defined. It is evident that this type of error will limit the precision of a measurement. Since the source of these errors cannot be easily identified, it is fortunate that statistical methods simplify the task of dealing with them. These procedures will now be treated briefly.

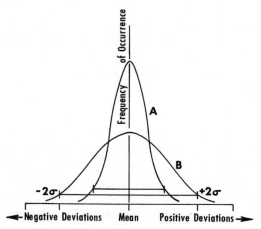

Fig. 3. Normal distribution of data. The method of measurement yielding curve A is inherently twice as precise as that giving curve B. The horizontal bars represent the relative uncertainty in both sets of data at the "95% level of confidence".

PRECISION MEASURES

Ordinarily a replicate set of measurements will show a scatter well approximated by the pattern called a *normal distribution*. This kind of scatter is illustrated in Fig. 3. While theoretically an infinite number of measurements would have to be made to achieve the smooth pattern of scatter represented in the figure, measures of precision based on the normal distribution may be derived and applied to small sets of 3, 4, or 5 measurements. Several terms must be defined and discussed. The arithmetic mean of a set of data, or more simply *mean* of the set, is a simple average. It is always more reliable than any individual result or another kind of average. This point is illustrated in Fig. 3, for it is seen that the data center on the mean value. In the ideal case where determinate errors have been eliminated, the arithmetic mean should approximate the accepted value for the result.

The most reliable measurement of precision is the *standard deviation*, σ. It is a root-mean-square type of quantity, defined as:

$$\sigma = \sqrt{\frac{\Sigma d_i^2}{n}} \tag{1}$$

where Σ indicates a sum, d_i is the deviation of a measurement from the mean, and n is the number of measurements made. When n is small, i.e., in all practical cases where no more than four or five replicate determinations are made, $n-1$ is substituted. The new expression is:

$$s = \sqrt{\frac{\Sigma d_i^2}{n-1}} \tag{2}$$

A different symbol s is assigned to the new expression to suggest that it is an estimate of the true standard deviation. The calculation of the estimated standard deviation, s, for a set of replicate measurements is illustrated in Table 2. In the table x_i designates a measurement, x, the arithmetic mean of the set of measurements.

TABLE 2

CALCULATION OF THE STANDARD DEVIATION FOR REPLICATE MEASUREMENTS

Sample	Data	$d_i = x_i - \bar{x}$	$d_i^2 = (x_i - \bar{x})^2$
1	1.50	−0.01	0.0001
2	1.48	−0.03	0.0009
3	1.55	+0.04	0.0016
4	1.52	+0.01	0.0001
Mean = 1.51	$s = 0.03$	$\Sigma d_i^2 = 0.0027$	$n - 1 = 3$

The merit of the standard deviation, or of any other precision measure, lies in the information it conveys about the reproducibility of a measurement. It can be shown that nearly 70 per cent of the time repetitions of the measurement will yield values falling within the limits $\bar{x} - \sigma$ and $\bar{x} + \sigma$, i.e., $\bar{x} \pm \sigma$. In other words, only three times out of ten will the value of the measurement be likely to fall outside this range. Some 95 per cent of the time the value will fall within the limits of $\bar{x} \pm 2\sigma$. For the data of Table 2, the $\bar{x} \pm 2\sigma$ figure would be 1.51 ± 0.06. These statements of reliability are often termed "levels of confidence."

Intuitively, one assumes that increasing the number of replications of the measurement will enhance the precision of the mean value. Statistically, it is established that the precision increases as the inverse square root of the number of observations, n, i.e., s_{mean} is proportional to $s/\sqrt{n}$. There is thus good reason even in careful work to limit the number of repetitions of a measurement to three or four, since additional measurements can improve the reliability only slightly.

A final point of interest is the handling of any widely divergent values in a set of data. There are really only two completely reliable criteria for rejecting such results. First, if a determinate error is believed or known to have affected a measurement which is well out of line with the other results in a set, the result may be legitimately rejected. Alternatively, previous experience with a particular instrument or technique will often be a guide in establishing that a value is out of the usual range. In other instances there are statistical tests that may indicate that a deviant result can be rejected, though all such tests are themselves subject to appreciable uncertainty. The reader is referred to the literature cited [1-6] at the conclusion of the Introduction for a detailed presentation of the use of these tests.

References

Good suggestions for research instrumentation are given by:
1. H. J. J. Braddick, *The Physics of Experimental Method,* Chapman and Hall, London (1954).
2. A. Weissberger, Ed., *Technique of Organic Chemistry,* Vol. 1, Interscience, New York, 3rd ed., (1959-60).
3. E. B. Wilson, *An Introduction to Scientific Research,* McGraw-Hill, New York (1952).
Useful references to the theory of errors are:
4. Y. Beers, *Introduction to the Theory of Error,* Addison-Wesley, Reading, Mass., 2nd ed. (1957).
5. R. B. Dean and W. J. Dixon, *Anal. Chem.* **23,** 636 (1951).
6. W. J. Dixon and F. J. Massey, *Introduction to Statistical Analysis,* McGraw-Hill, New York, 2nd ed. (1957).

Paper Chromatography

S. Mark Henry

CHROMATOGRAPHY is accurately described [1] as "those processes which allow the resolution of mixtures by effecting separation of all or some of their components in concentrated zones on or in phases different from those in which they are originally present, irrespective of the nature of the force or forces causing the substances to move from one phase to the other." One of the underlying principles of chromatography, that of preferential adsorption on various supports or adsorbents, was discovered by Tswett in the beginning of this century. He reported the separation of plant pigments by column chromatography in 1903. Block *et al.* [2] credit A. J. P. Martin and his co-workers, R. Consden, A. H. Gordon, and R. L. M. Synge, with development of paper chromatography to its present highly popular status. In 1938 Neuberger was interested in separating the neutral amino acids and observed that the partition coefficients of acetylated amino acids between water and an immiscible organic solvent differed for the various amino acids. In order to simplify the equipment and to enhance the separation of substances with very similar partition coefficients by increasing the number of theoretical plates, Martin and Synge [3] used an inert support (e.g., silica gel) to hold one of the phases (water) and passed the immiscible solvent through a bed of the water-containing silica gel. The ideal conditions for this type of chromatography employing two liquid phases were, first, that the solute be not absorbed by the supporting material and, second, that its distribution between the two liquid phases be not influenced by its concentration or by the presence of closely related solutes. These conditions were approached experimentally by Martin and Synge and by a number of other investigators. The procedure was, however, difficult and tedious and the preparation of the inert support left much to be desired.

In order to eliminate the preparation of silica gel and to reduce the quantity of material needed, Martin and his co-workers replaced silica gel with filter paper as the inert support. With the use of filter paper the acetylation of the amino acids was no longer necessary, and they could now be detected directly on the paper by treatment with ninhydrin (triketohydrindene hydrate). The technique has since been

13

extended to the separation of organic compounds of every conceivable type and many inorganic substances [4].

Chromatography on paper is in essence relatively simple. A droplet of solution containing a mixture of substances to be separated is applied near the end of a strip of filter paper. The same end is then immersed in the developing solution, usually a water-containing solvent, so that the solvent travels under the action of various forces along the paper and past the point of application. As a result of partition between aqueous and organic solvent phases, adsorption, ion exchange, and, perhaps, of other forces, the components of the mixture are moved away from the origin at different rates.

The purpose of this chapter is to present sufficient details of theory, methods, and applications of paper chromatography so that the reader might employ the necessary procedures to obtain qualitative and/or quantitative data with reference to the constituents of a mixture obtained from any biological source. This is not to be interpreted as indicating that the experimental biologist has no need for other analytical tools. Rather, one should regard paper chromatography not as a replacement for all other techniques but as a very useful supplement. Indeed, one occasionally finds that the information obtainable by paper chromatography is of a very general nature necessitating the employment of related techniques such as thin-layer chromatography, column chromatography, or electrophoresis and, more often than not, one or more of the spectrophotometric methods. Nevertheless, paper chromatography stands as a relatively inexpensive, rapid, simple, and effective analytical tool.

Theory

GENERAL

The dominant factor governing separation of mixtures of solutes on filter paper is ordinarily that of partition between two immiscible phases, one of which is usually water or some other relatively highly polar solvent. In Consden's early work it was found that excellent separations of amino acids occur on paper with solvents that are only partly miscible with water. The paper itself may be thought of as an inert support for the solvents between which partition occurs. The cellulose fibers in the paper have a strong affinity for the aqueous phase but not for the organic portion of the solvent. Indeed, the cellulose actually forms a hydrate consisting of up to 12.1 per cent, w/w, water. One ordinarily equilibrates the paper in the developing chamber in order to permit the aqueous vapors to be picked up by the hydrophilic cellulose. When the organic solvent flows past the sample on the paper, partition occurs between the mobile phase and the stationary aqueous phase bound by the cellulose. The organic portion of the solvent flows on carrying with it some of the solute. The amount left in the aqueous portion is a function of the partition coefficient of the solute. As the mobile phase reaches a section of the paper containing no solute, partition again occurs, some of the solute entering the stationary phase. Simultaneously, partition continues to occur at the previous position or "plate." With continuous flow of solvent, the effect of this distribution between the two phases is the transfer of the solute from the point of its application to a point some distance along the paper in the direction of solvent flow.

The processes which occur during the development of a filter paper chromatogram may be compared with the techniques of fractional distillation and continuous liquid-liquid extraction. Martin and Synge have developed a theory of chromatography based on its similarity to distillation with fractionating columns (cf. [2] for the detailed description of this theory). However, one must be careful in making such comparisons, for paper chromatography is frequently influenced by other factors such as surface adsorption to the cellulose and even ion exchange with polar constituents of the cellulose and with impurities in the paper.

Regardless of the relative importance of the various forces mentioned above, good results will be reproduced consistently if the following simple rules are observed:

1. Use sufficient solvent and an appropriate chamber so that the composition of the solvent will remain constant throughout development.

2. Maintain constant temperature.

3. Employ solvents in which the components to be separated have a low but definite solubility. If the substances are too soluble, they will appear at or near the solvent "front" of the chromatogram. If they are too insoluble in the solvent, they will remain at the point of application. If the factors of adsorption and ion exchange are neglected, the movement of a substance in a paper chromatogram is a function of its solubility in the developing solvent. Thus, solvents for water-soluble substances are usually water-containing organic fluids, whereas solvents for substances soluble in organic solvents but insoluble in water are often aqueous solutions of organic solvents.

4. Do not employ conditions which will cause excessively rapid development rates. The rate of solvent flow is dependent on the type of paper used, on the ratio of the width of the "wick," if one is used, to that of the paper chromatogram, on the composition of the solvent, and on the temperature of the atmosphere in which development occurs. While mechanical devices may be employed to hasten development, resolution is inevitably affected in an adverse manner.

R_f VALUES

In order to give a numerical value to the location of a spot on one- or two-dimensional paper chromatograms, the term R_f was introduced by Consden *et al.*, where:

$$R_f = \frac{\text{movement of spot in cm}}{\text{movement of advancing solvent front in cm}} \qquad (1)$$

Thus, if the solvent has moved 50 cm and the spot 25 cm, its R_f is 0.50. In many instances it is desirable to allow the solvent to run off the paper or to repeat the development with the same solvent in the same direction a number of times. Obviously in these instances an R_f value cannot be ascribed. Therefore, a small quantity of dye, such as bromocresol purple, is used as a marker and the final position of the spot is designated as R_{BCP}, i.e., the rate of flow relative to bromocresol purple. It is often useful to select one of the several constituents of a mixture as the reference point. For example, when chromatographing amino acids, proline may be substituted for "advancing solvent front" in the above formula so that the positions of the amino acids are then designated as $R_{proline}$. Such R designations are useful since the numerical values are constant regardless of the length of development. Factors which affect the actual R_f values include:

1. Composition of development phase.
2. Kind of paper.
3. Direction of paper fibers.
4. Manner of development (descending, ascending, ascending-descending, radial).
5. Length of paper used for development.
6. Distance of starting point from solvent.
7. Concentration of solute.
8. Presence of other substances.
9. Temperature of development.

The relationship between the partition coefficient of a solute and its chemical structure, the location of each of a homologous series of substances on paper chromatograms, and the value of paper chromatography in structural analysis have been discussed elsewhere [2].

R_f values are of use in many ways but primarily as an index or guide to the relative position of compounds with respect to each other. Tables of R_f values for numerous compounds of great diversity are available in the various chromatographic manuals [2,4, and others], the *Journal of Chromatography*, and in individual, scattered publications. A glance at these tables usually permits one to select an appropriate chromatographic solvent system for the particular group of compounds under study. It is emphasized, however, that R_f values must never be employed as the sole criteria for identification, for reported values may vary not only with any of the factors mentioned above but even with relatively minor differences in filter paper, in allegedly pure solvents obtained from different supply houses, with atmospheric conditions, and even with position of the paper in a chromatographic chamber (especially if the latter is not properly sealed).

CHROMATOGRAPHIC ARTIFACTS

A major difficulty in paper chromatography is the formation of several spots from an allegedly pure substance. The appearance of multiple spots may be due to one or more of the following causes:

1. The substance exists in various ionic forms, e.g.,

$$\begin{array}{ccc} COO^- & COONH_4 & COONH_4 \\ | & | & | \\ COO^-; & COO^- & ; COONH_4 \end{array}$$

2. The substance polymerizes during development.
3. The substance undergoes oxidation during development, e.g., methionine to methionine sulfoxide.
4. Oxidation may occur between application of the sample and development with the solvent.
5. The substance reacts with another compound in the mixture during drying on the paper, e.g.,

$$CH_3COCOONa, \quad NH_4Cl, \quad \underset{\underset{NH_2}{|}}{CH_3CHCOONa}, \quad HCl,$$

6. The compound is present in two isomeric forms, e.g., the *cis* and *trans* conditions of 2, 4-dinitrophenylhydrazones:

$$\underset{\underset{NHCH_6H_3(NO_3)_2}{\|}}{CH_3CCOOH}$$

7. Proteins to be chromatographed are easily denatured if the papers on which they have been applied are dried at room temperature. Denaturation may be avoided by drying at 10°C.

8. If the chromatograms are overloaded or if one or more substance reacts with the cellulose, a spot will remain at the origin, e.g., ascorbic acid.

Examples: The amine salts of strong organic acids or inorganic acids form two spots when chromatographed with acidic or neutral solvents ($R·NH_2$ and $R·NH_2·HR'$)[5]. Only a single spot is produced with most ammoniacal solvents or when the amines are salts of weak organic acids (mandelic, propionic, and citric). On the other hand, if tissue amines, such as adrenaline, noradrenaline, histamine, 5-hydroxy-tryptamine, etc., are chromatographed as their salts of CCl_3COOH, CF_3COOH, or picric acid, double spots are formed [6]. Fuller *et al.* [7] reported that both hydroxylamine and phenylhydrazine form a complex with an impurity in washed filter paper (Whatman 1, 3, 4) that chromatographs to give a yellow fluorescent spot.

DeVay *et al.* [8] and Zweig [9] have shown that when protein hydrolyzates or mixtures of amino acids are stored in dilute ethyl alcohol, glutamic acid and aspartic acid undergo partial esterification and consequently form multiple spots. They recommend that amino acid solutions be stored in 10 per cent, v/v, 2-propanol as described by Block et al. Amino sugars give double spots when developed in weakly basic or acidic solvents [10]. Carles and Lascombes [11] point out that aconitic acid is easily esterified and consequently an ethanolic solution gives two spots on a chromatogram. Methionine is so easily oxidized that it is inevitably found as two spots on paper chromatograms. On two-dimensional paper chromatograms, after development with phenol and certain other solvents in the first direction, any remaining methionine may be completely oxidized to methionine sulfoxide before development in the second direction. Under similar conditions, cysteine may be converted to cysteic acid, cystine disulfoxide, cysteine sulfinic acid, and cystine.

General Procedures and Equipment

The following outline describes the general procedure which one ordinarily follows in paper chromatography:

1. Preparation of sample.
2. Selection of filter paper.
3. Application of sample to paper.
4. Choice of solvent system.
5. Development of chromatograms.
6. Drying of chromatogram and detection of spots.
7. Quantitative estimation.

The basic equipment required can probably be found in almost any laboratory, even the most ill-equipped. Some of the standard laboratory items which may serve as adequate substitutes for the more expensive and elaborate commercially available equipment are indicated in the appropriate places. In addition to the actual chromatography apparatus, certain accessory instruments are highly desirable. Among these are a mechanical shaker for mixing solvents, a rotary vacuum evaporator, an X-ray viewing box, an oven, and an electric hair dryer for drying samples on the paper.

Ideally, a clean, air-conditioned room free of all volatile chemicals should be used for preparation and evaluation of chromatograms. A separate room, equipped with a fume hood and, if possible, constant temperature cabinets, is used for actual chromatographic development.

DESALTING OF SAMPLE

Methods for preparing samples for chromatography are necessarily modified according to the nature of the specific substances under investigation. However, regardless of the method selected, the final sample should be in a form compatible with chromatographic solvent and paper. Obviously, the sample cannot contain highly corrosive ingredients such as mineral acids in high concentration. In addition one should employ some procedure to remove inorganic salts since these generally cause streaking, discoloration, or other distortions on the finished chromatogram. For example, certain cations such as Al^{+++}, Fe^{++}, Ag^+, and Cu^{++} inhibit the ninhydrin reaction with alanine.

ION EXCHANGE. Ion exchange treatment is widely used for salt removal. Solutions containing free amino acids, for example, may be adsorbed on a column containing Amberlite IR$-$120 (H^+), Dowex 50 (H^+), and similar cation exchange resins. The strongly acidic amino acids, cysteic acid and taurine, pass through the column with other anions and nonionic material. The remaining amino acids are eluted from the column with 0.4 to 2.0N NH_4OH. Excess ammonia in the elutriate is evaporated *in vacuo* and the remaining cations are removed by percolation of the sample through an anion exchange resin such as Amberlite IRA$-$410 (CO_3^{--}) or Dowex 1 (Cl^-). The absorbed amino acids are eluted from the latter-mentioned resin with dilute acid.

CHEMICAL DESALTING. Chemical techniques for desalting are also dependent on the nature of the substances under investigation. To use amino acids once again, as an example, these may be converted to their camphorsulfonic acid salts which are insoluble in acetone. The solution containing the amino acids is first adjusted to pH 4 to 5, filtered, dried, and ground to a fine powder. The powder is then suspended in 0.2N *DL*-camphorsulfonic acid in acetone using 50 ml of solution per gram of amino acid. After being stirred for at least 1 hour, the residue is removed by filtration. The amino acid camphorsulfonates are decomposed with dry ammonia gas and the insoluble ammonium camphorsulfonate is removed.

Alternate solvents for the chemical removal of inorganic salts are acetone or methyl ethyl ketone containing 10 per cent N HCl, 1 per cent NH_4OH in butanol, or butanol saturated with $1N$ HCl. These are particularly useful for the separation of amino acids and related compounds from dried, defatted plant or animal tissues. The solutes are recovered simply by permitting the organic solvents to evaporate or by partition with water.

Pyridine containing up to 20 per cent, v/v, water is satisfactory for the extraction of sugars. If undiluted pyridine is added to an aqueous tissue extract, inorganic salts are precipitated and may be removed by filtration or centrifugation.

Modifications of the above procedures may be used for the separation of any organic substance from inorganic salts. However, recoveries of less than 100 per cent should be expected as a result of incomplete extraction or degradation during treatment.

ELECTROLYTIC DESALTING.   Desalting by electrolytic methods was the first of the various methods to gain wide usage since it is quite rapid (less than 5 minutes in some cases), does not change the original volume of solution, and is applicable to practically all classes of compounds. However, since required equipment is relatively complex, there has been a tendency for ion exchange and, to some extent,

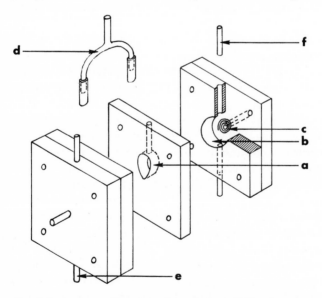

Fig. 1-1. Apparatus for microelectrodialysis [12]. The sections are constructed of Plexiglas 11 mm thick; each block is 8 cm square. (*a*) sample chamber; (*b*) electrode chamber; (*c*) coiled platinum electrode passing through end block to outside terminal. The block on the opposite side of (*a*) is constructed similarly; (*d*) water outlet; (*e*) and (*f*), tubing to connect apparatus with water lines.

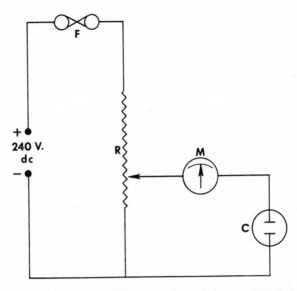

Fig. 1-2. Circuit diagram for electrodialysis using dc main [12]. *(C)* cell (Fig. 1-1); *(M)* ammeter reading to 500 ma; *(R)* variable resistance; *(F)* fuse.

chemical extraction to replace electrolytic desalters. The various types of electrolytic desalters are described by Block *et al.* [2].

ELECTRODIALYSIS.   In a related technique, commercially available ion exchange dialysis membranes serve as ion filters. Smith's modification of the apparatus described by Wood is shown in Fig.1-1. The dialyzer consists of a central, pear-shaped chamber and two electrode chambers, 2.5 cm in diameter, closed on the outer sides with sheets of Plexiglas. A coiled platinum electrode is fitted into each chamber and connected with a small metal screw which leads to the electrical contacts. Ion exchange membranes are placed between the central chamber and the two outer compartments and the assembled sections are bolted together. Samples are introduced and withdrawn through a hole in the top of the central chamber and water flows through the side chambers via holes through the top and bottom of each side block. To facilitate connection with a water supply and drain, glass tubes are fitted into these holes. The water flow serves to keep the temperature below 35°C and removes strong acid and alkali.

The circuit diagram shown in Fig. 1-2 includes a 500-w electric fire element to aid in preventing overheating of the cell. The cation membrane adjoins the cathode chamber and the anion membrane is on the opposite side. Initially, a current of 200 ma with a potential drop of not more than 45 v is employed. The current drops steadily as salts are removed from the sample. Accumulation of Na_2SO_4 deposits in the center chamber indicates that the current is flowing in the wrong direction. Applications of electrodialysis are discussed in detail by Smith [12]. A suitable dc power supply and an unmodified Wood electrodialyzer are available from the Shandon Scientific Co. (distributor: Consolidated Laboratories, Inc.)

ELECTROPHORETIC DESALTING.   One end of a strip of filter paper (3×30 cm) is placed in ammonium formate-formic acid buffer (0.1 ionic strength; see Ch. 3) of pH 2.3 or lower, the other end in ammonium formate-ammonia of pH 10.8 in any electrophoresis apparatus. A pH gradient then forms along the paper. The solution to be desalted is applied as a band at the center of the paper and a low dc current (ca. 50 v) is applied. The positive pole is at the pH 2.4 buffer chamber. The salts run off the strip into the buffer chambers, and the amino acids are retained according to their pK values. The filter paper is then eluted with water and the ammonium formate is removed by concentration *in vacuo* [13].

While any of the procedures discussed above may be used for desalting, caution is advised, especially when the chemical nature of the substance(s) under investigation is not completely known. Any one of the procedures may result in partial or complete degradation or loss along with the inorganic salts. It is always advisable to attempt chromatographic separation using tissue extracts intact or hydrolyzates or, if this is impossible, to determine the effectiveness of any procedure by doing recovery experiments using artificial but similar conditions.

CHROMATOGRAPHIC PAPERS

STANDARD GRADES.   Much is written in the early chromatography literature concerning the suitability of various types of paper obtained from several different sources. These are categorized in most chromatography manuals according to uniformity, texture, solvent speed, presence of impurities, etc. Ultimately, selection of a particular type of paper is governed by the material being chromatographed and several types should be tried routinely before deciding on any one for a long-range chromatographic study. Most laboratories appear to select from Whatman 1, 2, and 3 or any of the several Schleicher and Schuell papers. Eaton and Dikeman papers and Munktell papers are also used widely. Samples for evaluation purposes usually may be obtained from manufacturers.

MODIFIED PAPERS.   Procedures are described by Block *et al.* [2] for the chemical treatment of filter papers in such a way as to change the characteristics radically. For example, they may be alkylated to reduce hydrophilic properties and thereby provide for better separation of hydrophobic substances. They may even be impregnated with ion exchange resins so that they behave like open columns or thin-layer chromatograms. Impregnation with D-10-camphorsulfonic acid permits resolution of a racemic mixture of the amino acid DL-1-aminophenylacetic acid.

Modified chromatography papers are also available commercially from Whatman and other manufacturers. A completely nonabsorbent cellulose nitrate support may be obtained from Gelman Instrument Co. Uniform micropores in the sheets permit rapid separation.

Glass "papers" are discussed under thin-layer chromatography (Ch. 2).

Whatman and other papers are available in rolls of various widths and in sheets $18\frac{1}{4} \times 22\frac{1}{2}$ in., 23×23 in., 8×8 in., and several less commonly used dimensions.

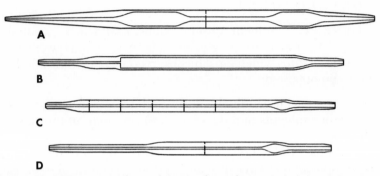

Fig. 1-3. Micropipettes for application of sample to paper. *(A)* transfer-type, standard; *(B)* transfer-type, self-filling; *(C)* graduated; *(D)* transfer-type, self-adjusting.

APPLICATION OF SAMPLE

Any convenient method may be used for application of material to the paper as long as the resulting spot is kept small (less than 5 mm) and, for quantitative purposes, uniform. Narrow bore glass tubes, such as used for melting point determinations, are very satisfactory. Self-filling micropipettes (Fig. 1-3) are generally used for quantitative determinations. These are available in sizes ranging from 1 to 10 μl (1μl = 1λ = 0.001 ml) for single spots and in larger sizes for multiple applications or mass chromatograms. The smaller sizes are available in disposable form.

If the quantity of sample applicable within an area of 5 mm diameter is insufficient, additional sample may be applied after the original sample has dried. A hair dryer or an infrared lamp may be used to decrease drying time. The paper rests on a glass plate or other support so that the point of application does not come into contact with a surface which might absorb the solution being applied. In ascending chromatography, the samples are normally placed 2 to 3 cm from the lower edge of the paper and are separated by a minimum distance of about 2 cm. In the descending method, the samples should always be applied so that they lie on the side of the antisiphon rod away from the solvent trough (see Descending Chromatography).

When large quantities of material are to be chromatographed, the sample is applied as a streak. Occasionally one finds an impedance of solvent flow resulting from samples thusly applied. In this case, the solvent at either end moves faster than in the center with the effect of pushing the moving components toward the mid-line of the chromatogram. This is avoided if the streak is applied discontinuously, i.e., in 2- to 4-cm segments separated by a gap of 1 to 2 cm.

DEVELOPMENT

GENERAL. Solvent systems found useful in separating various classes of compounds are given in a later section. However, there are a few basic rules which must be observed if good, reproducible results are to be obtained:

1. Use reagent grade chemicals and deionized or distilled water.
2. Store solvents and develop chromatograms at the same temperature.
3. Prepare only enough of any solvent system to use immediately. Decomposition occurs in many systems, such as phenol-water mixtures, and esters slowly form in mixtures of alcohol and acid.

CHROMATOGRAPHIC CHAMBERS. Chromatographic chambers of many types are commercially available. These vary in size from museum jars or battery jars to elaborate, insulated chromatographic cabinets such as the Chromatocab (Research Specialties Co.) which holds 18 × 22 in. chromatograms. Glass aquaria are used in many laboratories, but it may be necessary to coat the inner surfaces of these with paraffin to prevent deterioration of adhesives or exposed metal parts. Chambers constructed entirely of glass (Shandon Scientific Co.) obviate the necessity of coating with paraffin. The chamber must be constructed in such a way as to be able to support the chromatogram while one end is immersed in solvent. Tanks, jars, or cylinders used as chromatography chambers are covered with plastic film (Saran Wrap) and/or a glass plate.

ASCENDING CHROMATOGRAPHY. In the ascending method, the paper is supported by a device located at the top of the chamber while the lower end of the paper is immersed in solvent at the bottom of the tank. This technique in its simplest form is demonstrated in Fig. 1-4. In an ingenious modification of this, the upper cork is replaced by a glass plate on which rests a magnet. A paper clip is attached to the upper end of the sheet, which is then suspended from the top of the chamber by the magnet.

In larger tanks, a glass rod supported as illustrated in Fig. 1-5 is used to hold the upper end of the paper. Solvents are placed either in the bottom of the tank proper or in vessels of various types, such as a trough constructed of polyethylene, glass, or stainless steel. Upper supports are unnecessary in ascending chromatography if the paper is rolled into a cylinder and the juxtaposed edges joined by means of thread, staples, tape, or polyethylene clips (Fig. 1-6).

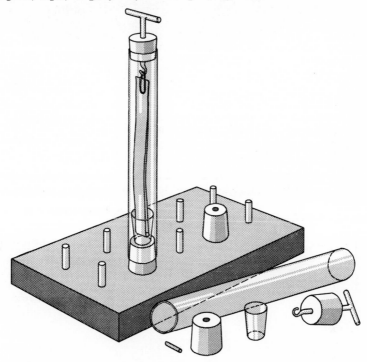

Fig. 1-4. Cylinders and accessories for ascending chromatography (Courtesy, Academic Press, Inc.) [2].

For chromatographing a dozen or more 8 × 8 in. papers, a simple glass, polyethylene, or noncorroding metal support may be used to hold parallel rods strung through holes in the upper ends of the papers. The more elaborate apparatus designed by Smith employs a metal or plastic rack consisting of two solid end plates connected by upper and lower rods to support the papers. Cylindrical sections of tubing separate the papers from each other. The frame fits into a solvent tray and the entire assembly (Fig. 1-7) is enclosed by the chromatographic chamber.

It should be borne in mind that the upward flow of solvent in ascending chromatography is eventually counteracted by gravity. This

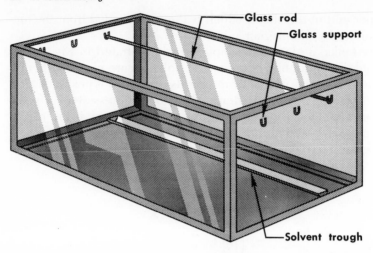

Glass rod

Glass support

Solvent trough

Fig. 1-5. Chromatography chamber for ascending or ascending-descending development [2]. Glass supports are affixed to the sides of the chamber with epoxy resin or paraffin. All joints are covered with a film of paraffin (Courtesy, Academic Press, Inc.).

becomes especially noticeable after the solvent has traveled to a height of about 25 cm. Development should be stopped at this point but, if adequate separation has not yet been attained, the dried paper may be reimmersed in the solvent (multiple development).

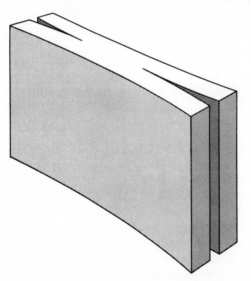

Fig. 1-6. Plastic clip [24] for joining vertical edges of paper cylinders for ascending chromatography in jars, wide mouth bottles, or cylinders. Staples, thread, or tape may be used in place of these (Courtesy, Academic Press, Inc.).

DESCENDING CHROMATOGRAPHY. In this procedure the solvent flows in a downward direction. The paper is held with its upper end in a solvent trough and passes upward and over an anti-siphon rod which suspends it away from the edges of the trough. The trough and rod are supported at the top of the chamber by any of several methods. Convenient steel clips or cradles (Fig. 1-8) to hold the trough and rods are available from several manufacturers. These rest on brackets attached to the sides of the chambers. As an alternative, one may use stainless-steel or glass racks or platforms supported on legs reaching to the bottom of the tank or attached to the sides. Smith's "universal" chromatography apparatus for 10 × 10 in. papers is similar to the equipment shown in Fig. 1-7 but is fitted with special trough assemblies that rest on the upper edges of two end plates when the apparatus is used for descending chromatography.

TWO-DIMENSIONAL CHROMATOGRAPHY. When large numbers of substances are to be separated on a single chromatogram, development in a direction perpendicular to the first and with a solvent system radically different from that used initially is often necessary.

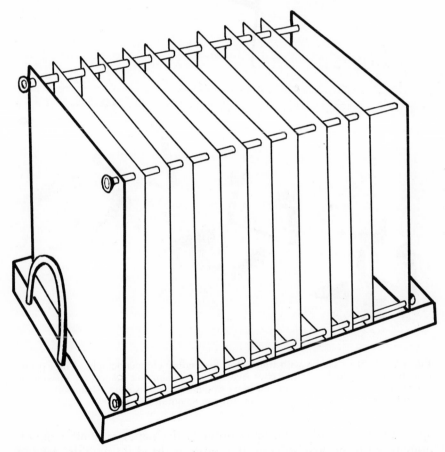

Fig. 1-7. Diagram of Smith's "universal" assembly for ascending or two-dimensional chromatography. Papers, suspended between rigid end plates, are separated by cylindrical spacers (Courtesy, Boyce Thompson Institute, Inc.).

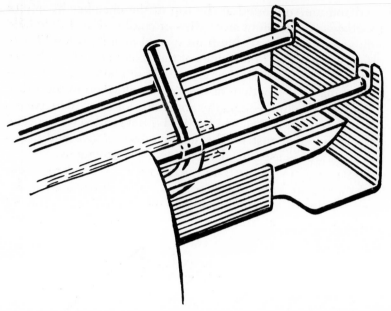

Fig. 1-8. (A) Steel cradle with trough for descending chromatography. Filter paper, held by a glass anchor rod, passes over an antisiphon rod (Courtesy, Kensington Scientific Corp.). (B) Steel clips for glass troughs of various sizes. U-shaped portion supports antisiphon rods (Courtesy, Kensington Scientific Corp.).

The sample is applied on one corner of the paper and, after development with the first solvent, the paper is dried thoroughly, rotated 90°, and developed in the second direction. It is essential that the first solvent be completely volatile. Solvent ingredients such as formic acid, phenol, etc., are difficult to remove from the paper and should be used only for development in the second direction.

RADIAL CHROMATOGRAPHY. Radial development, a modification well-suited for class room demonstration purposes, is rapid and requires a minimum of equipment. Two Petri dish tops or bottoms and a piece of ordinary circular filter paper are the basic requirements. Samples to be chromatographed are applied near the center of the paper disc which is then placed between the dish halves. The paper must be of a large enough diameter so that it extends several millimeters past the sides of the Petri dish chamber. Solvent is permitted to flow onto the center of the dish by any of serveral methods, the simplest of which is to make parallel cuts 2 mm apart from the edge of the paper disc to the center. The distal end of this wick is then placed in the developing solvent in the lower dish. Instead of fashioning the irrigating wick from the filter paper itself, one may use a rectangular strip of paper inserted into a slit in the center of the paper or a paper cone or cylinder positioned in the solvent dish with its upper end in contact with the filter paper.

The Kawerau apparatus utilizes a desiccator-type chamber with a thick-walled capillary tube which both delivers the solvent and supports the paper (Fig. 1-9). Chromatography paper supplied with the apparatus is slotted so that 5 samples can be analyzed simultaneously without interference at the edges. A typical chromatogram of 5 different samples chromatographed on slotted paper is shown in Fig. 1-10.

An important modification of radial chromatography is development in a centrifugal field. The filter paper is mounted on a centrifuge head and solvent is allowed to drip onto the center of the paper disc from an overhead reservoir. Development is complete in a matter of minutes but usually not without some loss of resolution.

SPIRAL CHROMATOGRAPHY. An interesting innovation in paper chromatography is the Chromatobox (Research Specialties Co.), which accommodates paper strips up to 5 cm wide and 50 cm long, yet measures only 8 cm in its longest dimension (Fig. 1-11). One end of the paper strip is anchored in a built-in trough containing 5 to 8 ml of solvent. The remainder of the strip is coiled around a band of embossed, flexible Teflon. The small volume of the chamber, sealed with a close-fitting lid, permits rapid saturation of the atmosphere with solvent vapor thereby decreasing development time.

The Chromatobox is especially useful for preliminary evaluation of developing solvents in a limited space and under similar conditions.

PAPER CHROMATOGRAPHY IN COMBINATION WITH ELECTROPHORESIS. Details of this procedure are given in Chapter 3. Suffice it to say here that two-dimensional chromatograms developed

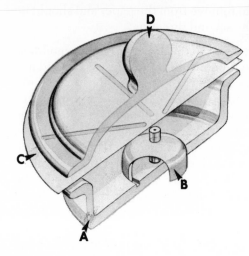

Fig. 1-9. Exploded sectional view of Kawerau circular chromatography apparatus. A filter paper circle *(C)* is held between the wide flanged, shallow dish *(A)* and cover *(D)*. A glass capillary tube for delivery of solvent is held in position and centered by a glass support *(B)* (Courtesy, Consolidated Laboratories, Inc.).

in the first direction by electrophoresis and in the second by conventional, vertical chromatography are characterized by better separation than can be obtained by either method alone. The combination of the two methods is especially useful for separating peptides.

VISUALIZATION

PHYSICAL METHODS.   Many compounds possess an innate color and can be observed on a chromatogram even during development. This is especially true of certain pigments found in plant extracts.

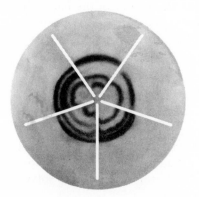

Fig. 1-10. Circular chromatogram on slotted filter paper (Courtesy, Consolidated Laboratories, Inc.).

Alternately, one may take advantage of the fluorescence or fluorescence-quenching properties of a compound or chemical adduct by viewing the dried chromatogram under ultraviolet light (240 to 260 mμ). The aromatic amino acids, for example, are easily detected by this method. After development with the butyl alcohol-acetic acid-water system and heating at 110°C for 10 minutes, all of the amino acids are detectable under ultraviolet light.

The paper itself may be slightly fluorescent, especially after development in certain solvent systems. Those compounds that absorb ultraviolet light appear as dark spots on the chromatogram. Contrast is increased by spraying the paper with a dilute alkaline solution of fluorescein or other similar reagent.

Radioactivity detection methods are used in conjunction with studies in which the metabolic fate of an isotopically labeled compound is determined subsequent to administration to an organism. The chromatogram on which labeled intermediates have been separated may be scanned manually with a Geiger counter (Ch. 14) or with an automatic device which advances the chromatographic strip past a detector and graphically records the radioactivity as a series of peaks on a chart. The corresponding regions of the chromatogram are then marked off. An alternate method, used largely with two-dimensional chromatograms, is to prepare an *autoradiogram* by placing the chrom-

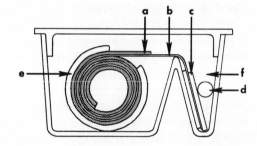

Fig. 1-11. Sectional view of Chromatobox. *(a)* Teflon band; *(b)* Paper strip; *(c)* Glass plates; *(d)* Glass rod; *(e)* Holding ring; *(f)* Solvent chamber (Courtesy, Research Specialties Co,).

atogram in contact with sensitive film (Kodak No-Screen X-ray film, with emulsion on both sides) for a suitable length of time. The exposure period depends on the kind and intensity of radioactivity. I^{131}, a gamma emitter, may give a good autoradiogram in 1 hour or less. S^{35} or C^{14} may require an exposure of 3 to 5 weeks because they are weak beta emitters. As a general rule, a spot easily detectable with a Geiger counter should produce a sufficiently darkened area in 1 to 2 days.

For good resolution it is necessary that the chromatogram and the X-ray plate be contiguous. A convenient method of accomplishing this is to place the paper and film, stapled together, between glass plates which then are bound with a few pieces of tape. The entire assembly is wrapped in aluminum foil or stored in any lightproof container. Lead-backed, cardboard film holders are available commercially (Kodak). Staples not only prevent the plate from shifting but provide marker holes by which the plate may be properly aligned with the chromatogram after development.

One may use this method also for visualization of metabolites by converting these to radioactive derivatives, e.g., C^{14}-labeled N-ethyl-maleimide adducts of sulfhydryl compounds. Autoradiographic detection is used also after neutron activation of chromatograms of unlabeled materials.

CHEMICAL METHODS.   Many of the reactions routinely used in the chemical laboratory for identification of compounds have been modified or used directly for detection and identification of substances on paper. These are discussed individually in later sections. Suffice it to say here that there are reagents, general or specific, for every class of compound. These are usually applied by spraying with an atomizer or aerosol spray or by drawing the paper through reagent contained in a wide, shallow vessel. A stainless-steel rod or a glass tube filled with lead shot and sealed at both ends may be used to weight the paper as it is being dipped in the reagent. The reagent should be prepared in a solvent in which the chromatographed substances are insoluble. Mineral acids, useful on thin-layer chromatoplates or glass paper chromatograms, are to be avoided in paper chromatography since these cause charring of the cellulose.

BIOASSAY TECHNIQUES.   Biological detection may be accomplished with intact chromatograms dried and placed in contact with a nutrient agar surface seeded with a suitable species of test organism. On a complete medium, growth inhibitors present on the chromatogram prevent growth in the areas immediately surrounding them. Nutrients or growth factors being assayed result in a zone of growth in a seeded medium deficient in the substance in question. Analogous results are obtained if the chromatogram is cut into strips and placed in tubes or on plates inoculated with test organism.

PREPARATION OF SAMPLES FOR CHROMATOGRAPHY

In rare instances, biological samples to be chromatographed are sufficiently pure in their natural state to permit analysis without additional manipulation. This is true, for example, in the case of certain secretions and exudates. More often, the biochemist is interested in separation of substances in such complex mixtures as plant sap, cellular fluids, and growth media, which contain numerous organic constituents plus inorganic salts. In such instances, fractionation of the material is necessary. The fractionation method selected depends on the nature of the various constituents, no single method being universally applicable. Extraction of tissues with 80 per cent ethyl alcohol (see Ch. 4, Column Chromatography) is satisfactory for non-volatile organic acids, amino acids, sugars, and related compounds.

If the initial homogenate is heated to boiling for 1 to 2 minutes, the method may be used for preparing protein for quantitative analysis of its constituent amino acids. It is suggested also that lipids be completely removed by extracting the protein with approximately 10 times its weight of acetone (twice), followed by hot benzene-ethyl alcohol (95:5, v/v) (twice), hot ethyl alcohol, and peroxide-free ether.

The fractionation method described by Roberts *et al.* [14] is somewhat more complex resulting in distribution of cellular constituents into 5 fractions and simultaneously providing considerable information with reference to solubility characteristics of various unidentified metabolites. The procedure is as follows:

1. Suspend 10 to 30 mg wet weight of washed cells or tissue in 4 ml of 5 per cent, v/v, trichloroacetic acid. Centrifuge the suspension after 30 minutes at 5°C. Recover supernatant fluid and remove the trichloroacetic acid by extracting with ether. Salts, amino acids, small peptides, nucleotides, and numerous other types of compounds are present in this fraction.

2. The cold trichloroacetic acid-insoluble residue is washed with distilled water and suspended in 4 ml of 75 per cent ethyl alcohol. Centrifuge after 30 minutes at 40° to 50°C. Decant the supernatant fluid and save. Suspend the alcohol-insoluble material in 4 ml of a solution containing 2 ml of ether and 2 ml of 75 per cent ethanol. After 15 minutes at 40° to 50°C, centrifuge the suspension and add the supernatant fluid to the 75 per cent ethanol-soluble fraction. This soluble material may be separated into two principle classes of compounds, i.e., proteins and lipids, by extraction with ether (step 5) or by chromatography on ion exchange resins or on paper.

3. The material insoluble in 75 per cent ethyl alcohol is suspended in 4 ml of 5 per cent trichloroacetic acid, heated in a bath of boiling water for 30 minutes, and centrifuged. The hot trichloroacetic acid (supernatant) fraction contains nucleic acids and nucleoproteins. The fraction is prepared for analysis by removing the trichloroacetic acid with ether and hydrolyzing in 0.1 to 10N HCl for 1 hour at 90° to 100°C to release purines, sugars, nucleotides, and inorganic phosphate from the protein.

4. The hot trichloroacetic acid-insoluble material is washed free of residual acid by suspending in acidified ethanol and centrifuging. The precipitate, the principal protein fraction, is dried with ether.

5. Add sufficient ether to the alcohol-soluble fraction (step 2) to give a 1:1 ratio with the 75 per cent ethanol. Add one-half the volume of water, mix thoroughly, and allow to settle. Remove ether phase and wash the remainder with a small amount of ether which is added to the first ether-soluble material, the lipid fraction. The alcohol-soluble, ether-insoluble fraction contains some types of proteins.

IDENTIFICATION OF SUBSTANCES

Specific spray reagents, discussed in a later section, are generally used for identification as well as location of substances on a chromatogram. In some cases identification may be accomplished by using a general reagent just to locate chromatographic position. The R_f value is then determined and compared to that of standard or known substance chromatographed on the same paper or mixed with an aliquot of the sample and *cochromatographed*. Among the more useful general reagents is iodine applied as a dilute spray in ethanol or as a vapor in a sealed chamber. The iodine produces spots either lighter or darker than the color produced upon reaction with the paper containing traces of solvent. After several hours, the iodine volatilizes and a second reagent may be used. Visualization by fluorescence, discussed above, is equally useful in determining R_f values, or comparing positions with known compounds.

Although cochromatography with standards in several solvent systems may be, at times, satisfactory for identification purposes, one should take advantage of other available methods when possible. First among these is the specific spray reagent. For example, ninhydrin, a general reagent for amino acids, gives a peculiar bluish-green color with β-alanine and aspartic acid. This is sufficiently specific that only one solvent system need be used.

Additional information concerning identification may be obtained by comparing chromatographic behavior of an untreated aliquot of the sample with that of a portion subjected to oxidation (with a drop of 30 per cent H_2O_2), reduction (with $LiAlH_4$), acetylation (with acetic anhydride), hydrolysis (with mineral acid), photolysis (ultraviolet light), etc. Some reactions such as oxidation may be conducted right on the paper. Oxidizable compounds in a mixture may be detected by spraying a dilute solution of performic acid on a two-dimensional chromatogram of the mixture after development and drying in the first direction. The chromatogram is then developed in the second direction with the same solvent system used in the first. All compounds except those oxidized should fall in a straight line on the paper.

Paper chromatography in conjunction with other techniques, such as spectrophotometric analysis, provides the surest means of identification.

PREPARATIVE CHROMATOGRAPHY

Separation of large quantities of material on paper is accomplished easily on a single large sheet (*mass chromatogram*) on which the sample is applied as a series of spots or streaks or as a single streak.

At each end of the streak, a single spot of the substance and, usually, one or more standard solutions are spotted. These "telltales" serve to indicate the position of the bands containing the components being separated. These bands are cut away from the remainder of the chromatogram and the substances on them are eluted with a suitable solvent. Purification of the substance may require chromatography in one or more additional solvent systems.

Even larger quantities may be separated on (a) thick sheets of filter paper, (b) several sheets of paper compressed between glass or plastic sheets, the entire assembly bolted together, (c) stacked paper discs of the same diameter compressed within a metal or plastic column, the *chromatopile*, or (d) a roll of filter paper wrapped around an inert core. With any of these methods one may experience uneven development, especially when large, unfractionated samples are chromatographed. Viewing of the paper under ultraviolet light frequently locates zones which serve as guides in determining the distribution pattern.

ELUTION

One of the least standardized techniques in paper chromatography is that of elution of materials from the paper subsequent to development. The author has obtained good results with the methods described below.

EXTRACTION TECHNIQUE. The section of paper containing the substance to be eluted is cut into small pieces which are then immersed in a minimum of 10 ml of a suitable solvent. After standing about 4 hours with occasional agitation, the fluid is filtered and collected. The procedure is repeated and the combined eluates are dried and reconstituted to the desired volume.

CHROMATOGRAPHIC ELUTION. Any chromatographic chamber adapted for descending chromatography is suitable for elution by the "continuous washing" or chromatographic technique. The 10-gal. aquarium tank (Fig. 1-5) for ascending chromatography may be provided with a solvent trough support by affixing rod supports about 1.5 in. apart on the end walls of the tank. The trough rests on parallel glass rods held by the supports.

The section of paper containing the sample to be eluted is threaded between two slits in the bottom of a paper wick or curtain. An 8 × 8 in. curtain can be cut to hold up to 10 samples depending on the size of the paper section to be eluted (Fig. 1-12).

If the curtain is manually saturated with elutrient, the actual elution process is completed rapidly. The entire sample may be recovered after as few as 5 drops have been collected. If the sample is not colored, it is advisable to collect several milliliters of solvent.

Quantitative Methods

Quantitative methods of chromatographic analysis on paper have been devised for many groups of substances. Highly refined techniques are available, for example, for amino acids, which have played such a prominent role in the development of chromatography. The methods usually involve measurement of color or fluorescence in-

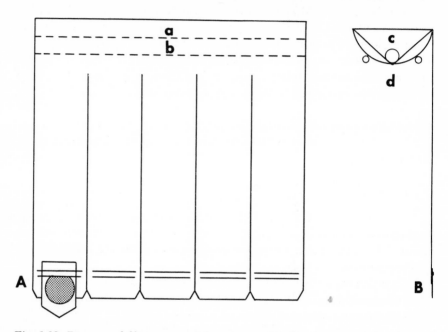

Fig. 1-12. Diagram of filter paper wick and assembly for chromatographic elution. (A) Front view of wick cut to accommodate 5 samples, 8 × 8 in. one of which is shown *in situ*. The paper is folded (*a* to *b*) and sliced with a razor blade for insertion of the paper section to be eluted. (B) End view of wick held in place by anchor rod (*c*) in trough supported by glass rods (*d*) (Courtesy, Boyce Thompson Institute, Inç.).

tensity either before or after elution of the spot from the paper. Measurement of spot area is also used with considerable success. In recent years, radioactive isotopes have been used with increasing frequency in quantitative measurements.

MAXIMUM COLOR DENSITY METHOD

Colored substances are measured directly on the paper after either one- or two-dimensional chromatography. Greater accuracy is obtained with the one-dimensional method since standards are chromatographed on the same sheet. The procedure of Block *et al.* [2] for quantitative estimation of amino acids in protein hydrolyzates follows:

PREPARATION OF SAMPLE. Proteins are hydrolyzed by refluxing in 6N HCl for 16 to 24 hours using 20 ml of acid for 200 mg of sample in a round bottom flask fitted with a glass condenser 75 to 100 cm long (Fig. 1-13). The contents of the hydrolyzing flask are transferred to a porcelain evaporating dish and dried on a steam bath to remove excess HCl. The humin is filtered off and the amino acid hydrochlorides are dissolved in 10 per cent 2-propanol. Hydrolysis with HCl is suitable for all amino acids except tryptophan. Hydrolysis with 14 per cent barium hydroxide is necessary for this amino acid. Barium is precipitated from the diluted hydrolyzate by adding solid carbon dioxide (dry ice). The barium carbonate is removed by filtration and/or centrifugation.

PREPARATION OF STANDARDS. Dissolve all amino acids except tryptophan and glutamic acid in dilute HCl, add sufficient water and isopropanol so that the final concentration is 10 μmoles/ml and isopropanol is 10 per cent. Prepare subdilutions (from 10 μM of standard with 10 per cent isopropanol) of 8, 6, 4, 2, and 1 μmoles/ml. Glutamic acid is incorporated in the stock solution at one half the concentration of the other amino acid, i.e., 5 μmoles/ml. Tryptophan standards in 10 per cent isopropanol should be prepared separately.

CHROMATOGRAPHIC PROCEDURE. Since one-dimensional chromatography does not separate all amino acids present in a protein hydrolyzate, several solvent systems are used as well as several types of paper. Samples are applied with a 1 or 2.5 μl pipette 2.5 cm from the bottom of the sheet and 2 cm apart. If more than 2.5 μl is required, a second application is made after the initial spot dries. Four to six replicate sheets are used, each sheet having at least one application of each level of standard and of each of the following concentrations of unknown:

2.5 mg of protein/ml
5.0 mg of protein/ml
10.0 mg of protein/ml
20.0 mg of protein/ml

The same pipette should be used for standard and unknown, and replicate sheets should be chromatographed simultaneously. Papers measuring 18 × 11 in. are chromatographed in an ascending direction in a chamber such as that shown in Fig. 1-5. A larger chamber is required for group H.

Prior to development, excess acid in the samples on the paper is neutralized by holding the sheet for 4 minutes over a trough containing 4N NH$_4$OH. It is advisable also to hydrate the papers to be developed in phenol by exposure to steam for about 15 minutes before immersion in the solvent.

Group A

Paper: Whatman 3. Size: 18 × 11 in. (long).

Solvent: Phenol-water (100 ml of 88 per cent liquid phenol plus 20 ml of H_2O). A small quantity of 8-hydroxyquinoline is added to the phenol before the addition of the water. Beakers containing 10 ml of 1 per cent NaCN and 25 ml of 0.3 per cent NH_4OH are placed in chamber. Treat hydrolyzate spots with 1:4 NH_4OH for 4 minutes.

Pipette: 2.5 λ (if necessary 1 λ).

Length of run: 23 cm.

Color reagent: 0.25 per cent ninhydrin in acetone.

Standards: 2, 4, and 8 μmoles/ml (if necessary 1 μmole).

Unknown to contain at lowest level (also apply two times and if necessary four times):

Aspartic acid	R_f 0.25	0.20 to 0.60 mg/ml
Glutamic acid	R_f 0.33	0.20 to 0.50 mg/ml
Serine	R_f 0.43	0.20 to 0.45 mg/ml
Glycine	R_f 0.48	0.12 to 0.30 mg/ml
Threonine	R_f 0.55	0.20 to 0.50 mg/ml

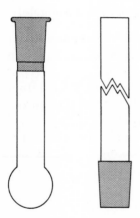

Fig. 1-13. Flask and condenser for acid hydrolysis of protein. Bulb of flask 3 to 4 cm in diameter. Condenser is 80 to 100 cm long with a 24/40 standard taper joint (Courtesy, Boyce Thompson Institute, Inc.).

Group B

Paper: Whatman 3. Size: 18 × 11 in. (long).

Solvent: 1-butanol-acetic acid-water (450:50:125, v/v/v).

Pipette: 1 λ (if necessary 2.5 λ).

Length of run: 23 cm; dry, and rerun three times for 23 cm (see Fig. 1-14).

Color reagent: ninhydrin.

Standards: 2, 4, and 8 μmoles/ml (if necessary 1 μmole).

Unknown to contain at lowest level:

Cystine	R_f 0.12	0.20 to 0.50 mg/ml
Lysine	R_f 0.18	0.25 to 0.60 mg/ml

Histidine	R_f 0.22	0.25 to 0.60 mg/ml
Arginine	R_f 0.26	0.25 to 0.70 mg/ml
Alanine	R_f 0.45	0.14 to 0.40 mg/ml
Tyrosine	R_f 0.60	0.25 to 0.65 mg/ml
Phenylalanine	R_f 0.80	0.30 to 0.70 mg/ml
Isoleucine	R_f 0.82	0.30 to 0.55 mg/ml
Leucine	R_f 0.85	0.30 to 0.55 mg/ml

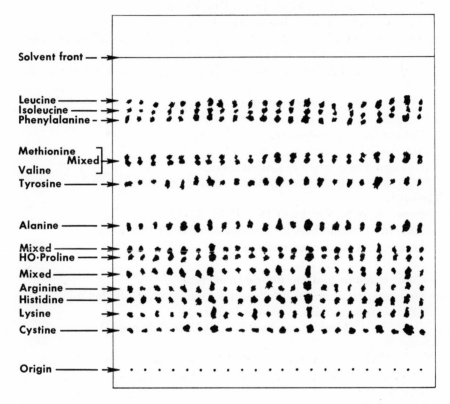

Fig. 1-14. Chromatography of Group B amino acids [2] (Courtesy, Academic Press, Inc.).

Group B₂

Solvent: Isoamyl alcohol-pyridine-water-diethylamine (50:50:35:2, v/v/v/v) in the presence of NaCN and aqueous phenol may be used for valine, methionine, tyrosine, isoleucine, leucine, and phenylalanine.

Length of run: 23 cm; dry, and rerun twice for 23 cm.

Group C

Paper: S. & S. 598. Size: 18 × 11 in. (long).

Solvent: 1-butanol-acetic acid-water (450:50:125, v/v/v).

Pipette: 5 λ (if necessary 2.5 λ).

Length of run: 25 cm.

Color reagent: diazotized sulfanilamide (Pauly reagent).

Standards: 2, 4, and 8 μmoles/ml.

Unknown to contain at lowest level:

Histidine R_f 0.17   0.30 to 0.70 mg/ml

Tyrosine R_f 0.40   0.20 to 0.70 mg/ml

Group D

Paper: Whatman 3. Size: 18 × 11 in. (long).

Solvent: lutidine-collidine-water (1:1:1, v/v/v).

Solvent contains 1 per cent $(C_2H_5)_2NH$ by volume. Beakers containing 5 ml of 1 per cent NaCN and 5 ml of aqueous phenol are placed in chamber. Treat hydrolyzate spots with 1:4 NH_4OH for 4 minutes.

Pipette: 2.5 λ (if necessary 1 λ).

Length of run: 25 cm.

Color reagent: ninhydrin.

Standards: 1, 2, and 4 μmoles/ml.

Unknown to contain at lowest level:

Valine R_f 0.36   0.15 to 50 mg/ml

Group E

Paper: S. & S. 598. Size: 18 × 11 in. (long).

Solvent: 1-butanol-acetic acid-water (450:50:125, v/v/v).

Pipette: 5 λ (if necessary 2.5 λ).

Length of run: 25 cm.

Color reagent: platinic iodide in acetone

Standards: 1, 2, and 4 μmoles/ml (if necessary 8 μmoles/ml).

Unknown to contain at lowest level:

Methionine R_f 0.50   0.15 to 0.60 mg/ml

Group F

Paper: Whatman 3. Size: 18 × 11 in. (long) or 18 × 20 in. (long).

Solvent: *n*-butanol-acetic acid-water (450:50:125, v/v/v).

Pipette: 5 λ.

Length of run: 25 cm for proline only; 46 cm for proline and hydroxyproline.

Color reagent: 0.2 per cent isatin in acetone. After spraying, air dry, put sheets in oven at 70° to 76°C for 10 minutes. Oven to be saturated with H_2O vapors. For hydroxyproline counter spray with color reagent G.

Standards: 1, 2, and 4 μmoles/ml.

Unknown to contain at lowest level:

Hydroxyproline R_f 0.20   0.25 to 0.60 mg/ml

Proline R_f 0.30   0.10 to 0.30 mg/ml

Group G

Paper: Whatman 3. Size: 18 × 11 in. (long).

Solvent: 2-butanol-3.3 per cent NH_3 (150:50, v/v).

Pipette: 2.5 λ or 5 λ.

Length of run: 25 cm.

Color reagent: *p*-dimethylaminobenzaldehyde (1 g) in a mixture of 10 ml of concentrated HCl and 90 ml of acetone. Prepare fresh just before use.

Standards: 2, 4, and 8 μmoles/ml.

Unknown to contain at lowest level:

             Tryptophan R_f 0.60   0.25 to 0.80 mg/ml

Group H

Paper: Whatman 3. Size: 18 × 22 in. (long).

Solvent: 2-butanol-3.3 per cent NH_3 (150:60, v/v) (3.3 per cent NH_3 is prepared by diluting 60 ml of 14.5 to 15.0N NH_4OH to 500 ml with water). A marker of bromocresol purple placed at the starting line permits one to follow the development as the solvent is allowed to drip off the paper. Bromocresol purple moves slightly ahead of phenylalanine.

Pipette: 1.0 λ or 2.5 λ.

Length of run: The bromocresol purple should travel 45 cm beyond the origin.

Color reagent: ninhydrin.

Standards: 1, 2, 4, 6, 8 μmoles/ml.

Unknown to contain at lowest level:

Lysine	0.25 to 0.60 mg/ml
Arginine	0.25 to 0.75 mg/ml
Tyrosine	0.25 to 0.65 mg/ml
Valine	0.20 to 0.50 mg/ml
Methionine	0.30 to 0.90 mg/ml
Isoleucine	0.30 to 0.60 mg/ml
Leucine	0.30 to 0.60 mg/ml
Phenylalanine	0.30 to 0.75 mg/ml

In practice, 5 μl solutions containing 1.25, 2.5, 5.0, and 10.0 μmoles of the compounds, which may be readily separated by one-dimensional chromatography or which are revealed by specific tests, are placed on the paper 2 cm apart. At the completion of the chromatogram, the circumferences of the spots are carefully marked in pencil, and the areas derived from the standards are plotted on semi-logarithmic paper against the concentrations. The quantity of material present in the unknown is then read from the standard curve prepared on the same chromatogram.

Accuracies of ±5 per cent are readily obtained by this method when the spot has distinct edges. If there is an overlapping or if the spot is distorted for any reason whatsoever, this method should not be used.

In case the circumference of the spot is fuzzy, a more successful outline can often be obtained by reproducing the developed chromatogram on photographic paper by means of the usual equipment for copying documents.

Giddings and Keller [15] have shown that the area of the spot is directly proportional to the log of the solute in the spot and that the length of the spot is proportional to the square root of the log of the spot content.

MEASUREMENTS AND CALCULATIONS

The colored spots obtained by reacting the amino acids with ninhydrin or other reagents are outlined in pencil using transmitted light. The spots are centered on a densitometer for determination of maximum color density. A calibration curve is prepared on semi-logarithmic paper by plotting per cent transmittance (abscissa) against concentrations of standards in mmoles/liter (ordinate). To calculate the per cent of each amino acid in the protein the following formula is used.

$$\text{Per cent amino acid} = \frac{\text{millimoles of amino acid} \times \text{molecular weight}}{\text{milligrams of protein/milliliter}} \quad (2)$$

The reproducibility of this procedure is in the order of ±5 per cent when two hydrolyzates of the same protein are analyzed on the same set of chromatograms.

Density measurements are not used in the case of methionine since the reagent (PtI_6) used for visualization gives a bleached spot on a colored background. In such cases, the area or length of the spot is used as a parameter of concentration.

AREA OR LENGTH OF SPOT

Fisher *et al.* [16] have described an excellent procedure for the quantitative estimation of substances on one-dimensional paper chromatograms. They found that when volumes of solution of constant size are applied to the paper, the areas of resultant spots were proportional to the logarithm of the concentration of material in each spot.

TOTAL COLOR OF SPOT

Colored, ultraviolet-absorbing, fluorescent, radioactive substances, etc., which have been separated on one-dimensional paper chromatograms, are scanned over the length of the paper strip using the appropriate equipment. The various scanning instruments include the devices which measure electrostatic discharge [17], electrical conductivity [18] and impedance changes [19]. The areas under the curves thus obtained are a function of the concentration of the material in each spot. Various manoses stained with aniline phthalate can be estimated with an error of ±1 to 2 per cent based upon the observation that the integral area of the density plot is proportional to the square root of the initial concentration. If the scan shows a Gaussian type distribution, the area is most easily obtained by:

$$A = hw \tag{3}$$

where A = area; h = height of the curve; and w = width of the curve at one half its height.

FLUORESCENCE

Mavrodineanu et al. [20] described a technique for the rapid estimation of fluorescent substances on paper chromatograms of plant tissues. The instrument selected for modification for this purpose is a Photovolt Corporation densitometer (Standard Transmission Density Unit Model 52-C) with a photomultiplier attachment (Multiplier Photometer Model 520-M). The fluorescence exciting light source was provided by a mercury vapor lamp (General Electric 4-watt germicidal lamp) provided with the instrument. An ultraviolet filter (U.G. 2, made by Schott, Jena) is inserted between the lamp and the aperture in a groove made for this purpose under the aperture mount. The ultraviolet beam passes through the aperture (diameter 0.5 cm), through the paper placed above the aperture, and reaches the photomultiplier tube of the search head after passing through a second filter in the search head. The latter filter with a maximum transmittance at 465, 495, 515, or 570 mμ is selected according to the fluorescence characteristics of the substances examined. Fluorescence emission, resulting from the presence of a suitable substance on the paper, is detected by the photomultiplier tube producing a deflection on the microammeter proportional to the amount of material on the paper. A typical standard curve for indole-3-acetic acid on a paper chromatogram developed with 2-propanol-water-ammonia (28 to 30 per cent) (80:15:5, v/v/v) in an ascending direction is given in Fig. 1-15 (see Ch. 10 for a brief discussion of densitometry).

PHOTOMETRY OF ELUTED SUBSTANCES

The large numbers of eluted substances in plant extracts make it difficult, if not impossible, to separate and measure these quantitatively by one-dimensional methods. Some excellent two-dimensional methods have been devised which greatly increase the potential for separation. Typical for these is the system for amino acids reported by Porter *et al.* [21]. Following chromatography, substances are located by virtue of their inherent color of fluorescence or by means of a suitable reagent. After outlining the spot and eluting the substance from the paper, the concentration is determined photometrically.

For amino acids, descending chromatography is carried out using aqueous phenol in the first direction and acidified 1-butanol in the second on Whatman 1 or 3. Mallinckrodt liquefied phenol (88 per cent

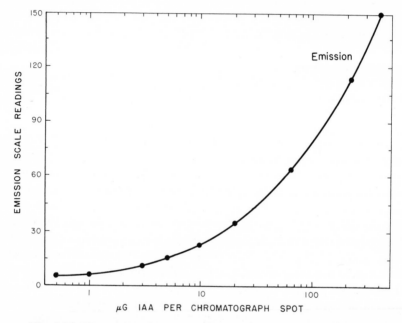

Fig. 1-15. Emission readings for different quantities of indole-3-acetic acid following chromatography. Fluorescence readings were made with a 465 mμ filter with a modified Photovolt densitometer (see text) (Courtesy, Boyce Thompson Institute, Inc.).

without preservative) is mixed 4:1, v/v, with water and adjusted to a pH of 5.5 to 5.8 with dilute NaOH. The second solvent, 1-butanol-acetic acid-water (90:10:29, v/v/v) is made fresh before use. A shallow pan of water is placed in the bottom of the chamber before development with phenol.

After the developed papers have been dried thoroughly, the amino acids are detected with 1 per cent ninhydrin in ethanol containing 0.1 per cent 8-hydroxyquinoline. The reagent is applied to the paper either by pipette or by immersion and the papers are heated for 30 minutes at 60°C in an atmosphere saturated with ethanol vapors.

The amino acid spots are identified, outlined in pencil, eluted from the paper, and the absorbance of the elutriate determined with a spectrophotometer. The absorbance of proline is read at 430 mμ, asparagine at 360, and all other amino acids at 570. Corrections for background are made by determining the absorbance of a solution obtained by eluting a section of the chromatogram which contains no amino acids.

Standard curves are prepared by plotting the absorbance of a number of standard, known concentrations of each amino acid against the corresponding concentrations of the amino acids. Alternatively, a regression equation is calculated for each amino acid using the appropriate absorbancies.

Except for the specific solvent systems and reagents used for the amino acids, this technique for quantitative analysis may be used for many other substances found in plant extracts. The accuracy of the method is fairly high providing sufficient material is chromatographed (10 to 40 μg for most amino acids).

ISOTOPIC METHODS

One of the most elegant methods for the quantitative determination of micro quantities of any reactive substance is the double-isotope dilution procedure of Keston *et al.* [22]. The material to be determined is reacted with a substance containing a radioisotope of known specific activity, then a known quantity of the resulting derivative labeled with a *different* radioactive isotope is added to the mixture and the compound isolated by paper chromatography. The quantity of the original compound is then calculated. The following example is adapted from Nuclear-Chicago Technical Bulletin No. 3.

The amino acids in a protein hydrolyzate are reacted with I^{131}-p-toluene-sulfonechloride (I^{131}-pipsylchloride) by the Shottan-Baumann method. Assuming that the amino acid mixture contained leucine and the pipsylchloride 50,000 counts/minute/micromole, then the iodine-labeled pipsylleucine that has been formed has a total activity of 50,000 leucine counts/minute. To the pipsylated hydrolyzate, 1.0 μM of S^{35}-pipsylleucine containing 20,000 counts/minute is now added. The pipsylleucine is separated by two-dimensional paper chromatography so that it is devoid of other pipsylated compounds. The total radioactivity is now measured. Then the spot is covered with aluminum foil to cut out the beta radiation of the S^{35} and the radioactivity due to I^{131} alone is measured. If 10,000 counts/minute for S^{35} is found (20,000 counts/minute of S^{35}-pipsylleucine having been added) this means that the spot now contains only 50 per cent of the original sample. If the observed value for I^{131}-pipsylleucine is 12,500 counts/minute, then the quantity of

I^{131}-pipsylleucine in the original hydrolyzate would be twice this value or 25,000 count/minute. Since the original I^{131}-pipsylchloride contained 50,000 counts/minute/micromole, the I^{131}-pipsylleucine would also contain 50,000 counts/minute/micromole, assuming that all of it reacted. This means that there was 0.5 μM of leucine in the original hydrolyzate.

If the presence of a contaminant is suspected, the spot can be cut into bands and only those portions which contain a constant ratio of I^{131} to S^{35} used for the calculations.

Substances containing sulfhydryl groups are converted to their C^{14}-N-ethylmaleimide adduct. These are chromatographed in the conventional manner in an acidic or neutral solvent and chromatographic positions are determined in any of the various ways listed. Although the N-ethylmaleimide adducts are easily detected by their

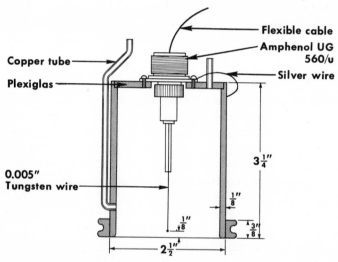

Fig. 1-16. End-window counting tube machined from 1/4-inch brass stock tubing (Courtesy, R. C. Fuller).

pink color after the chromatogram is dipped in dry isopropanol saturated with potassium hydroxide, this reagent is to be avoided since K possesses considerable natural radioactivity. The positions of substances labeled with C^{14} or other isotopes with relatively long half-lives may be accurately delineated by preparing autoradiograms of the intact chromatograms. Having located the spots, the radioactivity is measured either on the paper or following elution.

In situ measurements are made with a Geiger-Muller counter equipped with an end-window counting tube. The modified "Scott tube" (Fig. 1-16) described by Fuller [23] is especially well suited for paper chromatograms. The end window in this device is constructed from DuPont Mylar of 0.25 mil thickness. Any of several types of quenching gas, e.g., Q gas, may be used to displace air in the tube. The male plug of an amphenol connector for attachment to the input of a scaler unit is machined into the tube. A tungsten wire serves as the anode and the brass casing as the cathode.

Fig. 1-17. Vanguard 880 Autoscanner for paper strip chromatograms. Chart of recorder advances synchronously with the chromatogram which is drawn between twin window-less detectors (Courtesy, Vanguard Instrument Co.).

The radioactive area on the chromatogram is outlined in pencil and the surrounding area is covered with thin sheets of copper or aluminum foil. The counting tube is then placed over the spot and the radioactivity read off the scaling unit.

The Packard Model 460 Radiochromatogram Scanner performs the scanning automatically on either one- or two-dimensional chromatograms, presenting information relative to the location, zone shape, and amount of radioactivity. For scanning of one-dimensional strips, the Vanguard 880 Autoscanner (Fig. 1-17) (Vanguard Instrument Co.) is one of several highly recommended instruments equipped for 4 Pi scanning.

Quantitative radioactivity measurements *in situ* are severely limited with respect to accuracy because much of the radiation is absorbed by the chromatography paper, only the outermost portions of the sample, in the case of weak beta emitters, being detectable. Even 4 Pi scanners fail to give a true estimate of the activity since the type of drying procedure following chromatographic development strongly influences distribution of a substance within the paper. Reproducible, accurate determinations require elution from the chromatogram. Procedures for eluting substances from paper chromatograms are discussed above. If the substance is known to be highly radioactive, it is diluted following elution and a portion is dried on a sample pan for measurement by an end-window counter. Samples with low levels of radioactivity may be eluted directly into sample pans or into vials for scintillation counting.

Specific Applications

The various instruments described in the preceding sections are the same for paper chromatographic analysis of all types of natural products. The principal variables, viz., solvent systems and color reagents, are given in detail by Block *et al.* [2], Lederer and Lederer [4], and others, and a vast amount of similar data is published regularly in the *Journal of Chromatography* and miscellaneous publications. Procedures for some of the more common classes of substances of biochemical interest follow:

Although one must use special procedures for successful separation and identification of particular types of compounds, general or "universal" solvent systems may be employed for preliminary analysis of a crude extract. The procedures of Gordon and Hewel [24] not only provide fair separation of a great many compounds but have the advantage of being quite rapid. A fast-running paper, Whatman 4, is used with 2-propanol-pyridine-water-glacial acetic acid (8:8:4:1, v/v/v/v). After development for 2 hours, the paper is dried for 15 minutes in an air stream and sprayed with various color reagents. Before using certain reagents such as platinic iodide, pyridine must be removed either by drying for a longer period or by washing the chromatogram with acetone. A second solvent, 2-butanol-pyridine-water-glacial acetic acid (12:6:4:1, v/v/v/v) gives better separation of substances which have high R_f values in the initial system. Those with low R_f values are chromatographed in methanol-pyridine-water-glacial acetic acid (6:6:4:1, v/v/v/v) to obtain optimum resolution.

Preparation of extracts in 10 to 20 per cent methanol containing 1 per cent acetic acid pre-equilibrates the sample and inhibits microbial contamination during storage. Proteins should be removed either by boiling followed by centrifugation or filtration or by extracting with 50 per cent methanol. The latter also eliminates excessive amounts of salts or other substances with low solubilities in alcohol [25].

The reported R_f values for some 300 substances [26] serve as a useful guide to chromatographic fractionation of biological extracts. Subsequent to development in one of the above systems and elution from the chromatogram, the sample should be further analyzed by one of the more refined techniques to obtain better resolution of individual members of a particular class of compounds.

ALCOHOLS (Polyhydric)

SOLVENTS. The solvents given for separation of sugars (*quod vide*) are frequently used for sorbitol, dulcitol, mannitol, glycerol, and other polyhydric alcohols.

DETECTION. Spray with ammoniacal silver nitrate or a phenol red solution prepared from 0.05N sodium borate (pH 9.18)—phenol red (2 mg per ml in ethanol adjusted to pH 7 to 7.5 with dilute sodium hydroxide)—methanol (1:2:7, v/v/v). Sugars and sugar alcohols form yellow spots on a purple background [27].

ALKALOIDS

SOLVENTS. The compounds referred to as nitrogenous bases and others which constitute the alkaloids are so varied in structure and so numerous that no single solvent system is completely adequate for separation. However, preliminary chromatographic analysis may be performed with isoamyl alcohol (5 per cent, w/v), citric acid (9:1, w/v) on untreated paper or on paper buffered with 5 per cent monosodium citrate or 1 per cent potassium acid phosphate.

DETECTION. Ultraviolet light; iodine vapors or 1 per cent iodine in carbon tetrachloride applied as a spray; 0.5 per cent bromocresol green in ethanol; platinic iodide reagent (see Amino Acids).

AMINO ACIDS

SOLVENTS. In addition to the various solvents given in preceding sections, the following two-dimensional systems are especially useful:

1. Chromatograph in the first direction in *n*-butyl alcohol-acetic acid-water (450:50:125, v/v/v) and in the second direction with *n*-butyl alcohol-methyl ethyl ketone-water (2:2:1, v/v/v). A shallow dish containing cyclohexylamine [28] or 4N NH$_4$OH is placed in the chromatographic chamber with the second solvent.

2. An excellent system for the separation of amino acids, numerous sulfur-containing substances, and amines in plant extracts utilizes ethanol-tertiary butyl alcohol (58 per cent, v/v)-ammonium hydroxide-water (60:20:5:15, v/v/v/v) in the first direction. The second solvent is tertiary butyl alcohol-88 per cent (w/v) formic acid-water (14:3:3, v/v/v).

DETECTION.   There is a large number of reagents specific for the various kinds of amino acids. Some of those most often used are:

Ninhydrin: 0.25 per cent, w/v, in acetone. Amino acids, peptides, and some amines give a purple-blue color. When the reagent contains 0.5 per cent collidine, somewhat different and characteristic colors for some of the amino acids are obtained.

Pauly: Prepare sulfanilamide (1 per cent, w/v) in 10 per cent, v/v, hydrochloric acid; 5 per cent, w/v, $NaNO_2$; and half-saturated Na_2CO_3. To 5 ml of sulfanilamide solution, add 5 ml of $NaNO_2$ in a 100 ml separatory funnel. Shake for one minute and add 50 ml of *n*-butyl alcohol. Shake again for 1 minute and permit layers to separate during the next 4 minutes. The lower (aqueous) layer is applied to the chromatogram by means of an atomizer and the paper is then dipped into the Na_2CO_3 solution. Tyrosine gives a deep cherry-red color; histidine is yellow-orange.

Platinic Iodide: Mix, in the order given, 4 ml of 0.002M $PtCl_6$, 0.25 ml of 1N KI, 0.4 ml of 2N HCl, and 76 ml of acetone. Dry chromatograms are sprayed with or dipped in this reagent which produces a white spot on a pink background for the sulfur amino acids and some reducing compounds. Although many substances react immediately, it may be necessary to wait as long as 24 hours for others.

Ehrlich: Spray with a fresh solution of 1 g of *p*-dimethylamino-benzaldehyde in 90 ml of acetone and 10 ml of concentrated HCl for detection of tryptophan.

Periodate-Nessler: Spray with Nessler's reagent almost saturated with $NaIO_4$ for serine and threonine.

INDOLES AND OTHER CYCLIC COMPOUNDS

Indole, indole-3-acetic acid, tryptophan, tryptamine, isatin, and other aromatic compounds are extracted from tissue with butyl alcohol saturated with 0.1 to 1.0N HCl. For indoles, the extraction is conducted at $-10°C$ and, preferably, in an atmosphere of nitrogen. The excess solvent is evaporated under similar conditions. Ion exchange resins and mechanical desalters should be avoided in the case of these easily degradable substances.

Aromatic acids such as benzoic, cinnamic, and mandelic acids are extracted from macerated lyophilized tissue with ether. Extraction of the ether fraction with 2 per cent $NaHCO_3$ separates the acids from the neutral phenols which remain in the ethereal layer.

SOLVENTS.   The organic phase of *n*-butanol-acetic acid-water (4:1:5, v/v/v) is as suitable for indoles as for amino acids. 2-Propanol-ammonia-water (200:10:20, v/v/v) is used for indoles and phenolic acids. It is recommended that development proceed in the dark, at a low temperature (15°C), and in an inert atmosphere.

DETECTION.   *Ehrlich's reagent* is used for all substances containing the indole ring. Many aromatic substances can be detected
without color reagents by viewing them under ultraviolet light.

Phenols yield characteristic colors with *diazotized sulfanilic acid*.
This reagent is prepared by adding 25 ml of fresh 5 per cent, v/v,
$NaNO_2$ at 0°C to 5 ml of sulfanilic acid solution (0.9 g of sulfanilic acid
and 9 ml of concentrated hydrochloric acid, diluted to 100 ml with
water). The chromatogram is sprayed with 20 per cent, v/v, Na_2CO_3.

LIPIDS

Paper chromatography is not as suitable for the separation and
identification of lipids as is column-, gas-, or thin-layer chromatography. Nevertheless it is frequently used for determination of the
purity of lipids or as an aid in the identification of fractions obtained
by other methods. Many types of lipids have been chromatographed
with organic solvents on papers coated with a polar stationary phase.
Silicic acid-coated papers are prepared as follows: To 1 liter of distilled water in a 4-liter beaker add 280 g of NaOH pellets. Stir until
dissolved; cool; add 4 oz of silicic acid slowly with stirring. Cool to
room temperature and dilute with 500 ml of distilled water. Dip the
filter paper into the sodium silicate solution and then into 6N HCl
while still wet. After 10 to 30 minutes wash paper with distilled water
and dry [29].

SOLVENTS.   On acidic silicic acid paper, *n*-hexane separates
saturated and unsaturated hydrocarbons, fatty acid esters, and sterol
esters; benzene is used to chromatograph fatty acids, sterols, sterol
esters, and mono-, di-, and triglycerides; 5 per cent diethyl ether in
n-hexane is used for the above as well as for vitamin K, vitamin E,
coenzyme Q, hydroxy acids, and vitamins A and D_2.

Phospholipids, sulfatides, and glycolipids are separated with
chloroform and methanol in various ratios or with diisobutyl ketone-
acetic acid-water (40:25:5, v/v/v) on neutral silicic acid papers.

DETECTION.   A good general reagent for lipids is 0.001 per cent
Rhodamine 6G in 0.25M K_2HPO_4. More specific localization reagents
depend on the particular type of lipid. For example, ninhydrin will
react with phospholipids with free amino groups. A major limitation
in paper chromatography of lipids is that the extremely sensitive
methods employing mineral acids cannot be used for detection.

NUCLEIC ACID DERIVATIVES

The purine and pyrimidine nucleobases are liberated from parent
nucleic acids by hydrolysis with acid or alkali. Ten milligrams of
ribonucleic acid digested by boiling for 1 hour in 0.1 ml of 72 per cent,

w/w, perchloric acid releases guanine, adenine, cytosine, and uracil. Hydrolysis in 1N HCl under similar conditions gives guanine, adenine, cytidylic acid, and uridylic acid. Constituent nucleotides are obtained by digesting the nucleic acids with 0.3N potassium hydroxide. Potassium is precipitated as $KClO_4$ upon adjustment of the pH to 3.6 by addition of 60 per cent $HClO_4$ [30].

SOLVENTS. The bases, uridylic acid and cytidylic acid, are separated by chromatography with 2-propanol-water-hydrochloric acid (130:37:33, v/v/v). Nucleotides are separated in a solvent prepared by mixing 10 ml of concentrated NH_4OH with 329 ml of water and 661 ml of isobutyric acid. The pH is adjusted to 3.7.

Excellent separation of nucleotides is obtained on anion-exchange paper [31]. Distilled water (500 ml) is added to 100 g of a 50 per cent solution of polyethyleneimine (poly-EI).* Neutralize with concentrated hydrochloric acid and dilute to 2000 ml. Sheets of Whatman 1 washed with distilled water are immersed for 2 seconds in the poly-EI solution and then air-dried. The excess poly-EI and salt are removed by washing the papers several times with distilled water.

Ascending development with 1.0M NaCl for a distance of 10 cm is carried out in an open beaker. Better separation of slow-running compounds is obtained by washing the chromatograms with distilled water after initial development and rechromatographing in the same solvent. Ultraviolet light at 254 mμ is used to detect the nucleotides.

ORGANIC ACIDS

Methods for extracting and purifying organic acids are given in Chapter 4 on Column Chromatography. Mixtures of acids are prepared in 50 per cent, v/v, acetone. Standards should contain 2 mg per milliliter of solvent.

SOLVENTS. Although the solvent systems given in the chapter on column chromatography are suitable for separation of purified organic acids, an unfractionated plant extract may have to be chromatographed two-dimensionally. Cheftel *et al.* [32] recommend ethanol-ammonium hydroxide-water (80:5:15, v/v/v) for development in the first direction. The dried chromatogram is developed in the second direction with ethyl cellosolve-eucalyptol-formic acid (50:50:20, v/v/v). Oxalic, tartaric, citric, malic, maleic, malonic, succinic, fumaric, adipic, sebacic, glycolic, lactic, and aconitic acids are completely separated from each other.

DETECTION. Free acids are easily located on paper chromatograms with an acid-base indicator such as chlorophenol red, bromo-

---

* Obtainable as a 50 per cent aqueous solution of Polymin P from Badische-Anilin und Sodafabrik, Ludwigshafen, Germany.

cresol green, bromophenol blue, or methyl red. Dilute alkali is added to a 0.04 to 0.5 per cent, w/v, ethanolic solution of indicator until it is slightly alkaline.

More permanent records are obtained with the aniline-xylose reagent prepared by dissolving 1 g of xylose in 3 ml of water and mixing with 1 ml of aniline plus 96 ml of methanol. The chromatogram is dipped in the reagent, air-dried for 10 minutes, and heated at 105° to 110°C for 5 minutes or until brown spots appear on a yellow or cream-colored background.

PLANT PIGMENTS

Leaves from which chlorophyll is to be extracted are washed in cold water and stored for at least 30 minutes at 4°C. They are then ground in a Waring Blendor or in a mortar with sand. Ethyl ether, acetone, or methanol is added in the ratio of 50 ml per gram of fresh weight of tissue. The ether extract is further purified by filtration and is washed several times with distilled water.

Anthocyanins are extracted from petal tissues with methanol containing 1 per cent hydrochloric acid. Non-anthocyanin pigments are extracted with methanol. Carotenes are extracted into a solution consisting of equal parts of methanol and light petroleum (bp 60° to 70°C). After the addition of water, the lower (alcohol) layer is discarded and the petroleum fraction is dried with sodium sulfate.

SOLVENTS. The chloroplast pigments are separated on paper with organic solvents such as petroleum ether alone or containing a small percentage of alcohol. Using 0.6 per cent petroleum ether as a second solvent, discrete spots are obtained for neoxanthin, violaxanthin, and chlorophylls a and b [29]. Lutein and zeaxanthin chromatograph together and carotenes move with the advancing solvent front. Petroleum ether-diethyl ether-ethanol (30:10:0.1, v/v/v) solvent system is also used.

The flavonoid pigments, anthocyanins, and pterins have been chromatographed in a large number of solvent systems [2]. Two-dimensional chromatograms may be obtained with ethyl acetate-acetic acid-water (50:2:50, v/v/v) followed by n-butanol-acetic acid-water (4:1:5, v/v/v). The sample should contain 10 to 40 μg of each pigment.

DETECTION. In addition to the natural color of the pigments, identification of these substances is aided by characteristic fluorescent colors under ultraviolet light. The colors are intensified and modified when the chromatogram is sprayed with one of the following reagents: 1 per cent alcoholic ferric chloride, thorium chloride, aluminum chloride, or ferric perchlorate; 1 per cent aqueous lead acetate, basic lead acetate, or sodium carbonate; 2N potassium hydroxide in ethanol; equal parts of 0.1*N* silver nitrate and 5*N* ammonium hydroxide.

SUGARS

SOLVENTS.   Good separation is obtained with either *n*-butanol-pyridine-water (30:20:15, v/v/v); *n*-propanol-water (3:1, v/v); or 2-propanol-pyridine-acetic acid-water (8:8:1:4, v/v/v/v). Amyl alcohol-pyridine-water (4:3:2, v/v/v) is used to separate sugars by circular chromatography [34].

DETECTION.   The aniline hydrogen phthalate reagent is prepared from 1.66 g phthalic acid, 0.93 g freshly distilled aniline, and 100 ml of *n*-butanol saturated with water. The paper is sprayed and then dried at 105° to 110°C for 5 to 10 minutes. A second application of the reagent intensifies the spots.

Reducing sugars appear as brown spots with ammoniacal silver nitrate. The reagent is prepared by mixing equal volumes of 0.1*N* $AgNO_3$ and 5*N* NH_4OH. The sprayed chromatogram is heated as above. Photographic fixer (thiosulfate solution) may be used to remove background color (also see Polyhydric Alcohols).

VITAMINS – VITAMIN A

SOLVENT.   Acetonitrile containing 10 to 50 per cent water on Whatman 54 impregnated with 10 per cent, w/v, Dow Corning silicone stopcock grease in methylene chloride.

DETECTION.   Vitamin A, retinene, and other chromogens react with antimony trichloride applied as a saturated solution in chloroform.

VITAMIN D

SOLVENT.   Ethylene monoethyl ether-*n*-propanol-methanol-water (35:10:30:25, v/v/v/v) or 1-propanol-methanol-water (15:82:3, v/v/v) on Whatman 2 coated with 5 per cent liquid paraffin in petroleum ether.

DETECTION.   Antimony trichloride with heat.

THIAMINE AND ITS PHOSPHATES

SOLVENT.   *n*-Propanol-hydrochloric acid (2:1, v/v) on Whatman 1 impregnated with 0.2 per cent ethylenediamine-tetraacetic acid, Tetra sodium salt (Versene) at pH 8.5 and rinsed thoroughly with distilled water.

DETECTION.   Spray with alkaline ferricyanide (5 per cent $K_3Fe(CN)_6$ in 2*N* sodium hydroxide).

RIBOFLAVIN

SOLVENT. *n*-Butanol-acetic acid-water (4:1:5, v/v/v).
DETECTION. Ultraviolet light; intensify by spraying with 0.05*N* NaOH.

NICOTINIC ACID

SOLVENT. 80 per cent acetone or *n*-propanol in water.
DETECTION. 1 per cent benzidine in 50 per cent ethanol.

PANTOTHENIC ACID

SOLVENT. Water-saturated *n*-butanol.
DETECTION. Folin's reagent.

PYRIDOXINE

SOLVENT. Water-saturated *n*-butanol.
DETECTION. Ehrlich's reagent.

COBALAMINS

SOLVENT. Water-saturated *n*-butanol.
DETECTION. Bioassay.

VITAMIN C

SOLVENT. *n*-Butanol-acetic acid-water (25:6:25, v/v/v) in chamber containing H_2S.
DETECTION. Spray with ammoniacal silver nitrate prepared by dissolving 5 g of silver nitrate in water to which is added 10 ml of ammonium hydroxide. Dilute to 100 ml with water.

References

1. T.I.Williams and H. Weil, *Nature*, **170**, 503 (1952).
2. R. J. Block, E. L. Durrum, and G. Zweig, *A Manual of Paper Chromatography and Paper Electrophoresis*, Academic Press, New York, 2nd ed. (1958).
3. A. J. P. Martin and R. L. M. Synge, *Biochem. J.*, **35**, 91 (1941).
4. E. Lederer and M. Lederer, *Chromatography*, Elsevier Publishing Co., New York (1953).
5. A. H. Beckett, M. A. Beaver, and A. E. Robinson, *Nature*, **186**, 775 (1960).
6. G. B. West, *J. Pharm. Pharmacol.*, **11**, 595 (1959); *Chem. Abstr.*, **54**, 961 (1960).

7. R. C. Fuller, I. C. Anderson, and H. A. Nathan, *Proc. Natl. Acad. Sci. U. S.*, **44**, 518 (1958).
8. J. E. DeVay, A. R. Weinhold, and G. Zweig, *Anal. Chem.*, **31**, 815 (1959).
9. G. Zweig, *Anal. Chem.*, **31**, 821 (1959).
10. D. H. Leaback and P. G. Walker, *Biochem. J. Proc.*, **67**, 22 (1957).
11. J. Carles and S. Lascombes, *J. Chromatog.*, **3**, 90 (1960).
12. I. Smith, *Chromatographic and Electrophoretic Techniques*, Vol. 1, "Chromatography," Interscience Publishers, Inc., New York (1960).
13. J. C. Nichol, *Science*, **129**, 1549 (1959).
14. R. B. Roberts, P. H. Abelson, D. B. Cowie, E. T. Bolton, and R. J. Britten, *Studies of Biosynthesis in Escherichia coli*, Carnegie Institute of Washington (Publication 607), Washington, D. C. (1955).
15. J. C. Giddings and R. A. Keller, *J. Chromatog.*, **2**, 626 (1959).
16. R. B. Fisher, D. S. Parsons, and R. Holmes, *Nature*, **164**, 183 (1949).
17. G. G. Blake, *Anal. Chem. Acta*, **17**, 489 (1957); *Chem. Abstr.*, **53**, 114 (1959).
18. K. Bolewski, W. Loginow, and P. Towarz, *Przyjacio Nauk, Wydzia Mat.-Przyrod, Prace Komisji Mat.-Przyrod.*, **7**, 3 (1958); *Chem. Abstr.*, **52**, 15322 (1958).
19. M. Hejtmanek and J. Hejtmankova, *Chem. Listy*, **52**, 444 (1958); *Chem. Abstr.*, **53**, 979 (1959).
20. R. Mavrodineanu, W. W. Sanford, and A. E. Hitchcock, *Contrib. Boyce Thompson Inst.*, **18**, 167 (1955).
21. C. A. Porter, D. Margolis, and P. Sharp, *Contrib. Boyce Thompson Inst.*, **18**, 465 (1957).
22. A. S. Keston, S. Undenfriend, and M. Levy, *J. Am. Chem. Soc.*, **72**, 748 (1950).
23. R. C. Fuller, *Science*, **124**, 1253 (1956).
24. H. T. Gordon and C. A. Hewel, *Anal. Chem.*, **27**, 1471 (1955).
25. G. Sommer, *Z. Anal. Chem.*, **147**, 241 (1955).
26. H. T. Gordon, W. W. Thornburg, and L. N. Werum, *J. Chromatog.*, **9**, 44 (1962).
27. D. J. D. Hockenhull, *Nature*, **171**, 982 (1953).
28. M. Mizell and S. B. Simpson, Jr., *J. Chromatog.*, **5**, 157 (1961).
29. G. Rouser, A. J. Baumann, G. Kritchevsky, D. Heller, and J. S. O'Brien, *J. Am. Oil Chemists' Soc.*, **38**, 544 (1961).
30. G. W. Crosbie, R. M. S. Smellie, and J. N. Davidson, *Biochem. J.*, **54**, 287 (1953).
31. K. Randerath, *J. Chromatog.*, **10**, 235 (1963).
32. R. I. Cheftel, R. Munier, and M. Macheboeuf, *Bull. Soc. Chim. Biol.*, **35**, 1085 (1953).
33. H. H. Strain, *J. Phys. Chem.*, **57**, 638 (1953).
34. E. Kawerau, *Chromatog. Methods*, **1**, 7 (1956).

Thin-layer Chromatography

S. Mark Henry

History

HISTORICAL accounts generally credit the Russian botanist M. S. Tswett with being the first to realize the great potentialities of chromatographic techniques for separating and identifying materials. Tswett percolated dissolved compounds through a glass column packed with any one of more than 100 adsorbents. The solvent (eluant) distributed the various components of a mixture along the length of the column. Improvement of the adsorbents (including use of ion exchange resins, modified cellulose, etc.) and various modifications of the column, solvent flow control, temperature control, collection and detection techniques, and of other refinements resulted in column chromatography as it is known today. The Tswett technique also underwent metamorphosis in another direction and became paper chromatography. In a procedure employing elements of column and paper chromatography, Izmailov, Williams, and others achieved some success with adsorbents plated out on glass surfaces rather than packed in columns, but numerous difficulties with the technique prevented it from becoming an accepted method until Meinhard and Hall [1] demonstrated the feasibility of incorporating a binder into the absorbent to hold it to the glass support. Kirchner and co-workers [2, 3, 4] employed starch and gypsum binders, increased the size of the glass support, and further increased separation capabilities by developing in an ascending or descending direction instead of in the radial direction used by previous workers. Using mineral adsorbents, they achieved excellent separations and identification of terpenes from essential oils on long glass strips (chromatostrips) or plates (chromatoplates). Widespread use of the "open column" method followed the development by Stahl of an apparatus for preparing chromatoplates with uniformly thin layers of the adsorbent. In less than ten years, the technique, now known as thin-layer chromatography (TLC), has come to be used in virtually every area of biochemical research.

Theory

Partition chromatography, which plays a minor role in TLC, is discussed in the section on paper chromatography. Since TLC is primarily adsorption chromatography, adsorption principles will be discussed briefly. Any compound bound to an adsorbent such as aluminum oxide or silica gel by various physicochemical forces may be eluted with the proper solvent. The solvent establishes a competition between the adsorbed compound and the active areas of the adsorbent. When there is a greater affinity between solvent and adsorbent than between the compound and the adsorbent, elution occurs. Most important of the various factors responsible for elution is the nature of the eluting solvent and of the compound adsorbed. The adsorption affinity of a particular member of any class of compounds is determined by its chemical make-up. For example, the ease with which hydrocarbons become bound to an adsorbent increases proportionately with the number of double bonds. Most organic compounds can be classified in an order of adsorption affinity owing to the presence of functional groups. Lederer and Lederer give the following classification:

> Acids and bases
> Alcohols and thiols
> Aldehydes and ketones
> Halogen containing substances and esters
> Hydrocarbons

The first two classes of compounds above, with highly reactive functional groups, are most easily adsorbed. The others, in the order listed, are less strongly adsorbed.

The eluting ability of a solvent is proportional to its polarity. Trappe gives the "order of solvents" listed in Table 2-1 with reference to silica gel (silicic acid) and alumina. Polarity of a solvent system can be modified by mixing any two or more of the listed solvents thereby enlarging the number in the order of solvents.

Additional discussion of the theoretical basis of adsorption chromatography may be found in the writings of Lederer and Lederer [5], Zechmeister [6], Heftmann [7], Brenner and Pataki [8], and Wren [9]. However, the reader should not be misled by the apparent stress laid on the role of adsorption in TLC, for it is undoubtedly a complex interaction of adsorption, liquid-liquid partition, and, in some cases, ion exchange and diffusion that governs behavior of compounds on various coating materials.

Since reversed-phase TLC is used to some extent, particularly with lipids, brief mention is made of this procedure. In general the method depends on impregnation of the supporting medium (e.g., silica gel) with a hydrophobic material such as silicone or paraffin. The mobile phase, consequently, is usually a highly polar solvent such as methanol or dilute acetic acid. The extent to which any compound moves with the mobile phase is inversely related to the degree of interaction between the hydrocarbon chains of the compound and the nonpolar stationary phase; compounds with short chain lengths and small numbers of double bonds should move more rapidly than those with long carbon chains and large numbers of unsaturated bonds. This is exactly the reverse of that which one would expect with partition chromatography on nonimpregnated, hydrophilic supports.

Experimental

EQUIPMENT

APPLICATORS AND GLASS SUPPORTS.   Thin-layer chromatography is peculiarly attractive because of the simplicity of the equipment required. In fact, the method can be used on a small scale with materials already available in most laboratories. Of course, more elaborate equipment, available commercially, provides for a broader range of application and greater facility. The least expensive, but a very limited, procedure is that described by Peifer [10], who makes use of 8×10 cm glass plates used for lantern slides or 2.5×7 cm microscope slides as the glass support. A thin layer of adsorbent is applied by dipping the slides into a suspension of adsorbent, e.g., silica gel G (Merck) in chloroform or chloroform-methanol. These microchromatoplates may be used after drying them for less than 5 minutes in an oven or over a hot plate. Any small available container, e.g., a beaker covered with Saran Wrap, may be used as a developing chamber.

Larger chromatoplates or strips require the use of an applicator which may be either stationary or adjustable to permit the deposition of any layer up to 2000 μ. The equipment designed by Stahl is in

TABLE 2-1

Trappe's Eluotropic Series of Solvents*		
1. Petroleum ether	6. Dichloromethane	11. n-Propanol
2. Cyclohexane	7. Chloroform	12. Ethanol
3. Carbon disulfide	8. Ether	13. Methanol
4. Carbon tetrachloride	9. Ethyl acetate	14. Water
5. Benzene	10. Acetone	15. Pyridine

* Listed in order of increasing eluting power.

common use and is available commercially (Brinkmann). This applicator (Fig. 2-1) is designed to be used with glass plates measuring
200×200 mm. If an aligning tray is used, up to 5 plates can be prepared simultaneously. A 50×200 cm glass plate is placed at the
beginning and another at the end of the series of plates on the tray.
Two or more smaller plates or strips may be substituted for one
200×200 cm chromatoplate if desired. The applicator, positioned
on one of the end plates, is filled with a slurry of the coating material
and is slowly but steadily moved across the plates releasing a layer
of material through an aperture onto the plates.

A simplified version of the Stahl applicator is also available commercially (Research Specialties Co.). A 250 to 275 μ layer is obtained
with this nonadjustable instrument. The author has had excellent
results with a simple applicator constructed from Plexiglas (Fig. 2-2).
Two $35 \times 200 \times 6$ mm strips are joined with two $35 \times 35 \times 6$ mm end
pieces by means of Plexiglas cement. Working on a level surface, one
of the long strips is raised 250 μ (measured with a feeler gauge or brass
shim) prior to applying the adhesive. Stainless steel may be used in
place of Plexiglas. The leading edge should be rounded to permit
smooth passage from one plate to the next.

Another type of applicator, designed by Mutter and Hofstetter
(unpublished) and modified by Wollish *et al.* [11], also commercially
available (Kensington Scientific Corporation), permits regulation of
the thickness of the layer regardless of the thickness of the glass.

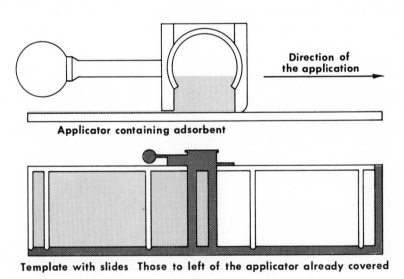

**Direction of
the application**

Applicator containing adsorbent

Template with slides   Those to left of the applicator already covered

Fig. 2-1. Desaga applicator for thin-layer chromatography according to
Stahl (15) (Courtesy, Desaga and Boyce Thompson Institute, Inc.).

Thus, one may use inexpensive window glass 100 mm wide and up to 300 mm in length. The construction data given by Wollish may be easily modified for construction of an applicator for larger plates. Another important feature of this apparatus is the use of a special gauge to assure accuracy in layer thickness.

The coating device designed by Miller and Kirchner and modified by Applewhite *et al.* [12] may also be used for the preparation of (12 mm wide) chromatostrips. Working drawings are available from the authors on request—Western Regional Research Laboratory, Albany, California.

Demole describes the application by hand as follows: Ten milliliters of silicic acid suspension is placed on the center of each plate and the liquid is immediately spread over the whole glass surface with a spatula. The plate is then rapidly tapped or shaken sideways several times so that the liquid film is distributed evenly. After partial drying at room temperature, higher temperatures are used for complete drying and activation. With proper mixing and application of the silica gel suspension, a 0.5 mm layer is obtained.

Uniform layers also may be obtained by using a glass rod supported at any desired distance from the plate either by rubber bands on the ends of the rod or by strips of metal foil on the edges of the plate.

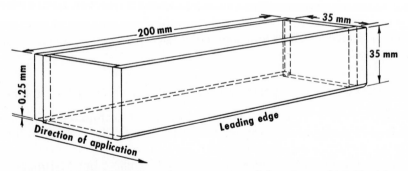

Fig. 2-2. Details of simple applicator constructed from 6 mm thick Plexiglas (Courtesy, R. H. Mandl and Boyce Thompson Institute, Inc.).

OTHER EQUIPMENT.   Other equipment that may be used in thin-layer chromatography is as follows:

Chromatographic Chamber.   Any transparent glass jar of suitable size may be used. Museum jars are especially well suited, but chambers designed especially to hold 200 × 200 mm plates are available from the various manufacturers of thin-layer apparatus. The chromatoplates are held erect either by leaning them against the chamber wall or by inserting them in plate holders commercially available. The chamber may be sealed by applying a layer of silicone stopcock grease to the top edges before lowering the plate glass cover. Chromatostrips 10 to 20 mm wide are developed in cork-stoppered test tubes of the proper diameter. Microchromatoplates or strips on glass microscope slides are developed in any suitable chamber such as a beaker or a staining jar.

Pipettes and Spotting Templates. Samples to be chromatographed are applied with a micropipette or with a microsyringe in 1 to 20 μl quantities per spot. As in paper chromatography, the resolution is greatly affected by the size of the spot at the origin; in no case should this exceed 0.5 cm. After some practice with micropipettes, ordinary melting point capillary tubes may be used for qualitative or semi-quantitative work. For application of samples to microchromatoplates, these tubes should be drawn out over a flame to provide as small a bore as possible.

As many as 20 different samples may be spotted on a 200-mm wide plate. These should be applied no less than 2 cm from the bottom edge of the plate and about 1 to 2 cm apart. A commercially available, transparent spotting template facilitates this operation.

Miscellaneous. Plates that have been coated with adsorbent are dried in air and activated by heating in an oven. For example, silica gel G is kept at 105°C for about 30 minutes. Aluminum or steel drying racks, suitable also for storing chromatoplates, are easily constructed, but these too may be obtained commercially. Coated chromatoplates and strips are stored in a large desiccator over calcium chloride or a similar desiccant. After long storage, it may be necessary to reactivate the plates.

ADSORBENTS AND OTHER COATING MATERIALS

SILICA GEL (SILICIC ACID). Silica gel was found by Kirchner to be the most satisfactory adsorbent for the production of uniform layers and for good resolution of lipids. Merck reagent-grade silicic acid, sifted through a 100 mesh sieve, will suffice, but Mallinckrodt silicic acid (100 mesh labeled "suitable for chromatographic analysis by the method of Ramsey and Patterson") is preferred. Chromatostrips are prepared as follows: Mix 85.5 g of silicic acid with 4.5 g of starch (Clinco-15, Amioca, or other rice starch) in a dry beaker. Slowly add 172 ml of distilled water and heat the mixture with continuous stirring on a steam bath until the temperature reaches 70°C. Cool the thickened mixture under tap water to about 32°C and then carefully add water with stirring until a thin paste that spreads rapidly and smoothly is obtained.

Demole [13] uses a modification of Reitsma's method for preparation of the adsorbent. Water (54 ml) is added to a mixture of 28.5 g of silicic acid and 1.5 g of rice starch. The mixture is heated to near boiling on a gas flame for 2 to 3 minutes until maximum thickening is attained. The slurry is then diluted with 20 to 30 ml of water, reheated rapidly, allowed to cool, and applied to the plate.

The glass strips or plates are coated with a 0.25 to 0.5 mm layer using one of the applicators (*vide supra*) and are activated by drying at 105°C for at least 15 minutes. The finished plates may be stored indefinitely in a desiccator over dry NaOH, KOH, or $CaCl_2$.

If corrosive agents such as H_2SO_4 are to be used in detecting compounds on the plates, 5 to 20 per cent, w/w gypsum (calcinated $CaSO_4$) is substituted for starch as the binding agent. Gypsum-bound silica gel forms a more delicate layer than the starch-bonded material and cannot be marked with soft pencil as in the case of the latter.

Commercially prepared silica gel containing gypsum is supplied as silica gel G for thin-layer chromatography according to Stahl (Merck). A 50 per cent slurry of this is prepared with water by mixing rapidly but thoroughly in a mortar or in a glass-stoppered flask. Thirty-five grams of silica gel G is sufficient for a 250 to 300 μ layer on 5 plates measuring 200 × 200 mm. The adsorbent must be mixed and applied to the plates within four minutes since hardening progresses rapidly after this period. For the preparation of microchromatoplates [10] on glass slides, etc., 35 g of silica gel G is suspended in 100 ml of chloroform or a mixture of chloroform-methanol, 2:1, v/v.

The microscope slides to be coated must be clean and dry. Two of these are dipped simultaneously into a beaker containing the adsorbent suspension, are lifted out, and are permitted to drain against the edge of the beaker. Partially dried plates may be exposed to steam or lightly sprayed with water to initiate hardening of the gypsum. It is necessary to activate only the water-treated plates by heating.

Microchromatoplates may be prepared by aligning up to 75 microscope slides on a template and applying the adsorbent with the Desaga apparatus [14]. The slurry, prepared by mixing 58 ml of water with 30 g of silica gel G, is shaken for 15 seconds in a capped bottle. After another 15 seconds, the applicator is filled with the suspension and the slides are coated. A drop of water beneath each slide holds it firmly in the template. When the adsorbent is dry the slides are removed with the aid of a spatula and are activated by heating as described above.

MODIFIED ADSORBENT LAYERS. The above directions are for preparation of neutral silica gel layers ordinarily used in thin-layer chromatography. It is frequently desirable to employ acidic, basic, or buffered layers, or a layer impregnated with fluorescent material or other chemicals to aid in detection. Some of these modifications are given below.

Acidic Layers. Substitute 0.5N oxalic acid [15] for water in preparing the slurry.

Alkaline Layers.   Use 10 per cent, w/v, silica gel G in 40 per cent, w/v, calcium hydroxide in water [16].

Citrate Buffer.   Prepare slurry with 25 g of silica gel G in 50 ml of 0.1M sodium citrate buffer, pH 3.3 [17].

Other Reagents.   The ability of many compounds to quench fluorescence may be used to advantage by incorporating fluorescent materials into the adsorbent. Kirchner *et al.* [2] use 0.15 g of zinc silicate and 0.15 g of zinc cadmium sulfide per 19 g of silicic acid. The phosphors are dry-mixed with the other components of the coating material. Reitsma [18] adds 0.004 per cent of Rhodamine 6 G to the adsorbent. For detection of derivatives of short-chain alcohols, aldehydes and ketones, acids, amines, and mercaptans, the commercial luminescent chemical #601 (du Pont) is satisfactory [19].

Sulfuric acid may also be incorporated into the adsorbent rather than used as a spray following development. The chromatoplates are coated with a slurry containing 50 g of silica gel G or 45 g of 100 mesh silicic acid and 5 g of plaster of Paris (gypsum) in 102.5 ml of chloroform-methanol-concentrated sulfuric acid (70:30:2.5, v/v/v). Developed plates are heated on an electric hot plate or with a heat lamp to char the organic compounds chromatographed.

Silicic acid as well as some of the other adsorbents may be prepared in a nonaqueous slurry for both standard plates and microchromatoplates. Müller and Honerlagen [20] use acetone instead of water with silica gel G in approximately a 1:2, w/w, ratio. The reader is cautioned that acetone and other organic solvents will mar the finish of plastic aligning and spotting templates.

ALUMINUM OXIDE (ALUMINA).   Calcinated calcium sulfate may be blended with Alcoa Activated Alumina to make a 5 per cent, w/w, mixture, or the adsorbent may be purchased ready-mixed as aluminum oxide G (Merck) or Fluka Alumina. This adsorbent is especially useful for the chromatography of steroids and water-soluble vitamins. The Merck product is prepared as a 1:2 slurry with water and the Fluka as 20:65, w/v.

Modified alumina adsorbents for TLC include basic alumina (pH 9) for adsorption and cation exchange and acid alumina for adsorption and anion exchange.

KIESELGUHR (DIATOMACEOUS EARTH).   This weakly adsorbing material, which is commercially available with gypsum binder, is used for the thin-layer chromatography of sugars, certain insecticides, and numerous other compounds.

CELLULOSE.   Powdered cellulose with gypsum binder also may be obtained commercially (Excorna; Machery, Nagel, and Company). One gram of cellulose is mixed with 6 ml of water, preferably with the aid of a mechanical stirrer. After a few minutes in air, the plates are dried in an oven at 100°C for 1/2 hour. Randerath and Struck [21] use gypsum-free cellulose powder MN 300 prepared as a 20 per cent, w/v, slurry with acetone for coating plates used for thin-layer chromatography of nucleic acid derivatives.

Suspensions of cellulose powder for chromatoplates also may be prepared by triturating 35 g of cellulose powder with 15 g of plaster of Paris and a minimum volume of methanol [10]. The resulting viscous mixture is diluted with methanol and chloroform to yield a final suspension containing 50 g of solids and 100 ml of chloroform-methanol (1:1).

ADSORBENTS FREE OF BINDING AGENTS. The presence of starch or plaster of Paris in adsorbents used for TLC may result in sample recovery problems since these materials are partially soluble in water and in many organic solvents. Adsorbents free of binding agents are supplied by several manufacturers but they are generally too coarse to provide good, thin layers. Adsorbents of a sufficiently small particle size so that adhesion to glass plates occurs without the use of binding agents are available from Woelm (Alupharm Chemicals). To coat 5 plates with a 300 μ layer of these, the following proportions are recommended:

Alumina (acid, neutral, basic)	35 g plus 40 ml water
Silica gel	30 g plus 45 ml water
Magnesium silicate	15 g plus 45 ml water
Polyamide	5 g plus 45 ml ethanol

After mixing in a stoppered flask, the plates are activated by heat in the usual manner. Polyamide and silica gel layers for partition chromatography are dried in air alone.

OTHER COATING MATERIALS; PLATES FOR REVERSED-PHASE CHROMATOGRAPHY. The reader is referred to the fine review by Mangold [19] for additional adsorbents, ion exchangers, and other coating materials which have been used in thin-layer chromatography.

Silica gel G or other adsorbents may be impregnated for reversed-phase partition chromatography either by immersion or by spraying with the proper hydrophobic material. Malins and Mangold [22] perform the impregnation by slowly immersing the plates at room temperature into a 5 per cent solution of silicone in diethyl ether. Winterstein *et al.* [16] use a 5 per cent solution of paraffin oil in petroleum hydrocarbon. Mangold [19] lists other impregnating materials that have been used by various investigators. This information may be further supplemented by consulting the reviews on paper chromatography of lipids by Rouser *et al.* [23] and on glass paper chromatography of lipids by Hamilton and Muldrey [24].

SOLVENT SELECTION
AND ADSORBENT ACTIVATION

Although it is frequently possible to select a good solvent by the empirical method, much time and effort may be saved by consideration of some of the principles of chromatographic separation. Of particular importance are the "eluotropic series of solvents" (see Table 2-1) and the relative adsorption characteristics of the class of compounds to be separated. Thus, knowing that saturated hydrocarbons are adsorbed poorly and unsaturated hydrocarbons are adsorbed according to the increase in the number of their double bonds and the degree of conjugation, one would employ a less polar solvent (high in the eluotropic series) for the former class, while a more polar solvent would be required for elution of the latter or of hydrocarbons with functional groups.

Utilizing these principles, Kirchner et al., using hexane as the solvent, have separated hydrocarbons from nonhydrocarbons, which do not move at all in this solvent. However, addition of ethyl-acetate (15 to 30 ml/100 ml hexane) gives excellent separation of the nonhydrocarbon components. Using ethyl acetate-hexane mixtures, excellent separation of oxygenated terpenes and other essential oil constituents is obtained [3].

The quantity of free water in the silica gel largely determines whether adsorption or liquid-liquid partition is primarily responsible for chromatographic separation. Therefore, silica gel plates to be used for adsorption chromatography with nonaqueous solvents must be activated by drying at 180°C for 1 hour. The plates are then stored in a dry atmosphere, e.g., in a desiccator over anhydrous $CaCl_2$. (Storage in a sealed container is also effective in preventing the silica gel from adsorbing alcohol, toluene, chloroform, and other volatile laboratory reagents.) Controlled deactivation of the silica gel plates for partition chromatography can be accomplished by placing the plates in atmospheres with different vapor pressures. Storage over a mixture of reagent-grade sulfuric acid with water, 1:1, v/v, will result in an increase in weight of 8 per cent due to the uptake of water. Over a saturated solution of calcium chloride hexahydrate, a 17 per cent increase occurs, sufficient for liquid-liquid partition chromatography. An increase to 32 per cent can be obtained with a saturated solution of ammonium sulfate. It is emphasized that the addition of water also weakens the adsorptive properties of silicic acid and alumina, thereby permitting the use of a less polar solvent for elution purposes.

Acetic acid-water (3:1 or 17:3, v/v) is useful for the separation of fatty acids and their methyl esters on silicone-impregnated plates [22]. Winterstein et al. [16] use methanol for the separation of carotenals on plates impregnated with higher paraffins. Since the technique is similar to reversed-phase partition chromatography on paper, any solvent system used with the latter [25] may be used with the thin-layer adaptation. Solvents for the separation of saturated from unsaturated nitriles are also given by Mangold [26]: a mixture of acetic acid-peracetic acid-water (65:10:25, v/v/v) or of acetonitrile-perhydrol-water (70:10:20, v/v/v) oxidizes all unsaturated lipids which then travel with the solvent front. Good separation of saturated nitriles is obtained with the same solvents on siliconized chromatoplates.

A useful method in selecting a suitable solvent is the *microcircular technique* of Stahl. When spotting a sample for chromatography, several aliquots are applied to a second plate coated with the same adsorbent. When the spots are dry, a few microliters of the chromatographic solvent are placed in the center of the sample spot with the aid of a capillary tube. Radial development occurs quite rapidly resulting in concentric rings of the components of the mixture. If these are not already colored, they may be detected with a suitable chromogenic spray or with ultraviolet light. This useful method gives an index of efficiency of the solvent applied.

Even more useful is unidimensional development with various solvents on microchromatoplates coated with the same adsorbent used on the larger plate. Numerous solvents may be so tested with excellent indications of the type of separation to be found on the larger plate.

DEVELOPMENT OF CHROMATOGRAMS

Although 200×200 mm are the standard dimensions for chromatoplates, a development of 100 mm usually gives satisfactory resolution of components. Therefore, if the samples are spotted close to the bottom edge of the plate, one may use the upper half of the plate for a second chromatogram by drying, reactivating, and reversing the plate after initial development. On the other hand, better results are frequently obtained, especially in partition chromatography, if the samples are applied at least 50 mm from the bottom of the plate, thus providing for a longer "equilibration" time before the solvent begins to exert its action on the sample. Saturation of the atmosphere by lining the insides of the chamber with solvent-saturated filter paper also aids in equilibration and speeds development time by one third. While many of the same techniques used in paper chromatography may be used for thin-layer chromatography, e.g., multiple development with the same or different solvents, descending, horizontal, or circular development, wedge strip development, etc., the most common procedure is to use a single solvent system and ascending development. Two-dimensional plates are, however, of special value in the case of samples containing a great many compounds to be separated, e.g., amino acids. The procedure does not differ from that used in paper chromatography (*quod vide*).

SPECIFIC SOLVENTS, ADSORBENTS, AND DETECTION METHODS

Thin-layer chromatography is such a highly flexible technique that the procedures used in one laboratory are seldom employed, without at least minor changes, by others. However, to serve as a guide in working with various classes of compounds, a cross section of some of the solvents, adsorbents, and detection methods is given below.

Most of the methods used for locating substances on thin-layer chromatograms have been taken directly or have been modified from those used in paper chromatography and electrophoresis. The chromogenic spray reagents are, in fact, even more efficient than on paper, perhaps due primarily to the tightness of the spots and the absence of impurities in thin-layer coating materials. One of the principal advantages in the use of noncarbonaceous layers is that one may use highly corrosive sprays for the detection of compounds on the chromatogram.

Some of the more important methods of separating and detecting various classes of compounds on thin layers are described below.

ACIDS.   Aliphatic dicarboxylic acids and other acids are applied as ammonium salts in methanol-water (1:1, v/v) to silica gel G plates which are developed with 96 per cent ethanol-water-25 per cent ammonia (100:12:16, v/v/v). Oxalic acid is applied as an aqueous solution. The solvent travels about 10 cm in 2 hours to give good separation [26].

Petrowitz and Pastuska [27] separate organic acids on silica gel G with either benzol-methanol-glacial acetic acid (45:8:4, v/v/v) or benzol-dioxan-glacial acetic acid (90:25:4, v/v/v). The R_f increases in both solvent systems with increasing number of methyl groups. Cis-trans isomers of unsaturated dicarboxylic acids are also separated. These are detected with soda-alkaline potassium permanganate solution to give yellow spots on a violet-green background.

Any of the common indicator dyes may be used for the detection of acidic compounds. A solution of 0.3 per cent bromocresol green in 80 per cent, v/v, methanol containing 8 drops of 30 per cent, w/v, sodium hydroxide per 100 ml is recommended [2]. Acids appear as yellow spots on a green background. The writer has used bromophenol blue (0.04 per cent, w/v, in ethanol) with equal success. Plates developed with solvents containing acetic acid are heated at 110°C to remove all of the solvent before an indicator dye is used.

ALCOHOLS.   Miller and Kirchner [3] list ten solvents for the separation of alcohols on silica gel. A 15 per cent, v/v, solution of ethyl acetate in hexane is very satisfactory.

To visualize the alcohols, chromatograms are sprayed with a 0.05 per cent solution of fluorescein in water and are then exposed to bromine vapor by blowing gently across the top of a bottle of bromine.

ALDEHYDES AND KETONES.   Ketones in oils are separated by development on silica gel plates with 10 per cent, v/v, ethyl acetate in hexane. Rietsma [18] uses a plate coated with silicic acid plus starch (28.5:1.5, w/w) and Rhodamine G.

This procedure is advantageous in that it not only detects ketones (and aldehydes), but indicates those that are heat- and acid-sensitive. Those compounds not immediately detectable under ultraviolet light may be revealed by spraying with a solution containing 0.4 g of 2,4-dinitrophenylhydrazine in 100 ml of $2N$ HCl. Spots are marked in visible and in ultraviolet light; the plate is heated at 105°C for 10 minutes and again inspected in visible and ultraviolet light. The terpenic ketone dinitrophenylhydrazone derivatives often have a color characteristic of the degree of unsaturation.

ALKALOIDS.   Alkaloids are isolated and identified by the procedure of Waldi *et al.* [28]. On the basis of behavior on silica gel G in various solvents ranging from chloroform or methanol to a mixture of chloroform-acetone-diethylamine (5:4:1, v/v/v), the alkaloid is placed into either of two groups. The R_f values, color reactions with the iodoplatinate reagent, and fluorescence characteristics under ultraviolet light aid in final identification.

The iodoplatinate used by Waldi is prepared by mixing equal parts of a 0.3 per cent aqueous platinic chloride solution with a 6 per cent aqueous solution of potassium iodide. The developed and dried plate is saturated with the spray reagent.

Dragendorff's reagent (see ref. 24) may also be used.

AMINO ACIDS.   One-dimensional chromatography on chromatoplates, as on paper, fails to resolve all amino acids generally found in biological material. However, the system described by Brenner and Pataki [8] gives fair separation of many amino acids and, perhaps more important, separates leucine from isoleucine. The amino acid mixture, dissolved in $0.1N$ HCl, is chromatographed on silica gel G with methyl ethyl ketone-pyridine-water-acetic acid (70:15:15:2, v/v/v/v).

Excellent separation of amino acids is obtained with a two-dimensional system [29]. The mixture is applied to one corner of a silica gel G plate and is chromatographed in the first direction with chloroform-methyl alcohol-17 per cent ammonia (2:2:1, v/v/v). The solvent travels 15 cm in about 75 minutes. After drying in an air stream for 20 minutes, the plate is developed in the second direction with phenol-water (75:25, w/w). The development time for the second solvent is about 180 minutes for 15 cm.

Phenylthiohydantoin derivatives of N-terminal amino acids, resulting from the degradation of peptides, may be chromatographed on silica gel layers [30]. A mixture of heptane-pyridine-ethyl acetate (5:3:2, v/v/v) separates the phenylthiohydantoins of glycine, proline, and leucine in about 30 minutes. These are detected with Feigl's I_2-sodium azide reagent (see ref. 24) after spraying with an aqueous starch solution if the chromatoplates contain gypsum. This step is not necessary if the adsorbent is bound with starch.

As on paper, amino acids may be detected with ninhydrin. Aromatic amino acids, ordinarily detectable on paper with ultraviolet light, are not readily discernible on silica gel layers. This difficulty is easily remedied by spraying the plates with a 10^{-4} per cent solution of fluorescein.

Sulfur amino acids and certain other basic nitrogen compounds are detected with the iodoplatinate reagent.

ANIONS. Inorganic halogen-containing substances are separated on silica gel G layers with acetone-n-butanol-concentrated ammonia-water (65:20:10:5, v/v/v/v). NaCl, KBr, and KI are detected with 0.1 per cent bromocresol purple in ethanol adjusted to neutrality with a drop of dilute ammonia. A 1 per cent solution of fluorescein is also used. The fluoride ion is visualized by spraying the plate with a 0.1 per cent solution of zirconium alizarin dye in strong hydrochloric acid [31].

CAROTENOIDS. β-Carotene, zeaxanthin, and other carotenoids are separated on silica gel containing starch by using n-hexane-ether (3:7, v/v) as the solvent [32]. Development is complete in about 15 minutes. The inherent color of these compounds permits one to observe the progress of development and separation.

CATIONS. 1. H_2S Group. Hg^{++}, Bi^{+++}, Cd^{++}, Pb^{++}, and Cu^{++} are separated on silica gel G with n- butanol-HCl (1.5N)-acetonylacetone (100:20:0.5, v/v/v). The chromatoplates are sprayed with 2 per cent potassium iodide in ethanol and dried. The plates are then exposed to ammonia vapor followed by exposure to H_2S. Characteristic colors are obtained [33].

2. $(NH_4)_2S$ Group. Develop on silica gel G with acetone-concentrated HCl-acetonylacetone (100:1:0.5, v/v/v). The developed and dried plate is placed in an atmosphere of ammonia and, on removal, is sprayed with 0.5 per cent, w/v, 8-hydroxyquinoline in 60 per cent, v/v, ethanol. Co^{++} and Cr^{+++} are detectable after NH_3. The oxine is required for detection of Fe^{+++}, Zn^{++}, and Mn^{++}. The plates are viewed in visible and ultraviolet light, the latter for the detection of Ni^{++} and Al^{+++} as well as others of this group.

ESTERS. A method for the rapid analysis of epoxy, monohydroxy, dihydroxy, and other esters as well as for mixtures of mono-, di-, and triglycerides is described by Vioque and Holman [34]. The esters are separated on a silica gel G plate with diethyl ether in hexane. Ten to thirty per cent diethyl ether is used depending on the types of esters to be separated.

The esters are located on the plates by reacting them with iodine vapors or by spraying with 2', 7'-dichlorofluorescein. Quantitative data are obtained by chromatographing several samples of the ester mixture on a plate. The components of one of these are then detected with 2',7'-dichlorofluorescein while the remainder of the plate is shielded from the spray. The rows of spots are then delineated and the silica gel in each parallel row is scraped off with a spatula and placed in a test tube. The esters are then converted to their hydroxamic acid derivatives and subsequently to colored complexes with ferric perchlorate. A colorimeter or spectrophotometer is used to ascertain the quantity of the colored derivatives.

An ingenious modification of the hydroxamic acid action is used by Demole [13] for the detection of esters. A piece of filter paper, moistened with hydroxylamine solution (vide infra) is placed in contact with the chromatoplates and held in place with a second glass plate and the whole is laid on a warm surface (30° to 45°C). The esters volatilize and are fixed on the impregnated paper where they are converted to hydroxamic acids. After 10 to 15 minutes, the sheet is removed and sprayed with a solution of 0.5N HCl containing 0.5 per cent ferric chloride. Violet spots appear in positions corresponding to those of the esters on the chromatoplate.

Preparations of Paper Impregnated with Hydroxylamine: Just before use, a solution of 7 per cent, w/v, of hydroxylamine hydrochloride is mixed with an equal volume of 12 per cent, w/v, potassium hydroxide. The mixture is sprayed on the paper which is used while still moist.

The fluorescein-bromine test described above is also used in the detection of esters.

ESTROGENS. Estrone, estradiol, and estriol, chromatographed on silica gel G with benzol-ethanol (9:1, v/v), are detected with antimony pentachloride (12 per cent, w/v) in carbon tetrachloride [35]. Estrone appears as dark brown, 17-β-estradiol as light brown, and estriol as red violet.

GLYCOSIDES. Several types of glycosides are separated on silica gel G chromatoplates with methylenechloride-methanol-formamide (80:19:1, v/v/v). A gradient technique may be used to separate aglycones from the glycoside mixture. The silica gel plate is developed first with chloroform-methanol (9:1, v/v) to distribute the glycosides over the first 6 cm of the plate. After removing the solvent by drying in an air stream, the plate is developed with chloroform-acetone (65:35, v/v). The second solvent moves the aglycones to the upper half of the plate, leaving all of the glycosides behind [36].

Visualization is accomplished by spraying the plate with a mixture of concentrated sulfuric acid and acetic anhydride (1:3, v/v). The plate is then heated for 15 minutes at 100°C. The chromogenic spray, antimony trichloride, prepared as a saturated solution in chloroform, is used for glycosides and several other classes of compounds. The chromatoplate is heated for 5 minutes at 105°C after being sprayed. Compounds not observed in visible light are frequently detected by viewing the plate under ultraviolet light.

INSECTICIDES. 1. Thiophosphoric Esters. Separation of Diazinon, Parathion, Meta-Systox, Malathion, Chlorthion, Fac, and Rogor is obtained on silica gel with hexane-acetone (4:1, v/v) as the solvent [37]. The esters are detected with 0.5 per cent palladium chloride in weak hydrochloric acid.

2. Chlorinated Hydrocarbons. Aldrin, Dieldrin, DDT, Perthane, hexachlorocyclohexane, and Methoxychlor are separated with hexane on aluminum oxide (Fluka). The positions of these are revealed by spraying with 0.5 per cent, w/v, N,N-dimethyl-p-phenylenediamine hydrochloride in sodium ethylate (1 g sodium in 100 ml ethanol). The plate is then sprayed with water and after 1 minute the spots may be discerned under ultraviolet light.

LIPIDS. Thin-layer chromatography is especially valuable in the separation of lipids into classes. Some of the solvents which have been used are listed in Table 2-2. In many cases, sufficient information is obtained from the silica gel separation so that no further analysis is necessary. More often, however, adsorption TLC must be followed by reversed-phase chromatography, gas-liquid chromatography, or other methods of analysis depending on the information desired. Fractionation by other methods may also precede thin-layer chromatography so that a relatively pure class of compounds will appear on the chromatoplate.

Many reagents have been employed for the detection of lipids on thin-layer chromatograms. These have been summarized by Mangold [19], who prefers to use several indicators consecutively. His technique consists of preparing duplicate chromatoplates, one of which is subjected to iodine (vapors or a 1 per cent, w/v, methanolic spray) which imparts a brown coloration to unsaturated compounds. After evaporation of the iodine (5 minutes) the plate is sprayed with the 2', 7'-dichlorofluorescein reagent. The reagent is prepared as a 0.2 per cent solution in ethanol. Lipids on silica gel G plates appear as bright yellow-green spots with ultraviolet light (270mμ). Finally, Mangold chars the lipids by spraying with saturated chromic-sulfuric

TABLE 2-2

SOLVENTS FOR THIN-LAYER CHROMATOGRAPHY OF LIPIDS ON SILICA GEL° [19]

Fats, oils, and waxes, oxygenated acids and their esters
Tetralin-hexane, 1:1, 1:3
Petroleum hydrocarbon†-diethyl ether, 95:5, 90:10, 80:20, 50:50
Petroleum hydrocarbon-diethyl ether-acetic acid, 90:10:1, 80:20:1, 70:30:2
Diethyl ether
Diisopropyl ether
Diisopropyl ether-acetic acid, 100:1.5
n-Propanol-concentrated aqueous ammonia, 2:1, followed by chloroform-benzene, 3:2, followed by carbon tetrachloride

Phospholipids, sulfolipids, and glycolipids
Chloroform-methanol-water, 70:22:3, 65:30:5, 65:25:4, 60:35:8
Chloroform-methanol-aqueous ammonia, 3:1, with 40 ml of concentrated aqueous ammonia/liter; 1:3 with 40 ml of concentrated aqueous ammonia/liter
Chloroform-methanol-aqueous sulfuric acid
Chloroform-methanol (containing 5% of 0.1N sulfuric acid) 97:3, 4:1‡
n-Propanol-water, 7:3
n-Propanol-aqueous ammonia (12%), 4:1
n-Propanol-concentrated aqueous ammonia, 7:3
n-Propanol-aqueous ammonia (12%), 4:1, followed by ethylene chloride-methanol, 49:1, followed by chloroform-acetic acid (96%), 95:5
n-Butanol-pyridine-water, 3:2:1

Steroids
Benzene, toluene, cyclohexane, hexane, dichloroethane
Benzene-ethyl acetate, 9:1, 2:1
Benzene-ethanol, 49:1, 95:5, 9:1
Cyclohexane-benzene, 4:1, 1:1
Cyclohexane-ethyl acetate, 19:1, 17:3, 9:1, 7:3

Bile acids
Upper phase of the system, toluene-acetic acid-water 10:10:1, 5:5:1
n-Butanol-acetic acid-water, 10:1:1

Triterpenoic acids and esters
Benzene, cyclohexane, methylene chloride, diisopropyl ether, ethyl acetate, butyl acetate
Cyclohexane-toluene, 4:1, saturated with formic acid
Diethyl ether-hexane, 1:1
Diisopropyl ether-acetone, 5:2
Diisopropyl ether-acetone, 5:2 with 5% pyridine
Ethyl acetate-methanol-diethyl amine, 14:4:3
Chlorobenzene-acetic acid, 9:1
Methylene chloride-pyridine, 7:2

° All ratios are v/v.
† Usually petroleum hydrocarbon, bp 60 to 70°C (mainly hexane).
‡ On silica gel G containing 10% ammonium sulfate.

acid solution. This reagent discloses unsaturated lipids as brown spots even before heating. Other compounds char at higher temperatures. There are few organic compounds that will not be detected by heating the chromatoplate over a hot plate or with a heat lamp until SO_3^{--} fumes appear. Mineral acid may also be sprayed as the concentrated reagent or may be diluted with water or combined with other reagents.

The second chromatoplate used by Mangold has a phosphor incorporated into the silica gel. The commercial luminescent chemical #601 is added to make a 1 per cent, w/w, mixture with silica gel G. Derivatives of short-chain alcohols, aldehydes and ketones, acids, amines, and mercaptans are easily detected with this reagent. Adsorbents containing 0.004 per cent Rhodamine 6 G or 0.04 per cent sodium fluorescein are equally useful. These may be used also as spray reagents after development of the chromatoplates. Rouser *et al.* [38] prepare Rhodamine 6 G as a 0.001 per cent solution in 0.25M dipotassium hydrogen phosphate. Greater sensitivity is achieved if the plates are observed while still wet under both short wave and long wave ultraviolet light.

NITRAMINE COMPOUNDS.   Compounds such as explosives containing nitramine are separated on silica gel G with petroleum ether (bp 40 to 60°C) in acetone (2:1.2, v/v). They are detected by spraying with 1 per cent diphenylamine in ethanol and exposing for 5 minutes to a 125 w mercury lamp (black glass filter removed). Blue-violet spots appear on a faint brownish background [39].

NUCLEIC ACID DERIVATIVES.   Purines, pyrimidines, nucleosides, and nucleotides chromatograph well on cellulose layers. A slurry is prepared by mixing 15 g of cellulose powder containing plaster of Paris with 100 ml of distilled water and shaking vigorously for 45 seconds. The suspension is applied to the plates with a spreader and allowed to dry overnight at room temperature. Plaster of Paris does not interfere with detection of the compounds when neutral or acid solvents are used.

Distilled water is used for the separation of purines, pyrimidines, and nucleosides. Saturated ammonium sulfate-1M sodium acetate-2-propanol (80:18:2, v/v/v) is used for the separation of 2'-adenosine monophosphate, 3'-adenosine monophosphate, 2'-guanine monophosphate, and 3'-guanine monophosphate. Tertiary amyl alcohol-formic acid-water (3:2:1, v/v/v) gives excellent separation of the nucleotides on cellulose; *n*-butanol-acetone-acetic acid-5 per cent aqueous ammonia-water (3.5:2.5:1.5:1.5:1, v/v/v/v/v) separates nucleotides on cellulose and silica gel.

Developed chromatograms are dried for 5 minutes at 100°C and the nucleic acid derivatives are detected by examination of the plate under ultraviolet light [21, 40].

PEPTIDE DERIVATIVES. Esters of N-substituted amino acids, dipeptides, and tripeptides are chromatographed on silica gel with chloroform-acetone (9:1, 8:2, v/v) or cyclohexanone-ethyl acetate (1:1, v/v). Chloroform-ethanol (9:1, v/v) is used for the separation of higher acyl-oligopeptide esters as well as acyl-, di-, and tripeptide esters with polar groups in the side chain. Compounds not protected at the carboxyl or amino end remain at the origin [41].

The same systems are used for the separation of carbobenzoxy, p-nitrocarbobenzoxy, trifluoroacetyl, tosyl, and phthalyl derivatives of amino acids up to pentapeptides containing glycine, alanine, leucine, valine, glutamic acid, tyrosine, and histidine as well as their methyl, ethyl, benzyl, and cyanomethyl esters.

The dried chromatograms are sprayed with a 0.05 per cent solution of morin (3,5,7,2',4'-pentahydroxyflavone). The intermediates are then detected by ultraviolet fluorescence or absorption.

PHENOLS. Phenols are separated with 15 to 20 per cent ethyl acetate on silica gel containing starch.

Diazotized p-nitroaniline, $FeCl_3$, and other reagents used in paper chromatography are used on thin-layers for detecting phenols. Mix immediately before use: 1 volume of an aqueous solution of 0.7 g p-nitroaniline and 9 ml of concentrated hydrochloric acid per 100 ml, 1 volume of 1 per cent sodium nitrate solution, and 2 volumes of 5 per cent sodium bicarbonate solution. After spraying, dry at 40 to 50°C. Phenols appear as brownish spots.

An alternate procedure is to apply 10 μg of each phenol or the mixture of phenols in methanol to the chromatoplate. Diazotized p-nitroaniline is then applied to the origin by means of an atomizer. The plate is dried for 10 to 15 minutes at 40 to 50°C and, when cool, is developed with n-hexane and ether (2:1, v/v). Characteristic colors are obtained by spraying the plate, after development, with 10 per cent sodium carbonate solution [13].

SUGARS. Excellent separation of sugars is obtained on Kieselguhr G layers buffered with acetate [42]. Thirty grams of Kieselguhr G is suspended in 60 ml of a 0.02M sodium acetate solution in water. The plates layered with this material are activated by heating at 100°C for 30 minutes. The solvent consists of a mixture of ethyl acetate and 65 per cent 2-propanol (65:35, v/v).

Prey et al. [43] list several other solvents for the separation of mono-, di-, and trisaccharides on silica gel and Kieselguhr, and describe an improved wedge strip technique for the separation of components present in unfavorable ratios.

Visualization of the sugars is accomplished by means of the anisaldehyde-sulfuric acid reagent prepared immediately before use by mixing 9 ml of 95 per cent ethyl alcohol with 0.5 ml of concentrated sulfuric acid plus 0.5 ml of anisaldehyde (anisic aldehyde). The plates are sprayed and heated 5 to 10 minutes at 90 to 100°C to produce characteristic colors with the different sugars.

SULFONAMIDES. Sulfanilic acid, sulfanilamide, and other sulfonamides are separated with chloroform-heptane-ethanol (1:1:1,v/v/v) on silica gel G. The *p*-dimethylaminobenzaldehyde reagent is used for visualization following chromatography [11].

TERPENES. Terpenes and other essential oil constituents are separated on silica gel containing starch or plaster of Paris as a binder. Hexane, carbon tetrachloride, chloroform, benzene, or 15 per cent ethyl acetate is used for development [2].

Use either 5 per cent, v/v, nitric acid in sulfuric acid or 20 per cent, v/v, antimony pentachloride in chloroform for visualization.

TETRAPYROLLIC PIGMENTS AND CAROTENOIDS. The porphyrins, bilirubin, and biliverdin are separated on silica gel plates with benzene-ethyl acetate-ethyl alcohol (90:20:7.5, v/v/v). β-Carotene, zeaxanthin, and other carotenoids are separated on silica gel using *n*-hexane-ether (3:7, v/v) as the solvent. Development is complete in about 15 minutes [32]. The inherent colors of the compounds permit one to observe the progress of development and preclude the use of additional reagents for visualization.

UBIQUINONES. Coenzymes Q_{10} (ubiquinones) are separated on silica gel G with benzene-chloroform (1:1, v/v) and are visualized by spraying the chromatoplate with Rhodamine B and viewing under ultraviolet light. Wagner *et al.* [44] employ this procedure for initial separation and isolation, but use reversed-phase thin-layer chromatography for further characterization and identification. For reversed-phase, acetone-water (9:1, v/v) saturated with paraffin is used as the chromatographic solvent on a silica gel G plate impregnated with paraffin (5 per cent in ether).

VITAMINS (FAT-SOLUBLE). Good separation of the fat-soluble vitamins is obtained on thin layers of alumina. Davidek and Blattna [45] apply dry aluminum oxide to a glass plate and obtain a fairly uniform layer by using a glass rod with a rubber band at each end as a spreader. The plate is held at an acute angle during development in any one of more than a dozen organic solvents.

The vitamins are applied to the plate in either petroleum ether or ethanol and are detected with 70 per cent perchloric acid or 98 per cent sulfuric acid. Charring agents are applied to the plates prepared with dry alumina by allowing them to be soaked up by the alumina in a direction perpendicular to that of development. A characteristic blue color is obtained when vitamin A is heated with sulfuric acid. The corresponding aldehyde, retinene, may be converted to a deeply colored Rhodamine derivative on the chromatoplate [46, 47]. The D vitamins are also detectable with antimony trichloride or tetrachloride or other reagents used for the detection of steroids on paper chromatograms. Vitamin E (tocopherol) is detected with a 20 per cent, w/v, solution of phosphomolybdic acid in ethanol [48]. The sprayed chromatoplates are dried at room temperature and are then treated with gaseous ammonia. The same reagent is used for the detection of alkaloids, uric acid, xanthine, creatine, and similar compounds. Vitamin K is easily detected on adsorbent layers containing sodium fluorescein. Tocopherols are separated on silica gel G or on aluminum oxide (Fluka) with benzene.

VITAMINS (WATER-SOLUBLE). Vitamins of the B-complex and vitamin C are chromatographed on silica gel G. If fluorescein (2 per cent, w/w) is incorporated into the latter, vitamin B_2 (riboflavin) is detected as a yellow fluorescent spot under long wave ultraviolet light. With short wave length (254 mμ) ultraviolet light, vitamin B_1 (thiamine), and nicotinamide are seen. The iodoplatinate reagent is used for biotin, but may also be used for the others listed above. Vitamin B_6 (pyridoxine) gives a blue color when sprayed with a 0.1 per cent solution of dichloroquinone-chloramide in ethanol followed by ammoniacal vapors. Calcium pantothenate is detected with ninhydrin. A violet color is observed when the plate is heated briefly at 160°C. The cyanogen bromide reagent may be used for the detection of pyridoxine [49].

IONOPHORESIS. Honegger [17] describes the ionophoretic separation of amines and amino acids on thin layers of silica gel G, Kieselguhr G, and aluminum oxide G. The same author also describes a combination of thin-layer ionophoresis and chromatography for the two-dimensional separation of these compounds. Separations by these methods are as good as and, in some respects, superior to results obtained with paper.

QUANTITATIVE METHODS

Quantitative determination of esters on thin-layer chromatograms by colorimetric analysis of hydroxamic acid-iron complexes is discussed above [49].

Any organic compound capable of being charred can be measured quantitatively by a somewhat similar method. In this case a densitometer rather than a colorimeter is used. Privett and Blank [50] employ a Photovolt densitometer (Model 52, 501A), with an attached stage for semiautomatic plotting of curves. The slit size is 1×7.5 mm. Substances to be measured are chromatographed on thin layers of silica gel G. The dried plates are then sprayed with 50 per cent aqueous sulfuric acid and are heated on a hot plate to char the organic compounds. Density readings are taken at 1 mm intervals between the origin and the solvent front and absorbance versus distance is plotted. Areas under the peaks are directly proportional to the amount of sample of any individual compound.

Peifer [10] uses a similar method for quantitative evaluation of substances on microchromatoplates. The latter are coated with silica gel G by dipping, are steamed, and are heat-activated prior to development. Absorbance measurements using a 1 × 3 mm slit are made prior to chromatography to correct for nonuniformity of the layer. The samples (standards and unknowns) are applied and chromatographed and the plates, after being dried, are sprayed with 29 per cent perchloric acid. On being heated, cholesterol and other lipids appear first as purple and then as brown to black spots.

Absorbance readings are taken at 1 mm intervals and are plotted against distance. With sufficient replicates, probable error is about ±5 per cent.

Measurement of spot area, frequently used in paper chromatography, is also applicable to thin-layer chromatography. For the (semi) quantitative estimation of tocopherols, for example, several different concentrations of the antioxidants are applied to a chromatoplate alongside mixtures containing the compounds to be measured. After development, the plate is sprayed with a solution of phosphomolybdic acid. The area of the resulting spot is proportional to the quantity of antioxidant [48].

Other quantitative methods used in paper chromatography, such as the quantitative measurement of radioactivity or the formation and measurement of radioactive derivatives, may also be used with little or no modification. For example, serial sections of a strip may be scraped off the plate into planchets or the adsorbent in the sections may be treated with a suitable eluant to free a compound of radioactivity-absorbing materials.

RECORDING CHROMATOGRAPHIC DATA

Because of the relatively thick glass support and the fragility of the adsorbent layer, thin-layer chromatograms are not as easily stored as paper chromatograms. However, the results are easily recorded by several methods. The spots may be traced or copied or photographed in either color or black and white. An Eastman Kodak Verifax copier has been used successfully by the author. Chromatoplates copied by this or similar instruments should first be wrapped in transparent plastic, especially when corrosive spray reagents have been used. Excellent photographs are obtained if the spots are outlined with a stylus. The layers themselves may be stored after stripping them off with an adhesive-backed tape. An alternate method is to infiltrate with Label Glaze (Fisher). The solution of polymerized resin, into which the plates are dipped, binds the adsorbent layer so that it can be stripped off the plate [51].

As with paper chromatograms, autoradiograms of compounds labeled with radioactive isotopes can be obtained. With gamma emitters, autoradiograms may be prepared from films removed from the plate with tape or Label Glaze. Beta emitters must be in direct contact with the X-ray film used for the autoradiogram. With modifications of the equipment normally used for scanning paper chromatograms, radioactivity scans of chromatostrips may be obtained.

Applications and Evaluation

SCOPE

A number of classes of compounds and many specific substances of interest to the biochemist and others are listed in the preceding pages. These are representative examples and are intended to serve as a guide for the thin-layer chromatographic separation of similar materials. Additional literature citations for numerous other compounds are to be found in the books by Stahl [52] and by Randerath [53] and in the reviews by Mangold [19] and Wollish [11] and are also available from the manufacturers of thin-layer apparatus.

The use of TLC in lipid research has been especially fruitful. In addition to being used for separation of numerous individual lipids, it has been applied to the following types of fractionations [19]:

ACCORDING TO CLASS OF COMPOUNDS. The types and numbers of functional groups determine the class separation of long chain hydrocarbons, alcohols, aldehydes, acids, mono-, di-, and triglycerides, and other lipids.

ACCORDING TO POSITION IN A HOMOLOGOUS SERIES. Alcohols (as 3,5-dinitrobenzoates), aldehydes and ketones (as 2,4-dinitrophenylhydrazones), and acids (as anilides) are separated on silicic acid layers. Reversed-phase partition chromatography on siliconized silicic acid layers is used for the separation of long-chain lipids. Good separation according to degree of unsaturation is also obtained by forming mercuric acetate adducts [54].

ACCORDING TO CIS-TRANS ISOMERISM OR POSITIONAL ISOMERISM. Menthol, neomenthol, isomenthol, and neoisomenthol are separated on silica gel G with either benzene, methanol, or mixtures of the two [55].

MICROCHEMICAL REACTIONS

Relative chromatographic positions should be considered merely as clues in identification of a compound. Additional information is obtained through the use of specific spray reagents imparting characteristic colors in some cases, but the formation of derivatives and/or the use of other chemical means are frequently required. TLC is an excellent medium for the analysis of compounds by all of the above methods. Miller and Kirchner [3] demonstrated its usefulness in their investigation of terpenes and other essential oil constituents. Identification of citral is cited as an example of identification through analysis of the reaction products. This compound is oxidized to geranic acid (with 30 per cent hydrogen peroxide and exposure to ultraviolet light) and is reduced to geraniol. The R_f values of the parent compound in numerous solvents on silica gel and of the two reaction products established the identity of the compound in question. The same authors give full details on the following reactions: oxidation, reduction, dehydration, hydrolysis, and preparation of 3,5-dinitrobenzoates, phenylhydrazones, and semicarbazones. Most of these are performed on the adsorbent layer using slight modifications of standard procedures (cf. refs. 55 and 56). Some reactions, such as preparation of 3,5-dinitrobenzoates, must be conducted on a micro scale in a small test tube prior to chromatography.

UNIVERSAL REAGENTS

TLC becomes even more simplified and advantageous if one makes use of the so-called "universal" reagents described by Ertel and Horner [57]. These strongly oxidizing mixtures show the presence of organic substances through a color change. One of these reagents is a solution of 3 g of sodium bichromate in 2 ml of water and 10 ml of sulfuric acid. The sprayed chromatoplate is heated for 10 minutes at 110°C. The organic substances appear as yellow-green spots on a red background. They become completely green if the plate is heated a second time.

The second "universal" reagent is prepared by carefully dissolving 0.5 g of potassium permanganate in 15 ml of sulfuric acid. Larger quantities of this explosive mixture should not be formulated. The dry chromatoplate is sprayed with the reagent after development. Compounds on the plate are white on a red background. The coloring of the background gradually increases as the silica gel absorbs water.

DETECTION OF OXIDIZABLE COMPOUNDS

Oxidizable compounds in a mixture are easily detected by the following procedure: Apply test substance in one corner of a 20 × 20 cm chromatoplate and develop with any appropriate solvent. Following development, dry the plate and spray uniformly with 5 per cent, v/v, hydrogen peroxide in ethanol. Dry the chromatoplate and develop in a direction perpendicular to the first with the same solvent. Oxidizable compounds are those that do not fall on a straight line connecting the majority of the spots. The method may be used for the detection of cystine and methionine on thin-layer or paper chromatograms.

REACTION TIME AND PREPARATIVE CHROMATOGRAPHY

TLC is especially useful in the rapid determination of reaction time and in the isolation of intermediates and reaction products. An example is the reaction between catalposide and Amberlite IRA-400-OH. The glucoside and the resin are mixed and heated at 80°C in water. Periodically, beginning immediately after mixing the 2 components, an aliquot of the mixture is spotted on a silica gel G chromatoplate. On developing in 20 per cent methanol in ether, it is found that the glucoside, an ester of p-hydroxybenzoic acid, is converted in less than an hour to the ester's alcohol component. Simultaneously, a third compound, the reaction product, appears on the chromatoplate. Formation of this product is complete in 8 to 10 hours [58].

The applicability of this method for the isolation of small quantities of intermediates of chemical reactions is increased by using thicker (1 mm) adsorption layers. From 50 to 100 mg of material can be separated on a single plate. Should even larger quantities be desired, a glass column filled with the same adsorbent and bedded in the same solvent used for the chromatoplate may be required.

FRACTIONATION MONITORING

Chromatoplates and strips are also of value in the monitoring of samples from fractionation systems. For example, aliquots collected automatically in tubes from a column may be checked rapidly for the presence of lipids or other compounds by applying a few microliters from each tube to a silica gel plate. The plate is then examined directly under ultraviolet light or is treated with one or more spray reagents such as 2',7'-dichlorofluorescein or sulfuric acid. The presence of mixtures in the tubes is ascertained by chromatographing the samples prior to use of a reagent for visualization.

COMPARISONS OF THIN-LAYER CHROMATOGRAPHY WITH OTHER METHODS

ADVANTAGES. Thin-layer or chromatostrip chromatography may be accurately considered to be a combination of paper and column

chromatography, providing most of the advantages of the latter procedures and few of the disadvantages. This "open column" method is
simple enough to be handled by *inexperienced personnel* with equipment that may be easily constructed in any small machine shop or
purchased from any of several manufacturers. The use of glass microscope slides, or lantern slides coated by the dipping technique,
eliminates completely the need for an applicator, template, etc., but
severe limitations are imposed as a result. The speed of TLC is,
perhaps, its greatest advantage. Excellent separation of components
of a mixture is usually obtained in 30 to 60 minutes with the proper
choice of solvent and adsorbent. Aqueous solvents may take somewhat longer. The rapidity of the method is especially noticeable in
two-dimensional chromatography. Paper chromatography of amino
acids on two-dimensional chromatograms requires at least 2 days;
similar separation of amino acids on chromatoplates can be accomplished in less than 5 hours. The sensitivity is also increased as a
result of lesser chromatographic diffusion even with larger quantities
of material than can be applied on paper. Relatively better separation
is, of course, another result of the tightness of the spots.

Ease of detection of compounds on chromatoplates is another
advantage over both column and paper chromatography. The inclusion of indicators such as fluorescein permits detection with or without the use of additional spray reagents. Corrosive spray reagents,
previously limited to glass paper chromatograms, are also used on
silica gel, alumina, and other thin layers to excellent advantage. The
importance of this lies in the fact that any organic substance is detectable, under proper conditions, by charring with mineral acid. Even
such inert compounds as camphor may be detected on silica gel by
spraying with a reagent such as a mixture of sulfuric and nitric acids.

While paper chromatography and column chromatography are best
conducted with large sheets of paper or large volume columns,
respectively, TLC is of such a nature as to be considered micro-
chromatography. The small size of the strips or plates is advantageous
not only in permitting the use of small chromatographic chambers,
hence less laboratory space, but also in providing ease of handling.

Randerath [40] compares the thin-layer and paper chromatography
of several types of compounds under similar conditions. Typical of
his results is the excellent separation of purine and pyrimidine bases
and their respective nucleosides on thin cellulose layers while the
same substances are scarcely resolved on paper under the same conditions. The same author states that comparable separations of nucleotides are achieved with *n*-butanol-acetone-acetic acid-5 per cent
aqueous ammonia-water (3.5:2.5:1.5:1.5:1, v/v/v/v/v) within 90 min-

utes on cellulose layers, 150 minutes on silica gel G, and 6 to 8 hours on paper.

Analogous results are obtained when the separation of amino acids on cellulose layers is compared with that on paper.

DISADVANTAGES. Although several reviews have stated that reproducible R_f values are difficult to obtain on thin-layer chromatograms, the author feels that the policy of chromatographing standard compounds each time (recommended also for paper chromatography) adequately compensates for this. Moreover, it is felt that the usefulness of R_f values is too frequently overstressed. It bears repeating that the chromatographic position of a spot, even in several solvents, must never be taken as the sole criterion for identification of the compound.

While elution of compounds from paper chromatograms (or collection of fractions from columns) is accomplished with little difficulty, some problems do arise with chromatoplates. For example, the use of water in eluting a compound from the adsorbent, previously scraped from the plate, is interdicted in the case of adsorbents containing a gypsum binder since the calcium sulfate is water-soluble. Quantitative recovery may also be difficult due to flaking or disintegration of the adsorbent during the process of removal from the plate. The use of 5 per cent, w/w, starch-bonded silica gel on adsorbents free of a binding material may be used in such cases. It is noted that the starch-bonded silicic acid is also of advantage in that the hardness of such a layer permits marking with a soft pencil directly on the adsorbent.

Glass Paper Chromatography

Chromatography on silicic acid-impregnated glass fiber paper is an important modification of the chromatostrip technique. The method was first used by Diekert and Reiser [59] for the separation of neutral lipids. Although glass paper chromatography has not been as fully developed as TLC, the two methods appear to be completely analogous in most respects. The principal difference is in the supporting material—flexible glass fiber in one case and solid strips or plates in the second. In addition, gypsum or starch binders are not required when glass fiber is used.

Most of that which has been said of TLC can be applied also to glass paper chromatography. Indeed, the speed of development is even greater in the latter and the use of charring as a means of detecting organic substances has been made quantitative. Details of the method are given in the review by Hamilton and Muldrey [24].

References

1. J. E. Meinhard and N. F. Hall, *Anal. Chem.*, **21**, 185 (1949).
2. J. G. Kirchner, J. M. Miller, and G. J. Keller, *Anal. Chem.*, **23**, 420 (1951).
3. J. M. Miller and J. G. Kirchner, *Anal. Chem.*, **25**, 1107 (1953).
4. J. M. Miller and J. G. Kirchner, *Anal. Chem.*, **26**, 2002 (1954).
5. E. Lederer and M. Lederer, *Chromatography*, Elsevier, Amsterdam (1953).
6. L. Zechmeister, *Progress in Chromatography* 1938–1947, John Wiley & Sons, Inc., New York (1950).
7. E. Heftmann, ed., *Chromatography*, Reinhold Publishing Co., New York (1961).
8. M. Brenner and G. Pataki, *Helv. Chim. Acta.* **44**, 1420 (1961).
9. J. J. Wren, *J. Chromatog.*, **4**, 173 (1960).
10. J. J. Peifer, *Mikrochim. Acta*, **1962**, 519 (1962).
11. E. G. Wollish, M. Schmall, and M. Hawrylyshyn, *Anal. Chem.*, **33**, 1138 (1961).
12. T. H. Applewhite, M. J. Diamond, and L. A. Goldblatt, *J. Am. Oil Chemists' Soc.*, **38**, 609 (1961).
13. E. Demole, *Chromatog. Rev.*, **1**, 1 (1959).
14. A. F. Hofmann, *Arch. Biochem.*, **3**, 145 (1962).
15. E. Stahl, *Pharm. Rundschau*, **1**, 1 (1959).
16. A. Winterstein, A. Studer, and R. Rüegg, *Chem. Ber.* **93**, 2951 (1960).
17. C. G. Honegger, *Helv. Chim. Acta*, **44**, 173 (1961).
18. R. H. Reitsma, *Anal. Chem.*, **26**, 960 (1954).
19. H. K. Mangold, *J. Am. Oil Chemists' Soc.*, **38**, 708 (1961).
20. K. H. Müller and H. Honerlagen, *Arch. Pharm.*, **293**, 202 (1960).
21. E. Randerath and H. Struck, *J. Chromatog.*, **6**, 365 (1961).
22. D. C. Malins and H. K. Mangold, *J. Am. Oil Chemists' Soc.*, **37**, 576 (1960).
23. G. Rouser, A. J. Bauman, N. Nicolaides, and D. Heller, *J. Am. Oil Chemists' Soc.*, **38**, 565 (1961).
24. J. G. Hamilton and J. G. Muldrey, *J. Am. Oil Chemists' Soc.*, **38**, 582 (1961).
25. R. J. Block, E. L. Durrum, and G. Zweig, *A Manual of Paper Chromatography and Paper Electrophoresis*, Academic Press, New York (1962).
26. D. Braun and H. Geenen, *J. Chromatog.*, **7**, 56 (1962).
27. H. J. Petrowitz and G. Pastuska, *J. Chromatog.*, **7**, 128 (1962).
28. D. Waldi, K. Schnakerz, and F. Munter, *J. Chromatog.*, **6**, 61 (1961).
29. A. R. Fahmy, A. Niederwieser, G. Pataki, and M. Brenner, *Helv. Chim. Acta*, **44**, 2022 (1961).
30. E. Cherbuliez, B. Baehler, and J. Rabinowitz, *Helv. Chim. Acta*, **43**, 1871 (1960).
31. H. Seiler and T. Kaffenberger, *Helv. Chim. Acta*, **44**, 1282 (1961).
32. E. Demole, *J. Chromatog.*, **1**, 24 (1958).
33. H. Seiler and M. Seiler, *Helv. Chim. Acta*, **43**, 1939 (1960).
34. E. Vioque and R. T. Holman, *J. Am. Oil Chemists' Soc.*, **39**, 63 (1962).
35. H. Struck, *Mikrochim. Acta*, **1961**, 634 (1961).
36. E. Stahl and U. Kaltenbach, *J. Chromatog.*, **5**, 458 (1961).
37. J. Baümler and S. Rippstein, *Helv. Chim. Acta*, **44**, 1162 (1961).
38. G. Rouser, J. O'Brien, and D. Heller, *J. Am Oil Chemists' Soc.*, **38**, 14 (1961).
39. J. G. L. Harthon, *Acta Chem. Scand.*, **15**, 1401 (1961).

40. K. Randerath, *Biochem. Biophys. Res. Commun.*, **6**, 452 (1962).
41. P. Schellenberg, *Angew. Chem., Intern. Ed. Engl.*, **1**, 114 (1962).
42. E. Stahl and U. Kaltenbach, *J. Chromatog.*, **5**, 351 (1961).
43. V. Prey, H. Berbalk, and M. Kausz, *Mickrochim. Acta.* **1961**, 968 (1961).
44. H. Wagner, L. Hörhammer, and B. Dengler, *J. Chromatog.*, **7**, 211 (1962).
45. J. Davidek and J. Blattna, *J. Chromatog.*, **7**, 204 (1962).
46. A. Winterstein and B. Hegedüs, *Z. Physiol. Chem.*, **321**, 97 (1960).
47. A. Winterstein and B. Hegedüs, *Chimia (Aarau)*, **14**, 18 (1960).
48. A. Seher, *Mikrochim. Acta*, **1961**, 303 (1961).
49. H. Gänshirt and A. Malzacher, *Naturwissenschaften*, **47**, 279 (1960).
50. O. S. Privett and M. E. Blank, *J. Lipid Res.*, **2**, 37 (1961).
51. J. Barrollier, *Naturwissenschaften*, **48**, 404 (1961).
52. E. Stahl, *Dunnschicht Chromatographie. Ein Laboratoriumshandbuch*, Springer-Verlag, Berlin (1962).
53. K. Randerath, *Dünnschicht Chromatographie*, Verlag Chemie, Weinheim Bergstr. (1962).
54. H. J. Petrowitz, *Angew. Chem.*, **72**, 921 (1960).
55. F. Feigl, *Spot Tests in Inorganic Applications*, Elsevier, Houston, Texas, 4th ed. (1954).
56. F. Feigl, *Spot Tests in Organic Analysis*, Elsevier, Amsterdam, 5th ed. (1956).
57. H. Ertel and L. Horner, *J. Chromatog.*, **7**, 268 (1962).
58. J. M. Bobbitt, *Chem. Eng. News*, **39**, 42 (1961).
59. J. W. Diekert and R. Reiser, *Science*, **120**, 678 (1954).

GENERAL

J. Chromatog., **9**, No. 3, (1962). Special thin-layer chromatography issue.

CHAPTER 3

Zone Electrophoresis

P. H. Plaisted

PROBABLY the first separation of complex mixtures by paper electrophoresis was reported by König [1] in 1937; but it was not until 1946, after the paper of Consden *et al.* [2], that the technique was intensively developed. Since 1946, hundreds of papers describing different apparatus, different techniques, or modifications of existing techniques have been published. The terms used to designate electrophoresis are many and varied. In some papers, such terms as "ionophoresis," "electrochromatophoresis," and "electromigration" have been used. *Zone electrophoresis*, as it is used in this discussion, is the separation of a complex mixture into definite zones or bands in a buffer stabilized by such media as paper or gel. Although paper is the oldest, it is also the most versatile and still the most popular support medium; therefore, this discussion will be centered on it. However, some of the newer techniques where gel is used as a support medium will also be included. The purpose of this chapter is to summarize representative types of apparatus and different techniques used to separate the major classes of compounds and certain specific ones.

Theoretical Considerations

Electrophoretic movement of particles, ions, or colloids, in filter paper or other support media, has advantages over liquid or free electrophoresis. The separation of each component into definite zones or bands facilitates isolation, and in many cases the components can be directly quantitated on the stabilizing medium. The simplicity of apparatus probably accounts for the popularity of both paper and gel electrophoretic separations.

Successful separation by paper or gel electrophoresis requires the understanding of a few basic facts. Migration of a particle in an electric field depends upon the sign and net charge, shape of the particle, and properties inherent to the particle. Factors external to the particle, such as ionic strength, concentration of the buffer, and ambient temperature, also affect resolution. The role that some of these factors play will be briefly discussed.

The magnitude of the net charge determines the velocity of migration, while the sign of the charge dictates the direction of movement. A charged particle bathed in an electrolyte attracts to it molecules or ions of opposite sign which are held to the particle. As the particle moves under the impulse of the electric potential, some of the oppositely charged molecules or ions which surround the particle move with it. Therefore, the particle does not move as an individual but instead moves in the center of a cloud of opposite charges. The algebraic sum of the charges on the particle and those surrounding it makes up the net charge. The increase in particle size caused by its cloud of ions also adds resistance to movement.

In many instances, the materials to be separated combine with components in the buffer system. Metallic ions and carbohydrates often move in an electric field as a complex rather than as individual ions or molecules. When complexing occurs, the net charge on the molecule may change from that calculated from theoretical considerations, and in some cases may even reverse that on the original ion.

The ionic concentration of the electrolyte affects separation in two ways. If the electrolytic system is too dilute, the separating material will streak toward the opposite terminal, thereby covering an abnormally large area on the finished electrophorogram. As the concentration of the buffer is increased, the ionic cloud surrounding the moving particle increases in diameter. This results in a change in the net charge on the particle, decreasing its original charge. Typically, an increase in electrolytic concentration decreases the mobility of the particle. The optimum concentration of electrolyte varies with the material being separated. In most cases, paper electrophoresis is carried out with an electrolyte having an ionic concentration near 0.1.

Ionic concentration of an electrolyte depends upon the valence of the ions in solution, not upon the specific chemical nature of the ions. The ionic strength of a solution can be calculated from the following formula:

$$\mu = \tfrac{1}{2}\Sigma CZ^2 \qquad (1)$$

in which C is the molarity (concentration) of each ion species present in solution and Z is its valence. The effect of valence on ionic concentration can be seen when a $0.05M$ NaCl solution is compared to a $0.05M$ CaCl$_2$ solution; the former has one-third the ionic concentration of the latter.

A change of temperature affects the electrolyte by altering conductivity, viscosity, and, under some conditions, concentration. The conductivity of an electrolyte increases with an increasing temperature. As particles tend to migrate faster in solutions of greater conductivity, a higher temperature indirectly produces greater migration

distance. Viscosity decreases with a corresponding increase in temperature. Water at 0°C has a viscosity of 1.7921 centipoises but drops to
0.8937 at 25°C. As viscosity exerts a retarding effect on movement of
particles, a decrease in viscosity tends to produce a corresponding
increase in particle migration. An increase in temperature also produces greater evaporation from the stabilizing medium. As evaporation progresses, the concentration of the remaining electrolyte is
increased unless the electrolyte is volatile. It can be readily seen that
temperature control is necessary for good reproducibility.

There are two other variables inherent in paper- or gel-stabilized
electrophoretic systems: heat generated by passage of the electric
current, and movement of electrolyte by electroendosmosis. The
passage of an electric current through a liquid electrolyte generates
heat in proportion to the current applied. Joule's law states that the
heat increases with the square of the current, and its quantitative
relationships are expressed in the following formula:

$$Q = \frac{RI^2}{A} \qquad (2)$$

in which Q is heat (calories per second); R is resistance of the medium;
I is current; and A is mechanical heat equivalent ($A = 4.185 \times 10^7$
ergs/cal). Therefore, temperature of the solution will increase rapidly
with a corresponding increase in current.

As the temperature of the electrolyte increases, the resistance
increases and evaporation also increases which, in turn, increases the
concentration of the electrolyte and increases current.

Electroendosmosis is the movement of an electrolyte in a capillary
system under the impulse of an electric potential. Such a phenomenon is characteristic of a solid-liquid interphase system. Buffer-
saturated filter paper is a solid divided by many small capillaries,
each liquid-filled. When an electric potential is applied, the electrolyte migrates along the walls of the capillaries, carrying with it any
uncharged particles. If a particle is migrating under influence of the
electric potential, it will buck the liquid flow when it moves toward
one pole, usually toward the anode, and will have its own velocity
plus the velocity of liquid flow as it moves in the opposite direction.
Therefore, the amount and duration of electroendosmotic flow have
a profound effect on the final position that compounds assume.

The electroendosmotic flow in the paper is followed by using some
compound which has no charge at the pH of the particular buffer
being used. Dextran, a polysaccharide obtainable in different molecular weights, is used with many buffer systems in which proteins
are separated. The nonmigrating marker is visualized with bromophenol blue, a dye which also stains the proteins. Low-molecular-

weight materials, such as glucose, 2,4,6-tri-O-methylglucose, or caffeine, are used when separating low-molecular-weight materials. The latter compound, used with buffers above pH 3.0, has the added advantage of being visualized on the dry electrophorogram with ultraviolet light (2537 Å). In some instances, dyes such as nitro-benzene-p-sulfonate [3] can be successfully employed.

Types of Compounds Which Can Be Separated by Electrophoresis

In the foregoing discussion it was pointed out that electrophoretic migration depends upon the net charge on the ion, molecule, or colloidal particle. The degree of ionization of many compounds or functional groups depends upon the pH of the electrolyte in which they are bathed.

The migration of amphoteric compounds and proteins depends upon the hydrogen ion concentration of the electrolyte. A pH below the isoelectric point of the compound will cause ionization, pre-dominantly from the basic groups, causing the compound to migrate toward the cathode. When the pH is raised above the isoelectric point of the compound, the acidic group is predominantly ionized and the compound migrates toward the anode. If the pH of the electrolyte is the same as the isoelectric point, no migration occurs even though an electric potential is applied [4].

Many compounds which do not possess an electric charge when bathed in an electrolyte can be complexed with some other molecule or ion which, in turn, will impart an electric charge to the complex. Carbohydrates and polyvalent alcohols complex with borate ions. Other complexing agents, such as sodium arsenite, basic lead acetate, sodium hydroxide, or germanate [3, 4], can be used. Many inorganic ions can be separated by using the complexing technique.

Types of Instruments

The types of electrophoretic apparatus that will be described fall into two general categories: those employing paper as the stabilizing medium, and those using gels. Basically, there are many points of similarity between the two types. The electrodes, buffer vessels, and power supply can be used interchangeably between paper and gel apparatus. The physical nature of gels dictates a different means of support than that which is used for paper. The following discussion will describe instruments and methods of use in each category.

PAPER ELECTROPHORESIS

The popularity of paper electrophoresis stems from the advantages that filter paper offers, namely, ease of handling, simplicity of equipment, and ease in isolation of separated materials. The individual compounds moving as spots or bands on the paper often make it possible to quantitate directly many of the separated materials.

The speed of separation depends upon the potential applied across the electrodes. Separations using electric potentials of 20 v/cm of paper length and below are generally considered low voltage electrophoretic separations, while separations using potentials higher than 20 v/cm are classified as high voltage separations. The design requirements of apparatus for each category are different and representative pieces of equipment for each group will be discussed.

All types of paper electrophoretic apparatus have three things in common — paper, buffer, and sample. Before describing the individual types of apparatus, some general characteristics of these three will be discussed.

PAPER. The electrophoretic migration of charged particles in paper depends, to a large extent, on the type of paper used. At the usual pH ranges, cellulose has negatively charged groups which cause adsorption of some compounds, especially proteins. The degree to which materials adsorb depends upon the basicity and purity of the paper. Generally speaking, electrophoresis paper should contain at least 96 per cent α-cellulose. Typically, a good grade of filter paper which can be used for chromatography can also be used for electrophoresis.

The choice of paper will dictate to a large extent the speed of migration and the electroendosmotic flow. If relatively large amounts of material are to be isolated, a thick paper such as Whatman 3 or 3MM can be used. The ratio of electroendosmotic flow to migration can be reduced by using Whatman 4, 5, or 50. Whatman 1 or a comparable paper can be used to separate smaller amounts of material.

Diffusion of the sample is often greater in the thicker papers, Whatman 3 or 3MM, than in the more compact ones similar to Whatman 1, 5, or 50. The greatest diffusion occurs when thick papers, which hold more moisture, are used in low voltage electrophoretic separations. Presumably, this diffusion is a result of the longer time needed for separation with low voltage.

SAMPLE. The sample can be applied to the filter paper either before or after the paper is moistened with the electrolyte. Critical work requires that the sample be applied to the moist paper after it is arranged in the apparatus. If the concentration of the sample is low and more than one application per spot is necessary, dry papers are used. The buffer is applied to the dry paper with a pipette or similar instrument. The electrolyte is allowed to wet the sample area by capillarity, the liquid front approaching from both sides of the sample and meeting at the sample. This technique squeezes the sample into a smaller area, thereby sharpening the sample zone. A measured amount of sample can be applied with a micropipette or, for qualitative work, with a flame-smoothed melting-point tube.

BUFFER. Probably the single greatest reason for poor resolution and poor reproducibility in paper electrophoresis is a surplus of electrolyte (buffer) in the paper. Actually, the filter paper is capable of holding much more liquid than most types of apparatus can handle. Two types of electrophoretic apparatus, the hanging strip and the horizontal closed strip, have design modifications which guard against surplus electrolyte staying in the paper. In the hanging strip, the paper is elevated above the buffer compartments and gravity drains the surplus electrolyte. In the horizontal closed-strip apparatus, the dampened paper is held between two insulated plates which can squeeze out surplus electrolyte.

The correct amount of liquid in the paper can be obtained by allowing the wet paper to hang for a few minutes until the liquid sheen has disappeared. Another method is to place the wet sheet between two blotters and gently roll the blotters.

The actual composition of the buffers is varied, depending upon the types of materials being separated. Many different types, ranging in pH from less than 2 to over 11, have been used. A typical electrophoretic buffer is not concentrated; the ionic concentration may range from 0.05 to approximately 0.1.

It is often advantageous to rid the paper of buffer before reacting the separated materials to make them visible. Some organic buffers can be removed by aeration, while others need to be washed from the paper with acetone or some other appropriate solvent that does not dissolve the separated materials.

LOW VOLTAGE APPARATUS. Many different kinds of low voltage apparatus have been devised. Space permits discussion of only a few. Those apparatus which have the paper hanging from a central rod or support are called *hanging strip*. When the paper is supported on a horizontal frame with each end dipping into a buffer compartment, the apparatus is classified as *horizontal strip*. The latter type of equipment has two subdivisions. In one, evaporation from the paper is permitted, and in the second, evaporation is prevented. A third type of low voltage apparatus is that in which *continuous electrophoresis* is carried out.

Hanging Strip. An example of a hanging strip apparatus is seen in Fig. 3-1. Electrodes, either carbon or platinum, are inserted into the buffer compartments but are separated from the paper. This ensures that electrolyte products formed at each electrode will not diffuse into the paper. Electrolyte is poured into each of the buffer compartments, and the liquid level is equalized by a connecting tube which must be closed before the electric potential is applied to remove the possibility of an electric short. The paper, previously dampened with electrolyte, is suspended over the central rod, with

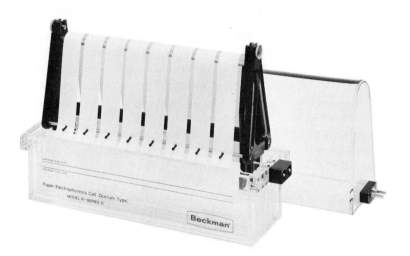

Fig. 3-1. An example of a hanging strip electrophoresis apparatus. The paper strips are supported on a removable rack with each strip in contact with a wick which is immersed in the electrolyte solution. This alleviates the need for cutting the ends of the electrophorograms when the strips are removed from the apparatus. The plastic cover protects the apparatus during a run (Courtesy, Spinco Division of Beckman Instrument, Inc.).

each end dipping 2 to 3 cm into the buffer compartments, and is left to equilibrate until the liquid sheen disappears. Creasing the paper should be avoided, for this breaks the fibers.

The sample is applied at the center or apex of the sheen-free paper with a micropipette, flame-smoothed melting-point tube, or special wire applicator. In some instances, when the migration distance and direction are known, the sample is spotted off-center and allowed to migrate up and over the central rod.

After separation is completed, the paper is removed from the apparatus, and the ends which had dipped into the electrolyte are cut off. This precaution is necessary to prevent the surplus liquid in the ends of the paper from migrating into the drier areas thus displacing the separated materials. Papers are dried either at room temperature or at an elevated temperature.

Some commercial types of apparatus have special racks for holding the paper (Fig. 3-1). These can be removed from the apparatus at the end of a run and the papers dried directly on them. Such racks facilitate handling the wet papers.

Evaporation of buffer from the dampened paper can be kept to a minimum by reducing the current or by cooling the apparatus. A more complete discussion of the effect of evaporation on separation is found in the following section.

Horizontal Strip—Evaporation Permitted. Some authors refer to this design as the moist chamber apparatus. The reason for this is discussed below.

In the horizontal strip apparatus where evaporation is permitted, the paper is held horizontally on a rack supported at each end by a buffer compartment (Fig. 3-2). Operation of the apparatus, preparation of paper, and spotting of sample are similar to the methods described for the hanging strip.

Separation of material in a horizontal strip apparatus where evaporation is permitted has characteristics common to the hanging strip apparatus. The passage of an electric current through the paper

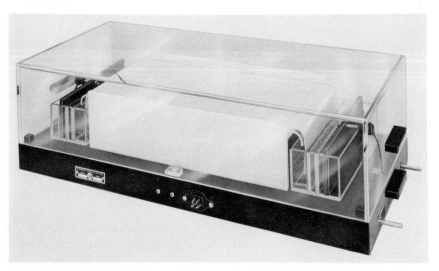

Fig. 3-2. An example of a horizontal strip (evaporation permitted) electrophoresis apparatus (Courtesy, Research Specialties Co.).

creates resistance which, in turn, raises the temperature of the paper and promotes evaporation. The evaporation from the paper produces a flow of liquid from both buffer compartments toward the center. The electroendosmotic flow, usually toward the cathode, sets up an added liquid flow. Therefore, liquid is flowing toward the cathode under the impulse of electroendosmotic flow plus evaporation replacement. A liquid flow toward the anode is caused only by the replacement of evaporated electrolyte. As a greater liquid flow is toward the cathode, the point of liquid equilibrium on the paper is displaced from the center toward the cathode. If an ion is placed at the point of neutral liquid flow and migrates toward either pole, it is bucking a continuously increasing stream in either direction. Eventually the ion may come to a point of equilibrium with respect to the electric potential, net ionic charge, and liquid flow. Any movement in one direction will be countered by either the electric potential or the liquid flow. This explains why some compounds such as amino acids reach the same relative position on the paper irrespective of where they are originally spotted.

Horizontal Strip—Evaporation Prevented. The fundamental design of apparatus in this category (Fig. 3-3) is similar to the one in

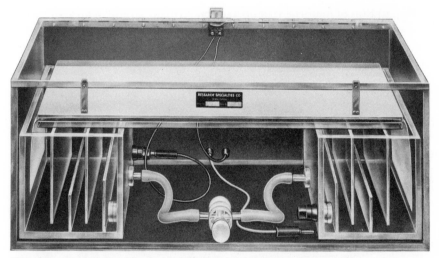

Fig. 3-3. An example of a horizontal strip (evaporation prevented) electrophoresis apparatus (Courtesy, Research Specialties Co.).

which evaporation is permitted. The paper is supported on a horizontal rack with each end dipping into electrolyte filled compartments. Instead of having the upper surface of the paper exposed to air, it is covered with an insulated plate made of plate glass or some similar material.

The upper and lower plates, with the paper sandwiched between them, are held together with laboratory clamps. In some types of apparatus, the weight of the upper plate is enough to maintain the correct pressure on the paper. In order to ensure good reproducibility if the two plates are clamped together, the clamps are placed in the same position each time and screwed to approximately the same tension. Evaporation can be reduced if the edge of the glass is sealed with grease or tape.

Operation of the apparatus is relatively simple and similar in many respects to that previously described. The electrolyte is placed in the compartments with the same precautions as to leveling of the liquid as previously discussed. The dampened paper is placed on the apparatus after it has lost the liquid sheen. A sample is applied to the paper, either at the center or displaced toward either electrode, and the electric potential applied. If the top plate has holes drilled in it for sample application [5], a slightly different technique is used for applying the material to be separated. The wet paper is placed in the apparatus, the top plate attached, and the electric potential applied for a short time (20 to 30 minutes) before the sample is spotted on the paper through the holes in the upper plate. The edges are then covered with grease or tape before the separation is started.

After the run is completed, the ends of the paper are cut off before removing the top plate. If the top plate is removed before the ends saturated with electrolyte are cut off, liquid will quickly migrate into the drier areas of the paper causing displacement of the separated materials. The paper is dried and the separated components made visible.

Continuous Electrophoresis. In continuous electrophoresis, a sheet of filter paper is suspended in a vertical frame with the upper edge dipped into a buffer filled vessel. The electrolyte migrates down the paper, finally drips off the lower serrated edge, and can be collected in a series of test tubes. The electric potential is applied at right angles to the flow of the buffer. A sample is slowly but continuously fed onto the paper near the upper edge. If no electric potential is applied, the sample will be carried to the drip point (serration in the bottom edge) directly under the point of application by movement of the buffer. When the electric potential is applied, the ions migrate to different drip points, depending upon their speed of migration in the electric field and the velocity of the liquid flow.

The two forces acting upon the particles to be separated are electric potential and hydrodynamic flow. Therefore, in order to achieve good resolution, a homogeneous electric field and even flow of buffer over the paper are necessary. Peeters *et al.* [6] have devised a continuous electrophoresis apparatus that has been successfully used in our laboratory (Fig. 3-4). The electrodes, which are threaded through a labyrinth system, are continuously flushed with a fresh source of buffer. The top of the paper curtain is cut into tabs that are continuously wet by dripping buffer onto them. Trickle-feeding the paper in this manner eliminates the electric shunt which otherwise exists between the electrodes of a buffer trough system. Since the buffer feed for each electrode is separate, experiments using two or three different buffers at the same time can be carried out.

As continuous electrophoresis is fundamentally a preparative technique, the type of paper used is generally thick, such as Whatman 3 or 3MM, although Whatman 1 can be used.

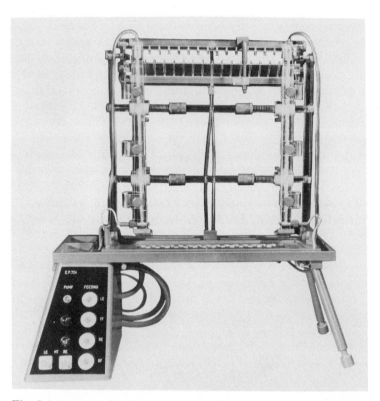

Fig. 3-4. An example of a continuous electrophoresis apparatus. The paper curtain is held between the two upright electrode containers with each of the top tabs bent into its separate drip compartment (Courtesy, Scientific Industries, Inc.).

As the separation achieved in two-dimensional electrophoresis is a vector of the electric potential and buffer flow, greater resolution is often obtained by using a relatively high voltage gradient across the electrodes. High electrical potential with relatively low current can be obtained by using electrolytes with low ionic concentration. The minimum usable ionic concentration has to be found for each type of separation. If the buffer is too dilute, protein samples may denature and lower molecular weight compounds show a much wider separation band than is necessary. Better resolution is obtained when the mixture to be separated is diluted with the buffer used on the curtain.

Generally speaking, the compounds to be separated should possess less conductivity than the electrolyte in use. If the conductivity is too great, it can be reduced by diluting the sample.

The rate of electrolyte flow down the paper is critical for good resolution. The type of filter paper used will partially control the flow; thinner compact papers afford slower flow (and better resolution) than the very thick, coarse papers. However, the flow of the electrolyte down the paper can be controlled to a degree by moving the drip trough [6] apparatus forward or backward.

Another variable which has been utilized to advantage is the addition of an inert material, such as glycerol or propylene glycol, to the electrolyte. These substances do not affect the pH of many electrolytic systems even when used in relatively high concentrations (10 to 20 per cent, v/v) [7].

The use of high electric potential causes a temperature rise in the paper which, in turn, may cause excessive evaporation to take place. If the salts of nonvolatile buffers are not flushed out of the paper by new electrolyte, an uneven electric field develops on the paper with an accompanying increased resistance which, in turn, causes a rise in temperature. Too high a temperature will adversely affect some samples and result in decreased resolution. The use of volatile buffers does not cause heating to such a marked degree.

The sample is applied by a mechanically operated syringe or a small paper wick inserted into a cup which contains the sample and which is mounted near the top center of the paper. The paper wick is so arranged that the tapered end rests against the paper curtain. Irrespective of which method is used, it is important to have the sample fed onto the paper at a slow, constant rate. A flow rate of 0.2 ml per hour has been recommended [8]. The location of the wick or device for applying the sample to the paper depends upon the migrating characteristics of the components in the sample. If the apparatus devised by Peeters *et al.* [6] is being used, the sample components separate into straight lines, and the angles between the different components are constant for similar samples. This information can be used to compute the correct sample location on the paper.

At the end of the separation, the components can be located on the paper by drying it and treating it with an appropriate reagent or by examining it under ultraviolet light. The components of the separated material are found in the collecting tubes corresponding to the pattern seen on the paper.

HIGH VOLTAGE APPARATUS. High voltage electrophoresis is carried out with an electric potential higher than 20 v/cm of paper length. Proteins have not been separated successfully with high voltage, but polypeptides, amino acids, organic acids, carbohydrates, and many other low-molecular-weight materials respond well to this type of separation. The short time required, which in most cases is less than 45 minutes, prevents diffusion, thereby allowing two materials which have close mobility values to be separated.

The main problem involved is removal of the heat generated by the electric potential, for doubling the voltage quadruples the heat. A reduction in heating can be accomplished by lowering the buffer concentration, but this expedient can only be used in certain cases. More efficient methods of heat removal are obtained by attaching cooling plates to the paper support or by immersing the paper in a nonpolar liquid. Actually, wet paper conducts heat better than dry and consequently would be desirable in high voltage electrophoresis; however, under such conditions the buffer migrates too rapidly. Therefore, relatively dry strips (ratio of air-dried paper to buffer strip 1:1.2 [9]) are generally used. The paper strip can be prepared by passing it through a solution of buffer and removing the excess moisture by careful blotting or squeezing between two rollers.

Many different types of high voltage apparatus have been designed, each incorporating some method of removing heat. All of these different apparatus fall into two general categories: those that remove the heat with solid heat exchangers, and those that use liquid heat exchangers. An example from each category will be described.

Solid Heat Exchangers.   The basic design of apparatus in this category is shown in Fig. 3-5. The paper is supported on a flat surface which, in turn, is cooled by running tap water [10] or by a refrigeration system [11]. Since the cooling plates are usually constructed of metal, an insulating material, such as plate glass or thin (0.006 in.) polyethylene, separates the paper from the cooling plates. Buffer compartments contain a baffle system or the electrodes are in a different compartment from the paper wicks but are connected by a bridge (Fig. 3-5). Platinum electrodes are advisable, for they can be washed readily and inserted into a new buffer. As the half-dry paper has a tendency to absorb moisture from the buffer compartments, the paper is separated from the buffer with a cellophane membrane (dialysis tubing) which encases a paper wick saturated with the electrolyte and dipped into the buffer compartment. This allows an electric contact between the electrolyte and paper, yet reduced electroendosmotic flow.

The sample is spotted on the paper either when the paper is dry or after the buffer has been applied. The cellophane ends of the wicks are laid on top of the paper, the top plate or cooling unit is attached, and the electric potential is applied for the desired time. A constant pressure should be applied to the paper for good reproducibility. Some high voltage apparatus have inflatable cushions above the paper

(Gilson Medical Electronics). This inflatable unit can be pumped to a constant pressure each time the apparatus is used. In other designs, the weight of the top plate is kept constant by laboratory screw clamps tightened to the same degree for each separation.

No special precautions are necessary after completing the separation. The top plate assembly is removed, wicks taken off, and the paper placed on a drying frame. For best results, the paper should be dried horizontally.

Liquid Heat Exchangers. One of the most efficient methods of removing heat generated in the paper strip is to have the heat exchange medium in direct contact with the paper. The use of a liquid heat exchanger fulfills this requirement. A convenient apparatus is diagramed in Fig. 3-6. The semidry paper ready for electrophoresis with the sample applied is arranged in the apparatus. The two buffer compartments are filled and the cooling liquid, usually a nonpolar organic liquid, such as carbon tetrachloride, chlorobenzene, chloroform, or Varsol, is added to the inner container until the paper is

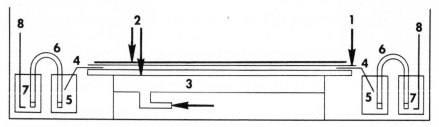

Fig. 3-5. Diagram of a high voltage electrophoresis apparatus with cooling plates attached. The paper *(1)* is sandwiched between the upper and lower cooling plates *(2)*, which are cooled with the circulating liquid *(3)*. The paper is connected to the buffer compartments *(5)* through the wick *(4)*. The inner buffer compartment *(5)* is connected to the outer one *(7)*, which contains the electrodes *(8)*, by a paper or gel bridge *(6)* (After Michl [9]) (Courtesy, Boyce Thompson Institute, Inc.).

completely covered. The latter compound, Varsol, produced by Standard Oil of New Jersey, is recommended. Some commercial apparatus have racks which hold the paper. In this case the paper is mounted on the rack then submerged in the cooling liquid. Often the liquid needs to be kept cool; this can be accomplished by circulating water through coils immersed in the coolant. The organic cooling liquid serves two functions, namely, cooling and inhibiting the siphoning of the buffer from the electrode compartment down the paper. The organic cooling liquid should be immiscible with the buffer system, easily removed from the paper, and nonflammable. As most of the organic liquids used for this purpose have some solubility in water, it is necessary to have the organic phase in equilibrium with the buffer before immersing the paper. Some of the physical characteristics of the organic liquids used as coolants are shown in Table 3-1.

TABLE 3-1

PHYSICAL CHARACTERISTICS OF ORGANIC COMPOUNDS USED AS COOLANTS

Compound	Thermal conductivity, calories/cm sec (°C)	Solubility in H_2O (g/100 ml)	Vapor pressure (mm Hg at 20°C)	Density at 20°C
Carbon tetrachloride	0.000252	0.08(20°)	90.99	1.595
Chlorobenzene	0.000302	0.05(20°)	8.76	1.106
Chloroform	0.000288	0.82(20°)	156.6	1.489
Heptane	0.000337	0.005(16°)	40.0(22.4°)*	0.690
Toluene	0.000349	0.063(25°)	18.4*	0.866
Varsol†	–	Nil	2.07(38°)	0.792(15.5°)

* A 1 to 7% mixture in air may explode.
† From Standard Oil Company of New Jersey.

The operating technique of a liquid cooled apparatus is similar to that which has been described. A sample is applied to the semidry buffered paper, the paper inserted into the apparatus, and separation started. After the separation is completed, the paper is removed, and aerated to remove the coolant and buffer. The separated materials are rendered visible by the appropriate technique.

PAPER ELECTROPHORESIS AND PAPER CHROMATOGRAPHY

A combination of electrophoresis and paper chromatography will separate a greater number of compounds with better resolution than can be obtained with either technique alone. Both low and high voltage electrophoretic apparatus can be used; best results are obtained with high voltage equipment.

Different commercial apparatus have been designed to accommodate 18 × 22 in. sheets of filter paper (Brinkman Instruments Inc., Gilson Medical Electronics, Servonuclear Corp.). Apparatus of these types are constructed so that the electrophoretic separation is carried out with the paper hanging vertically, the top end immersed in a buffer compartment which contains the negative electrode, and the bottom end dips into the positive electrode compartment. The paper is surrounded by some liquid coolant similar to those previously described. Cooling coils may be inserted in the liquid coolant and tap water or some other cooling liquid passed through them.

The sample to be separated is applied a short distance in from one edge of the buffered paper. Whatman 1, 3, 3MM, or other type papers are used. Many commercial apparatus have racks which hold the paper and facilitate placing the paper in the apparatus. A potential, ranging from 20 v/cm to 60 v/cm, is used. The time of separation depends upon the sample under investigation and the voltage applied. After completion of the separation, the paper is removed, aerated to remove the coolant, then turned 90°. The choice of solvent and method used depends upon the sample and desires of the operator. Butanol-acetic acid-water (4:1:5, v/v/v) descending can be used for peptides and amino acids.

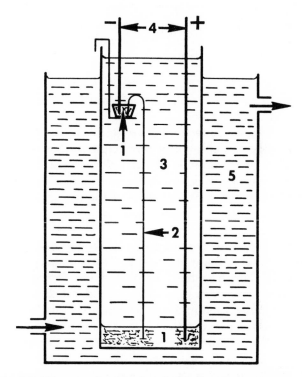

Fig. 3-6. Diagram of a liquid-cooled high voltage electrophoresis. The paper (2) is suspended between the two buffer compartments (1) which contain the electrodes (4). The coolant (3) is maintained at a constant temperature by immersing the apparatus in a circulating water bath (5) (Courtesy, Boyce Thompson Institute, Inc.).

GEL ELECTROPHORESIS

The popularity of gels as buffer-supporting media for electrophoretic separations probably stems from the high resolving power, lack of sample adsorption to the gel matrix, and speed of separation. The separation of proteins by paper electrophoresis is limited because many proteins adsorb on the paper. Gel electrophoresis reduces adsorption to a minimum; in fact, in most cases no adsorption is noticed. Some of the new polyacrylamide gels, presumably working by a combination of molecular filtration and electrophoresis, are able to resolve many more materials from a single sample than is found by the conventional paper technique. The disadvantage in using gels to stabilize the buffer is the difficulty of removing the separated compounds, especially if the technique is used for preparative purposes. For separating different protein components, gels give excellent reproducibility and high resolution.

Although many different apparatus have been designed to accommodate gels, only two different types will be discussed: those designed for starch gel, and those designed for polyacrylamide gels or, as commonly referred to, disc electrophoresis.

STARCH GEL ELECTROPHORESIS. The apparatus used for starch gel electrophoresis is similar in many respects to that used for paper. Buffer compartments, electrodes, and power supply can be used interchangeably. The gel troughs, often made of Plexiglas, are relatively shallow but the length and width are determined by the number of samples and length of separation time. A 20 cm × 25 or 30 cm trough is adequate for most separations. The gel can be removed easily if the ends and sides of the trough are removable.

Starch gel electrophoresis is carried out either in the horizontal or vertical position (Fig. 3-7). Electroendosmotic flow is reduced if the apparatus is arranged with the gel trough in the vertical position and the cathode at the top. The starch gel is cast in the trough by gently heating the hydrolyzed starch with the appropriate buffer. When a viscous liquid is obtained, the air is removed from it by boiling under vacuum for 1 to 2 minutes. The hot starch is poured into the trough, covered with a plastic sheet or vaseline, and allowed to harden.

A connection between the electrode compartments and starch gel is obtained with two or three layers of heavy filter paper with the ends which are in contact with the gel encased in a cellophane membrane. The filter paper wicks can either be cast into the ends of the gel trough or, if the trough has the ends removable, be placed in direct contact with the gel after it has hardened.

The sample is mixed with the same buffer as is used in casting the gel. This sample buffer mixture is placed in a small slot made by removing a segment of gel, 1 to 5 mm thick, near the center of the block. A very small sample can be inserted into the block by first absorbing it onto filter paper, then placing the filter paper in a slit in the gel. The sample area is covered with a waterproof covering and separation is started.

Hydrolyzed starch used for casting the gel can be purchased from Cannought Medical Research Laboratories, University of Toronto,

Fig. 3-7. Diagram of a starch gel electrophoresis apparatus. The outer electrode compartment *(1)* which contains the electrodes *(6)* is separated from the inner one *(3)* but an electrical connection is maintained by the window *(2)* stuffed with glass wool or cotton. The starch gel is cast in box *(5)* and connected to the electrolyte with wicks *(4)* (Courtesy, Boyce Thompson Institute, Inc.).

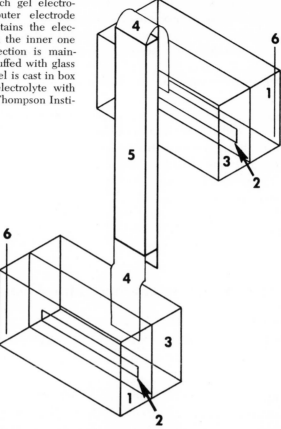

Canada, or the starch can be prepared by the method of Smithies [12]. Buffers used in the preparation of the gel can range in pH from 3 to 11. Good results for separating some proteins are obtained with a borate buffer pH 9 to 9.2 [12].

Starch gel electrophoresis is carried out at low voltages. The heat created by higher voltage is not dissipated fast enough unless very thin layers of gel are used with special provisions for heat removal.

After separation has been completed and the gel removed from the apparatus, the block can be sliced horizontally with a taut wire; one layer is used to locate the sample, while the second is reserved for some other use.

DISC ELECTROPHORESIS. Polyacrylamide has recently been used as a buffer-stabilizing medium. Electrophoresis of proteins in the gel resolves many more components from the same sample than are resolved by paper electrophoresis. The short time and high resolving power contribute to the popularity of this technique; approximately 20 to 30 minutes are needed for maximum separation.

The apparatus for disc electrophoresis is relatively simple. Polystyrene refrigerator dishes with ⅜ inch holes drilled around the periphery of the bottom can be used for one electrode compartment. A similar dish with holes cut in the top to match those in the bottom of the first container will serve for the second buffer compartment. Electrical grommets are inserted into the holes in the bottom of the container to hold the sample tubes and keep the electrolyte from leaking out. The apparatus is arranged with one dish on top of the other separated by the length of the sample tube. Electrodes are inserted into the two compartments; the cathode is in the top. A commercial apparatus is available from Canal Industrial Corp.

The sample tubes are arranged in the apparatus, electrolyte added, and the electric current applied. A constant current of 5 ma per tube for a 20- to 30-minute period will separate most material. Higher currents cause heating which, in turn, results in abnormal migration, such as twisted fronts.

Methods of Separating Major Classes of Compounds

The successful use of zone electrophoresis as an analytical tool is based upon two facts: the materials being studied can be separated into discrete spots or bands and can be visualized. There is no one general procedure which can be used to separate all classes of compounds, nor is there any single method which can be employed to visualize the separated components. Generally speaking, the components within a group will respond in a similar fashion both to performance in different buffer systems and to methods of visualizing them. Separation of certain compounds within a group may require special treatment. A detailed discussion of the conditions needed to achieve maximum resolution of different types of compounds is beyond the scope of this section, but a brief summary of some of the conditions that affect resolution and methods of visualizing some of the major groups will be described.

PROTEINS

The use of paper electrophoresis to separate blood serum proteins has been investigated extensively, but much less information is available on the separation of plant proteins. Although some of the techniques used for separation of blood proteins can be used for plant materials, modifications of these techniques may produce better results; the exact modification depends upon the plant material being studied.

The disadvantage of filter paper as a support medium for separating plant proteins is that many proteins adsorb onto the cellulose fibers. Starch gel and polyacrylamide, used in place of paper, will separate various components with little or no adsorption of protein to the support medium.

Irrespective of whether proteins are separated on paper or in gel, they need to be visualized for either locating or quantitating. As proteins contain many basic and acidic groups, different dyes which react with these groups are used to visualize the separated components.

Successful resolution of proteins depends upon attention to many details which are described in various books on electrophoresis [13–16]. Only generalities will be discussed in the following sections.

PAPER ELECTROPHORESIS. The extraction and concentration of solutions of plant proteins are not discussed in this section. It is assumed that a solution of proteins is available for electrophoretic separation.

Practically any type of low voltage electrophoretic apparatus can be used to separate proteins. Any good grade of filter paper will suffice as a support medium. Buffer systems ranging from pH 3.1 (aluminum lactate) to pH 9.7 (sodium glycinate) have been used to separate the proteins of wheat [17]. In many cases where hydrogen bonding interferes with separation, the addition of compounds such as urea, which decreases hydrogen bonding, gives improved resolution. Good resolution of blood serum proteins is obtained with a pH 8.6 barbiturate buffer with an ionic concentration ranging from 0.05 to 0.083. Although plant proteins will not show the same characteristic separation as blood serum, the characteristics of blood serum can be used as a general guide. It is anticipated that maximum resolution of a particular type of plant protein will require considerable modification of buffer pH and concentration from that used for blood.

Separation time varies from 6 hours to more than 12 hours. Generally speaking, the greater the ionic strength of the buffer, the longer it takes to achieve separation.

The separated protein components on the filter paper can be located by dyes, ultraviolet light, radiotracers, or nitrogen determinations. Probably the most practical and certainly the most popular method of visualizing the proteins is to stain them with dyes such as bromophenol blue, Amido Black 10B, light green S.F., Azocarmine G., Nigrosin, or Sudan Black. Sudan II and Oil Red O are used for lipoproteins, while periodic acid-Schiff reaction [13] is used for proteins containing carbohydrates.

The procedures for staining proteins vary with the dye being used, but certain aspects of the technique are common to all. The electrophorogram is removed from the apparatus, and dried at 110° to 120°C for 30 minutes to denature the protein. The paper is then immersed in a solution of the stain for the appropriate time, removed, drained, and surplus stain removed by washing repeatedly in some solvent that will dissolve the stain. Finally, the paper is dried and observed.

STARCH GEL ELECTROPHORESIS.   Starch gel, as a support medium for various buffers, offers advantages over filter paper. Fewer proteins adsorb onto the gel particles than onto paper, and better resolution of the proteins is obtained with the starch gel than with filter paper. The gel can be handled in much the same manner as filter paper; therefore, it can be used for qualitative and quantitative determinations or for micro preparative purposes.

The gel is prepared with many different types of buffers ranging from pH 1.7 to 11.5 [12]. Material such as urea can also be incorporated into the gel. In fact, the gel can be cast containing a buffer of one pH, while a second type of buffer at a different pH can be used in the electrode compartments. Such a discontinuous system has been shown to give improved resolution.

Starch gel electrophoresis, like paper, requires a relatively long time for complete separation. Usually, with gels of average thickness, an overnight separation is adequate. Extremely thin gels cast in troughs equipped with cooling devices can tolerate a higher voltage which, in turn, reduces separation time.

Protein separations in starch gel are similar to the separations on paper in one respect; they have to be visualized. Usually the gel containing the separated materials is cut horizontally with a taut wire and one half of the slab is used for locating the materials, while the second half is retained for some other test. Many dyes that are used for detection of proteins on filter paper can also be used with starch gel. Similar to paper electrophorograms of proteins, the separated materials in the gel have to be denatured and the gel hardened for handling. Smithies [12] used a mixture of methanol-water-acetic acid (50:50:10, v/v/v) containing a concentrated protein dye to harden the gel, and to denature and dye the proteins. Many of the dyes discussed under paper electrophoresis of protein can be used with starch gel.

If the protein needs to be removed from the starch gel before staining, it can be done either electrophoretically or mechanically. Electrophoretic removal of the protein is carried out by overlaying the gel sections with a dilute salt solution and applying an electric potential across the salt-gel interphase. The protein migrates from the gel to the salt solution from which it can be isolated [18]. Mechanically, the proteins can be separated from the gel by trituration followed by centrifugation to separate the gel particles from the solubilized protein. The mechanical method results in some soluble starch associated with the gel going into the protein fraction. If it is desirable to remove the trace of starch, the protein can be chromatographed on a column of Dowex 2-X8 with tris buffer as described by Paillerets *et al.* [19].

DISC ELECTROPHORESIS. Electrophoretic separation of protein mixtures in polyacrylamide gels produces the greatest resolution in the shortest period of time of all the different electrophoretic techniques discussed. Since the separated, stained proteins appear as small discs stacked on top of each other, this method was called disc electrophoresis.

The technique was designed fundamentally for separation of blood serum proteins, but it can be adapted for many other types. In the most commonly used procedure, one end of an open-ended, cylindrical glass tube, measuring 7×0.5 cm id (Canal Industrial Corp.) is fitted with a rubber stopper and the tube, standing upright on the stopper, is half-filled with a solution of acrylamide, catalyst, and buffer. The solution is overlaid with 0.1 ml of water and, after polymerization (20 to 30 minutes), the water is replaced with a second acrylamide solution which polymerizes upon exposure to light. The sample of proteins mixed with another portion of photosensitive acrylamide solution forms the third and uppermost layer. The rubber stopper is removed, the tube is inserted into the electrophoresis apparatus and a current of 6 to 8 ma is applied for a 20- to 30-minute period. After the separation is complete, the gel is removed and stained with such protein dyes as Amido-Schwarz in 7 per cent acetic acid. The background stain is removed electrophoretically using 7 per cent acetic acid in both electrode compartments with a current of 15 ma per tube. Reisfeld *et al.* [20] have described a technique for separating basic proteins; Chang *et al.* [21] used disc electrophoresis to separate soluble *Neurospora* proteins, and Ornstein and Davis [22] used this technique to separate proteins from blood serum. As different plant proteins might require other buffers at different pH values from those methods which have been described, modifications would have to be made in order to achieve maximum resolution.

PEPTIDES

A mixture of simple and complex peptides can be separated by a combination of electrophoresis and paper chromatography as described by Katz *et al.* [23], and Rodbell and Fredrickson [24]. Peptides, totaling 1 to 2 mg of amino nitrogen, are spotted on an 18×22 in. sheet of Whatman 3 or 3MM paper, and descending chromatography is carried out for 16 hours or longer using *n*-butanol-acetic acid-water (4:1:5, v/v/v). After chromatography is completed and the papers dried, a pencil line is drawn from the origin to the other edge of the paper, parallel to the direction of solvent flow. This is a guide for applying the buffer. Typically, a volatile buffer, such as glacial acetic acid-pyridine-water (10:1:289, v/v/v, pH 3.7), is used. The separation pattern obtained can be varied by using other types of buffers. As this system draws considerable current, it will be necessary to cool the paper. If the instrument described in the preceding section under electrophoresis and chromatography is used, the liquid bathing the paper will need to be cooled. Although this instrument is recommended for peptide separation, other instruments which can be adapted to accommodate large sheets of filter paper can also be used. Irrespective of which instrument is used, cooling of the paper during the separation is recommended.

The type of separation obtained can be altered by using different chromatographic solvents or buffers of different pH. If electrophoresis is carried out first, a volatile buffer should be used. This buffer will leave no salts on the paper to interfere with chromatography. The separated peptides can be rendered visible with ninhydrin, 0.5 per cent in absolute methanol, ethanol, or acetone (w/v). If the peptides are to be hydrolyzed, a light spraying with a dilute ninhydrin reagent, 0.025 per cent in absolute ethanol, will bring out the peptides as pale purple spots; these can be eluted and hydrolyzed to their amino acids [25].

AMINO ACIDS AND AMINES

Amino acids can be separated by either high or low voltage paper electrophoresis. High voltage typically produces the best resolution in the shortest time (20 to 30 minutes) thereby reducing the possibility of diffusion. The type of filter paper used dictates to a degree the amount of amino nitrogen that can be applied to the paper.

The migration rate of individual amino acids depends to a great extent on the pH of the buffer used. Typically, the migration rate of the acidic amino acids increases as the pH decreases. As the pH is increased above 7, the migration rate of the basic amino acids increases faster than the others. A small change in buffer pH can mean the difference between resolving and not resolving amino acids which have similar mobilities. Gross [26] resolved alanine, γ-aminobutyric, serine, the leucines, asparagine, glycine, hydroxyproline, and tryptophan on Whatman 3MM in a pH 2.0 buffer (0.15M formic acid-2M glacial acetic acid, 1:1, v/v) with 90 v/cm. Many other combinations can be separated.

The greatest resolution, similar to that obtained for the peptides, is obtained by using a combination of high voltage electrophoresis and chromatography. The apparatus and technique are similar to that described for peptide separation. Efron [27] used a closed strip, high voltage apparatus for electrophoresis, followed by chromatography. She was able to resolve over 40 amino compounds.

The separated amino acids can be rendered visible on the paper with ninhydrin, 0.5 per cent (w/v) in absolute methanol, ethanol, or acetone. Reagents which react with specific amino acids such as are used for paper chromatography will produce satisfactory results on electrophorograms.

The conditions necessary for amino acid separation are adequate for separating aliphatic amines. These can be visualized with the same ninhydrin reagent used to detect amino acids [28].

Aromatic amines have successfully been separated with low voltage in a pH 2.7 HCl-KCl buffer (ionic concentration of 0.004). Most amines will migrate toward the cathode unless the molecule contains a strongly negative group such as SO_3H or COOH. These compounds can be detected on the paper with p-nitrobenzenediazoniumfluoborate as described by Hanot [29].

CARBOHYDRATES AND RELATED COMPOUNDS

Carbohydrates are neutral compounds, but the molecules can be complexed with boron, molybdenum, germanium, or similar materials, after which the complex will migrate in an electric field.

All types of paper electrophoretic apparatus can be used to separate complexed carbohydrate mixtures. Similar to all low-molecular-weight materials, high voltage separation gives superior resolution in the shortest period of time.

The electroendosmotic flow, which affects the migration rate and final position of the compounds on the paper, is followed with various nonmigrating markers such as 2,4,6-tri-O-methylglucose. Since different electrophoretic apparatus cause the carbohydrates to migrate varying distances under similar conditions of buffer pH and ionic concentrations, an internal standard of glucose is often used. The final position that the carbohydrate attains is referred to as the ratio of its distance of migration to that of glucose on the same electrophorogram. This distance is referred to as the M_g value. Numerous tables have been constructed listing the M_g values of many polyhydroxy compounds [3].

Although many different buffer systems are used to separate carbohydrates, the most popular and easiest to prepare is a pH 9.2 sodium tetraborate (19.1 g $Na_2B_4O_7 \cdot 10H_2O$ per liter). Under these conditions, the carbohydrates migrate toward the anode. Other buffers and methods of handling them are discussed by Frahn and Mills [3].

The carbohydrates on the dried electrophorogram are detected with many of the same reagents used to visualize them on paper chromatograms. Aniline phthalate will detect the reducing sugars on electrophorograms that are buffered with sodium tetraborate. Glucose alone, in the presence of other carbohydrates, can be visualized on borate buffered papers by neutralizing the electrophorograms with a dilute pH 7.0 buffer, and by then spraying with Glucostat (Worthington Biochemical), a preparation of glucose oxidase. When buffers other than borate are used, special visualizing agents help [3].

MISCELLANEOUS MATERIALS

Complex mixtures of many materials, other than those previously discussed, can be separated by electrophoresis. In some cases, electrophoresis gives resolution superior to paper chromatography. The following section briefly describes some conditions which will resolve charged substances of low molecular weight.

The nucleotides of the various purine and pyrimidine bases are separated by either low or high voltage electrophoresis. High voltage separation is preferred. The monophosphates are easily separated on Whatman 1, 3, or 3MM in a pH 3.5 to 4.1 citrate or acetate buffer, each with ionic concentration about 0.1. As these compounds are relatively heat stable, the separation is done at room temperature. The di- and triphosphates, being more heat-labile, require cooling during separation.

The separation of the mono-, di-, and triphosphates of a given purine or pyrimidine base in a pH 3.5 to 4.1 buffer is good, but in a mixture of the mono-, di-, and triphosphates of adenine, guanosine, cytidine, and uracil, all of the nucleotides will not be separated. Some have similar mobility values, and these will occupy areas so close together that separation is not likely. For example, at pH 4.1 guanosine triphosphate, adenosine triphosphate, uridine diphosphate, and cytidine triphosphate have similar mobilities and are not separated.

The different isomers of a given nucleotide are separated by using a borate buffer described under *Carbohydrates and Related Compounds*. This buffer contains borate ions which complex with the free hydroxyl groups. As the position of the free hydroxyl groups varies with each isomer, the degree of borate complexing also varies which, in turn, varies the net molecular charge.

Nucleotides and nucleosides are visualized on the dried electrophorogram by viewing them under ultraviolet light. The nucleotides appear as dark blue spots on a light blue background.

Organic acids are among the easiest organic compounds to separate. All types of paper electrophoretic apparatus and any good grade of filter paper can be used to achieve separation. The type of organic acid to be separated dictates the buffer to use. Generally speaking, buffers higher than pH 7.0 are used to separate weak acids, i.e., C_1 to C_{10} aliphatic acids [28]. Those acids which readily ionize may require a stronger buffer such as a mixture of 0.75M formic acid plus M glacial acetic acid (1:1, v/v) [30]. Reagents, such as bromophenol blue in ethanol, used to detect organic acids on paper chromatograms, can also be used on electrophorograms.

The separation of inorganic ions by paper electrophoresis, especially at high voltages, is fast and produces good resolution. Preparation of the inorganic ions for electrophoretic separation is very important but is outside of the scope of this discussion. The kind of ions being separated determines the pH and type of buffer which need to be used. In many cases, ions move better on the electrophorogram when complexed with some agent. Gross [31, 32], Jakovac and Lederer [33], and Lederer [15, 34] have separated anions and cations by electrophoresis. Detection techniques for separated materials depend upon the ions being separated. Many of the detection devices used in paper chromatography of inorganic ions can be applied to electrophorograms [13].

The compounds discussed in the above section do not exhaust the list of those which can be separated by electrophoresis. As previously pointed out, any material that possesses an electric charge, or can be complexed with another molecule which will give it an electric charge, will migrate in an electric field. The exact conditions of buffer pH and strength, time, and detection device may have to be determined. Electrophoresis can be used for separating complex mixtures and, in conjunction with paper chromatography, offers a method of resolving mixtures that either technique alone will not resolve.

References

1. P. König, *Actas Trabaljhas Congr. Sud-Americano Chem.*, **3**, Rio de Janeiro e Sao Paulo, **2**, 334 (1937).
2. R. Consden, A. H. Gordon, and A. J. P. Martin, *Biochem. J.*, **40**, 33 (1946).
3. J. L. Frahn and J. A. Mills, *Australian J. Chem.*, **12**, 65 (1959).
4. H. J. McDonald, *J. Chem. Educ.*, **29**, 428 (1952).
5. A. B. Foster, *Chem. Ind. (London)*, **21**, 1050 (1952).
6. H. Peeters, P. Vuylsteke, and R. Noë, *J. Chromatog.*, **2**, 308 (1959).
7. E. L. Durrum, *J. Am. Chem. Soc.*, **73**, 4875 (1951).
8. M. Zaitlin, *J. Chromatog.*, **1**, 186 (1958).
9. H. Michl, *Chromatog. Rev.*, **1**, 11 (1959).
10. D. Gross, *J. Chromatog.*, **5**, 194 (1961).
11. A. E. Pasieka, *Can. J. Biochem. Physiol.*, **39**, 1313 (1961).
12. O. Smithies, *Advan. Protein Chem.*, **14**, 65 (1959).
13. R. J. Block, E. L. Durrum, and G. Zweig, *A Manual of Paper Chromatography and Paper Electrophoresis*, Academic Press, New York, 2nd ed. (1958).
14. I. Smith, *Chromatographic and Electrophoretic Techniques*, Interscience Publishers, New York, 2nd ed. (1960).
15. M. Lederer, *An Introduction to Paper Electrophoresis and Related Methods*, Elsevier, New York (1955).

16. M. Bier, *Electrophoresis: Theory, Methods, and Application,* Academic Press, New York (1959).
17. J. H. Woychik, J. A. Boundy, and R. J. Dimler, *Arch. Biochem. Biophys.,* **94**, 477 (1961).
18. P. Bernfeld and J. S. Nisselbaum, *J. Biol. Chem.,* **220**, 851 (1956).
19. C. de Paillerets, J. Moretti, and M. F. Jayle, *Bull. Soc. Chim. Biol.,* **41**, 1285 (1959).
20. R. A. Reisfeld, U. J. Lewis, and D. E. Williams, *Nature,* **195**, 281 (1962).
21. L. O. Chang, A. M. Srb, and F. C. Steward, *Nature,* **193**, 756 (1962).
22. L. Ornstein and B. J. Davis, Preprinted by Distillation Products Industries (Div. of Eastman Kodak Co.) (1962).
23. A. M. Katz, W. J. Dreyer, and C. B. Anfinsen, *J. Biol. Chem.,* **234**, 2897 (1959).
24. M. Rodbell and D. S. Fredrickson, *J. Biol. Chem.,* **234**, 562 (1959).
25. C. B. Anfinsen, S. E. G. Åqvist, J. P. Cooke, and B. Jönsson, *J. Biol. Chem.,* **234**, 1118 (1959).
26. D. Gross, *Nature,* **176**, 72 (1955).
27. M. Efron, In *Chromatographic and Electrophoretic Techniques,* I. Smith, ed., Interscience Publishers, New York, 2nd ed. (1960), p. 150.
28. D. Gross, *Nature,* **184**, 1633 (1959).
29. C. Hanot, *Bull. Soc. Chim. Belges,* **66**, 76 (1957).
30. D. Gross, *Nature,* **178**, 29 (1956).
31. D. Gross, *Chem. Ind., (London),* **26**, 1597 (1957).
32. D. Gross, *Nature,* **180**, 596 (1957).
33. Z. Jakovac and M. Lederer, *J. Chromatog.,* **2**, 658 (1959).
34. M. Lederer, *J. Chromatog.,* **1**, 86 (1958).

Column Chromatography

Leonard H. Weinstein and Henry J. Laurencot, Jr.

COLUMN CHROMATOGRAPHY is the separation of a mixture of substances into its various components by the processes of selective adsorption, partition, ion, or electron exchange, or filtration in a column of porous material.

The Russian botanist, Mikhail Tswett (1872-1919) is generally held to be the discoverer of the chromatographic process, although an American chemist, David Talbot Day (1859-1925), had already been experimenting in this area. Day was able to separate crude oil into several fractions by passing it through finely pulverized Fuller's earth. He did not, however, recognize the analytical and industrial significance of his discovery.

In his classical experiments on *adsorption chromatography*, Tswett resolved a petroleum ether extract of plant chloroplast pigments in a column of calcium carbonate. The pigments were separated into colored zones from top to bottom according to the degree each component was held by adsorption. Strongly adsorbed pigments displaced the more weakly held ones and forced them down the column. The phenomenon is therefore a continuous process of adsorption and desorption of solutes to and from the liquid phase and the surfaces of the adsorbent. Separation was accomplished by passing a stream of pure solvent through the column. Tswett stated that the adsorption phenomenon he described was not restricted to the chromatography of chloroplast pigments but that all kinds of colorless and chromogenic molecules are subject to the same laws.

In 1941, A. J. P. Martin and R. L. M. Synge developed a chromatographic column containing a finely divided solid, called the *support*, on which a solvent is adsorbed with such tenacity that it will not migrate, while solutes are not retained by adsorption. The solutes participate in a partitioning between the *stationary* phase in which they are held in a fixed position, and the *mobile* phase, in which they migrate. The name *partition chromatography* has been given to this phenomenon. The mixture to be separated is distributed between the two liquid phases, and separation depends on the distribution of the components of the mixture in the mobile and stationary phases. A component which interacts with the stationary phase is retarded with respect to others that interact less. Martin and Synge visualized the supporting medium as being divided into a number of regions, or *plates,* with perfect equilibrium between the solute in the mobile and stationary phases existing in each. Solutes passing through a column having a large number of theoretical plates will be subject to a number of extractions, and thus more efficient separation. In the case of a 1 × 20-cm column of silica gel, with water as the stationary phase and chloroform as the mobile phase, there are 104 theoretical plates.

In *ion-exchange chromatography,* the stationary phase comprises a polymeric structure with fixed charge sites to which oppositely charged ions are affixed. These latter ions may be competitively exchanged with ions of a similar charge contained in the mobile phase, thus preserving electronic neutrality. The rate of movement of an ionizable material through the column depends upon its degree of ionization, the concentrations of other ions, and the relative affinities of the various ions in the solution for charged sites on the resin. Using a cationic resin, H^+ ions attached to the resin may be exchanged for Na^+ ions or other suitable positively-charged ions in the mobile phase. On the other hand, Cl^- ions of an anionic resin may be exchanged for OH^- ions in the mobile phase. A further application of an anionic resin will be seen in a later example where a mixture of organic acids is sorbed on an acetate-form resin and the acids subsequently displaced individually with acetic and formic acids. Some general references are given at the end of the chapter [1-9].

Factors Affecting Chromatographic Separation

PARTICLE SIZE OF THE SUPPORTING MEDIUM

Good chromatographic separation is dependent upon uniform flow rate of the chromatographic solvent, and this, in turn, is dependent to a great extent upon the particle size and uniformity of the supporting material. It is therefore important that the supporting material used be graded into particle sizes and that the most suitable particle size for a given application be used.

As the particle size of an adsorbent decreases, the sorption equilibrium on the column increases. This permits flow rates through the column to be increased without impairing separation. However, adsorbents of very small particle size will offer considerable resistance to flow, and one must then resort to pressure flow of the eluting liquid. This is best brought about by the use of liquid pumps. Compressed gases may also be used at relatively low pressures but should be avoided if pressures in the order of 4 atm (60 psi.) or greater are employed.

SIZE OF COLUMN

As mentioned earlier, the size of the column may be critical to successful separation of a mixture of substances. This is due, in part, to the fact that homogeneous packing and uniform particle size are critical aspects of column chromatography. When particle sizes are not uniform, the interstitial areas between particles will vary and chromatographic bands may not be straight. If two consecutive elution bands are close together and not perpendicular to the direction of flow, the separation between the bands leaving the column will not be complete and a certain amount of mixing will occur between them. On a long and narrow column, slight deviations in the uniformity of zones will not be as critical as on a short and wide column.

RATE OF FLOW

A uniform and low flow rate will result in a more satisfactory sorption equilibrium and more uniform zone formation than a fast flow rate when the particle size is uniformly small. As a result, the separation of individual components of a mixture will be more efficient. It is not usually possible to determine visually the uniformity of separation of components during the chromatographic procedure, however, since they are rarely chromogenic. In instances in which the components are chromogenic and chromatographic separation is unsatisfactory, certain steps may be taken to correct the situation. If the front is diffuse, the flow rate should be decreased. If this does not improve separation, a finer particle size of chromatographic medium should be used. In some instances, a combination of decreased flow rate and particle size may be required. A sharply differentiated but uneven front usually signifies improper or uneven packing of the column. Occasionally, a decreased flow rate will correct this condition, but, if not, repacking of the column will be necessary.

The rate of flow through a column may be controlled either by adjustment of the flow rate into the column or at the outlet of the column. Flow into the column is commonly controlled by a pump, by gas pressure, or by a leveling bottle. Flow out of the column is usually controlled by an adjustable clamp and a small piece of rubber or Tygon tubing, a stopcock, or a needle valve. Most accurate flow is obtained by employing a proportioning pump to deliver solvent into the column under pressure or to pull the eluate stream through the outlet tube of the column.

Supporting Media for Column Chromatography

ADSORPTION COLUMN CHROMATOGRAPHY

Among the most commonly used inorganic adsorbents for column chromatography are alumina and related substances. Alumina is usually the material of choice when a new mixture of substances is being chromatographed, since it is a good adsorbent for most substances, has a large capacity, is insoluble, relatively inert, and easily obtainable. Carotenes, fat-soluble vitamins (such as vitamins A and E), coenzyme Q, steroids, alkaloids, porphyrins, proteins, and many other substances have been separated with alumina.

A number of activated charcoals and carbons from animal and plant sources, such as blood, bone, wood, sugar, etc., are available. They have been used to achieve separation of such nitrogen-containing compounds as aromatic amino acids and purine and pyrimidine ribotides, and of lipids and carbohydrates.

Many clay minerals, such as montmorillonite, attapulgite (Fuller's earth), kaolinite, bentonite (an ore of montmorillonite), and talc, have been used as adsorbents. The clays and related inorganic materials have been used to separate phospholipids, vitamin A, unsaturated fatty acids, and carotenes.

Kieselguhrs, diatomaceous earths, and filter aids are often employed to improve solvent flow rate through columns of such absorbents as clays and silicic acid. In some instances, however, they may themselves be used as adsorbents. For example, Kieselguhrs have been found to be useful adsorbents for high-molecular-weight materials such as proteins.

Silicic acid and silica gels are good adsorbents for polar substances and have been used to separate terpenes and steroids by adsorption chromatography. Recently, several polyamides, such as nylon 6 and nylon 66, have come into general use for the separation of polyphenols, flavanols, and flavanoids.

Miscellaneous organic substances, such as cellulose powder, cellulose acetate, confectioner's sugar, and starch, have been often employed as adsorbents. Among the applications of these materials is the separation of carbohydrates on cellulose.

PARTITION COLUMN CHROMATOGRAPHY

Many of the same supporting media are used for both adsorption and partition chromatography. Silica gel is one of these, and it was also the first inert carrier used for partition column chromatography. Silicic acid columns, supporting the polar phase, are used for the separation of lipids by the nonpolar solvent. Silica gel and silicic acid are also used to separate aromatic acids, 2,4-dinitro-phenylhydrazones of keto acids, anthocyanidins, N- acetyl amino acids, and many other substances.

Kieselguhr and diatomaceous earths, when applied to partition chromatography, have been used to separate proteins, aliphatic acids, di- and trihydric alcohols, glycolipids, etc.

Starch is used for partition chromatography of chlorophylls, ribonucleotides and nucleic acid, purines and pyrimidines, and peptides.

Cellulose powders can be employed wherever paper chromatography has been successfully used and therefore have wide application. Among the applications of cellulose are separation of amino acids, 2,4-dinitrophenylhydrazones of keto acids, sugars and sugar derivatives, phospholipids, and flavanoids.

Powdered rubber is used in the reverse phase separation of C_8 to C_{18} fatty acids, and glass powders and beads have been applied to the separation of lipoproteins.

ION-EXCHANGE   COLUMN   CHROMATOGRAPHY

Ion-exchange materials contain either anionic- or cationic-exchange sites. In some cases, they may occur in the same exchangers. Both the anionic and cationic types may act as exchangers, catalysts, or sorbents, singly or in combinations of these properties.

Inorganic cation exchangers include the zeolites, clays, and aluminosilicates. The hydrous oxides of tetravalent metals, such as zirconium, thorium, titanium, and tin, are anionic or cationic according to pH. The phosphates, molybdates, tungstates, and vanadates of tetravalent metals are predominantly cation exchangers. They exhibit great resistance to radiation and temperature extremes, have a high column capacity, and show great selectivity towards simple inorganic ions. The principal uses of these materials are in water-softening applications.

Inorganic anion exchangers are represented by the synthetic zeolites, hydrous oxides of iron and aluminum, aluminosilicate gels, powdered greensand, and some clays. They have been used in water-softening applications and for removal of fluoride from water.

Natural organic ion exchangers of cellulose and wool, silk, horn, humus coals, and other proteinaceous substances exhibit some limited exchange capacities owing to the presence of free amino and carboxyl groups.

Synthetic organic ion exchangers are by far of the greatest importance. They are usually classified according to the dissociation behavior of the acid or base forms; cation exchangers are thus classified as weak or strong acid types and anion exchangers as weak or strong base types.

Synthetic organic cation exchangers of the sulfonic acid type are represented by sulfonated coal, phenolsulfonic acid resins, and sulfonated polystyrene-divinyl-benzene resins. Strongly acidic cation exchangers are represented by the commercial resins Dowex 50 and Amberlite IR-120. They are typically used for the separation of amino acids, peptides, and nucleic acids, and their derivatives. Duolite C-10, a sulfonic acid resin, is employed for the separation of alkaloids. Amberlite IRC-50 is a carboxylic acid type resin of the weak acid type. Resins of this group can be buffered at specific pH values and are used for the separation of alkaloids and other organic bases of high molecular weight which are strongly bound to resins of the sulfonic acid type and removed with difficulty.

Synthetic organic anion-exchange resins of the weak base type, such as Amberlite IR-4B, Amberlite IR-45, and Dowex 3, are polymers of primary, secondary, or tertiary amines with styrene-divinylbenzene.

Polymers of styrene-divinylbenzene with quaternary ammonium groups are represented by the strongly basic anion-exchange resins, Amberlite IRA-400, Amberlite IRA-410, Dowex 1, and Dowex 2. These resins are employed for the separation of sugars and other carbohydrates, nucleotides, and nonvolatile organic acids.

A number of ion-exchange celluloses have found wide application in column chromatography for the fractionation of high-molecular-weight ionic substances. A major advantage of these materials is their ability to release, selectively, materials under mild elution conditions. Among the anion-exchange celluloses, diethylaminoethyl cellulose (DEAE) has wide application in the chromatography of enzymes, hormones, and proteins. Triethylaminoethyl cellulose (TEAE) is used for the separation of acidic proteins, and a mixed amine cellulose (ECTEOLA) for the separation of nucleic acids. Carboxymethyl cellulose (CM), used in the fractionation of certain enzymes and other proteins, has had the greatest application among the cation-exchange celluloses. Sulfoethyl cellulose (SE) has similar applications.

GEL FILTRATION

In a column packed with small swollen gel particles, solutes of large molecular size are excluded from the gel and emerge from the column without retardation, while solutes capable of diffusing into the interior of the particle are retarded. The whole process is carried out without changing the solvent. Hydrophilic gels, such as starch, synthetic xerogels, dextran gels, and calcium phosphate gels, are used for the desalting of colloids and proteins, the separation of polysaccharides, of amino acids from peptides and proteins, of nucleotides and nucleic acids, of enzymes and soluble cofactors, fractionation of histones, and purification of enzymes. Organophilic gels are applied to the separation of substances soluble in organic solvents. Vulcanized rubber latex columns have been used for the separation of polymers of low-molecular-weight compounds.

Chromatographic Procedures

ELUTION ANALYSIS

The chromatographic column, packed with the supporting material, is rinsed with the starting solvent. The sample is then introduced onto the bed and forms a region called the *starting zone*. If possible, the sample should be dissolved in the first solvent, and then introduced into the column in the smallest possible volume. This procedure tends to keep the *elution bands* more discrete. When the sample is not soluble in the first solvent, it is added to a small amount of supporting medium in a small beaker and is thoroughly mixed with a glass rod to obtain a friable powder. More of the supporting medium is added if necessary. The solvent in the column is then lowered until it reaches the surface of the bed. The sample-support mixture is then introduced carefully, and a small amount of solvent is added to raise the liquid level to just above the surface of the sample. With a small stirring rod. the newly introduced material is gently stirred to remove air bubbles and to wet thoroughly the supporting material, while care is taken not to disturb the portion of the bed added previously.

After the sample has been introduced into the column, the solvent to be used, or the first of several solvents in some instances, is added to a suitable reservoir attached to the top of the column. This solvent is called the *eluting agent* or *eluant*. Usually the eluant contains the same ion as that initially on the column. The process of elution is now begun. Individual substances of the sample mixture begin to move through the column, depending upon the characteristics of the substance in relation to the supporting material. If these characteristics are different for the various components of the sample, they will begin to separate from one another, and will finally appear in separate zones, more or less discretely separated. As the elution is continued, the separation becomes more distinct, and, if the characteristics of the column are satisfactory, the separated individual constituents will leave the lower end of the column where they may be collected.

Elution may also be achieved, in some instances, by the introduction into the column of several eluting agents in a predetermined sequence. The first eluting agent is always one of low elution power, and, with each subsequent change, an agent of higher elution power is introduced. This is often done by increasing the concentration of a single eluting agent, by introduction of a new ionic species into the eluting agent, or by introducing a new solvent. This sequential elution procedure is used when the range of retention between the most weakly and most strongly held constituents is very great.

A serious drawback to this procedure is the possibility of having a single compound appear in two discrete peaks. This may occur when one component of the mixture is not entirely eluted with the preceding olvent. The sequential addition of the next eluant, with a greater eluting power, will remove the remainder of the component, thus resulting in what appear to be two peaks. This deficiency may be overcome to a great extent by *gradient* elution.

In gradient elution, the composition of the eluant is changed continuously. This change is accomplished by using a mixture of solutions with continuously increasing elution power. This is usually done by constant alteration of pH or increasing ionic strength, or both. Several devices for gradient elution are shown in Fig. 4-1. Container (a) is always filled with a relatively weak eluant, often water, while container (b) has a more concentrated eluant. In Fig. 4-1 A, and B, the stronger eluting agent is forced by gas pressure or with a proportioning pump into container *(a)*, where it is thoroughly and continuously mixed. Concomitantly, there is a movement of eluting solution from container *(a)* into the column, since the system is closed. The expression

$$C = C_0(1-e^{-k}) \tag{1}$$

defines the concentration produced, where C_0 and C are the concentrations of the solutions entering and leaving the mixing flask, respectively, and k is the ratio of the volume of eluate collected at any time to the fixed volume of the mixing flask. Thus, initially, the first volume of solution entering the column consists essentially of only the weaker eluting solution. As the elution proceeds, the concentration of the stronger eluant in container (a) increases as does its eluting power. The device shown in Fig. 4-1 A will result in a logarithmic gradient, while that in Fig. 4-1 B will result in a linear gradient. The device shown in Fig. 4-1 C is used in conjunction with a proportioning pump and also yields a linear gradient. Gradient elution has several advantages: *(1)* Elution peaks are discrete, *(2)* single components yield single peaks, and *(3)* substances having widely separate properties can be separated in a single operation.

FRONTAL ANALYSIS

In *frontal analysis*, the sample solution is continuously passed through the column until the adsorbent is saturated with solutes and the composition of the influent and effluent liquids is the same. In this procedure, only the front-running solute emerges pure, hence the name frontal analysis. Subsequent fractions are mixed. Thus, the first fraction, A, will be pure. Fraction B will contain A, fraction C will contain A and B, etc. This procedure is of limited use for quantitative analysis.

DISPLACEMENT ANALYSIS

Displacement analysis does not result in complete separation of individual components of a mixture. This is because the boundaries

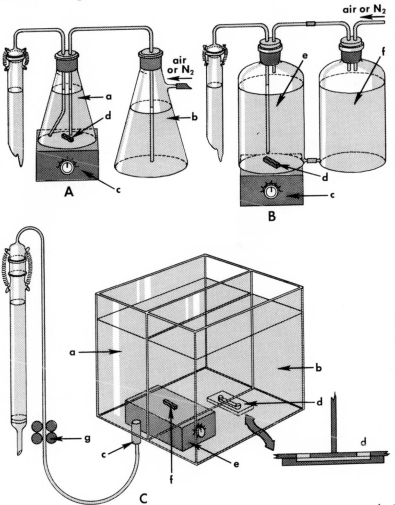

Fig. 4-1. Types of equipment employed for gradient elution (A) Apparatus producing a logarithmic gradient. (a) mixing flask; (b) reservoir flask; (c) magnetic stirring motor; (d) magnetic stirring bar. (B) Device producing linear gradient. (e) mixing flask; (f) reservoir flask; (c) magnetic stirring motor; (d) magnetic stirring bar. (C) Compartmented plastic box for producing linear gradient. (a) mixing compartment; (b) reservoir compartment; (c) outlet tube; (d) connecting channel between compartments; (e) magnetic stirring motor; (f) magnetic stirring bar; (g) proportioning pump.

of the zones as they travel down the column are in contact with each other, resulting in some mixing. In *carrier displacement analysis,* suitable carrier substances are added to the mixture to be separated. These carriers then serve to divide each component by forming bands between them.

Packing of Columns

Both dry and wet packings of columns are commonly used. If the dry method is employed, small amounts of the supporting medium are poured into the chromatographic tube and each aliquot is tamped firmly into place. This process is repeated until the column is adequately filled. The column is then thoroughly washed with the first solvent. The wash displaces air (which may interfere with elution), washes out impurities, and prepares the column in a suitable condition for sorption and elution.

Wet packing is most commonly used and results in more homogeneous columns. The support is prepared in the solvent to be used subsequently or in some other suitable liquid. The slurried material is introduced into the column, and the suspending liquid is allowed to flow out slowly. Before the solvent reaches the top of the supporting medium, an additional amount of slurry is added. This is continued until the desired amount of supporting material has been introduced. Gentle air pressure or suction may be applied to the column to expedite the flow of bedding liquid. The column is closed off before the liquid level reaches the top of the supporting medium; otherwise, air will be introduced, and it will be necessary to rebed the column. When the supporting material is prepared in a liquid not being used for elution, the slurry is introduced into the column, and most of the liquid is drained off, after which the packed material is washed with several bed volumes of the solvent to be employed. Certain combinations of liquids should be avoided. For example, if the supporting medium is introduced in water and the column is subsequently eluted with an ethanol-containing solvent, air bubbles will form. Preparing the column bed in ethanol followed by elution with an aqueous solvent is satisfactory.

Equipment

Basically, the successful separation of a mixture by column chromatography requires only the correct selection of a column, the supporting medium, the chromatographic solvent, and a reservoir to contain the solvent.

TYPES OF COLUMNS

The separation of mixtures of compounds by column chromatography does not necessarily require elaborate equipment. The supporting medium is contained in a tube, usually circular in cross section, commonly of glass, and somewhat constricted at the bottom end (Fig. 4-2). A number of other materials are suitable for chromatographic columns and, in some instances, may be essential for certain applications. Direct observation of the separation of compounds which absorb ultraviolet light or fluoresce may be achieved by the use of quartz columns. Some investigators have used stainless steel, polyethylene, lucite, polyvinyl chloride, or cellophane for various applications. The column is sometimes constructed so that it may be opened or sliced longitudinally or laterally.

The size of the column may be critical to successful separations of mixtures of materials. A height/diameter ratio of 10 or 20 to 1 is often employed, although, for some separations, long columns having a ratio of 100 to 1 are not uncommon.

The stationary phase is usually supported in the column by a fritted glass disc, although glass wool, glass filter cloth, perforated discs of porcelain, polyethylene, stainless steel, or porous discs of polyethylene are often used.

FRACTION COLLECTORS

In order to achieve separation of mixtures, the eluate must be divided into fractions, the number of which depends upon the materials being separated, the technique employed, the solvent used, etc. Collection of fractions may be carried out manually by counting drops or by collecting known volumes of eluate in small graduated cylinders. This technique, however, is extremely tedious and wasteful of time. For this reason, an automatic device called a *fraction collector* is generally used. Many fraction collectors are available commercially, and they may be obtained over a wide range of prices (Fig. 4-3).

All commercial fraction collectors are designed to hold test tubes or bottles of common dimensions. The rack is generally available in the form of a circular reel containing several rows of concentric perforations, although square or oblong racks are also available with some instruments.

There are several means of sequentially introducing known aliquots of the column eluate into the tubes. One method is based upon a time-actuated mechanism whereby the eluate is dispensed into a tube for a preset time interval, at the end of which the rack is automatically moved one position. A change in the flow characteristics of the column, however, may with time result in increasingly smaller fractions. Aliquots of relatively constant volume may also be obtained by

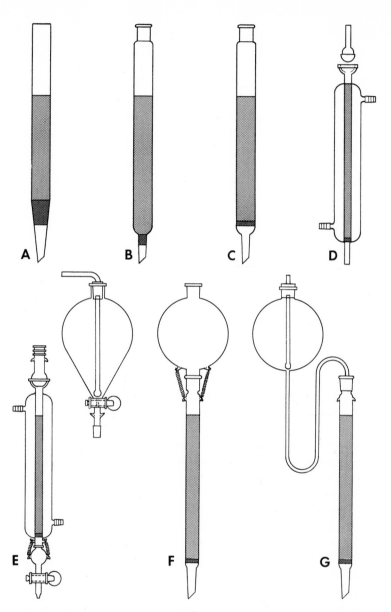

Fig. 4-2. Types of columns and reservoir flasks. (A) Glass tubing drawn out at end to accommodate glass wool filter. (B) Standard chromatographic column with filter in outlet tube. (C) Same as (B) with porous or perforated disc of fritted glass, polyethylene, porcelain, etc. (D) Water-jacketed column for separation of mixtures at controlled temperatures. (E) Water-jacketed column and reservoir flask adapted for separation of lipids. (F) Column fitted with reservoir flask which conveniently holds solvents for washing and charging of supporting material, or for subsequent elution. (G) Column with Mariotte bottle, which may be raised or lowered to control flow rate of solvent.

the use of small volumetric siphons. With such devices, constant volume is usually maintained, although some variation may occur due to a change in composition of the chromatographic solvent. Since siphoning is never completely quantitative, a small amount of liquid will be held up in the siphon and will mix with the next fraction. This is not usually a serious problem.

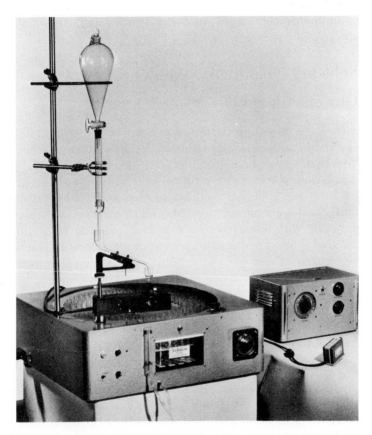

Fig. 4-3. Automatic fraction collector with drop-counting assembly (Courtesy, Technicon Instruments Corp.).

Automatic counting of drops by interruption of a light beam directed at a photoelectric cell is also available. In this type of instrument, the reel is actuated after a predetermined number of drops has been counted. Although this technique appears, on the surface at least, to be of great accuracy, it is imperative that all drops be of the same size. During gradient elution or after a change in composition of a chromatographic solvent, drop size is often affected. Even during elution with a single solvent, drop size will change as the solute concentration of the various chromatographic zones is changed.

Still other fraction collectors are based upon collection of fractions of constant weight. Here again, as the gradient of a chromatographic solvent changes or as a band of material emerges from the column, small changes in weight may occur.

It can be seen readily that none of the techniques for the collection of uniform fractions is foolproof, and one can generally expect a small variation in the size of fractions. Under the usual circumstances of column chromatography, however, these variations are of no appreciable significance.

Selected Quantitative Methods of Column Chromatography of Plant Materials

In order to demonstrate the principles and techniques of column chromatography under laboratory conditions, three relatively simple quantitative or qualitative methods have been selected for detailed discussion. Each of these procedures utilizes a different supporting medium and different methods of elution. It is hoped that the inexperienced chromatographer who masters these will then have little difficulty with other more complicated methods. It should be pointed out that there are alternate column chromatographic methods for the separation of each of these groups of biological materials covered below, but each of these methods has been found to be very satisfactory under most circumstances.

SEPARATION AND IDENTIFICATION OF NONVOLATILE ORGANIC ACIDS BY ANION-EXCHANGE CHROMATOGRAPHY

PREPARATION OF RESIN. Very fine particles present in chloride-form Dowex 1-X8, 200 to 400 mesh resin, are removed by sedimentation or elutriation. In sedimentation, the resin is suspended in about 3 volumes of distilled water and allowed to settle for 10 minutes. The fines are then decanted. The coarser resin is then resuspended in water, again allowed to settle for 10 minutes, and the fines are again decanted. The fines should be saved for possible future use, but the coarser resin will be further processed for use in organic acid separation. In elutriation, 300 ml of wet resin is transferred with water to a 2-liter separatory funnel supported on a ring stand. Distilled water is run into the bottom of the funnel at a flow rate of about 250 ml per minute. The standard taper joint at the top of the funnel is fitted with a one-hole rubber stopper, a large inverted Y-tube, and a rubber hose leading to a Buchner funnel. Washing is continued until the water above the resin is clear.

The resulting coarser-mesh resin is transferred with water to a large column or to a 500 ml burette with a plug of glass wool at the bottom. Water is run out of the bottom of the column, and additional resin is added until it is nearly full. Channeling should be avoided by not allowing the resin to run dry. A reservoir of at least 1-liter capacity is fitted to the top of the column (Fig. 4-2 F). A separatory funnel with an appropriate rubber stopper on the outlet tube is also suitable. The reservoir is then filled with $3M$ sodium acetate. The stopcock on the separatory funnel and the outlet tube of the column are then opened to allow the sodium acetate to pass through the resin. The flow from the column is adjusted to about 10 ml per minute. Small aliquots of the effluent liquid are checked occasionally with a dilute solution of silver nitrate to determine the presence of chloride ion. Charging is continued until there is no detectable chloride ion remaining. The resin is then thoroughly washed (5 to 10 bed volumes) with distilled or, preferably, deionized water. The acetate-form resin may be stored in water or in ethanol until used.

EXTRACTION OF PLANT TISSUES.   Place 10 to 15 g of freshly harvested or 1 to 2 g of finely ground lyophilized tissue in a VirTis 45 Homogenizer, a Waring Blendor, or other suitable homogenizer, with sufficient ethanol to yield a final ethanol concentration of 70 to 80 per cent. With fresh tissue, assume that 90 per cent of the weight is water. Homogenize the sample for about 1 minute. Transfer the homogenate to a centrifuge tube or bottle, washing out the grinding chamber and blades with 80 per cent ethanol. Centrifuge the homogenate for about 5 minutes. Decant and save the supernatant liquid. Suspend the residue in about 50 ml of 80 per cent ethanol and place in a water bath at about 45° to 50°C for 15 minutes, stirring occasionally. Centrifuge and combine the supernatant liquids. Repeat this extraction and centrifugation procedure three additional times or until the supernatant liquid is colorless.

PREPARATION OF EXTRACT FOR CHROMATOGRAPHY. The 80 per cent ethanol extract of the plant tissues may be used directly. Some workers, however, prefer to reduce the volume and to remove chlorophyll prior to chromatography. In the latter instance, reduce the volume of the supernatant liquid about four fifths under a stream of air, or nitrogen, or in a rotary vacuum evaporator. Transfer the remaining liquid to a separatory funnel and extract with benzene, petroleum ether, or chloroform until pigments and lipids are removed. If desired, the volume of the aqueous phase may be further reduced.

REMOVAL OF FREE AMINO ACIDS AND AMIDES.   The plant extract contains the free amino acids and amides, nonvolatile organic acids, sugars, and other neutral substances, as well as small quantities of many other materials, both organic and inorganic. Since amino acids are ampholytes, several of them (such as aspartic and glutamic acids) might be taken up on Dowex 1 resin and would be removed during elution, interfering with the separation of some of the weaker nonvolatile organic acids. It is therefore desirable to remove the amino acids and amides prior to the chromatographic separation under discussion. This is accomplished by passing the extract through a bed of hydrogen-form Dowex 50 resin, 200 to 400 mesh. For each 10 g of fresh plant tissue extracted, use a 1 × 5-cm bed of resin. It is convenient to use a reservoir flask, as shown in Fig. 4-2 *F*. If the extract is still in the ethanolic form, slurry the resin in ethanol before preparing the column. If in the aqueous form, prepare the resin in water. Place a loose plug of glass wool over the top of the resin. Pass the extract through the appropriate column at a flow rate of 1 to 2 ml per minute. When all of the extract has run through the resin, wash the column thoroughly, allowing the washings to combine with the effluent liquid. The effluent liquid now contains the nonvolatile organic acids, sugars, and other anionic and neutral substances. If desired, the amino acids and amides may then be removed from the Dowex 50 resin with ethanolic and aqueous ammonia solutions. For each 5 cm of resin, the following elution sequence may be used: 40 ml of 0.4N ammonium hydroxide in 80 per cent ethanol, 15 ml of water, 15 ml of 4N aqueous ammonium hydroxide, followed by a 15 ml water wash. The eluates are combined and taken to dryness in preparation for further separation.

SORPTION OF NONVOLATILE ORGANIC ACIDS. Prepare a 1 × 10-cm column of acetate-form Dowex 1 resin bedded in ethanol for ethanolic extracts or in water for aqueous extracts. Place a loose pad of glass wool or a filter paper disc over the top of the resin to prevent agitation. Pass the extract through the column at a flow rate of 1 to 2 ml per minute. When the extract has run through the resin, wash with two or more bed volumes of water, combining the washings with the effluent liquid. The effluent contains soluble sugars and other neutral substances. Leave a head of water in the column and close it off at the outlet tube.

GRADIENT ELUTION OF NONVOLATILE ORGANIC ACIDS. Prepare the equipment for gradient elution as shown in Fig. 4-1 *A, B,* or *C*. The device shown in Fig. 4-1 *A* is very satisfactory. Into the 250-ml Erlenmeyer mixing flask place a magnetic stirring bar and 200 ml of deionized or glass-distilled water. Fill the reservoir (500-ml or 1000-ml suction flask) with 2.5N acetic acid. It is convenient to make the connection between the two flasks with polyethylene "quick disconnects." Secure the column to the elution apparatus, turn on the magnetic stirrer, and gently apply air or nitrogen pressure to the side tube of the reservoir flask. If a peristaltic pump is used, place it between the mixing flask and the column. The chromatographic solvent is passed through the resin at a flow rate of 1 ml per minute, collecting a total of 3 ml per test tube. A total of 300 ml is collected on an automatic fraction collector. The reservoir is then removed and replaced with one containing 6N formic acid. The mixing flask is not changed. An additional 100 3-ml fractions are then collected.

TITRATION OF ORGANIC ACIDS.   The amount of the various acids eluted is determined by titration of the free acids after evaporation of the eluting solvent with a stream of air. Evaporation is accomplished by placing the test tubes in a rack and immersing them in a water bath at about 45°C containing about 5 cm of water. A glass manifold is placed into each row of tubes (Fig. 4-4). The manifold tubes are of such a length that the capillary openings are about 2 cm above the liquid surface of the sample. Air is blown through the manifold at such a rate that the liquid surface of the sample is agitated without excessive splashing. Complete evaporation usually takes between

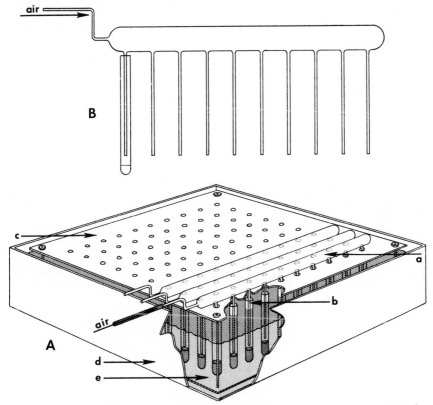

Fig. 4-4. Device for evaporation of volatile solvents following column chromatography. (A) (a) Glass manifold with capillary outlet tubes; (b) capillary outlet tube positioned in test tube; (c) stainless steel or galvanized metal rack which accommodates 100 test tubes; (d) stainless-steel or galvanized metal pan for holding water; (e) warm water. The drying device is positioned on hot plates, which in turn are connected to variable transformers for temperature regulation. Inset (B) shows details of manifold design.

$1\frac{1}{2}$ and 2 hours, depending upon the temperature of the water bath and the rate of air flow through the manifold. Complete evaporation is difficult to detect visually, and it is best to determine this by cautious smelling above each tube while the air stream is on. Losses of certain acids may occur if the tubes are dried for an excessive time after evaporation is complete.

When the tubes are dry, add about 1 ml of CO_2-free water to each tube. Titrate the tubes with 0.01N NaOH (or a higher normality, if necessary) to the phenol red end point. A sharper end point is obtained using a mixed indicator containing 5 parts of 0.02 per cent ethanolic bromocresol green and 1 part of 0.02 per cent methyl red.

IDENTIFICATION OF ACIDS. When titration results in milliliters are plotted against tube number, a series of peaks will appear, each of which will usually represent a single compound. The order in which a number of important nonvolatile acids are eluted is shown in Fig. 4-5. More positive identification of the acids is usually desirable. In this instance, combine and evaporate to dryness the eluates from

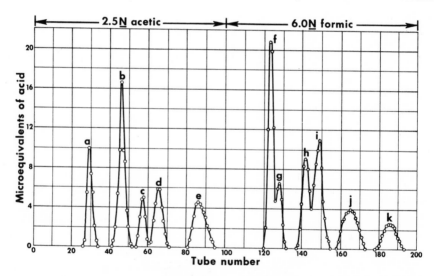

Fig. 4-5. Separation of nonvolatile organic acids on a 1 × 10-cm column of acetate-form Dowex 1-X8 resin by gradient elution with 2.5N acetic acid (tubes 1 to 100) and 6N formic acid (tubes 101 to 200). Flow rate, 1 ml per minute; fraction volume, 3 ml. *(a)* Shikimic acid; *(b)* quinic acid; *(c)* glyceric, glycolic, glutaric acids; *(d)* pyrollidone carboxylic acid; *(e)* succinic acid; *(f)* malic acid; *(g)* citramalic acid; *(h)* tartaric acid; *(i)* citric and malonic acids; *(j)* fumaric acid; *(k)* α-ketoglutaric acid.

the tubes representing each peak. To each sample, add a small amount of hydrogen-form Dowex 50 resin, 20 to 50 mesh and a few drops of water to dissolve the acid and remove Na^+. Spot a small aliquot of the unknown liquid on Whatman 1 chromatography paper with a micropipette or a melting-point tube. Spot appropriate standards along the starting line and develop the chromatogram in a suitable solvent by ascending chromatography. Three excellent solvents are n-butanol-glacial acetic acid-water (100:6:25, v/v/v), ethyl ether-88 per cent formic acid-water (5:2:1, v/v, upper phase), benzyl alcohol-t-butyl alcohol-isopropyl alcohol-water-88 per cent formic acid (15:5:5:5:0.5, v/v/v/v/v). After the solvent front has traveled a suitable distance, the papers are removed and dried. Acid spots are then made visible by spraying with 0.04 per cent bromophenol blue in ethanol, to which has been added 6N NaOH until the color is reddish-blue by transmitted light. Acid spots appear as yellow spots against a blue background. Comparison of R_f's of unknown and known substances in the solvent systems described, as well as the position of elution from the column, should allow identification of known acids.

CALCULATION OF RESULTS. The total volume of NaOH required for titration times normality of the NaOH will give total milliequivalents of acid. Milliequivalents times the molecular weight of the identified acid divided by titratable carboxyl groups yields milligrams of acids.

SEPARATION OF ANTHOCYANINS AND OTHER FLAVANOIDS BY CHROMATOGRAPHY ON CELLULOSE POWDER

PREPARATION OF CELLULOSE POWDER. Cellulose powder for column chromatography may be obtained commercially. It is easily prepared, however, by boiling scraps of filter paper for 2 to 20 minutes in dilute nitric acid (5 ml concentrated nitric acid per 100 ml of water). The resulting pulp is transferred to a Büchner funnel, and then, under suction, nitric acid is removed by washing thoroughly with water, followed by ethanol or methanol, and finally with diethyl ether. When dry, the powder is ready for use.

EXTRACTION OF PLANT TISSUES. Anthocyanins and other flavanoids are removed from flower petals or other plant tissues by extraction with 0.02 per cent ethanolic or methanolic HCl. Homogenize or steep fresh or dried tissue in the acidic alcohol solution for a period of time suitable to the tissue being extracted. Collect the supernatant liquid by centrifugation or filtration. Reextract the residue and clarify the supernatant liquids until no more pigments are removed. Dry the combined supernatant liquids under a stream of air. If desired, the pigments may be partially purified and separated from other alcohol-soluble constituents of the tissues. Dissolve the residue in a small amount of alcoholic HCl. Add 10 volumes of diethyl ether, cover the container, and allow the flocculent precipitate to form and settle for about an hour. Remove the precipitated pigments by centrifugation or filtration. Redissolve the precipitated pigments in alcoholic HCl and reprecipitate with ether. Repeat this process a third time. The precipitated pigment is again dissolved in a small volume of alcoholic HCl and is stored until further use.

PREPARATION OF COLUMN AND CHROMATOGRAPHIC SEP-ARATION OF FLAVANOIDS.   A number of solvents are suitable for the separation of flavanoids, but *n*-butanol-glacial acetic acid-water (4:1:5, v/v/v, upper phase) is among the best. A 1 × 30-cm column is satisfactory for the separation of relatively small quantities of pigment. Slurry the cellulose powder in the chromatographic solvent. Pour the slurry into a chromatographic column containing a pad of glass wool, a fritted glass disc, or other suitable filter at the bottom, and fitted with means of controlling the flow rate from the outlet tube of the column. Allow the liquid to drain through the column by gravity or with slight air pressure until the solvent has nearly reached the top of the cellulose powder. Add more of the slurried cellulose powder if necessary.

The material to be chromatographed may be added to the column in a number of ways. By one method, a desired amount of the pigment concentrate and a small amount of dry cellulose powder are placed in a small beaker. Mix with a glass rod, adding more powder until a friable mixture is obtained. Carefully transfer the mixture to the top of the column. Add a small amount of chromatographic solvent and gently stir only the pigmented portion with a small glass rod to re-move air bubbles. Place a clean porous or perforated disc in the column on the surface of the cellulose powder. Carefully fill the column with chromatographic solvent by means of a pipette. Connect a reservoir flask and fill it with solvent. Open the outlet tube of the column adjusting the flow rate to about 1 ml or less per minute. Separation of the flavanoids can be readily seen as the chromatogram develops. The yellow flavanoids move most rapidly, while anthocy-anins will separate behind them. Separation will occur in the follow-ing order of decreasing speed: quercitrin, quercetin, isoquercitrin, callistephin, chrysanthemin, pelargonin, quercineritrin, antirrhinin, and cyanin.

Since the separation can be easily followed visually, individual fractions may be collected manually by changing collecting tubes at the appropriate time. If the chromatographer is interested in a distinct qualitative separation, it is best that the transitional areas between bands be discarded since there may be a small overlapping of pig-ments. It is imperative that a slow rate of solvent development be used in order to obtain sharp fronts and discrete bands.

After collection, the pigments may be further identified by one-dimensional paper chromatography. More complete authentication is carried out by hydrolyzing the flavanoid in HCl, separating the aglycone from the sugar, or other esterified moiety with isoamyl alco-hol, followed by paper chromatographic identification.

SEPARATION OF LIPID MIXTURES BY
SILICIC ACID CHROMATOGRAPHY

PREPARATION OF SILICIC ACID.   Silicic acid, specially prepared for. lipid separation, is now available commercially (Bio-Rad Laboratories, Berkeley, Calif.). If desired, however, satisfactory material may be obtained by the following procedure: Mallinckrodt silicic acid, 100 mesh, and prepared for chromatographic analysis by the method of Ramsey and Patterson, is used. Place 200 g of silicic acid and 400 g of $\frac{3}{4}$-inch porcelain bells in an Abbé mill for 10 to 12 hours. Transfer the ground silicic acid to a 2-liter glass cylinder. Add absolute methanol to the 2-liter mark and suspend the silicic acid by vigorous agitation. Allow the particles to settle for 30 minutes and decant and discard the liquid. Repeat suspension and decantation once again with methanol and twice with diethyl ether. Air dry the remaining silicic acid (about 75 per cent of the starting material). When dry, store in a clean, closed container.

EXTRACTION OF PLANT LIPIDS.   Grind a suitable amount of fresh plant material (5 to 10 g) in a mortar under liquid nitrogen. Transfer the powder in portions to 300 ml of boiling iso-propanol and homogenize for 1 to 2 minutes in a VirTis 45 Homogenizer or Waring Blendor. Filter the hot material through a Büchner funnel with suction. Wash the residue with 200 ml of hot iso-propanol. Remove the filter cake and blend it with hot iso-propanol-chloroform (1:1, v/v), and filter the homogenate. Wash the filter cake with 200 ml of the iso-propanol-chloroform mixture, followed by 100 ml of chloroform. The residue is now essentially free of pigments and lipids. Combine the filtrates and concentrate to 40 ml in a water bath at 40°C in a rotary vacuum evaporator. Flush nitrogen into the flask just prior to releasing the vacuum to prevent oxidation of double bonds. Dilute the concentrate to 200 ml with chloroform and add it dropwise to a separatory funnel containing 200 ml of water. Remove the chloroform layer (lower) and wash the emulsion, if one has formed, with chloroform. Combine the chloroform fractions. Repeat the entire process four times. Take the chloroform fraction to dryness in a rotary vacuum evaporator, not exceeding a temperature of 40°C. Be sure to flush flask with nitrogen prior to releasing the vacuum. As the extract nears dryness, add small amounts of benzene to facilitate removal of traces of water. Dissolve the lipids in 5 ml of starting solvent (n-hexane) for chromatography.

PREPARATION OF COLUMN.   The apparatus shown in Fig. 2E is recommended for lipid separation (Scientific Glass Co.). The column dimensions are 18 × 250 mm. The column is water-jacketed, and the temperature is controlled by continuous circulation of water at 25°C. Temperature control is essential since increased temperatures reduce the adsorption of lipids on silicic acid, resulting in rapid elution. The bottom of the column is fitted with a coarse sintered glass disc to support the silicic acid. A disc of Whatman 1 filter paper is placed over the glass disc prior to the introduction of silicic acid. The 1200-ml solvent reservoir fits into the female glass joint of a short segment which, in turn, connects to the column with a ball and socket connection. The solid glass plunger in the reservoir maintains an air pocket above the column, thereby preventing back diffusion of solutes from the column into the reservoir.

Before use, dry a portion of silicic acid overnight at 115°C. Weigh an 18-g aliquot and introduce it into the column with gentle tapping until the silicic acid has settled. Place a disc of Whatman 1 filter paper over the top of the silicic acid. Run tap water at about 25°C through the water jacket of the column.

The following procedure is used for separation of neutral lipids, followed by separation of phospholipids. Complete the dehydration of the silicic acid by carefully introducing 10 ml of diethyl ether. When the ether just reaches the top of the bed, repeat with 30 ml of acetone-diethyl ether (1:1), and finally with 20 ml of diethyl ether. Wash the column with *n*-hexane for 7 to 10 hours to remove any ether. Introduce the lipid preparation carefully with a pipette. When it has drained just to the top of the silicic acid, carefully introduce 10 ml of *n*-hexane. Attach the reservoir containing 90 ml of *n*-hexane and begin the elution. Adjust the flow rate to 1 ml per minute with nitrogen, if necessary. Collect 10-ml fractions on a fraction collector. The first solvent removes hydrocarbons. Continue the elution with the following solvents and amounts: 15 per cent benzene in *n*-hexane (v/v), 100 ml, sterol esters; 5 per cent diethyl ether in *n*-hexane, 500 ml, triglycerides and fatty acids; 15 per cent diethyl ether in *n*-hexane, 500 ml, unesterified sterols; 30 per cent diethyl ether in *n*-hexane, 200 ml, diglycerides; diethyl ether, 100 ml, monoglycerides. For phospholipids, the elution is continued with the following solvents: chloroform-methanol, 4:1 (v/v), 500 ml, phosphatidylethanolamine and/or phosphatidylserine; chloroform-methanol, 3:2, 500 ml, phosphatidylcholine and inositol phosphatide; chloroform-methanol, 1:4, 500 ml, sphingolipids and other polar phospholipids.

QUANTITATIVE ESTIMATION OF LIPIDS. Transfer each tube collected during the neutral lipid separation to individual, clean, tared weighing bottles. Evaporate to dryness in a vacuum oven at about 58 to 60°C. Reweigh. Plot tube number against weight in milligrams.

Phospholipids are estimated by total phosphorus determination of the contents of each tube. Transfer 2-ml aliquots of each tube to individual acid-washed test tubes. Take them to dryness under a stream of air in a device such as that shown in Fig. 4-4. When dried, remove the tubes and add 0.5 ml of digestion mixture (nitric acid-perchloric acid-water, 1:1:1, v/v) and a small acid-washed Hengar granule or a quartz chip. Digest the contents of the tube for 20 to 30 minutes by placing them in a 12-inch diameter cast-iron pipe cap containing 100-mesh carborundum and heated from below with a Bunsen burner. Cool the digests and add 6 ml of water. Add 0.5 ml each of the following reagents in order: 70 per cent perchloric acid; Amidol (2.5 g of 2,4-diaminophenol dihydrochloride, 46.0 g of sodium bisulfite in 200 ml of water); and 5.0 per cent ammonium molybdate (w/v). Mix the sample thoroughly between each addition. Read the molybdate blue color formed within 30 minutes on a spectrophotometer at 660 mμ. Prepare a standard curve with 10, 20, 30, 40, 50μg of P as orthophosphate following the same procedure. Calculate the amount of P in each aliquot from the standard curve and plot total μg P in each tube against tube number.

It should be pointed out that some modifications in the amount and composition of solvent may be required depending upon the tissues used.

References

1. P. Alexander and R. J. Block, *A Laboratory Manual of Analytical Methods of Protein Chemistry*, Vol. I, Pergamon Press, New York (1960).
2. Anonymous, *Dowex: Ion Exchange*, The Dow Chemical Co., Midland, Mich. (1959).
3. C. Calmon and T. R. E. Kressman, *Ion Exchangers in Organic and Biochemistry*, Interscience Publishers, New York (1957).
4. H. G. Cassidy, *Fundamentals of Chromatography*, Interscience Publishers, New York (1957).
5. E. Heftmann, *Chromatography*, Reinhold, New York (1961).
6. R. Kunin, *Ion Exchange Resins*, John Wiley & Sons, New York (1958).
7. J. K. Palmer, *Agr. Expt. Sta., New Haven, Bull.*, **589**, (1955).
8. O. Samuelson, *Ion Exchangers in Analytical Chemistry*, John Wiley & Sons, New York (1953).
9. I. Smith, *Chromatographic and Electrophorétic Techniques*, Vol. I, Interscience Publishers, New York (1960).

C H A P T E R   5

Gas Chromatographic Methods

H. P. Burchfield and Eleanor E. Storrs

CHROMATOGRAPHY is the most versatile technique currently available for the analysis of complex mixtures of biological origin. The process is carried out by selectively partitioning the components of the mixture between a stationary solid or liquid phase and a mobile liquid or gas phase. The stationary phase may be filter paper, a granular active solid, or an inert solid impregnated with a liquid. The mobile phase may be a liquid, a mixture of liquids, or a gas. The use of a gas as the mobile phase was suggested by Martin and Synge in 1941 [1], but it was not implemented until the work of James and Martin [2] on gas-liquid chromatography and the work of Cremer and Prior [3] and Cremer and Müller [4] on gas-solid chromatography. Since then, the use of the technique has penetrated almost every area of analytical and biochemical research.

The concept of replacing the moving liquid phase in conventional chromatography with a gas is a simple one, yet it has led to revolutionary changes in techniques and vastly improved efficiencies of separations because of the unique physical properties possessed by gases as opposed to liquids. Some of the important advantages that have resulted from this innovation include improved separation of closely related compounds, fast analysis time, the detection of submicrogram quantities of solutes, and the possibility of making analyses over a wide range of temperatures.

This chapter is directed to the experimental biologist whose main concern is to obtain a practical working knowledge of the subject, unencumbered by complex mathematical treatment. Readers who wish to pursue individual topics in more depth are referred to recent treatises by Burchfield and Storrs [5], Dal Nogare and Juvet [6], and Littlewood [7]. The operation of individual gas chromatographs is not described in detail, since so many variations in design are possible. At present, about thirty companies manufacture instruments, most of which differ in several important respects from one another. However, they are all based on the same general principles and contain essentially the same component parts. Therefore, careful study of the fol-

136

lowing material, with collateral reading of the operating instructions supplied with individual makes of gas chromatographs, should provide sufficient information for the intelligent use of this versatile and fascinating technique by experimental biologists.

Nature of the Process

Gas chromatography can be accomplished with either a liquid sorbed on an inert particulate support or with an active solid as the stationary phase. Alternatively, the liquid can be coated on the internal surface of a long capillary tube with very small bore. Each of these procedures has special advantages that overlap only slightly. However, all forms of gas chromatography are more efficient in many respects than methods using a liquid as the mobile phase because of unique features conferred by the low viscosity and high diffusivity of gases and vapors.

GAS-LIQUID CHROMATOGRAPHY (GLC)

The column in gas-liquid chromatography is a glass or metal tube, usually about 0.5 cm in internal diameter and 1 to 20 meters long. The tube is packed uniformly with a finely divided, free-flowing powder prepared by impregnating an inert solid with a liquid of low volatility. The solid support should be absorbent in the sense that it will be capable of imbibing and holding the stationary liquid without becoming greasy, but not adsorbent in the sense that it will bind components of the sample being analyzed by secondary valence bonds. The main physical requirement for the liquid is that it must not be eluted from the column at the operating temperature employed.

A sample of the mixture to be separated is flash-evaporated at one end of the column and swept into it by a constantly flowing stream of carrier gas, such as hydrogen, helium, or nitrogen (Fig. 5-1). The components of the sample are carried through the column at different rates, which are governed by their partition coefficients between the gas phase and the stationary liquid phase. Ideally, they emerge from the other end of the column at different times. Their presence in the emerging carrier gas is detected by chemical or physical means, and the response of the detector is fed into a strip chart recorder. Generally, differential detectors are used, and the data are presented as a series of peaks spread out along a longitudinal time axis (Fig. 5-2). Each peak represents a discrete chemical compound, or a mixture of compounds with identical partition coefficients. The time required for each component to emerge from the column is characteristic of the compound and is known as its retention time. The area under the peak is proportional to its concentration in the sample. This constitutes the principal primary information derived from the chromatogram.

It may be helpful to review briefly some elementary principles governing the rate of travel of chemical compounds through columns packed with a stationary liquid phase. Each compound has a characteristic partition coefficient, which is given by Equation (1).

$$K = \frac{\text{weight of solute/ml stationary phase}}{\text{weight of solute/ml mobile (gas) phase}} \tag{1}$$

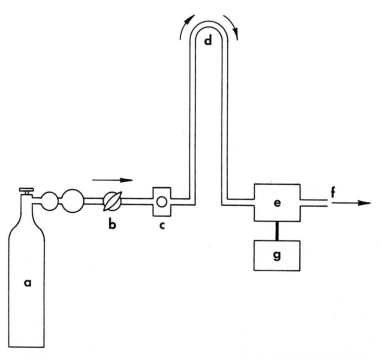

Fig. 5-1. Basic design of a gas chromatograph, arrows showing the direction of gas flow. (*a*) gas cylinder with reducing valve; (*b*) constant-pressure regulator; (*c*) port for injection of sample; (*d*) chromatographic column; (*e*) detector; (*f*) exit line; (*g*) strip chart recorder (Courtesy, Academic Press).

Therefore, if the partition coefficient of compound A is small, the amount of compound dissolved in the stationary liquid phase will be small compared to that in the gas phase. Consequently, the compound passes through the column rapidly, since it is not retarded by the stationary liquid. If the partition coefficient of compound B is large, the greater proportion of it resides in the solvent (stationary phase); therefore, passage through the column is slow, and this material passes through the detector and registers a peak at a later time than compound A. It must be remembered that the solute present in the gas phase is in dynamic equilibrium with the same solute in the liquid phase at all times. The vapor molecules cannot be swept through the column with the carrier gas, leaving the dissolved molecules behind; the only effect is to retard passage in proportion to the partition coefficient of the compound.

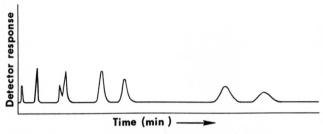

Fig. 5-2. Typical chromatogram showing separation of a hydro-carbon mixture. Note peak broadening at increased retention times (Courtesy, Academic Press).

The basic principles governing the separation of chemical compounds by gas chromatography are simple, but unfortunately, like most other systems, behavior is not ideal. Therefore, mathematical treatment of conditions as they supposedly occur in columns is moderately complex. This topic has been dealt with adequately by Keulemans [8] and others and so will not be repeated here. Nevertheless, it may be worth while to point out a few consequences of departures from ideality, since they affect the symmetry and shape of chromatographic peaks and often must be dealt with experimentally. These are:

1. *Tailing.* Under ideal conditions, peaks on gas chromatograms should be symmetrical and resemble Gaussian distribution curves. This situation is often approximated in GLC, but sometimes the recorder pen does not return to the base line as rapidly on the descending side of the peak as it leaves it on the ascending side. This results in asymmetric peaks and is called tailing. Generally, tailing in GLC arises from adsorption of the solute on active sites of the solid support. It can be reduced and sometimes eliminated by deactivating the support. Peak asymmetry occurs when adsorption isotherms are nonlinear— that is to say, when the partition coefficient of a compound between the mobile and stationary phases varies with the amount present. However, at the low solute concentrations used in GLC, solutions generally behave ideally, and tailing arises mostly from interaction of the solute and the solid support.

2. *Leading.* Leading is said to occur when the front or leading edge of the chromatographic peak is elongated and the rear or descending side is straight. It occurs when the column is overloaded to such an extent

that the solute molecules interact with one another within the stationary liquid. The concentrations in gas chromatography are usually too low for leading to be a serious problem. However, if 2 to 3 mg of a polar compound is chromatographed on a nonpolar stationary phase, asymmetry of this type is observed frequently.

3. *Peak Broadening.* If samples injected into a chromatograph were carried through the column as homogeneous plugs of vapor, peak width would be independent of the time they remain in the column. In practice this is not true. Peaks broaden perceptibly, so those recorded first are high and narrow, whereas those representing slower moving components tend to become lower and wider, even though the areas under them remain the same. This results from the fact that the vapor molecules diffuse longitudinally as the sample moves through the column; thus the longer the sample remains in the column, the broader will be the peaks. This problem has been treated mathematically by van Deemter *et al.* [9] and later by Kieselbach [10]. The simplest form of the van Deemter equation is given by Equation (2), where

$$\text{HETP} = A + B/u + Cu \qquad (2)$$

HETP is the height equivalent to a theoretical plate; u is the velocity of the carrier gas; A is a constant that accounts for the effect of "eddy" diffusion of the vapor; B is a constant that accounts for the effect of molecular diffusion of the vapor in the direction of the long axis of the column; and C is a constant proportional to the resistance of the column packing to mass transfer of solute through it. Therefore, it is seen that peak broadening (as measured by high values for HETP) results from diffusion of the solute, certain physical characteristics of the column, and slow flow rate of the carrier gas. This latter quantity, of course, is related directly to the length of time the sample remains in the column.

GAS-SOLID CHROMATOGRAPHY (GSC)

Gas-solid chromatography differs from gas-liquid chromatography in that the stationary phase is an active solid or adsorbent, such as charcoal or silica gel, instead of a liquid. Consequently, the passage of gases and vapors through the column is retarded differentially by adsorption rather than by partition. Adsorption isotherms are rarely linear; hence peaks in GSC are asymmetric more often than in GLC. This can be corrected sometimes by treating the active solid with a small amount (about 0.5 to 1.5 per cent) of nonvolatile liquid. Sometimes larger volumes are used, in which case the method becomes a hybrid of adsorption and partition chromatography.

Historically, gas-solid chromatography was developed a short time before gas-liquid chromatography [3,4]. GSC has been used to some extent recently for the separation of fairly high-molecular-weight hydrocarbons [11], but its main value is for the analysis of permanent gases.

The method of chromatography described in this and the foregoing section is termed *elution analysis*, since a compact plug of vapor is applied to a column and swept through it or eluted with carrier gas. However, two other methods, "frontal analysis" and "displacement analysis", are possible. They are not employed in any of the methods described in this chapter, or for that matter in analytical work generally, and consequently will not be discussed here. The reader who is interested in details of these techniques can find them in general texts such as those of Keulemans [8] or Phillips [12].

CHROMATOGRAPHY USING CAPILLARY COLUMNS

Capillary column chromatography is a branch of gas-liquid chromatography in which the stationary phase is coated on the inside wall of a capillary tube, the wall thus serving as the solid support in lieu of an inert particulate solid such as a diatomaceous earth [13]. The same principle has been used recently to obtain separations in wide bore ($\frac{1}{8}$ inch) columns. This method of supporting the liquid phase is mentioned separately here, since it has developed into an independent technique from both a practical and theoretical point of view. Capillary columns are efficient and can be made very long, since they are coiled in the form of helices which occupy a relatively small amount of space. Glass and metal columns 100 to 300 ft in length are used routinely; they have efficiencies as high as several hundred thousand theoretical plates. With these, separations that would be impossible by ordinary physiochemical methods are achieved rapidly and precisely.

The roles of capillary and conventionally packed GLC columns overlap only to a minor extent. The methods tend to supplement one another rather than compete. Packed columns can be prepared with a greater variety of selective stationary liquids and will yield fractions of pure compounds large enough for identification by ordinary chemical and physical methods. Packed columns contain a stationary liquid sorbed on a particulate solid support. By contrast, capillary columns have been used with a smaller variety of stationary liquids, are more difficult to prepare reproducibly, and yield samples too small for characterization by the usual methods. However, they have high plate   efficiencies and are suitable for separating mixtures having wide boiling-point ranges without programing the temperature.

In general, capillary columns have not received the widespread acceptance that was once predicted for them, the limiting factor appearing to be poor reproducibility in performance from column to column. Recently, more emphasis has been placed on the development of packed columns with low stationary liquid/solid support ratios to achieve the separation of thermolabile compounds at low temperatures.

Nomenclature

A committee appointed by the Analytical Section of the International Union of Pure and Applied Chemistry (IUPAC) has recommended standard terms and units for gas chromatography [14]. These are employed in this chapter in so far as is practical. Only those terms which will be of immediate use to the experimental biologist are defined below. The reader is referred to the text by Burchfield and Storrs [5] for a more complete treatment of the subject.

CHROMATOGRAM

A chromatogram is a plot of the detector response versus time or volume of the carrier gas. Idealized chromatograms obtained with differential and integral detectors for one component are shown in Fig. 5-3. With integral detectors, the chromatogram appears as a ser-

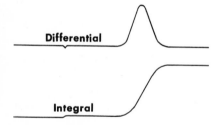

Fig. 5-3. Relationship between the peak obtained with a differential detector and the step obtained with an integral detector (Courtesy, Academic Press).

ies of steps, and the height of each step is proportional to the amount of component which it represents. With differential detectors, each component (or mixture of components) is represented by a peak, and the amount present is proportional to the area under the peak.

RETENTION TIME

Retention time (uncorrected) is the time which elapses between the injection of a sample and the appearance of the peak maximum.

RETENTION VOLUME

Retention volume (uncorrected) V_R is the volume of gas required to elute the compound under study and is given by

$$V_R = t_R F_c \tag{3}$$

where t_R is the retention time, the time for the emergence of the peak maximum after injection of the sample, and F_c is the volumetric flow rate of the carrier gas measured at the outlet pressure and the temperature of the column.

GAS HOLDUP

Gas holdup V_M is the uncorrected retention volume of a nonabsorbed sample and is the volume of carrier gas required to transport such a sample from the point of injection to the point of detection at column outlet pressure. It includes contributions due to the interstitial volume of the column, and the effective volumes of the sample injector and the detector. It can readily be determined for any column by elution of some material for which the partition coefficient is very small compared with its value for other solutes. Gases such as nitrogen, air, or the noble gases are normally employed for this purpose. The peak often produced by the presence of small amounts of air during the sample injection gives this information and is referred to as the "air peak."

NET RETENTION VOLUME

Net retention volume V_N is given by

$$V_N = \frac{3(\rho_i/\rho_o)^2 - 1}{2(\rho_i/\rho_o)^3 - 1} (V_R - V_M) \tag{4}$$

where V_R is the uncorrected retention volume, V_M the *gas* holdup volume, ρ_i the inlet pressure of the carrier gas, and ρ_o the pressure of the carrier gas at the outlet.

RELATIVE RETENTIONS

Retention volumes may be expressed relative to the retention volume of a standard component on the same column at the same temperature. Relative retention r is given by

$$r_{1,2} = \frac{V_{R1}}{V_{R2}} \tag{5}$$

where the subscripts refer to components 1 and 2. Component 2 is the standard. Relative retentions measured from the point of injection can only be considered independent of column dimensions if $V_M \ll V_{R1}, V_{R2}$.

Factors Influencing Peak Resolution

Two independent factors determine whether any given pair of compounds can be separated from one another by gas chromatography. These are the separation factor (equivalent to relative retention) and the column efficiency. Both must be taken into account in selecting stationary phases, column length, temperature, and other parameters. The separation factor is a measure of the relative *positions* of two peaks on a chromatogram, and column efficiency is a measure of the *narrowness* of the peaks. Once the separation factor for any pair of compounds is known, it is possible to calculate the number of theoretical plates required to achieve any specified degree of resolution. The interplay between these two factors is illustrated in Fig. 5-4.

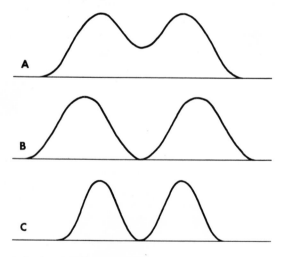

Fig. 5-4. Factors influencing peak resolution; *(A)* unresolved peaks; *(B)* resolution by change in separation factor; *(C)* resolution by increase in column efficiency (Courtesy, Academic Press).

Chromatogram *A* shows two peaks that are not resolved satisfactorily. Better separation can be achieved by shifting the relative positions of the two peaks (chromatogram *B*) while keeping peak width constant or, alternatively, by maintaining the peaks at the same positions and making them narrower (chromatogram *C*). The first procedure requires a change in separation factor; the second, a change in column efficiency.

SEPARATION FACTOR

The separation factor, α, is the ratio of the retention volumes of the two compounds to be separated, or

$$\alpha = \frac{V_{R1}}{V_{R2}} \tag{6}$$

where the subscripts refer to components 1 and 2.

The separation factor is a measure of the distance between the apices of the two peaks to be separated. If this value is unity, the compounds cannot be resolved no matter how efficient the column. However, the separation factor may be quite large and the peaks still not be resolved because they are too broad, and therefore overlap. This situation can be corrected by improving the column efficiency, or increasing the column length, or both, so that narrower peaks are obtained in relation to their distance from the air peak.

Separation factors can be adjusted by changing the stationary phase or the column temperature. They depend only on the ratio of the partition coefficients of the two solutes between solvent and carrier. If this value cannot be improved by adjusting the temperature, it is necessary to change the stationary liquid. Fortunately, liquids are available having a great deal of selectivity based on polarity. Consequently, it is usually possible to find a liquid that will provide the required degree of separation even though the boiling points of the solutes are practically identical, since their partial vapor pressures when dissolved in the solvent may differ.

COLUMN EFFICIENCY

Column efficiency is measured by the number of theoretical plates. In a separation process that can be carried out in discrete steps, such as countercurrent extraction, perfect equilibration of the solute between two phases is established at each step, and the phases then are separated. Each step is termed a theoretical plate. However, in a chromatographic column the solute is in constant motion down the column, and perfect equilibrium cannot be established at any one point. Consequently, the best that can be done is to calculate the height of column that will give a separation equivalent to one theoretical plate. This quantity is termed the height equivalent to a theoretical plate (usually abbreviated as HETP). The number of theoretical plates in a gas chromatographic column depends on a number of factors, including the rates of diffusion of the solute in the two phases, the uniformity of column packing, the thicknesses of the layers of stationary liquid, and the nature and flow rate of the mobile phase. The number of theoretical plates can be increased within limits, by increasing the column length, and it is reduced slightly by an increase in diameter.

The number of theoretical plates can be calculated from fundamental column parameters by the van Deemter equation, but from the standpoint of establishing practical operating conditions for any given column it is necessary to calculate it from values determined experimentally. Several equations have been developed for doing this, but they do not all give the same results. However, each is a measure of peak sharpness in relation to retention volume, and they all give about the same relative values. The IUPAC committee on gas chromatographic terminology [14] recommends Equation (7).

$$n = 16\left(\frac{\text{retention volume}}{\text{peak width}}\right)^2 \qquad (7)$$

The theoretical plate number varies with the nature of the solute giving rise to the peak used for measurement, as well as with column characteristics. Therefore, the compound used to make the calculation should be specified in reports of results, since differences in the number of theoretical plates can be obtained on the same column during the same run if values are calculated from two different peaks. The units for retention and peak width in the above equation must be consistent so that their ratio, n, is dimensionless. If the corrected retention volume is used, the observed peak width must also be corrected for pressure drop across the column.

When the number of theoretical plates is known, the height equivalent to a theoretical plate can be calculated from Equation (8),

$$\text{HETP} = L/n \qquad (8)$$

where L is the *effective* length of the chromatographic column.

Basic Instrumentation

The chromatograph illustrated in Fig. 5-5 is representative of many commercial instruments equipped with temperature programing, a thermal detector, and a flame ionization detector. The controls are contained in the module to the right, and the column is located in the oven situated on the left.

The standard chromatograph consists of four major units: a source of carrier gas, a column, a detector, and a recorder. The cylinder of carrier gas supplies the mobile phase which is most often nitrogen, helium, or argon. Helium is generally the choice for thermal detectors, argon for beta-ray ionization detectors, and nitrogen for flame ionization detectors. The carrier gas cylinder is equipped with a two-stage diaphragm reducing valve for controlling the flow of mobile phase, and is connected to the chromatograph through a constant pressure regulator which is standard on most instruments.

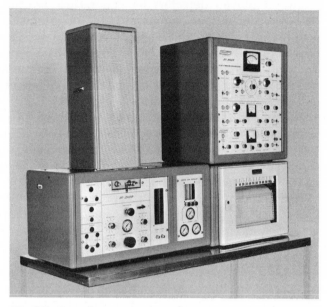

Fig. 5-5. Gas chromatograph with temperature programing, thermal detector, and flame ionization detector (Courtesy, Mikro-Tek Co.).

The chromatographic column is housed in an oven that can be adjusted to any desired temperature. Temperature programing units which permit the temperature of the column oven to be raised linearly with time at any predetermined rate are available for most instruments. This feature is useful for chromatographing samples containing components best eluted over a wide temperature range. The chromatographic column must be easy to replace, and the connections must be gastight. Columns are often attached with knurled thumbscrews sealed with O rings, Swagelok quick-connect fittings, or other devices.

The sample is injected through a sample injection port just before the chromatographic column. Most often the port is covered with a self-sealing diaphragm through which samples can be injected with a hypodermic needle. The injection port is heated by a separate heater, and the temperature is usually maintained about 50°C above the column temperature to ensure rapid volatilization of the sample, which is then swept onto the column as a plug of vapor by the carrier gas.

The detector is usually housed in an oven separate from the column oven, and the temperature is maintained at column temperature or slightly higher. Many types of detectors are commercially available, and the choice depends upon the specific application. The most commonly employed detectors for general use are the hydrogen flame detector, beta-ray ionization detector, and thermal conductivity cells. The hydrogen flame and beta-ray ionization detectors are very sensitive, detecting around 10^{-10} to 10^{-13} mole of compound. They are the detectors of choice for work with capillary columns and trace analysis generally. The hydrogen flame detector requires a source of hydrogen and air in addition to the carrier gas.

Thermal conductivity cells are useful for chromatographing larger samples, being sensitive to about 10^{-8} mole of material. These detectors are most useful in preparative gas chromatography or for qualitative analysis where samples are to be collected. These detectors are discussed in more detail later in this chapter.

The last component of the gas chromatograph is a standard 0 to 1 mv or a 0 to 10 mv recorder which is sometimes equipped with an integrator for automatic measurement of peak areas.

Sample Introduction

The introduction of accurately measured samples into the gas chromatograph often constitutes a major problem because of the small amounts of material that are used. Sometimes this difficulty can be avoided by inclusion of an internal standard or by normalizing peak areas, but situations still occur where the amounts of materials applied to the column must be known accurately. This problem is aggravated when capillary columns and ionization detectors are used, since as little as 1 μg of material may be chromatographed.

With ionization detectors, carrier gas flow can be stopped to introduce the sample without destabilizing the base line. In this case, the plug sealing the injection port is removed, and the sample is applied directly to the column. With most instruments, however, the sample is introduced against the back pressure of the column with the carrier gas flowing. Therefore, liquid samples are injected through self-sealing diaphragms with hypodermic syringes or through specially designed injection ports with micropipettes. Both liquid and solid samples can be introduced by sealing them in glass or metal capillaries and releasing the contents by melting or crushing the capillaries in the carrier gas stream. Gas samples are often introduced through valves specially designed for this purpose.

LIQUID SAMPLES

The fastest and most widely used method for introducing liquid samples is with a syringe fitted with a hypodermic needle. Almost all commerical and laboratory-built chromatographs contain injection ports designed for this purpose.

Samples also can be introduced into gas chromatographs with micropipettes. In the method of Tenny and Harris [15] one end of the pipette is introduced into the instrument through a special attachment which replaces the self-sealing injection port standard on most instruments. Once the pipette is inside the instrument, the sample is blown from it with carrier gas. This method was developed before leakproof syringes capable of withstanding the pressure of the carrier gas became available. They are less convenient than syringe injection, and now they are no more accurate.

Very small samples are needed with capillary columns. These cannot be measured accurately by syringe or pipette methods. Therefore, the usual procedure is to inject a much larger sample and vent the greater proportion of it to the atmosphere by means of a split-stream system. Generally, only 0.01 to 0.001 per cent of the sample injected is used. Reproducibility is only fair, and partial fractionation of high-boiling liquids sometimes occurs before the sample enters the column.

To obtain optimum peak resolution, the sample should be introduced into the carrier gas stream as a homogeneous plug of vapor, insofar as this is possible. For liquid samples, the temperature of the injection block governs the rate of vaporization and therefore the extent of mixing of the vapor with carrier. This can have a profound effect on column efficiency.

In general, injection block temperatures are held at 50° to 100°C above column temperature to ensure flash evaporation. However, care must be taken to make sure artifacts are not created through pyrolysis or isomerization of sample components, for even though a compound may be stable at the column temperature, it could decompose or rearrange at the injection temperature. Therefore, the injection temperature should be controlled entirely separately from the column temperature, and the block should be equipped with its own thermocouple connected to a read-out meter.

SOLID SAMPLES

Solid samples are generally introduced into gas chromatographs by first dissolving them in a suitable solvent. However, if this is undesirable, they can be sealed into glass capillary tubes. The tubes are then introduced into the gas stream, brought up to vaporization temperature, and crushed or broken *in situ* with a suitable mechanical device. It has been reported that volumes of 0.004 to 0.5 μl can be introduced with a reproducibility of 10 per cent [16].

GAS SAMPLES

Permanent gases differ basically from liquids and solids in the manner in which they are collected in the field and introduced into the gas stream of the chromatograph. Liquids are injected in volumes of a few microliters or less and expand suddenly by flash evaporation within the confines of the instrument. Gases, on the other hand, are introduced in volumes ranging from 0.25 to 25 ml. The larger samples are used when trace elements are being analyzed; if the sample exceeds 2 per cent of the retention volume of the component of interest, poor peak resolution will be obtained. Consequently it may be necessary to concentrate trace components by specialized techniques useful exclusively for samples of this type.

Small gas samples can be injected into any standard gas chromatograph with a syringe fitted with a hypodermic needle. Often, medical syringes are used, but they tend to leak around the barrel. Escape of gas can be reduced by greasing the plunger lightly with mineral oil. However, in some instances this may change the composition of the gas mixture by dissolving one of the components selectively. This is likely to be particularly important in the analysis of respiratory gases containing anesthetics. Loss of gas without lubrication can be minimized by using a gastight syringe. Such syringes are made with a stainless-steel plunger coated with Teflon resin and have a Teflon tip.

However, the most accurate method for introducing reproducible plugs of gas into a chromatograph is through gas sampling valves especially designed for this purpose. These may be manually or electrically operated. Manual valves are supplied as standard or optional equipment with most commercial instruments.

Preparation and Properties of Chromatographic Columns

The chromatographic column is the heart of the instrument, and therefore special care must be taken in its selection or preparation. Unlike detectors, most columns are prepared in the laboratory by the individual investigator. However, the biologist who wishes to employ one of the more commonly used columns can often purchase it complete with packing from various instrument manufacturers. Sometimes packing ratios, diameters of tubing, and other information are not furnished. These should be ascertained before accumulating data for publication.

Three types of columns are described in this section: the GLC column, the GSC column, and the capillary column. The first two can be employed interchangeably in any standard chromatograph. However, capillary columns require an instrument equipped with an ionization detector having small effective volume, and the injection system must be modified so that very small samples can be introduced.

COLUMNS FOR GLC

THE SOLID SUPPORT. The solid used to support the stationary liquid is usually porous in order to absorb large quantities of solvent and still remain dry to the touch and free-flowing. Diatomaceous earths are employed most often although other materials having lower absorptivity have been used in special applications. The support should not be too soft, since the particles will fragment on grinding, and it should pack uniformly into a column for maximum efficiency.

The particle size of the support is very important, as this property will affect both column efficiency and flow rate of the mobile phase. Finely divided solid supports yield packings with highest plate efficiencies. However, they impede passage of gas through the column, thereby making a higher inlet pressure necessary to maintain the same flow obtainable with coarser packings. This leads to a higher ratio of inlet to outlet pressure, unless flow is impeded by placing a restriction on the end of the column. If the pressure ratio exceeds 1.5 to 2.0, part of the column will not be used efficiently, since the rate along its length will not be uniform owing to the compressibility of the carrier gas. Therefore, a compromise must be sought between column efficiency and flow rate in selecting particle size. This is comparatively easy to do, for impedance to flow continues to increase with decreasing particle size, whereas column efficiency tends to level off. Therefore, the best size distribution for most applications is around 50/60 U.S. mesh. If it is necessary to obtain higher plate efficiency, a finer support may be used, but this will decrease flow rate or else make a bigger pressure drop across the column necessary. A packing with a narrow particle size range will give better results than one with a wide range, even though the average size is the same, because small particles will fill in voids between large ones and thus increase impedance. Fines should be removed for the same reason. This can be done by water elutriation or by wet-screening the support between two sieves of different mesh sizes.

The most commonly used solid supports are Celite 545, C-22 firebrick, and Sterchamol 22. Chromosorb is a red powder similar to C-22 firebrick, and Chromosorb W a white powder similar to Celite 545. In some publications, firebrick is referred to as Silocel. Standard and acid-washed grades of these are available commercially from many manufacturers of chromatographs and auxiliary equipment. Mesh ranges (U.S.) currently available include 40/60, 60/80, 80/120, 100/120, and others. There has been a marked tendency in recent publications to report the use of narrow size ranges.

⌐Adsorption of solutes on the solid support results in asymmetric peaks due to tailing. This is particularly noticeable in the chromatography of polar compounds, or when the stationary liquid is nonpolar.⌐Tailing is not so much of a problem with polar liquids, as the liquid tends to deactivate the "active" sites on the solid. Tailing can be reduced and sometimes eliminated by chemical treatment of the packing. Hydrochloric or sulfuric acid is used to remove iron, and the product is dried and finally treated with methanolic sodium hydroxide. More elaborate methods are used to deactivate supports for the chromatography of polar materials. Alkali treatment of the support also reduces the tendency of labile compounds to dehydrate or isomerize during chromatography.

A number of papers have been published on the deactivation of supports by treatment with chemicals which form films over the solid particles. These include dimethyldichlorosilane [17], hexamethyldisilazane [18], and metallic silver [19]. Another procedure for deactivating solid supports when nonpolar stationary phases are used is to include a small amount of a polar material in the liquid. Compounds used for this purpose include sodium caproate [20] and synthetic detergents [21].

There has been a recent trend toward the chromatography of high-boiling compounds at low temperatures through use of small sample size and low liquid-to-solid packing ratios. Of course, this requires an inactive support, since the film of liquid coating the solid is very thin and opportunities for adsorption are magnified correspondingly. However, since the amount of stationary phase is small, supports with little or no sorptive capacity can be used. Small glass beads have been employed as well as metal beads. The lowest amount of packing that can be used without getting adsorption on glass beads is about 0.15 per cent, and the upper practical limit about 3 per cent. Adsorption appears to be about the same on glass beads, stainless-steel beads, or silvered beads. However, diatomaceous earths, either silanized or unsilanized, are very satisfactory general support materials, especially for low packing ratios.

Other solid supports which have been investigated include carborundum, porous Teflon, crushed unfused Vycor, crushed crystalline quartz, Fluorpak (Fluorocarbon Co.), and crushed, unglazed tile.

THE STATIONARY LIQUID. ⌐Selection of the stationary liquid is the most important choice to be made in developing a gas chromatographic method, for it determines whether any given pair of

solutes can be separated. A few general guides can be given to properties that are most desirable, but beyond this the selection must be
governed by the nature of the individual problem. Extremes in whatever solvent properties are considered desirable are evaluated first,
and further testing is guided systematically by the results obtained.
However, the initial selection must depend always on the polarities
and volatilities of the compounds being separated.

The liquid selected as the stationary phase must be substantially
nonvolatile and thermally stable at the operating temperature of the
chromatograph. As a general rule, the partition liquid should boil at
250° to 300°C above operating temperature; however, the maximum
allowable vapor pressure in each individual case is governed by the
sensitivity of the device used for detection. If the solvent bleeds from
the column excessively, detector background will be high, the base
line unsteady, column life short, and fractions collected from the
effluent gas contaminated with liquid phase or its decomposition
products. Therefore, it is obvious that solvents such as dimethyl
sulfoxide and dimethylsulfolane, which give excellent separations
at room temperature, cannot be used for the separation of high-boiling
liquids. As the operating temperature is increased, the choice of
solvents becomes more and more restricted and finally becomes the
limiting factor in setting the upper limit. Thus, only irradiated asphaltenes, polyphenyl tars, and eutectic mixtures of inorganic salts can
be used at temperatures above 350°C for any length of time. Mixtures
of sodium, potassium, and lithium nitrates supported in conventional
manner on crushed firebrick are the most heat-stable stationary
liquids available currently and have been evaluated for the separation
of a number-of types of organic compound [22]. Resolution is low
compared to organic liquids, but retention volumes are also low,
permitting the use of long columns.

Other physical properties that must be considered include melting
point and viscosity. The stationary phase should be liquid at column
temperature, and low viscosity is desirable. If the liquid phase is
highly viscous at operating temperature, the time required for equilibration of the solute between the mobile and stationary phases will
be increased and column efficiency diminished correspondingly.
However, viscosity is not so critical a factor in making the selection
as vapor pressure.

Once the physical requirements which the stationary liquid must
meet are known, it is necessary to select one that will give good
separation factors for the solutes being analyzed. Usually a value for α
of about 1.1 or over will suffice, the degree of peak separation being
dependent on the plate efficiency of the column. If compounds having
the same polarity and different boiling points are to be separated, a

nonpolar liquid phase will prove most satisfactory. The most commonly used liquids belonging to this class include squalane, the Apiezon greases, silicone oil, and esters of high-molecular-weight alcohols and dibasic acids. If compounds must be separated according to polarity—that is, by unsaturation or degree of aromaticity—a polar liquid should be used. Examples are polyethylene glycols, polyesters prepared from short-chain dibasic acids and dibasic alcohols, ethers and esters of carbohydrates, and derivatives of ethylenediamines. Sometimes superpolar liquids, such as solutions of silver nitrate in ethylene glycol, are used to resolve closely related olefins. Often, good separations can be obtained if the solvent can form secondary valence bonds with one or more of the solutes, charge transfer complexes being an example. In some instances, better separations can be achieved on two columns in series containing different stationary phases than on either column alone. Comparable results are often attained by mixing the two liquids and using a single column.

Recently, there has been considerable interest in the development of liquids which are suitable for use at low packing ratios (1 per cent or less on the solid support) for the separation of high boiling liquids at intermediate temperatures (180° to 250°C). Thus, the methyl silicone rubber, SE-30, has proved to be very useful for the chromatography of steroids at temperatures below their decomposition points. Thermally stable polar liquid phases for use in similar applications are also available. One of these is silicone polymer QF-1, a fluorinated alkyl silicone supplied by the Dow Corning Co. This liquid will permit the separation of cholesterol from cholestanol, which is not achievable on SE-30. Other stationary liquids which are useful at low packing ratios include silicone XE-60, Versamide, and neopentyl glycol succinate.

SELECTION OF PACKING RATIOS. The ratio of stationary liquid to solid support is an important variable in preparing columns for GLC, since it influences retention volumes, column efficiencies, operating temperature, and degree of adsorption of solutes on the solid support. Furthermore, the permeability of the column to the mobile phase is lower at high packing ratios because there is less free space in the column for the passage of the gas. Ideally, the liquid should be spread over the internal and external surfaces of the support in the form of a thin film, but in practice it is not. The liquid enters the smaller pores first, owing to capillarity, the larger pores becoming filled as the packing ratio is increased. As a result, molecules of solute in the gas phase must diffuse a distance, d_g, from interparticle space through unfilled pores before they reach the surface of the liquid. The average distance that solute molecules must diffuse in the liquid phase is given by d_f, or the film thickness. The relative rates at which the solute diffuses in the two phases are determined by the ratio of its diffusion coefficients in them, D_{liq}/D_{gas}.

Since diffusion takes place much more rapidly in gases than in liquids, the former is of relatively little importance in influencing mass transfer. The influence of the thickness of the liquid film and the diffusion coefficient of the solute in it are given by the third term of the van Deemter equation, as shown in Equation (9) where K is the partition coefficient of the solute

$$\text{HETP} = A + B/u + \frac{8}{\pi^2} \frac{KF_{liq}/F_{gas}}{(1 + KF_{liq}/F_{gas})^2} \cdot \frac{d_f^2}{D_{liq}} u \tag{9}$$

between the liquid and gas phases, F_{liq} is the volume fraction of the column occupied by liquid, F_{gas} is the volume fraction of the column occupied by gas, d_f is the film thickness of the liquid, D_{liq} is the diffusion coefficient of the solute in the liquid phase, and u is the velocity of the carrier gas. When the solid support is porous, as is usually the case in gas chromatography, the thickness of the liquid film will be proportional to the packing ratio. Therefore, column efficiency in terms of the height equivalent to a theoretical plate should decrease as the amount of liquid phase is increased. The change, however, will not be directly proportional to the square of the film thickness, d_f, since the ratio F_{liq}/F_{gas} will increase also, because of the change in the relative proportions of the column volume occupied by the two phases. The van Deemter equation does not provide a quantitative description of the variation in column efficiency with packing ratio because of the approximate nature of the assumptions made in its derivation. Nevertheless, it indicates clearly that HETP will increase as the liquid layer becomes thicker, because of increased resistance to mass transfer.

In practice, many workers use packings containing 15 to 40 per cent liquid. Others recommend lower figures, in the range of 8 to 20 per cent; ratios of from 0.5 to 5 per cent are used for very high-molecular-weight compounds such as steroids and alkaloids. It is likely that the optimum varies with the solute-solvent combination under investigation, and also with other considerations. Thus, if it is necessary to collect fractions of eluted materials for chemical analysis, comparatively large samples must be applied to the chromatographic column. This necessitates high packing ratios to avoid overloading. If, on the other hand, rapid separation is required, a low packing ratio is indicated to reduce retention volumes. However, if the solid support is adsorptive, low ratios will lead to tailing. In summary, high ratios result in somewhat lower plate efficiency and high retention volumes, and are needed for the chromatography of large samples. Low packing ratios give low retention volumes, require small samples, may result in tailing, and yield higher column efficiency.

The smaller retention volumes achieved with low packing ratios can be sacrificed in order to operate at lower column temperatures, often with very beneficial results. Thus, fair peak resolution is obtained on chromatographing mixtures of mono-, di-, and triethylene glycols on Carbowax 1000 at packing ratio of 40:100 and a temperature of 180°C [23]. When the packing ratio is reduced to 12:100, the peaks are not resolved. However, when the temperature is reduced to 150°C, sharp peaks and good resolution are obtained with a 12:100 ratio. This principle has been used for the chromatography of heat-labile organic compounds at several hundred degrees below their boiling points. Solid supports with low adsorptive capacities are used, and packing ratios are reduced to 1 per cent or less. Of course, it is necessary to use small samples and correspondingly more sensitive detectors.

COLUMN DIMENSIONS. Columns 1 to 2 meters long are satisfactory for most purposes. However, the number of theoretical plates obtainable increases with length. Consequently, columns 10 to 20 meters long are not uncommon for the resolution of solutes with low separation factors. Some packed columns may have efficiencies as high as 3000 theoretical plates per meter, but in other cases this value may be as low as 200, particularly with solid supports having low specific surfaces. Columns 0.2 to 2 cm in internal diameter are used for quantitative analysis, sizes of 0.4 to 0.6 cm being most common. GLC columns do not lose efficiency seriously when the diameter is increased.

Columns are made of glass, stainless steel, or copper. The choice of the material is important, for sensitive compounds may react or isomerize catalytically at the column walls. This often leads to artifacts, especially in the analysis of terpenes. The shape of the column must be considered also. Columns are most efficient when packed straight and then bent to the desired shape.

However, this is not practical with glass columns or economical in the case of stainless steel. Hence, when these materials are used, coiled columns are loaded with packing under vacuum.

Coiled columns are slightly less efficient per unit length than straight ones, but this is not serious for 0.5-cm analytical columns if the diameter of the coil is 15 cm or more.

PREPARATION OF THE COLUMN. The stationary liquid is usually dissolved in an organic solvent, such as dichloromethane, acetone, or ethyl acetate, and is mixed with the solid support in a large evaporating dish. The solution is heated with stirring to drive off the solvent. If the equipment is available, it is more convenient to mix the solid and solution of stationary phase in a round-bottomed flask and remove the solvent in a rotary vacuum evaporator. The powder should be dry to the touch and free-flowing before it is used to pack the column.

To fill a straight column, the bottom end is stopped with a 1-cm plug of glass wool. The column is supported in a vertical position, and a powder funnel is attached to the top with a short length of plastic tubing. The packing is placed in the funnel and sifted into place by vibrating the column. This is best accomplished by holding the bottom portion of the column against the flattened drive shaft of a motor rotating in a vertical position. The tube is rotated and moved up and down against the shaft during filling. If a vibrator is not available, the packing can be settled into place by tapping the tube sharply with a blunt instrument. However, a vibrator is recommended.

The column is filled to within 1 cm of the top and sealed with a plug of glass wool. It is then bent to the required shape or spiraled around a mandril. For the former, a tube bender is very convenient. Connection to the chromatograph is usually made with thumbscrews sealed with silicone O rings or Swagelok fittings.

Columns are conditioned by passing the mobile phase or another inert gas through them at the maximum use temperature or above. The exact conditions depend on the thermal stability of the packing and the sensitivity of the detector. Usually treatment for 24 to 72 hours will suffice. If a variety of columns are to be used with an ionization detector, it is convenient to have substitutes conditioning at all times in a special apparatus built for the purpose. Otherwise, a considerable waiting period may ensue before detector background is low enough for use.

COLUMNS FOR GSC

The active solids employed most frequently in GSC include molecular sieve, silica gel, activated charcoal, and alumina. These are often activated, or sometimes deactivated, prior to use. Molecular sieves are synthetic metal aluminosilicates having three-dimensional pores. Three grades are available, 13-X, 4-A, and 5-A, the numbers referring to the pore sizes. They are the most efficient materials known for separating oxygen from nitrogen, but carbon dioxide is adsorbed irreversibly by them except at elevated temperatures. Silica gel is used most often for the separation of carbon dioxide from air and light hydrocarbons. It does not resolve oxygen and nitrogen. Activated charcoal is good for separating hydrogen from air. It will also separate oxygen from nitrogen, but not so efficiently as molecular sieve.

Peaks obtained on GSC columns often tail badly, since adsorption isotherms of gases on them are nonlinear. This can be reduced by coating the active solid with a small amount of strongly adsorbed stationary liquid. For example, 1.5 per cent squalane has been used to reduce tailing on furnace black [24].

GSC columns are packed and installed in the chromatograph in the same manner as GLC columns.

PREPARATION AND USE OF CAPILLARY COLUMNS

In preparing capillary columns, the stationary liquid is coated on the internal surface of the tubing in a layer about 3 to 5μ thick. Despite the thinness of the film, capillaries can be used for prolonged periods before the stationary phase is eluted. The bore of the tubing is generally 0.01 to 0.1 cm, and the length 15 to 45 meters. Generally 2 to 4 mg of liquid per 10 meters of tubing is applied. The liquid is dissolved in a nonpolar volatile organic solvent, and this solution is forced into the capillary by pressure or suction. Once the tube is filled, the liquid is forced out of it with carier gas, and the coating is formed from what adheres to the walls. Gas pressures used in filling the column vary from 2 to 100 psig, and for blowing out the plug of liquid from 40 to 100 psig. So far, no absolutely reproducible method has been developed for preparing them. Consequently, variable results are obtained on commercial columns as well as on those made in the laboratory.

The thickness of the liquid layer and its uniformity must be controlled carefully for optimum results. The gas selected to introduce and sweep out the liquid must be clean and dry. Also, the interior of the column itself must be dry and free of organic matter. Materials of construction include glass, copper, and stainless steel, the latter being used most widely. Metal columns must be treated chemically before packing to destroy "acid centers" and so minimize catalytic breakdown of labile compounds. Copper columns may contain a film of oxide that causes tailing. This also can be removed by chemical treatment.

Because of the small amount of stationary liquid used, sample sizes must be kept very small, of the order of 1 μg. To do this, a normal-sized sample is injected, and most of it is vented to the atmosphere in a ratio of 100:1 to 1000:1 by a stream-splitter placed between the injection port and the column. This procedure is not very reproducible, particularly for high-boiling compounds, since the sample may be fractionated partly before it enters the column. Therefore, sample introduction and application of the stationary liquid to the column are major problems that are still incompletely solved.

Detectors

High detector sensitivity and versatility are a direct consequence of using a permanent gas as the mobile phase in chromatography. The properties of gases make possible the measurement of differences in thermal conductivity, ionizability of organic molecules, heats of combustion, and other similar properties for the detection of solutes in column eluates. These measurements would be impractical if not impossible in the liquid phase. With them it is possible to determine automatically the amounts of solutes present in column eluates, and in almost unbelievably low amounts. Thermistor detectors will respond to 10^{-8} mole of solute, and ionization detectors will record the presence of as little as 10^{-12} mole of an organic compound in the mobile phase.

High detector sensitivity coupled with automation is invaluable for the detection of trace components and the analysis of minute amounts of biological fluids. In addition, there are other hidden values which are not at once apparent. The capacity to detect small amounts of organic compounds makes it possible to use very small sample sizes and therefore obtain high column efficiencies in terms of theoretical plates. Moreover, small sample sizes can be coupled with low liquid/solid packing ratios. This makes possible the chromatography of organic compounds at column temperatures several hundred degrees below their boiling points and thus enormously increases the versatility of the method. Of course, gas chromatography in capillary columns would be unfeasible from a practical point of view were it not for the extreme sensitivity of ionization detectors.

Detectors can be classified in several ways: according to the manner in which the chromatographic data are presented; according to principle of operation; or according to universality of response to a variety of chemical compounds. Data are presented as integral or differential curves, depending on the method. Integral detectors measure the cumulative amount of all the compounds which pass into them during the course of analysis. An example is the titration cell, in which the total amount of standard alkali required to neutralize a series of acids eluted from the chromatographic column is measured. The chromatogram appears as a series of steps plotted against time, the height of each step being proportional to the amount of component present in the sample. Differential recorders measure the instantaneous concentration of solute vapor in the sensing part of the cell. The solute vapor is spread out in a longitudinal direction, so that all of it does not enter the cell at once. The concentration of vapor in the leading and trailing ends of the plug is less than in the center. Consequently, the chromatogram appears as a series of peaks, the amount of each component of the sample being proportional to the area under the peak it generates.

A large number of properties have been used as the basis for detection. However, the overwhelming majority of detectors in actual use are based on measurement of the differences between the thermal conductivities of the solute and the mobile phase, or measurement of the electric currents produced by causing the solutes to ionize. Thermal detectors are rugged, easy to build, and moderately sensitive. However, they are susceptible to changes in temperature and to the flow rate of the mobile phase. Ionization detectors are much more sensitive and are more stable with respect to changes in operating parameters. In the past, thermal detectors have been used most extensively, but ionization detectors, which have higher sensitivity, have now supplanted them in most biological applications.

Thermal detectors are universal in that they respond in a greater or lesser degree to the presence of all the components of a sample unless one of them happens to be identical to the carrier gas. Ionization detectors are semiuniversal in that they respond to most organic compounds but not in a marked degree to inorganic compounds. For most work, universality of response is very desirable. However, in some instances it is impossible or inconvenient to resolve all the components of complex mixtures on the column. When this occurs, it is possible sometimes to use a selective detector which "sees" only a selected group of compounds possessing some specific property or component in common. For example, a coulometric detector has been developed that responds only to compounds containing halogen and sulfur. This makes extensive pretreatment of the sample or complete resolution of all its components on the column unnecessary in order to obtain useful analytical results. Consequently, selective detectors can be extremely valuable and should be considered along with universal detection methods during the development of new analytical procedures.

THERMAL DETECTORS

Thermal detectors are still supplied as standard or optional equipment on many makes of gas chromatographs. They respond to chemical compounds of all types and are moderately sensitive to organic vapors when the carrier gas is hydrogen or helium. As little as 10^{-8} to 10^{-5} mole of solute can be detected in the carrier gas, depending on type, cell geometry, and operating temperature. Thermal detectors are very sensitive to temperature changes and should be thermostatted to within 0.05° below 100°C, and to within 0.1°C above this temperature to secure a stable base line. Therefore, a considerable wait often ensues if the oven is opened between runs to change columns or if the temperature must be changed. Similarly, detector response is influenced by the flow rate of the mobile phase, and therefore this also must be kept constant. Consequently, it is not feasible to stop the flow of carrier gas to apply a sample, since the base line of the recorder would not become established quickly enough on restarting the flow.

Therefore, the sample must be injected through a self-sealing diaphragm against the back pressure of the column.

The basic component of the thermal detector is a small resistance element made of a semiconductor (thermistor type) or a platinum or tungsten wire (katharometer type). Two of these elements are used in each cell, one serving as the detector and the other as a reference unit. A typical circuit arrangement is shown in Fig. 5-6. The detector

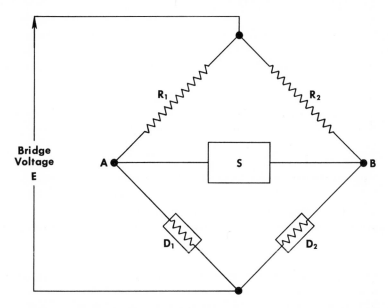

Fig. 5-6. Wheatstone bridge arrangement for thermal conductivity cell (Courtesy, Academic Press).

element (D_1) and the reference element (D_2), together with resistances R_1 and R_2, form a Wheatstone bridge across which a bridge voltage (E) is impressed. This serves to heat the resistance elements in the detector to a constant temperature. The variable resistances are then adjusted to zero the potential drop across AB, which feeds the recorder (S). This adjustment is made with pure carrier gas flowing through D_1 and D_2 so that the amount of heat carried away from the elements by conduction and convection remains constant. Under these conditions, the recorder pen will draw a straight line at the base of the chart. If a solute vapor passes through D_1, the resistance element will change in temperature because of the difference in thermal conductivity between the solute and pure carrier gas. If hydrogen or helium is used as the mobile phase, the temperature of the element in D_1 will increase, as all other gases have lower thermal conductivities and hence will conduct heat away from it less rapidly. This change in temperature will cause the resistance of the element in D_1 to increase, since a substance with a high temperature coefficient of resistance is chosen for construction. Meanwhile the resistance of the element in D_2 will remain the same, as the gas flow system is arranged so that pure mobile phase only flows through this side of the cell. As a result of the difference in resistance between the elements D_1 and D_2, a potential imbalance is created across AB which activates the recorder pen to draw a peak.

To operate properly, the resistance elements must be heated to a temperature above that of the cell block, in order to conduct heat away from the elements to the block at a rate which depends on the thermal conductivity of the surrounding gas and the difference in temperature between the element and the walls of the housing. In actual practice, the sensing cell and the reference cell cannot be made to balance exactly with pure carrier flowing through them. Therefore the circuit is so designed that the signal arising from this inequality can be balanced with an opposing signal by means of an adjustable zero control.

When hydrogen or helium is the carrier gas, the peaks are always in the same direction, as all other materials have lower conductivities. However, with nitrogen, the temperature of the element in D_1 will become higher or lower, depending on whether the solute passing through it has a lower or higher conductivity than nitrogen. Therefore negative peaks are obtained for some substances. To avoid this, a polarity switch is usually installed on the chromatograph to reverse the direction of the signal.

Thermal conductivity is a unique characteristic of each chemical compound which does not vary in an exact way with molecular weight or other characteristics. Therefore the T/C cell must be calibrated by measuring its response to known amounts of pure compounds if accurate results are required. But approximate results can be obtained on most organic compounds if hydrogen or helium is used as the mobile phase, since the spread between the conductivities of the carrier and solutes is great enough to minimize differences between the various solutes.

IONIZATION DETECTORS

Ionization detectors are inherently more sensitive than thermal detectors, responding to as little as 10^{-10} to 10^{-12} mole of solute in the carrier gas. Basically, most ionization detectors operate on the same principle; an organic compound is ionized, and the ions (or electrons) formed are used to carry an electric current. The magnitude of the signal is then recorded with or without intermediate amplification. A number of ionization detectors have been described in the literature, but only two have found widespread use as yet. These are the argon detector and the flame detector. Consequently, this discussion will be confined to them.

In general, ionization detectors are considerably less sensitive to temperature changes and fluctuations in the flow rate of the carrier gas than are thermal detectors. Furthermore, the signal-to-noise ratio is so high that reference cells are not needed. Because of their extreme sensitivity, they are always used in capillary column chromatography. However, this should not obscure the fact that they can be exceedingly helpful in conjunction with packed columns, particularly for the detection of trace components or where the use of very small samples is desirable.

ARGON DETECTOR

In the apparatus developed by Lovelock [25], argon is the carrier gas, and atoms of it are excited to a metastable state by ionizing radiation as they enter the detector. The argon atoms remain in this condition until they collide with atoms or molecules possessing ionization potentials lower than the excitation potential of the noble gas, whereupon the organic molecules ionize and are detected. Since the excitation potential of argon is 11.6 ev, it will ionize most organic compounds (C_1 and C_2 hydrocarbons being excepted) but not inorganic gases such as oxygen, nitrogen, and carbon dioxide, since their ionization potentials are too high.

Three types of argon detectors are now in common use. These are the simple detector, the small detector for use with capillary columns, and the triode detector. Signals from these detectors range between 10^{-6} and 10^{-12} amp. The triode detector is about 1000 times more sensitive than the first argon detector and has at least 100 times the signal/noise ratio of the flame ionization detector. It responds more or less uniformly to high-molecular-weight substances, but extensive calibration is required for low-molecular-weight compounds.

Argon detectors are used to greatest advantage in the trace analysis of steroids, fatty esters, and related compounds where molecular weights are fairly high, and where separations are carried out in an inert atmosphere. They are less useful than flame ionization detectors for the direct measurement of air pollutants or volatiles stripped from aqueous media, since their response is quenched by the presence of water vapor or oxygen in the mobile phase.

FLAME DETECTOR

Organic compounds yield ions when burned in a flame, and, if two electrodes at a potential difference of about 150 v are inserted in it, differences in the conductivity of the flame can be measured as the solutes elute from the chromatographic column and are burned. This is the principle on which the flame ionization detector is based. The degree of ionization that occurs in a flame is much greater than would be predicted from the ionization potentials of organic compounds. It has been suggested that this is caused by the formation of carbon aggregates and their subsequent ready ionization due to the low work function of solid carbon.

In operation, nitrogen or a similar inert gas is used as the mobile phase for chromatography. The column effluent is mixed with hydrogen, and this mixture fed into the flame jet of the detector. The jet is a thin-walled metal tube which also acts as an electrode. The other electrode is a metal filament held a few millimeters above the flame. A current of filtered sweep air is passed through the detection chamber to remove dust particles and water of combustion. As organic compounds pass through the detector, they are burned in the flame and give rise to an ionization current which is measured and recorded. Background current is of the order of 10^{-11} amp, depending on detector design.

The detector is insensitive to temperature changes, vibrations, and small fluctuations in the flow rates of carrier and flame gases. For hydrocarbons, response is roughly a function of carbon number, but rather large deviations from this are encountered for low-molecular-weight compounds containing functional groups. The detector does not respond to inorganic vapors such as air, carbon dioxide, water, ammonia, or hydrogen sulfide. However, unlike the argon detector, it yields a high response to methane and ethane.

The flame ionization detector has proved very useful in gas chromatography. It is sufficiently sensitive for use with capillary columns or conventional columns prepared at low packing ratios, and at the same time its response is not quenched by the presence of water vapor or oxygen in the gas stream as is the case with the argon detector. Unlike the latter, it responds to low-molecular-weight organic compounds such as methane and ethane but is essentially insensitive to all inorganic gases. Although not as sensitive as the argon detector, it has a greater over-all range of applicability. In most cases, it would be the detector of choice for a laboratory limited to a single instrument.

Selection and Regulation of the Carrier Gas

Use of a permanent gas as the mobile phase is the salient feature distinguishing gas chromatography from other forms of chromatography. Yet comparatively little attention is given to factors influencing selection of the gas because the choice is limited, being confined at present to hydrogen, helium, nitrogen, air, argon, neon, and carbon dioxide. However, these gases, as well as others that might be used, possess individual chemical and physical characteristics that often determine whether a particular type of analysis is feasible or not. Careful attention should be given to properties that influence flow rate, detector sensitivity, selectivity of detector response, and chemical stability in the gas stream. Furthermore, the flow rate of the carrier gas should be selected to obtain optimum resolution of peaks, and variations in rate should be kept to the minimum to ensure reproducible retention volumes and good detector performance. Some of these factors are treated briefly in this section.

FACTORS INFLUENCING CHOICE OF CARRIER GAS

VISCOSITY AND DIFFUSIVITY. Gases are much less viscous than liquids, this being the principal reason why gas chromatography is a rapid method of analysis compared to liquid-liquid or liquid-solid chromatography. Nevertheless, considerable differences in viscosity occur between them, so some leeway in the selection of this operating parameter is possible. Hydrogen is the least viscous of all gases, as befits its low mass, but helium is more viscous than any other material listed except the other noble gases and oxygen (Table 5-1).

TABLE 5-1
PHYSICAL PROPERTIES OF GASES AT 0°C*

Gas	Molecular (or atomic) weight	Diffusion coefficient (cm²/sec) Into H₂	Into CO₂	Viscosity (micropoises)	Thermal conductivity (× 10⁵)	Ionization potential (ev)
H₂	2	—	0.550	83.5	41.6	15.6
He	4	—	—	186.0	34.8	24.46
CH₄	16	0.625	0.153	102.6	7.21	14.5
NH₃	17	—	—	91.8	5.22	11.2
Ne	20.2	—	—	297.3	—	21.47
CO	28	0.651	0.137	166	—	14.1
N₂	28	0.674	0.144	156.3	5.81	15.51
Air	—	0.611	—	170.8	5.83	12.8
C₂H₆	30	0.459	—	—	4.36	—
O₂	32	—	—	189	—	12.5
H₂S	34	—	—	—	—	10.42
Ar	39.9	0.77	0.14†	209.6	—	15.68
CO₂	44	0.550	—	141	3.52	14.4
C₃H₈	44	—	—	—	3.58	—
SO₂	64	—	—	115.8	—	13.1

* Data compiled from the literature.
† At 20°C.

At the other extreme, sulfur dioxide, with a molecular weight of 64, has a lower viscosity than any member of the series except methane, ammonia, and hydrogen. This irregular behavior should make it possible to select a pure or mixed carrier with almost any combination of values for viscosity, diffusivity, and thermal conductivity desired, since these properties do not vary in a parallel manner.

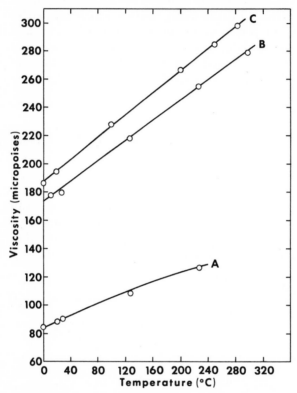

Fig. 5-7. Change in viscosity of gases with temperature. (A) hydrogen; (B) nitrogen; (C) helium (Courtesy, Academic Press).

It is important to realize that the viscosities of all gases increase with temperature (Fig. 5-7). This factor is particularly important when the temperature of the chromatograph must be changed during an analysis. The viscosity of the gas will change also and so will the flow rate. If constant mass or linear flow is required by the characteristics of the detector, or for other reasons, a suitable regulating valve must be included upstream from the injection block.

Another inherent property of gases that must be considered is diffusivity. This is measured by the diffusion coefficient which is a function of viscosity, density, and degree of molecular interaction.

Data for the diffusion of a number of gases into hydrogen and into carbon dioxide are shown in Table 5-1. It can be seen that all gases diffuse into hydrogen at a relatively high rate, but the tendency becomes less as molecular weight increases. On the other hand, diffusion rates into carbon dioxide are low. This suggests that better resolution of gas chromatographic peaks will be obtained by employing nitrogen, argon, and carbon dioxide as carriers rather than by choosing gases with high diffusivity, such as hydrogen and helium, since there will be less longitudinal diffusion of the solute during transport through the system. To oversimplify the situation, carbon dioxide will tend to carry the sample through the column as a compact plug, whereas in hydrogen the plug will spread out. Consequently, some workers believe the use of high-molecular-weight gases to be advantageous where other factors are not overriding.

THERMAL CONDUCTIVITY. The thermal conductivity of the carrier gas is an important property only when katharometers or thermistors are used as detectors. Since these have been supplanted by ionization detectors except for preparative gas chromatography and the analysis of permanent gases, this topic will not be dealt with in depth here. It will be sufficient to say that mobile phases having high conductivities (hydrogen or helium) should be used for the measurement of organic compounds with T/C cells. Generally, the conductivities of the mobile phase and solute should differ as widely as possible to obtain maximum sensitivity. For a more extended discussion, the reader is referred to the text by Burchfield and Storrs [5].

EXCITATION AND IONIZATION POTENTIALS. Excitation potentials are important only when a noble gas is used in conjunction with an ionization detector as a means of conserving radiation energy temporarily. In this case, the excitation potential of the gas should exceed the ionization potentials of the compounds to be measured (Table 5-1). Argon detectors exhibit small (and sometimes negative) responses to permanent gases when they are present in massive quantities, but they are not used to their fullest advantage in this application. Consequently, they should not be employed to detect materials having ionization potentials greater than 11.6 ev. This excludes most of the inorganic gases except ammonia and hydrogen sulfide, as well as C_1 and C_2 hydrocarbons.

CHEMICAL REACTIVITY OF CARRIER GAS. Generally, highly reactive carrier gases should be avoided. Hydrogen may reduce organic compounds in hot-wire detectors, and oxygen or air can cause breakdown of some column packings at high temperatures. Presumably gases such as hydrogen chloride, sulfur dioxide, ammonia, and hydrogen sulfide could find application because of unique physiochemical characteristics were it not for their noxious or corrosive properties.

However, in some instances special advantages may accrue through use of a reactive gas, and it should therefore always be considered as a means of augmenting the versatility of the method. The reducing power of hydrogen, for instance, can be utilized to simplify detection and calibration in the chromatographic analysis of aldehydes obtained by oxidation of amino acids [26]. The aldehyde vapors in a hydrogen carrier are passed through a heated column packed with nickel-Kieselguhr located between the column and detector. The aldehydes are hydrocracked to methane and water, and the latter compound is removed in a drying tower. Thus, the only material to pass through the detector is methane. This simplifies calibration, since the carbon number of the aldehyde and the response of the detector to methane are the only data required to obtain quantitative results. Furthermore, the detector can be operated at room temperature without danger of condensing sample components.

The reaction of carbon dioxide gas with aqueous alkali to form solutions of alkali metal carbonates forms the basis of a unique detection system originally developed by Janák. Low-molecular-weight hydrocarbons are eluted from a column with carbon dioxide, and the mixed gases are collected in a burette filled with sodium hydroxide solution. The carrier gas is absorbed quantitatively, but light hydrocarbons accumulate above the liquid and are measured volumetrically. Undoubtedly analogous results could be obtained with hydrogen chloride, ammonia, or sulfur dioxide, should special circumstances warrant their use.

PURITY OF CARRIER GAS.   Many industrial cylinder gases of commercial grade contain varying amounts of water and organic vapors which are introduced during cleaning and refilling of the tanks. Steadier base lines can be obtained and column life prolonged by inserting a drying column containing silica gel or molecular sieve between the gas cylinder reducing valve and the chromatograph inlet valve. This is particularly important for polyester packings, since they are hydrolyzed readily by water at high temperatures.

RATE OF GAS FLOW AND ITS REGULATION

SELECTION OF OPTIMUM INLET AND OUTLET PRESSURES. In liquid-liquid or liquid-solid chromatography, both the volumetric flow rate and the linear flow rate are invariant across the length of the column, since, for all practical purposes, the mobile phase is incompressible. However, gases are highly compressible, and this salient fact must be taken into account in calculating retention volumes or in selecting operating conditions. In a gas chromatograph, the pressure at the inlet side of the partition column must be of necessity higher than the outlet pressure for flow to take place. Consequently, the pressure varies continuously from p_i (inlet pressure) to p_o (outlet pressure) along the length of the column. Since this is true, the linear velocity of an imaginary point carried along by the gas stream must increase as it approaches the outlet of the column. Hence, the linear flow rate of the gas increases with distance from the inlet side of the column (x), even though the volumetric flow rate at the column exit (milliliters per minute) is constant. The linear flow rate at any point within the column is directly proportional to the pressure gradient (dp/dx), inversely proportional to the viscosity of the gas (η), and directly proportional to the permeability of the column packing (ϕ), as shown in Equation (10).

$$u = -\frac{\phi}{\eta}\frac{dp}{dx} \tag{10}$$

On making suitable substitutions in Equation (10) and integrating between limits, Equation (11) results, where l is the length of the chromatographic column,

$$\frac{x}{l} = \frac{(\rho_i/\rho_o)^2 - (\rho/\rho_o)^2}{(\rho_i/\rho_o)^2 - 1} \tag{11}$$

x is the distance of any arbitrary point from the inlet side of the column, ρ is the gas pressure at that point, ρ_i is the inlet pressure, and ρ_o is the outlet pressure. Since ρ_i, ρ_o, and l are constant under any given set of operating conditions, it is possible to calculate the pressure (ρ) at any point x within the column. Furthermore, since pressure within the column is inversely proportional to linear gas velocity, it is possible to compute the velocity relative to inlet velocity (u/u_o) at any relative distance (x/l) from the inlet side of the column at various arbitrary ratios of inlet to outlet pressures (ρ_i/ρ_o). When this is done, and the results are plotted, a family of curves is obtained showing how the linear velocity of the gas changes along the length of the column at different inlet-to-outlet pressure ratios.

From these data it is found that pressure ratios of three or more result in rapid increases in linear gas velocity toward the outlet side of the column. An optimum flow rate exists for every chromatographic separation, on either side of which column efficiency as measured by HETP (height equivalent to a theoretical plate) diminishes. Therefore, to operate a column at maximum efficiency, the linear flow rate should be constant, insofar as this is possible, and should be regulated at the optimum value along the entire length of the column. When this is not the case, part of the column is being operated inefficiently. Thus, high inlet-to-outlet pressure ratios result in suboptimum performance.

However, many times it is necessary (for practical reasons) to decrease the time required for the elution of a particular component. This can be done by increasing the inlet pressure or decreasing the outlet pressure, or both, and it is necessary to know which procedure is most satisfactory. Keulemans [8] has considered this problem for a hypothetical column operated at an inlet pressure of 1 atm and an outlet pressure of 0.25 atm, which has a ratio of outlet velocity to inlet velocity (u_o/u_i) of 4. When the outlet pressure is decreased by a factor of 2.5, the residence time of the gas is decreased by only 9 per cent, whereas the velocity ratio is increased to 10. However, if the outlet pressure is held constant and the inlet pressure is increased by 15 per cent, residence time drops by 15 per cent, while the velocity ratio increases to only 4.6. Therefore, increasing the inlet pressure is more effective than decreasing the outlet pressure for shortening residence times, and, moreover, it does not increase the velocity gradient within the column as much.

For this reason and others, it is best to operate chromatographs with the outlet at atmospheric pressure or higher and at a value for p_i/p_o between 1.1 and 2. Operation with the outlet under reduced pressure may result in inefficient utilization of part of the column.

SELECTION OF OPTIMUM FLOW RATE. Selection of flow rate is based frequently on personal preference or expediency. Some chromatograms contain as many as 20 to 30 peaks, and it would be impossible to select a value optimum for all of them. If a column temperature has already been selected, a low flow rate will give the best presentation of data for compounds with low retention volumes, and a higher rate is preferable for compounds retarded to a greater extent by the column packing. If both groups are of interest, a compromise must be sought. Values reported in the literature generally range between 20 and 200 ml of gas per minute, measured at the column outlet. A rate of 100 ml/min is about average for a 2-meter column 0.5 cm in diameter and is at least a good starting point if no background of information is available on the column characteristics and partition coefficients of the sample components. Of course, the volumetric flow rate must be changed in proportion to the cross-sectional area if tubing of a different bore is used to keep the linear flow rate constant.

All carrier gases are available in compressed form in cylinders. These are fitted with two-stage diaphragm reducing valves to regulate the pressure of the gas delivered to the chromatograph. The chromatograph itself is usually equipped with a regulating device.

Most commercial chromatographs have pressure regulators only at the inlet. A wider range of operating conditions can be obtained if a regulator is also placed at the outlet.

MEASUREMENT OF FLOW RATES. Flow rates must be measured accurately for the computation of retention volumes and continuously to determine if fluctuations occur during a run. Usually two types of indicator are used: a soap film flowmeter for precise work, and a rotameter (float meter) or Venturi (orifice) meter for constant observation. The rotameter and orifice meter respond to changes in temperature and should be located within the column oven. The soap film meter is accurate to within 1 per cent and gives virtually no back pressure. These meters can be obtained from many laboratory supply houses and manufacturers of chromatographs.

Regulation

and Selection of

Operating Temperatures

Control of column and detector temperature is a vital factor in gas chromatography, for the temperature influences reproducibility of retention volumes, base-line stability, and constancy of peak areas. Moreover, inadequate heating of the injection block lowers column efficiency, and condensation of solutes in the exit lines prevents collection of fractions. Consequently, it is more important to consider the over-all effects of temperature rather than to focus attention on any one component part of the instrument. Once adequate means are available for adjusting temperatures with the requisite precision, optimum conditions must be selected for the particular separation being attempted. This requires studies of changes in retention volumes with respect to temperature and studies of the influence of temperature on separation factors and column efficiencies. Finally, the thermal stabilities of the solutes and stationary phase must be considered. All these factors must be weighed in arriving at operating specifications.

If the mixture to be analyzed is complex and contains components that boil at temperatures as much as 100° to 200°C apart, no single temperature may be satisfactory. In this case, it may be necessary to increase the temperature of the chromatographic column during the analysis, either stepwise or continuously, to achieve the separations desired. Alternatively, the sample can be prefractionated before chromatography by ancillary physical methods such as fractional or azeotropic distillation.

REGULATION OF TEMPERATURE

The temperature of all the component parts of a chromatograph must be controlled to obtain optimum performance. There are two general methods of accomplishing this. The first method is to place all the component parts of the chromatograph in the same oven. This is inexpensive, simplifies instrumentation, and reduces repair and maintenance problems to the minimum. However, flexibility is lost, and analysis times may be lengthened. Some problems cannot be handled satisfactorily with this type of equipment. The other method is to thermostat the major components of the chromatograph separately. This increases the number of instrumental adjustments that must be made, but at the same time it greatly enhances the versatility of the method. Instruments of both types are available commercially, and, as would be expected, the greater the degree of temperature control, the greater is the cost. The choice is governed by the nature of the problem. Many routine analyses can be handled satisfactorily on an instrument equipped with a single control. However, on research instruments, the temperature of the injection block, the column, and the detector should be regulated separately.

INJECTION BLOCK TEMPERATURE.   See the section on Sample Introduction, Liquid Samples on page 148.

COLUMN TEMPERATURE.   Chromatographic columns are operated at temperatures varying from $-200°$ to $500°C$ and the range is expanding continually. Zero and subzero temperatures are achieved most conveniently by immersing the column in a liquid coolant. This may be a wet ice bath, an ice-salt bath, a solvent-dry ice bath, or a liquefied permanent gas such as nitrogen, depending on the requirements of the analysis. The columns are usually coiled and placed inside a Dewar flask containing coolant.

For operation above room temperature, the column can be heated in an oil bath, a vapor bath, or an air oven, or it can be wrapped with heating tape. Enclosure of the column in an air oven is the most widely adopted means of controlling column temperature. Regardless of the method of regulation, accurate adjustment of temperature is necessary to secure reproducible retention volumes. Control within $0.1°C$ is desirable over the entire operating range.

DETECTOR TEMPERATURE.   The detector should usually be operated at or slightly above the highest column temperature employed to avoid condensation of solute vapors in it. The line leading from the column to the detector should be as short as possible and should be heated. When ionization detectors are used, precise temperature control is not critical. However, it is desirable to maintain the detector at or slightly above the highest column temperature used to avoid condensation of solutes. There are exceptions to this. If tritium is used as a radiation source in an argon or electron capture detector, it is not advisable to heat the detector above 210°C. However, it may be possible to use considerably higher column temperatures by employing small sample sizes to avoid condensation of the solutes.

TEMPERATURE OF THE OUTLET. Collection of fractions for rechromatography or identification is often impossible because solute vapors condense in the line leading from the detector. Consequently, the exit line should be wrapped with insulated resistance wire or with heating tape and the temperature controlled either by the detector thermoregulator or independently. If the fractions are collected through a hypodermic needle attached to the exit line, this must be heated also, particularly if high-boiling compounds are being chromatographed. This can be accomplished by enclosing the needle in a short metal tube approximately its own length and about 1.5 cm in diameter. The metal tube is wound with resistance wire and insulated, and the temperature is adjusted by means of a variable transformer.

SELECTION OF COLUMN TEMPERATURE

Column temperature is one of the most important operating parameters to be established in developing a new gas chromatographic method. If the temperature is too low, the solutes may not be eluted from the column, or, if they are, the peaks will be very broad owing to longitudinal diffusion in the carrier gas during the long residence time within the column. If the temperature is too high, the solutes will emerge without resolution. Generally, there is some intermediate temperature at which separation factors are at the maximum and the column operates with high plate efficiency. Location of this range and determination of whether solutes and stationary phases are stable under these conditions constitute one of the major tasks in arriving at optimum operating conditions.

RELATION OF RETENTION VOLUME TO TEMPERATURE. The principal effect of increasing column temperature is to decrease the partition coefficient of the solute between the mobile and stationary phases. In other words, a greater proportion of the compound being chromatographed is present in the vapor phase; therefore, it travels through the column faster if a constant flow rate of carrier gas is assumed. A secondary effect is reduction of the proportion of space occupied by the mobile phase within the column, caused by thermal expansion of the stationary phase. The net effect is reduction of retention volumes by about 5 per cent for each degree of temperature increase, the exact value depending on the temperature range and amount of interaction between the solute and the stationary phase. The quantitative dependence of retention volume on column temperature can be expressed by an Antoine equation having the form of Equation (12),

$$\log V_g = L + \frac{M}{T\rho_L} = \frac{\Delta H}{2.3RT} + k \tag{12}$$

where V_g is the specific retention volume of the solute, L, M, and k are empirical constants, ρ_L is the density of the liquid phase at column temperature, T is the absolute temperature of the column, R is the gas constant (1.987 cal deg^{-1} mole^{-1}), and ΔH is the partial molar heat of solution of the solute vapor in the stationary liquid.

Changes in the density of the stationary liquid, ρ_L, with respect to temperature are comparatively small. Therefore, it is possible to evaluate the experimental constants L and M with satisfactory accuracy by plotting $\log V_g$ against $1/T$. When this is done, straight lines are obtained, each with a slope (M) and intercept (L) characteristic of the compound being investigated (Fig. 5-8). This is an extremely

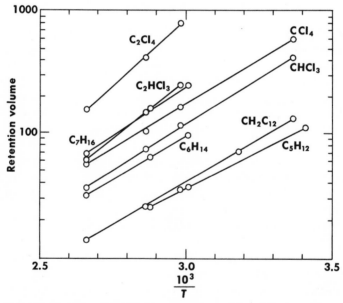

Fig. 5-8. Change in logarithm of retention volume with respect to reciprocal of absolute temperature for hydrocarbons and chlorinated hydrocarbons (Courtesy, Academic Press).

valuable method for evaluating data, since a great deal of information can be obtained from readings taken at relatively few temperatures. From such plots, it is often possible to tell whether a separation is feasible at any given temperature. For example, the curve for C_7H_{16}

(Fig. 5-8) has a different slope than the curve for C_2HCl_3, and the two intersect at a reciprocal temperature of 2.85. Consequently, it would be impossible to separate these compounds at a temperature corresponding to this value, since their retention volumes are identical.

In view of the usefulness of this relation, the change of retention volume with temperature should be determined and the results reported for at least two temperatures as far apart as is practicable.

RELATION BETWEEN COLUMN EFFICIENCY AND TEMPERATURE. It is sometimes stated that column efficiency as measured by HETP increases with increasing column temperature. Peaks become narrower at higher temperatures because the solute does not remain in the column as long, and thus there is less time for longitudinal diffusion to take place. However, peak narrowness alone should not be taken as evidence of improved column performance. The theoretical plate number of a column is proportional to the square of the ratio of the retention volume to the peak width (Equation 7). Hence, as the retention volume becomes smaller, the number of plates decreases, and thus the two factors operate against one another. Consequently, it is the *ratio* of volume to width that must become larger; a reduction in width alone will not suffice. The peaks may be sharper, but they could also be closer together so that the per cent overlap is not reduced.

RELATION BETWEEN SEPARATION FACTORS AND TEMPERATURE. Column efficiency is not the only criterion determining whether a separation is feasible. Separation factor is frequently more important, and this, too, is temperature-dependent. In general, separation factors for members of a homologous series diminish with increasing temperature, but this may not be universally true. It is often true because the velocity ratio for the movement of two solutes through the same column is an exponential function of their heats of solution in the stationary phase and the absolute temperature, as expressed in Equation (13), where u_A is the linear velocity of component A, u_B is the linear velocity of component B, T is the absolute temperature, and H_A and H_B are the heats of solution in the liquid phases of the two components, respectively.

$$u_A/u_B \cong e^{-(H_A - H_B)/RT} \tag{13}$$

In general, the *difference* in heats of solution between two members of a homologous series of compounds does not change greatly with temperature. Hence if T increases while H_A and H_B remain the same, the ratio of the velocities, or in effect the separation factor, will diminish.

The importance of this in GLC is illustrated by the fact that the classically difficult separation of *m*-xylene from *p*-xylene can be achieved on a nonselective column packing [27]. At room temperature these two isomers are easily separated on a 50-ft column containing dinonyl phthalate, the separation factor being 1.05 (Fig. 5-9).

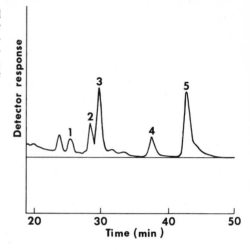

Fig. 5-9. Resolution of *m*-xylene and *p*-xylene on a nonselective stationary phase (dinonyl phthalate) at room temperature: *(1)* ethyl benzene; *(2)* *m*-xylene; *(3)* *p*-xylene; *(4)* *o*-xylene; *(5)* styrene [27] (Courtesy, Academic Press).

No separation is obtained at 80°C, although the column efficiency as measured by HETP remains the same. Low temperatures are advantageous in GSC also. Argon cannot be resolved from oxygen on a molecular sieve at room temperature. However, by reducing the temperature to −72°C, good separation is obtained.

INFLUENCE OF TEMPERATURE ON SOLUTE AND SOLVENT STABILITY. Not least among the factors arguing for choice of the lowest operating temperatures consistent with practical retention volumes is the fact that many solutes are thermally unstable. This can lead to loss of components through chemical reaction with column packings, production of artifacts through pyrolysis, and isomerization of unsaturated compounds.

Many of the more selective stationary liquids are volatile or decompose at high temperatures, and this places a ceiling on their usefulness. Common difficulties include unstable base lines on recorders, arising from excessive elution of the stationary phase or its decomposition products through the detector, and contamination of solute fractions collected from the column effluent. Bleeding is particularly serious with ionization detectors, since background is often prohibitively high. Apiezon L, high-vacuum silicone grease, and polyethylene have been used at temperatures ranging from 150° to 350°C. Higher temperatures can be employed with conditioned silicone gum rubber, irradiated asphaltenes, and inorganic salts. However, none of the organic packings now available will survive prolonged use at 500°C.

TEMPERATURE PROGRAMING

There is no optimum column temperature for chromatographing complex mixtures of compounds having widely separated boiling points. At high temperatures extremely volatile compounds are not resolved, and at low temperatures high-boiling components are not eluted. At intermediate temperatures peaks arising from low-boiling components are likely to be crowded, whereas those of high boilers may be inconveniently broad because of high residence times in the column. The most satisfactory way of resolving such mixtures is by programing the temperature so that each group of compounds is eluted at the temperature best suited for the separation of its components.

The preferred method for accomplishing this is to regulate the power supply to the column heater so that the temperature increases linearly with time. If the flow rate of the carrier gas is controlled also, peak areas are reproducible to within 3 per cent over a sixfold change in heating rate.

Programing the temperature spreads out peaks which appear early in isothermal runs at high temperatures and sharpens up peaks which have long retention times at low temperatures, thereby resulting in more uniform presentation of the data. There has been considerable discussion over whether programing temperature actually increases column efficiency. This is an interesting point but from a practical outlook perhaps irrelevant since there is little doubt that it simplifies the analysis of complex mixtures with wide boiling-point ranges. However, it must be kept in mind that the formula for calculating the height equivalent to a theoretical plate in temperature-programed chromatography is not the same as that used for isothermal conditions.

Fraction Collection

Gas chromatography is by itself an excellent method of qualitative analysis. Retention volumes (V_g) of chemical compounds on specified liquid phases are independent of all operating parameters except temperature. They are characteristic and reproducible and so can be used for tentative identification. Further confirmation can be obtained by running unknowns, together with standards, on several liquids differing in polarity to make certain that peaks do not overlap fortuitously. Moreover, it is possible to assign some unknown compounds to certain homologous series and determine their molecular weights by means of retention volumes obtained on polar and nonpolar liquids. Nevertheless, final confirmation of identity must be sought through chemical tests or instrumental methods of analysis.

To do this, samples must be collected in pure form, uncontaminated by column packing or fractions which precede them through the chromatograph. Samples for analytical columns are ordinarily small, so special methods are needed for their collection. If larger samples are required, specially constructed preparatory columns can be used for separation. Unfortunately, none of the chemical or instrumental methods currently in practice is sensitive enough to analyze the minute amounts of materials eluted from capillary columns. Consequently this section will be concerned with collection of fractions from packed columns having ordinary dimensions.

A number of methods can be used. The vapor eluted from the chromatograph can be condensed in a chilled U-tube, absorbed by cotton wool moistened with a solvent, or trapped in a solvent. Regardless of the method, it is essential that the sample be free of contaminants, particularly with optical methods of analysis. The two principal sources of contaminants are the carrier gas and the column packing. Volatile impurities in the carrier gas can usually be removed by passing the gas through a cold trap situated between the cylinder and the pressure regulator of the chromatograph. The trap can consist of a coiled metal tube immersed in coolant. It will operate more efficiently if filled with finely divided metal shot to increase the surface and act as a heat-transfer agent.

Contamination from the column usually results from bleeding caused by insufficient conditioning or from operation at a temperature too high for the particular packing. Interference from this source will be recognized immediately if the spectra of all the samples collected resemble one another and that of the stationary liquid or its decomposition products. The only remedies are to increase conditioning time, reduce operating temperature, or change the liquid phases. Insertion of a cold trap between the column and the collector will be of value only for compounds with very low boiling points. Reasonably pure fractions can be obtained from columns packed with Apiezon L or silicone grease at temperatures of 240° to 260°C and below.

Loss of samples through condensation in lines leading from the column to the collector is another potential source of difficulty in the analysis of high-boiling materials. The exit lines in some chromatographs are not heated, and in others heating is insufficient. If samples are to be collected, the exit lines should be wrapped with heating tape or insulated resistance wire and heated to column temperature or slightly above. Heating should be continuous from the column exit to the point of collection, since a cold spot anywhere along the route can cause trouble in the collection of high-boiling sample components.

Samples also may be lost through failure to condense them in the trap. For the collection of volatile components, the trap should be cooled in an ice bath, a dry ice bath, or a liquid nitrogen bath, depending on the boiling points of the compounds. Efficiency can be increased by filling the trap with an inert particulate solid, such as very pure quartz sand or finely divided glass beads, to increase the surface available for condensation. Of course, the compounds must be extracted from the packing, and this entails an extra step. Active solids such as silica gel or charcoal can be used in traps, but if possible this should be avoided, since some sample components may not be desorbed quantitatively when the trap is warmed.

High-boiling compounds also may be lost through incomplete condensation, since they may form fogs consisting of a cloud of charged particles when the carrier gas is cooled suddenly. The particles are extremely small and will not condense in ordinary cold traps. If the hot vapors are allowed to condense in a trap at room temperature, fogging is reduced considerably, particularly if a thermal gradient is established between the chromatograph and the trap, so that cooling is slow. However, fogging is eliminated entirely and sample recovery is practically quantitative if the carrier gas is passed through a tube containing a plug of cotton wool moistened with solvent. This sorbs the sample, so that an aerosol does not form. Other methods for sample collection involving auxiliary solvents include bubbling the carrier gas through a small quantity of solvent contained in a micro test tube or mixing the carrier gas with heated solvent vapors which are then condensed. The latter method results in considerable dilution of the sample but may be a useful means of avoiding premature condensation in the lines.

Losses due to aerosol formation can be overcome without dilution of the sample with solvent by imposing a high voltage generated by an induction coil across the exit end of the cold trap. This acts on the same principle as a Cottrell precipitator and results in condensation of the fog in the tube, thus reducing loss of sample [28]. Recovery of essential oils was increased from about 10 to over 90 per cent by this device, the trap not being cooled in either case. None of the compounds tested formed a fog that could not be precipitated.

Regardless of how samples are collected, they must be recovered from the trap in some form suitable for optical or chemical analysis. If a solvent is used, it is often expedient to choose one that is also a suitable medium for the type of analysis contemplated. For example, hexane and methanol are good choices when the solutes will be analyzed by ultraviolet spectrophotometry, and carbon disulfide and carbon tetrachloride are best for infrared work, since they transmit electromagnetic radiation in these regions. If optical properties are not a paramount consideration, and the solutes must be recovered by evaporation, a solvent with a low boiling point should be chosen.

Sometimes it is possible to recover liquid samples without a solvent and so eliminate one step in the analysis. To make this possible, the trap should be designed so that the sample accumulates in a declivity or capillary tip from which it can be withdrawn by a hypodermic needle equipped with a syringe. A U-tube or a straight glass tube can be modified for this purpose. When samples are collected in straight glass tubes or U-tubes without narrow declivities, it is usually necessary to wash them out with solvents because of the small volume of the condensed liquid.

Most of the procedures discussed above are intended for the collection of single fractions. However, multiple-fraction collectors have been described in the literature and are available commercially from many manufacturers of chromatographs and auxiliary equipment.

Quantitative Analysis

Gas chromatographs are suitable for quantitative analysis as well as for the separation of chemical compounds. When operating conditions are adjusted satisfactorily and peak parameters are measured carefully, accuracy should be within a few per cent. Results obtained on instruments equipped with integral detectors are easy to interpret, since the height of each step in the chromatogram is directly proportional to the amount of solute present (see Fig. 5-3). Furthermore, the response of the detector is frequently related to some accurately known or easily predictable property of the molecule, such as acid value or molecular weight. Consequently, extensive calibration is unnecessary.

However, most chromatographs are equipped with differential detectors, and with these the fundamental analytical parameter is the area of the peak rather than its height. This must be measured indirectly. Furthermore, the responses of many detectors vary with the nature of the compound being measured in a way that is often unpredictable. Special attention must therefore be given to calibration and computation of areas under curves. Discussion of these topics will occupy the major part of this section.

PARAMETERS INFLUENCING PEAK DIMENSIONS

PEAK HEIGHT.   Measurement of peak height is useful in quantitative analysis only when all operating parameters can be reproduced exactly from experiment to experiment. Careful adjustment of flow rate is particularly important, since peaks broaden and become lower with increasing residence time in the column, owing to longitudinal diffusion of the solute in the mobile phase. Consequently, peak heights will vary with the retention volumes of the compound even when the detector response is approximately the same. Furthermore, peak height is not directly proportional to reciprocal flow rate so that it is inconvenient to correct values mathematically if this parameter differs from experiment to experiment. Both relative and absolute peak heights increase with temperature even when the flow rate is kept constant; thus, it is necessary to construct a calibration curve under the same conditions used for analysis. Other variables that must be controlled include filament current when katharometers are used and secondary factors such as the column length and porosity of the packing, since these factors influence flow rate when the pressure differential is constant. Consequently, peak height is not a very satisfactory measurement for many purposes.

However, peak height is easy to measure and is useful for routine analysis when operating conditions can be reproduced exactly. It has been employed mostly for the analysis of compounds with short retention times such as permanent gases, since peaks are very narrow and high, and large responses are obtained for comparatively minor changes in sample composition. Obviously peak height measurements are most sensitive at low retention volumes where ratios of width to height are very small, and they become progressively less useful with increasing residence times of the solutes in the column.

PEAK AREA. Peak area increases with decreasing flow rate; however, the relation between area and the reciprocal of the rate is linear so arithmetic corrections for variations in this parameter are made easily. Furthermore, peak areas produced by different chemical compounds do not change relative to one another when the rate is changed. Temperature variations have very little effect on absolute areas and no observable effect on relative areas. If the detector is a katharometer, increasing the filament temperature will increase absolute but not relative areas. Consequently, absolute area is more independent of operating conditions than height but not so much so as relative area. The vast majority of chromatograms are quantitated by area measurements.

CALIBRATION METHODS

Calibration is required to ascertain the response of the detector-recorder system to the presence of a known amount of solute passing through the sensing cell. Detector sensitivities will vary by many orders of magnitude, depending on the principle on which they operate and on cell geometry. The need for calibrating each instrument is therefore obvious. This would be comparatively simple were it not for one unfortunate fact; the detectors in most common use do not respond to the presence of different chemical compounds in a uniform way either on a molar or on a weight basis. There are, however, differences between detectors that must be considered before deciding whether calibration is necessary.

The responses of thermal conductivity cells vary considerably with the nature of the solute, particularly when the carrier gas is nitrogen. With hydrogen or helium, differences are smaller because of the greater conductivity spread between mobile phase and solutes.

More uniform response is obtained with other detector types. The flame ionization method yields moderately consistent results for hydrocarbons when computations are made on a weight basis, the response per mole increasing roughly with carbon number. However, much lower responses per unit weight are obtained from alcohols and chlorinated hydrocarbons so that once more rather extensive calibration is required to obtain quantitative data. The performance of the argon ionization detector is somewhat more predictable for compounds with high molecular weight, but it must be calibrated to obtain accurate results with a number of compounds having molecular weights under 150. Thus, the response per mole and the response per unit mass obtained on alkanoic acids increases markedly with increasing carbon number (Table 5-2). Conversely, the response of this detector to other compounds has been found to decrease strongly with rising molecular weight up to a value of 100. Thus, the argon detector gives consistent results when the molecular weight is above 150 to 200 but should be calibrated otherwise.

TABLE 5-2

PEAK AREAS OF FATTY ACIDS PER MOLE AND PER UNIT MASS[*]

Compound		Relative peak area per mole	Relative peak area per unit mass
Butyric acid	(C_4)	0.09	0.16
Valeric acid	(C_5)	0.35	0.54
Caproic acid	(C_6)	0.53	0.72
Enanthic acid	(C_7)	0.74	0.90
Caprylic acid	(C_8)	0.86	0.94
Pelargonic acid	(C_9)	1.00	1.00
Capric acid	(C_{10})	1.09	1.00

[*] Relative to those of pelargonic acid.

Aside from variability of detector response, the other major problem in constructing a calibration curve is the introduction of an accurately measured sample into the chromatograph. This can be done now with fair reproducibility in the 0.5 to 10-μl range with some of the newer syringes that have been developed. Direct calibration on medium- and large-sized samples is therefore possible. However, alternative methods are available that do not require an accurate knowledge of the size of the sample introduced into the chromatograph. These are the internal standard method and the internal normalization method. In the internal standard method a known amount of standard, for which the detector response has been determined, is added to the sample. The mixture is chromatographed, and the concentration of the unknown is computed from its peak area relative to that of the standard. In the internal normalization method the areas of all the peaks on the chromatogram are measured, and the *total* area is divided into the area of the peak generated by the component of interest.

Applications in Biology

The applications of gas chromatography to the solution of biological problems are many and varied [5]. For example, gas-solid chromatography can be used for measuring respiratory and photosynthetic gases, while gas-liquid chromatography can be used to measure the volatile compounds responsible for food aromas, terpenes and essential oils, lipids, and even nonvolatile compounds, such as amino acids and oligosaccharides, after first converting them to volatile derivatives. Gas chromatography is sometimes used to analyze these materials directly. However, a more satisfactory approach is first to separate the sample into groups of related compounds by ancillary procedures such as distillation, liquid-liquid partition, liquid-liquid chromatography, ion-exchange chromatography, or thin-layer chromatography. The gas chromatographic step is then used for the final analysis. This provides for better resolution than when the method is used directly.

When writing up gas chromatographic procedures, the operating parameters should be stated clearly and concisely so that others can reproduce the conditions. A standard form for the presentation of chromatographic methods, has been developed by the authors. An example is given as follows:

CHROMATOGRAPHY OF VOLATILE COMPOUNDS

Chromatograph	Perkin-Elmer Model 154-A with gas sampling valve
Column dimensions	200×0.635-cm od copper tubing
Solid support	Johns Manville C-22 firebrick (40/60 U.S. mesh), water-washed
Stationary phase	Carbowax 1500, a polyethylene glycol supplied by Union Carbide Chemicals (20:80)
Temperature	45°C

Carrier gas	Helium at approximately 100 ml/min. Inlet pressure: 1280 mm Hg. Outlet pressure: atmospheric
Detector	Thermistor at 5.6 v
Recorder	0 to 10 mv; 1 second
Sample size	About 3 to 5 μl
Analysis time	About 30 minutes to diacetyl

Parameters such as operating temperature, nature of the carrier gas, column temperature, and detector type should be included. Of special importance is the nature of the stationary phase and the dimensions and material of construction of the column. Even when these parameters are stated explicitly, results may sometimes be difficult to reproduce owing to variability in the solid support, catalytic decomposition at the column walls, etc. The preparation of a good gas chromatographic column is still an art rather than a science.

PERMANENT GASES

Permanent gases of interest to the biologist include oxygen, carbon dioxide, and nitrogen, since these are important in respiration, photosynthesis, and nitrogen fixation by soil bacteria. Atmospheric argon is of secondary interest since it can interfere in the analysis of oxygen. Nitrogen and oxygen are easily resolved from one another on molecular sieve. However, carbon dioxide is not eluted from this stationary phase except at high temperatures. Therefore, for a complete analysis of the atmosphere, two columns are used, either in series or parallel. Molecular sieve is used to separate oxygen from nitrogen, while silica gel is used to resolve carbon dioxide from other constituents of the atmosphere. At room temperature, argon is eluted with oxygen. The error in the oxygen analysis due to the presence of argon can be corrected for mathematically or the two gases can be resolved from one another by chromatographing at very low temperatures. Alternately, argon can be used as the carrier gas to swamp the response from atmospheric argon. In this procedure, sensitivity to other atmospheric gases is reduced.

Organic compounds present in the atmosphere due to air pollution or exudation from vegetation may also be of interest to the biologist. These are usually not chromatographed directly. Instead, an air sample is passed through the cold trap which contains an active, or in some cases, an inert solid. Trace organic components are condensed or sorbed on the solid. They are then desorbed with heat and flushed into the chromatograph. The same stationary phases are used for separating them that are employed in the analysis of low-molecular-weight hydrocarbons and oxygenated compounds. These include liquids such as di-*n*-butyl phthalate, alumina modified with propylene carbonate, squalane, and ethylene glycol containing 30 per cent silver nitrate. This latter substance is particularly useful for separating alkanes from alkenes and resolving isomeric olefins.

VOLATILE COMPOUNDS

Volatile compounds are defined arbitrarily as materials containing one, or rarely, two functional groups, and not more than 8 to 10 carbon atoms. They are found in the steam or vacuum distillate from fruits and vegetables, or in the condensate obtained on freeze-drying these products. They are usually mixtures of lower fatty acids, amines, carbonyl compounds, thiols, and sulfides, alcohols, and esters. Often they are chromatographed as complex mixtures, but better results are obtained by prefractionating them. Thus, fatty acids may be isolated as a group by distilling-off neutral and basic compounds from alkaline media, and recovering the free acids after acidification through distillation or extraction. Carbonyl compounds can be isolated as a group by precipitation with 2,4-dinitrophenylhydrazine, while thiols and sulfides can be separated by the formation of compounds with salts of heavy metals. After isolation, the various groups are chromatographed separately.

Complex mixtures of volatiles have been chromatographed on a wide variety of liquid substrates at temperatures ranging from 0° to 175°C. A typical set of operating parameters is presented above. No single set of conditions is satisfactory for all materials. Usually it is best to chromatograph complex mixtures on both polar and nonpolar liquids to obtain the maximum number of peaks. Very often, additional information can be obtained by collecting unresolved fractions and rechromatographing them on a stationary liquid having different characteristics.

TERPENES AND ESSENTIAL OILS

Gas chromatography is an excellent tool for the separation characterization and quantitative analysis of essential oils. Separations of components that formerly took days by tedious chemical and physical means, or were impossible by these older methods, can be accomplished in minutes.

Terpene hydrocarbons and related oxygenated terpenoids are the main constituents of essential oils. The oils may be chromatographed directly, or prefractionated into hydrocarbons and oxygenated hydrocarbons prior to chromatography. Generally, the latter is accomplished by liquid-solid chromatography on silica gel, but preparative scale gas chromatography can be used also, since the terpenes as a group are eluted well ahead of the oxygenated compounds. The oxygen-containing compounds are sometimes further subdivided into carboxyl, hydroxyl, and carbonyl compounds.

Chromatography of terpene hydrocarbons can be carried out using stationary liquids such as poly (polyethylene glycol adipate), Carbowax 4000, squalane, or didecyl phthalate at temperatures ranging from 100° to 150°C. Sesquiterpenes can be chromatographed on polyesters and nonpolar phases such as Apiezon M at temperatures in the range of 160° to 190°C. Oxygenated terpenoid mixtures can be separated on phases such as sucrose diacetate hexaisobutyrate, and polyesters at temperatures ranging from 120° to 170°C. Usually, special precautions must be used in the chromatography of terpenes and related compounds since these are labile materials and the production of artifacts is common.

LIPIDS

Gas chromatography has proved to be more successful for the analysis of lipids than for any other group of compounds. Here again, prefractionation is desirable before injection of the sample into the chromatograph. This is usually accomplished by liquid-solid chromatography on silica gel, or thin-layer chromatography. These techniques separate the sample into fractions consisting of sterol esters, triglycerides, sterols, fatty acids, and phospholipids.

Some lipids are chromatographed directly while others are converted to volatile derivatives. The following compounds are structurally modified before injection: phospholipids, sterol esters, higher fatty acids, O-alkyl glycerols, and higher aldehydes. Sterols and higher fatty alcohols may be chromatographed either unchanged or as derivatives. Hydrocarbons are chromatographed unchanged. Recently, considerable success has been attained in the chromatography of triglycerides without prior chemical modification.

Lipids are usually chromatographed on both polar and nonpolar stationary liquids to attain optimum resolution. Chromatography of the methyl esters of the higher fatty acids on nonpolar liquids such as Apiezon M results in separation according to boiling point. Thus, the C-14, C-16, and C-18 fatty acids are resolved readily by this technique. By contrast, chromatography on polar phases such as the polyesters leads to improved separation according to unsaturation. Thus, the saturated acids are eluted ahead of the monoenes, the monoenes ahead of the dienes, and the dienes ahead of the trienes. By plotting retention volumes obtained on the two phases against one another, a graph is obtained which is very useful for identification purposes. Thus, the number of carbon atoms as well as the degree of unsaturation of any given fatty acid can be obtained by finding its position on the grid shown in Fig. 5-10.

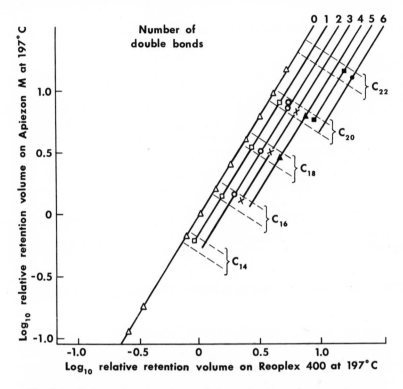

Fig. 5-10. Relation between $\log_{10}$ relative retention volume on Apiezon M and $\log_{10}$ relative retention volume on Reoplex 400 for methyl esters of saturated and unsaturated fatty acids (Courtesy, Academic Press).

NONVOLATILE COMPOUNDS

Compounds which are ordinarily considered to be nonvolatile can be separated by gas chromatography by first converting them to volatile derivatives. Thus, amino acids can be separated as their N-acetyl-n-amyl esters or as their N-trifluoroactyl methyl esters. Oligobasic acids can be chromatographed as their methyl esters and mono- and oligosaccharides can be separated after converting all of their OH groups to OCH_3 groups. Excellent methods of separation have been developed for many of these materials, but some problems still remain to be solved in quantitating the results. It is highly probable that gas chromatography will continue to grow in usefulness in this field with continued advances in technology.

References

1. A. J. P. Martin and R. L. M. Synge, *Biochem. J.*, **35**, 1358 (1941).
2. A. T. James and A. J. P. Martin, *Biochem. J.*, **50**, 679 (1952).
3. E. Cremer and F. Prior, *Z. Elektrochem.*, **55**, 66 (1951); *Chem. Abstr.*, **45**, 9334h (1951).
4. E. Cremer and R. Müller., *Z. Elektrochem.*, **55**, 217 (1951); *Chem. Abstr.*, **45**, 9335a (1951).
5. H. P. Burchfield and E. E. Storrs, *Biochemical Applications of Gas Chromatography*, Academic Press, New York (1962).
6. S. Dal Nogare and R. S. Juvet, *Gas-Liquid Chromatography*, Interscience, New York (1962).
7. A. B. Littlewood, *Gas Chromatography, Principles, Techniques, and Applications*, Academic Press, Inc., New York (1962).
8. A. I. M. Keulemans, *Gas Chromatography*, Reinhold, New York (1959).
9. J. J. van Deemter, F. J. Zuiderweg, and A. Klinkenberg, *Chem. Eng. Sci.*, **5**, 271 (1956).
10. R. Kieselbach, *Anal. Chem.*, **33**, 23 (1961).
11. C. G. Scott and D. A. Rowell, *Nature*, **187**, 143 (1960).
12. C. Phillips, *Gas Chromatography*, Academic Press, New York (1956).
13. M. J. E. Golay, In *Gas Chromatography*, D. H. Desty, ed., Academic Press, New York (1958), p. 36.
14. D. Ambrose, A. T. James, A. I. M. Keulemans, E. Kovats, R. Rock, C. Rouit, and F. H. Stross, *Pure Appl. Chem.*, **1**, 177 (1960).
15. H. M. Tenny and R. J. Harris, *Anal. Chem.*, **29**, 317 (1957).
16. R. L. Bowman and A. Karmen, *Nature*, **182**, 1233 (1958).
17. E. C. Horning, E. A. Moscatelli, and C. C. Sweeley, *Chem. Ind. (London)*, **28**, 751 (1959).
18. J. Bohemen, S. H. Langer, R. H. Perrett, and J. H. Purnell, *J. Chem. Soc.*, **112**, 2444 (1960).
19. E. C. Ormerod and R. P. W. Scott, *J. Chromatog.*, **2**, 65 (1959).
20. E. Bayer, In *Gas Chromatography*, D. H. Desty, ed., Academic Press, New York (1958), p. 333.
21. O. Harva, P. Kivalo, and A. Keltakallio, *Suomen Kemistilehti*, **B32**, 52 (1959).
22. W. W. Hanneman, C. F. Spencer, and J. F. Johnson, *Anal. Chem.*, **32**, 1386 (1960).
23. R. D. Ring, In *Gas Chromatography*, V. J. Coates, H. J. Noebels, and I. S. Fagerson, eds., Academic Press, New York (1958), p. 195.
24. F. T. Eggertsen, H. S. Knight, and S. Groennings, *Anal. Chem.*, **28**, 303 (1956).
25. J. E. Lovelock, *J. Chromatog.*, **1**, 35 (1958).
26. A. Zlatkis, J. F. Oró, and A. P. Kimball, *Anal. Chem.*, **32**, 162 (1960).
27. W. A. Wiseman, *Nature*, **185**, 841 (1960).
28. P. Kratz, M. Jacobs, and B. M. Mitzner, *Analyst*, **84**, 671 (1959).

Freeze-drying, or Drying by Sublimation

N. W. Pirie

THE DISAPPEARANCE of snow, and the drying of frozen clothing in air at temperatures well below the freezing point of water, are so generally familiar that the beginnings of freeze-drying cannot be given a date. The phenomenon became a matter for laboratory study in 1811 when Leslie [1, 2] found that water would freeze and then "waste away" in an evacuated vessel connected with one containing sulfuric acid, parched oatmeal, or porphyritic trap rock. Wollaston [3] got the same effect in an inverted, evacuated U-tube with a bulb at each end; a little water in one bulb froze and then sublimed over into the other when the latter was put in a freezing mixture. It is clear from reading these three papers that their authors understood exactly what they were doing and the matter was put on a firm basis by Regnault's [4] measurements of the vapor pressure of ice at various temperatures and Gibbs' enunciation, in 1876, of the phase rule and his definition of the triple point where the water:ice:water-vapor system is in equilibrium in the absence of another component. The potentialities of this technique of drying were not then exploited, but they must have been fairly generally known for the prolific French novelist About [5] wrote a romantic story about a man who was freeze-dried over calcium chloride in a vacuum and then resuscitated. As one character remarks "il ne manque de rien que d'humidité." It is difficult to believe that About had not seen freeze-dried tissue and noted that it retained its original form, but Altmann [6] is generally credited with having introduced the technique into histology. It was used to preserve viable microbial cultures by Shackell [7] and Hamner [8]. There has, in recent years, been a great increase in interest in these applications of the technique and they are described in detail in several symposia [9-12] and reviews [13, 14].

The preservation of texture gives the technique its main attraction for the food industry and for histologists and bacteriologists. The method has an obvious advantage with thermolabile substances such as penicillin and most proteins, but even thermostable substances, when dried unfrozen, may have a horny or scaly texture so impervious to water that the outer skin prevents drying from going to completion in any reasonable time. The open, feathery, texture of most freeze-dried products quickens the final stages of drying when the limiting factor is the escape of water vapor and not the access of heat. Furthermore, the shrinking sheet of a protein or polysaccharide, when it is drying unfrozen, often pulls chips of glass from the surface of the container. Freeze-drying is therefore often a valuable technique, not only for preserving bulk preparations of a substance, but also for making a specimen from which aliquots can be taken for analysis. When substances with large molecular weights are being handled it is generally easier to do the analyses on material that is in equilibrium with moist air, and then correct all of them by a moisture determination, rather than to try to weigh out separate lots of dry material.

The problems involved in drying by sublimation can be considered under four headings. The solutions adopted for each problem depend on the quantity of material to be dried and the number of containers among which it is convenient to distribute it, on the conflicting demands of convenience and economy, and on the temperature to which it is considered safe to expose the dry material. The four headings are: the type of container used, the means used to introduce into the container the energy needed to supply the latent heat of fusion-plus-evaporation, the means used to sequestrate the water vapor, and the means used to drive water vapor from the material to the sequestrator. There is little need for comment on the last for, almost universally, the difference in water vapor pressure between the two ends of the system is relied on to cause the movement. Meryman [15] described a small unit in which a fan circulates air at a temperature below 0°C through a desiccant and over the material to be dried so that, at the same time, it introduces the necessary energy and carries away the water vapor. This principle may well be useful when many small samples have to be dried; it may also have applications on a large scale, because the drying-up of materials kept in cold storage for a long time is already one of the problems of the food industry. But the method does not seem to have been used extensively.

The Container for the Material Being Dried

VACUUM DESICCATOR

A vacuum desiccator is the simplest and most satisfactory vessel for freeze-drying quantities up to 50 ml. Success depends on attention to several points of detail. The material to be dried must be disposed in a suitable vessel, such as a Petri dish, so that no part of it is more than 1 cm thick; it must be supported in a manner that minimizes heat conduction; the desiccant must have a surface adequate to cope with the rate at which water vapor reaches it during the first phase of drying and, if it is liquid, there should be some means of stirring it or a light diluted layer will lie on top of the dense fresh desiccant and prevent access of water to it. Figure 6-1 shows an arrangement which has proved satisfactory since 1930 [16]. The dish of material to be dried is supported on a glass tripod; it should be well above the level of

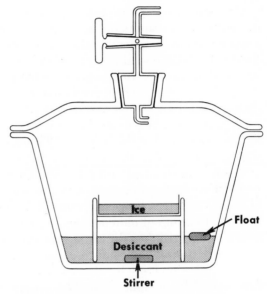

Fig. 6-1. Diagram showing the arrangement of materials in a vacuum desiccator.

the desiccant but below the level at which it could be struck by the lid of the desiccator should that move suddenly during opening. The stopcock should, naturally, be carefully greased so that it can be turned off, as soon as a satisfactory vacuum has been established, without fear of leakage. The inner end of the inlet tube should point horizontally, for, if it points either upward or downward, excessive care is needed when the stopcock is opened—the jet of air, coming into an evacuated vessel, may dislodge the wisp of material remaining when a dilute solution has been dried. When sulfuric acid is used as desiccant a piece of iron encased in a glass tube, which can be moved by a magnet, should lie at the bottom to act as a stirrer, and it is convenient to have a float in the acid to show when it is spent and needs changing.

If the material to be freeze-dried has already been concentrated by vacuum distillation, or has been deaerated in some other way, it can be frozen *in situ* by evaporative cooling. If it contains the normal amount of air, it is likely to froth when pressure falls in the desiccator and this may cause loss. The fluid should then be prefrozen in a refrigerator. With small samples there is a risk of thawing during transfer from refrigerator to desiccator but this is easily overcome by freezing the dish, or dishes, in a container made of cork or paraffin wax (according to one's whim in attaching more importance to low conductivity or high specific heat) and putting both dishes and container in the desiccator. In this way it is easy to handle samples as small as 0.5 ml.

Mechanical pumps are now so common that few will try to freeze-dry with a water pump, but a good water pump is perfectly satisfactory if attention has been paid to the other aspects of the system and if the fluid to be dried contains very little material of low molecular weight. At one time various tricks were used to improve the final vacuum; 1 to 2 ml of ether or strong ammonium hydroxide can be put in a separate dish so that their vapors will displace residual air. With this arrangement some skill is needed to know the right amount to use and the best moment to shut the stopcock. These, obviously, can be used only with sulfuric acid as the desiccant.

When a mechanical pump is used there is no need for the refinement of air ballast because, with the wide, short, pathway available to water vapor in a desiccator, nothing is gained by taking the pressure below 1 to 2 mm of mercury; even the simplest pump will do that in 1 to 2 minutes and in this time very little water will condense in the pump. It is only when the freezing point of the fluid to be dried is significantly lowered by the presence of soluble substances with low molecular weights that these simple arrangements will prove unsatisfactory.

MANIFOLD

When many small samples have to be dried, for example, serum distributed in 1 ml quantities in ampoules, they can be mounted on a manifold after prefreezing, or the whole set, complete with manifold, can be frozen in a cold chamber before being attached to the water-absorbing system and pump. The risk of frothing makes it inadvisable to attach an unfrozen ampoule to the manifold and let it freeze by evaporation. Greaves [17] suppressed frothing by centrifuging the rack full of ampoules in the vacuum chamber during evaporative freezing. Figure 6-2 shows a suitable rack for the purpose; it can be lightly constructed because 7g is sufficient.

When ampoules are being dried, the manifold is simply a suitable length of 1 to 2-cm diameter pipe with side tubes every 2 to 3 cm along it. Something more elaborate is needed with larger quantities and there are many variations in design. A common all-glass manifold is illustrated in section in Fig. 6-3. Four or more ports are arranged round the lower part of an invaginated vessel, and there is an outlet near the top for the pump attachment; sizes, naturally, vary but they are generally in the range 6 to 15 cm outside diameter and 15 to 35 cm length. A few points need attention. The gap between the outer vessel and the invagination must leave ample room for the passage of vapor after the layer of ice has formed. The ports should have funnel-shaped seals because a knob of ice often grows opposite each port and may obstruct it if the tube is sealed neatly onto the outer vessel; there should be no port at the very bottom because the ice layer is not always coherent and flakes may fall back into a vessel in that position and have to be evaporated off again. For this reason it is a mistake to have the ports sloping downward as in the fraction collector of a distillation unit.

Fig. 6-2. Rack in which samples are centrifuged during evaporative freezing. The centrifugation suppresses frothing (Courtesy, Edwards High Vacuum, Ltd.).

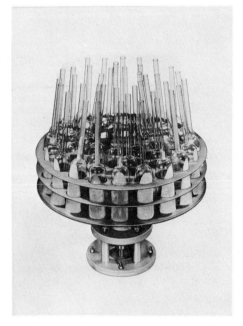

If the system is vacuum tight, as it should be if the vessels attached to the ports have properly greased ground-glass joints, a stopcock can be fitted to the pump outlet so that the unit can be left to finish drying without having the pump running. But it must be run for several hours before this is done because air dissolved in the material being dried is released only slowly during drying and it will spoil the vacuum. Furthermore, the water vapor carries residual air with it out of the containers toward the vessel where ice collects. Its return by diffusion is slow so that a difference in gas composition builds up in the two sections of the apparatus; there is a preponderance of water vapor where evaporation should be proceeding and of air where water vapor should be condensing. This soon brings drying to a stop.

A manifold drier differs from a vacuum desiccator in that there is much more opportunity for complete gas mixing in the latter, so that it is prudent to keep the vacuum pump running continuously on the former.

Figure 6-4 shows the parts of a commercially available unit. A refrigerant is put in the central flask and the cover, carrying in this model six ports, an ampoule manifold, and the pump outlet, is sealed onto the heavy glass container, shown on the left, by means of a rubber O ring in a groove on the underside of the cover.

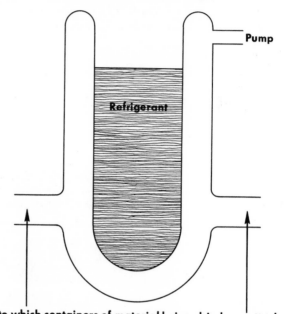

Pump

Refrigerant

Ports to which containers of material being dried are attached.
Fig. 6-3. An all-glass manifold suitable for drying several samples at once.

The vessels that are to be attached to the ports and hold the material being dried must obviously be able to withstand external atmospheric pressure. For this reason, thin-walled spherical flasks are often used but they are ill-adapted to the job because it is difficult to freeze a uniform layer of fluid over a spherical surface. Cylindrical bottles are ideal. Enough of the solution is put in each to give a 1-cm layer over the inside surface and the layer is frozen onto the surface either by rotating the vessel slowly in a cold bath or by centrifuging it about its axis in a cold room [17].

TRAY

Unless there is some other advantage, such as sterility, to be gained by the use of several bottles to hold the material being dried, a manifold is seldom used with volumes of solution greater than 1 liter. Instead the solution is put into trays and these are stacked in a container. One of many commercial models is shown in Fig. 6-5; the decision whether to buy a complete unit, or build it, depends on the importance attached in different institutes to convenience or economy. Morrison and Pirie [18] prefer the latter and use industrial 7.5 and 15 cm glass tubes as containers. Their arrangement, shown in Fig. 6-6, has the added convenience of being easily rearranged to suit different types of drying tray or material to be dried. The increase in the scale of working, made possible by the use of trays, accentuates the problems of heat input, pumping, and the final sequestration of the evaporated water, but these will be discussed in the appropriate sections.

Methods of Supplying Heat
to the Material Being Dried

When a stream of cold dry air is used to carry water vapor away from the material being dried [15] the air also brings in the energy to supply the necessary latent heat. It is more difficult to supply this in

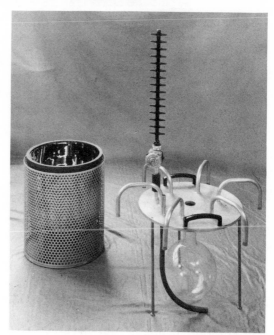

Fig. 6-4. A commercial manifold for drying several samples at once (Courtesy, Edwards High Vacuum, Ltd.).

an evacuated system and, if it is not supplied, an equilibrium is soon established; the temperature of the material being dried falls until the vapor pressure of the ice in it is equal to the vapor pressure of water at the point where it is sequestered. In practice, some heat gets in and raises the temperature of the material so that drying can proceed. When small quantities are being dried in glass vessels, uncontrolled conduction and radiation are generally adequate; too much heat may come in, in this way, so that it may be wise to insulate a set of ampoules on a manifold during the first few hours of drying. In dull weather, or at night, evaporation in a desiccator can be hastened by keeping a light shining on it. Because the white surface of most freeze-dried products is a poor absorber of light, the idea of putting a black metal gauze on top of the material has its advocates, but I am not convinced that the advantages outweigh the extra trouble.

The containers round a manifold of the types shown in Figs. 6-3

Fig. 6-5. A commercial model with trays for use with volumes greater than 1 liter (Courtesy, Edwards High Vacuum, Ltd.).

and 6-4 soon get covered with hoar frost. Any method, such as blowing a stream of warm air past them or keeping them immersed in a warm bath, that will keep the outside of the container warm is therefore advantageous. Choice is restricted by the thermal sensitivity of the dried material, for the part in contact with the container wall will come to the external temperature as soon as it is dry. In a normally lit and warmed laboratory a 5-mm layer of material will dry in 24 hours. Because of the poor thermal conductivity of the dry felt surrounding still undried material, the necessary time increases sharply with increasing thickness so that layers thicker than 1 cm should not be used; it saves time to dry in successive batches.

Trays in a glass container pick up heat satisfactorily by radiation but it is advisable to warm the outside of the container by means of a coil of electrically heated wire [18]. In an opaque container of the type shown in Fig. 6-5 the trays rest on shelves that can be heated by electricity, or hot air, or water. Several of the articles in recent reviews and symposia on freeze-drying give an overidealized picture of the conduction of heat into a tray, with the frozen mass remaining in firm thermal contact with the metal, heat flowing through the mass, and evaporation taking place from the upper surface. If the process is

Fig. 6-6. Unit used at Rothamsted Experimental Station. It can take different types of trays, and material can be put directly into the tubes.

interrupted before drying is complete, it is obvious that there is evaporation down the edges of the mass and, after that, along the layer between the mass and the tray so that heat has soon to penetrate dry felt and vapor escapes as a horizontal sheet between the tray and the charge. This insulates the charge from the source of heat; the consequent inefficiency has stimulated much ingenuity in devising other means for getting the heat in. The essential conditions for freeze-drying impose a set of incompatible requirements so that all that can be hoped for is a least objectionable system rather than an ideal one.

The rate of evaporation can be approximately doubled if heat is supplied by conduction from both sides. This is managed in commercial practice by pressing a heated perforated plate against the exposed surface, but the arrangement is not suited to laboratory scale work. Radiant heaters mounted between the trays will warm the upper surface of the tray below them, and the attractive possibility exists that a wavelength of maximum emission could be found to which the overlying dry felt would be transparent, so that energy could penetrate directly to the drying surface. This would minimize the risk of overheating the surface layer in the course of getting enough heat through to the ice. Levinson and Oppenheimer [19], studying the application of heat from outside glass vessels, claimed that the surface temperature of the emitter should be between 400° and 700°C; this has not been confirmed, and it seems a dangerously high temperature to use if the heaters are being put inside a freeze-drying container.

The dielectric properties of the material being dried can be used to dissipate energy in it. In principle, a slab of frozen material absorbs energy when it lies between, but not in contact with, plates connected to a source of alternating current. It is acting as the dielectric in a condenser and the "loss factor" is a measure of the inefficiency with which the polarization of structures within the slab can reverse in phase with the electric field. The loss factor for water is a few thousand times that for ice; the loss factor for frozen materials such as tissues or foods is intermediate [20], but it is so small that to get useful rates of energy dissipation it is necessary to increase the frequency of alternation enormously. Although, formally, the material being dried resembles the dielectric in a condenser, it is generally more convenient to have a separate generator that feeds short radio waves into the drying chamber along a wave guide rather than to have it inside the chamber. Meryman [21] uses 2500 Mc per second and Hopkins [22] 10,000 Mc. This is the most favored range because at lower frequencies there is more dissipation of energy by ionization [23, 24] which is both wasteful and potentially damaging to the material being dried.

Centimeter waves penetrate the dry felt and produce heat throughout the material within—especially in water either free or bound in hydrated particles. From these particles the heat travels by conduction to the crystals of ice. So long as the ice crystals are small, as they will be with material frozen quickly, this is not, in principle, a disadvantage; it does however introduce an element of metastability into the system for, if there should be local overheating, because water vapor cannot escape freely from part of the material, that part would thaw and preferentially absorb energy. Careful control is therefore needed or the center may melt because heat is not being conducted fast enough to the evaporating surfaces. This is a hazard that does not arise when heat gets into the mass by conduction or radiation; the outer, dry layer may then get overheated, but the heat finally reaches the ice at its surface where evaporation is freest. In practice, microwave sources are so expensive that units are seldom large enough to give a dangerous rate of heating; they are more often used to complete the drying of material that has been partially dried in some other way.

Electrical energy can also be introduced into a frozen mass by electrical conduction. The direct use of the mass of frozen material as the resistance in an ac circuit is not practical because the region of contact between the electrodes and the mass would probably heat up and dry first, thus breaking the circuit. Eddy currents induced in the slightly conducting mass by high frequency ac in a coil surrounding it (as in the forms of cooking from within outward that are sometimes used) are a possibility, but expense and the very low conductivity of the ice limit their use.

The difficulties discussed in the last few paragraphs arise primarily from the poor thermal conductivity and transparency of material that has already been dried. An obvious solution is to remove this, and Greaves [25] describes an arrangement in which the material to be dried is frozen in the form of a hollow cylinder, the inside of which is scraped by a slowly moving blade. The cylinder is mounted vertically with an axial radiant heater so that the dry material falls continuously into a collecting tray below. When granular material is being dried in a horizontal cylindrical container, the mass can be rearranged by a stirring paddle mounted axially so that fresh material is brought from time to time to the surfaces where it picks up heat by conduction or radiation [18]. There is scope for development here. One disadvantage of any arrangement that disturbs the material, before drying is complete, is that light particles move very readily in the high-velocity winds in an exhausted container. If the depth of an extensive surface of ice is diminishing by evaporation at 1 mm per hour into a vessel at 0.1 mm pressure, the vapor comes from the surface at nearly 1000 miles per hour.

We have discussed methods for increasing the rate of transmission of energy into the charge. These two factors limit the desirable rate: it must not overtax the capacity of the sequestering system, and the rate of water vapor production at the ice surface must be small enough to allow the vapor to get through the dry felt. The pressure with which we are concerned, in applying the phase rule to freeze-drying problems, is not the pressure in the apparatus as a whole, it is not even the pressure immediately above the drying mass (which will be higher because of the pressure difference needed to drive the vapor to the sequestering system), but it is the pressure at the ice surface. This is controlled by the rate of evaporation there and the thickness and texture of the already dried material. The position was analyzed theoretically by Stephenson [26]; by studying the behavior of pieces of tissue during freeze-drying he showed that observation agreed with theory.

When it is necessary to preserve the texture of the material being dried, either because it is to be studied histologically, or to improve the physical appearance of a food when it is later reconstituted, there is general agreement that it is important to freeze the material quickly so as to make the crystals of ice in the material as small as possible. Microcrystallinity is also essential if an adequate system of escape channels is to be maintained, for the larger the ice crystals the larger the pieces of material between them. Optimal conditions for drying are given when all the channels are of comparable size, rather than when some are large because large ice crystals have evaporated from them, whereas the pieces of material that are actually being freeze-dried are relatively impervious because of the small channels in them.

When dilute solutions of water-soluble macromolecules are being dried, the texture that results when freezing is completed in 1 to 2 hours is satisfactory, but more care is needed to ensure quick freezing when the concentration of dissolved material exceeds 50 g/liter or with lipoproteins and similar substances that may form relatively impervious layers. This factor probably explains the failure [27] of the technique with some substances. With pastes, granules, and the moist cakes from a filter press, it is particularly difficult to get a dry product with a uniform, soft texture; to achieve such a texture the freezing must be completed in 1 to 2 minutes [18].

Sequestration of Water Vapor

The simplest way to get rid of the vapor produced when ice evaporates is to let it flow through the pump and this is done in many of the steam-ejector pumps used in large-scale drying of foods. No one recommends the technique on a laboratory scale and it will not be further considered. When the water vapor is kept inside the system it can be condensed on a cold surface or absorbed by a desiccant.

COLD SURFACES

The vapor pressure of ice at different temperatures is set out in Table 6-1.

TABLE 6-1

VAPOR PRESSURE OF ICE AT DIFFERENT TEMPERATURES

Temperature (°C)	0	−10	−20	−30	−40	−50	−60
Vapor pressure (mm Hg)	4.6	1.9	0.8	0.3	0.1	0.03	0.01

Obviously, the lower the temperature of the condensing surface, the lower can be the temperature of the evaporating surface for the same pressure difference between them, and the smaller will be the risk of contaminating the pump by untrapped water vapor. For most purposes a condenser at −20° or −30°C would be adequate, but in small-scale work in units similar to those illustrated in Figs. 6-3 and 6-4, solid CO_2 is used because it is available commercially. Its temperature is −78°C and its latent heat of vaporization 137 cal/g. To improve the transfer of heat between the condenser surface and the CO_2, a liquid such as acetone is put in the refrigerant vessel; it should not be more than two thirds full because, during the phase of drying when water vapor is being condensed rapidly, CO_2 gas boils out briskly. A minimum of 5 g of CO_2 will be needed for each gram of water to be condensed but, because of the inevitable leakage of heat into the system, 8 g should be available.

With a tray drier, especially if it is to be used regularly, it is more economical to use a mechanical refrigerator to cool the condenser. Suitable units are supplied by all the firms that specialize in freeze-drying equipment. The simplest arrangement is to have the coils, into which the working fluid of the refrigerator expands, inside a vessel with a wide (>4 cm) connection to the container holding the trays; there is then direct condensation onto the cold coils, and there is no need for external thermal insulation because the vessel holding the coils is evacuated. There are two disadvantages in this arrangement. The coils and vapor in them have a small heat capacity so that the maximum rate at which vapor can be condensed, even for brief periods, is limited to the rate at which the mechanical refrigerator can dispose of heat; the layer of ice that grows on the coils is a poor conductor and it is not feasible to remove it from them while the unit is running.

The small heat capacity of the system, or reserve of cold in it, is of little consequence if the material is frozen before being exposed to vacuum, because the initial rate of evaporation is not then greater than the rate that will be attained when heating is started—and the refrigerator must be able to cope with this. An efficient 3/4 hp refrigerator will be able to handle the vapor produced by the absorption of 100 w by the material being dried, i.e., with a peak evaporation rate of 2 g a minute. But evaporative freezing produces vapor very much faster than this. Even under conditions of perfect thermal insulation, 120 g of water have to evaporate to freeze 1000 g initially present and already at 0°C (at 0°C the latent heats of fusion and evaporation are 79.6 and 594, respectively), so that freezing would take the best part of an hour if water vapor is only allowed to reach the refrigerator at a rate that will not overload it. The commonly used phrase "snap-freezing" is misleading. The reticulum of ice crystals that forms quickly gives a solid appearance to material that is only one quarter frozen; after that, complete freezing may take a considerable time. A refrigerator with the necessary capacity to deal with the inflow of heat during rapid evaporative freezing would be uneconomical in the later stages of drying. Some form of "cold storage" unit is therefore used. A unit in which the refrigerator cools a brine tank and the brine is pumped through the condenser is effective for this purpose. Alternatively, the main load during freezing can be carried by a separate condenser immersed in a cold tank. The condenser used by Morrison and Pirie [18] for this purpose is illustrated in Fig. 6-7. Vapor comes in through the 7.5-cm opening and condenses on the wall of an 11-cm diameter steel tube, which has 2000 copper rods butt-welded to its outside to ensure good thermal contact with 35 per cent methanol that is kept permanently in a tank in one corner of a deep freeze. Air and any uncondensed water vapor pass out through the central 2-cm tube to a commercial condenser and thence to the pump. With this unit, 5 to 6 kg of water can be frozen in a minute and after an hour or two, when the flow of vapor is small, a direct connection is opened between the drying manifold and the conventional condenser so that this special condenser can be removed; drying is then completed in the normal way.

As the layer of ice thickens on a condenser its efficiency falls; this is less serious than is sometimes thought because by that time the rate of evaporation is falling too, so that the condenser has less work to do. Nevertheless, arrangements have been described in which the condenser is cylindrical and cooled by circulating brine; the ice that forms on it is scraped off by a slowly moving knife and falls into a sump below. This elaboration seems to have little application on a laboratory scale.

There is some disagreement about the temperature at which the condenser should be maintained to get maximum evaporation from a surface maintained at a given temperature. Obviously the temperature, and therefore the water vapor pressure, at the condenser must be lower than that at the evaporator or there would be no movement of vapor. Theory and observation [28, 29] led to the conclusion that nothing was gained by maintaining a condenser temperature such that the pressure there was less than 55 per cent of that at the evaporator, but Harper and Tappel [30] dispute both the theory and the observations and find that the rate of evaporation can be increased by lowering the vapor pressure at the condenser more than this. It must, however, be remembered that mechanical refrigerators become increasingly less efficient as their operating temperatures fall.

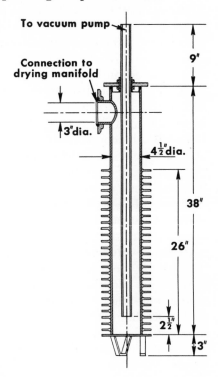

Fig. 6-7. A separate condenser, immersed in a cold tank, for ensuring very rapid freezing.

CHEMICAL DESICCANTS

For small-scale, or infrequent, freeze-drying, water vapor is most conveniently sequestrated by a chemical desiccant. Two types must be distinguished clearly: those that give a definite new phase on hydration so that the vapor pressure over the partly hydrated desiccant remains relatively constant until hydration is nearly complete, and those in which the vapor pressure increases steadily as water is absorbed. In the first category are phosphorus pentoxide and magnesium perchlorate with negligible vapor pressures, calcium sulfate which exerts 0.004 mm during the formation of the hemihydrate, and calcium chloride which exerts 0.2 to 0.3 mm. Anhydrous alumina, silica, potassium hydroxide, and sulfuric acid have negligible vapor pressures. With the first two the pressure rises to about 0.2 mm when 1 per cent of water has been absorbed and to about 1.7 mm for 7 per cent. As soon as its surface is moist, the pressure over potassium hydroxide stays at about 0.8 mm until all the solid has dissolved. The vapor pressure over sulfuric acid rises to 0.3 mm when it has absorbed one quarter of its weight of water, and to 1 mm with one third. Sulfuric acid is cheap but has the defect that if organic matter gets into it, either as vapor or in droplets dispersed by bubbling, SO_2 will be formed and may harm the material being dried.

The suitability of a desiccant depends not only on the amount of water it can absorb, and the pressure at which it absorbs it, but also on the rate of the absorption. Granular desiccants that do not become sticky when hydrated have an obvious advantage in this respect; those that become sticky, such as phosphorus pentoxide and calcium chloride, must be distributed in trays giving an area about ten times that of the ice that is being evaporated or the rate of absorption may be too low to maintain freezing in a normally heated and lit laboratory. Only sulfuric acid is mobile enough to be stirred with arrangements similar to that shown in Fig. 6-1.

The state of hydration of calcium chloride is easily judged by its moist appearance, and that of sulfuric acid by the sinking of a suitable float in it. The state of the other desiccants is not so easily assessed and, if the same charge is being used on successive runs, it is wise to keep a record of the amount of water that has been absorbed.

Heat is evolved by all these desiccants when they absorb water. This raises their vapor pressure during the period when drying is most rapid and there is most need for efficient water absorption; furthermore, there is the risk that a glass vessel holding the desiccant will crack should the heating be uneven. Because chemical desiccants are generally used only on a small scale, the dissipation of this heat does not raise serious difficulties, but if more than 200 g of ice is being evaporated in a vessel which contains both the ice and the desiccant, for example the unit described by Payne *et al.* [31], it is wise to watch the internal temperature.

It is not practical to regenerate sulfuric acid or phosphorus pentoxide in the laboratory. The advisability of regenerating the other desiccants is simply a matter of economics; it is probably not worthwhile with calcium chloride, oxide, and sulfate, whereas it is wasteful not to regenerate alumina, magnesium perchlorate, and silica, for regeneration only requires a well-ventilated oven maintained at 260°C for the first two hours and at 120°C for the last hour. Regenerable liquid desiccants, such as ethylene glycol and lithium bromide solution, have been used on an industrial scale because they open up the possibility of continuity in the working of a freeze-drier, but they seem to offer no advantages in the laboratory.

Pumps

Rotary mechanical pumps are used almost exclusively in laboratory freeze-drying; they are smaller and faster than reciprocating pumps; oil or mercury vapor pumps give an unnecessarily high vacuum; steam ejectors are inconvenient for small-scale use; and filter pumps, as already mentioned, have to be handled with considerable skill if they are to be effective. The relative merits of the pumps produced by different makers are as much a matter of personal opinion as the merits of motor cars, but they can be discussed quantitatively in terms of pumping rate and ultimate vacuum and they can be divided qualitatively into those with air ballast and those without.

Provided care has been taken to make sure that the joints and openings in the system do not leak, a 1/4 hp pump will be adequate for a unit with a volume less than 5 liters. For larger units it is necessary to use a larger pump; 1 hp is adequate up to 50 to 100 liters. It is the time taken to get the system down to about 3 mm that is important because, at pressures below this, the water vapor flowing toward the condenser carries residual air with it toward the pump; at this pressure, therefore, there is a sudden increase in the rate of fall of pressure. The desirable final vacuum depends on the arrangements used to sequestrate the water; obviously, if the pump attains a lower pressure than that of the water vapor at the surface of the condenser or desiccant, vapor will be transferred from them to the pump. The sequestration of water vapor is never complete so that vapor moves slowly into the pump if it is kept running continuously, and this is essential both because of unavoidable small leaks and, as has been pointed out, because air will collect in the neighborhood of the condenser. It is therefore wise to use a pump with air ballast, that is to say, one in which air is admitted during the latter part of each revolution of the pump so that it can carry away the water vapor that would otherwise condense in the pump. On most makes of pump the air-ballast inlet can be shut. Because the pumping rate is smaller when ballast is used, the ballast inlet should be kept shut until a satisfactory working vacuum has been reached (0.1 to 0.5 mm) and then only opened to the extent needed to keep the pump oil free from water. If there is any turbidity in the oil in the sight glass of the pump more air should be admitted until the oil is clear.

Pressure Gauges

For most purposes a McLeod gauge is satisfactory. To make a reading on this, a column of mercury is moved so as to imprison a sample of vapor and then to compress it to 1/100 or 1/1000 of its original volume; the pressure the vapor then exerts is given by the difference in height between the mercury that is compressing the sample and a parallel column still exposed to vacuum. There are many variations in detail but the principle is the same in all, and the imprisoned gas is finally measured at room temperature and under a pressure of several millimeters of mercury. Water vapor will remain in that form and exert a pressure more or less in accordance with Boyle's law for as long as the pressure is less than the vapor pressure of water at the temperature of the instrument. At higher pressures it condenses, and the pressure recorded is that due to air or other noncondensable gases. When a McLeod gauge is used to measure the pressure in a freeze-drier, water will generally enter, so the reading is valid only when the pressure exerted on the imprisoned sample of vapor is small. The condensation of water can be avoided by interposing a desiccant between the gauge and the drier. At low pressures a minute or two must be allowed between readings so that the chamber into which the vapor is compressed can re-equilibrate with the system as a whole.

Continuous readings can be made with a Pirani gauge. In this, two similar wires are heated electrically to the same extent, one sealed *in vacuo* and the other exposed to the system being studied; the difference in temperature between the two wires is measured, and it is a function of the pressure. In theory the instrument should be calibrated for each gas mixture on which it may be used because of the different thermal conductivities of gases, but the largest error that water vapor is likely to introduce on an air-calibrated instrument is 8 per cent, which is not significant in this particular application. The dust and organic vapors which gradually contaminate the exposed filament introduce larger errors and necessitate frequent recalibration.

In an ionization gauge the conductivity of the vapor between two fixed electrodes is measured; ionization is maintained either by a hot filament or by a radioactive source. The conductivity is a function of the gas pressure, but this type of gauge has little application in freeze-drying because it has to be calibrated for each type of gas mixture and its effective working range is lower than that used in normal freeze-drying.

Residual Water and the Completeness of Drying

When substances with a definite composition and small molecular weight are being dried it is, as a rule, easy to determine the end point. A series of hydrates may be formed but each has a characteristic vapor pressure and will lose water to an environment with a lower water vapor pressure. At pressures lower than the last of these steps the final weight of the substance will be independent of the precise pressure. Very prolonged drying sometimes introduces secondary changes [32] but this phenomenon is recognized by changes in the general properties of the substance being dried; the change in its water content is immeasurably small. When substances with a large molecular weight are being dried the position is quite different, presumably because water is held by them in many different ways; some of it is held avidly. This effect is accentuated with the unfractionated, or only partially fractionated, mixtures that are generally freeze-dried. The water content of material like this is a matter of arbitrary definition. Material that has reached constant weight at one temperature and pressure will lose weight at a higher temperature or lower pressure. The smell in an oven in which biological material is being dried makes it perfectly obvious that more than water is being lost and that the convention that "dry matter" is what is left after a sojourn at 100° or 105°C is arbitrary. At temperatures in this neighborhood, even with purified proteins, dehydration merges into decomposition. Chemical methods for determining water introduce a completely new set of conditions; they are convenient and repeatable but there is no reason to assume that what is being measured is free water in the accepted sense. Both these methods destroy the material on which the determination is made. Beckett [33] and Heckly [34] describe units in which the water released from a substance at any desired temperature is measured manometrically without destroying the specimen.

Besides these difficulties in definition, freeze-dried material presents the practical difficulty that its open, fluffy, texture presents an immense surface for the reabsorption of water and, if it has been dried over phosphorus pentoxide, the first traces of water are absorbed with an avidity comparable to that of phosphorus pentoxide. It is therefore usual to distinguish between primary and secondary drying and to use special precautions in handling the material after the latter.

Primary drying is complete when the material has reached room temperature, or whatever higher temperature is deemed safe, in the presence of a properly functioning sequestering system. The latter condition is easy to ensure but, for the reasons stated in the section on supplying heat to the material being dried, it is not so easy to determine the temperature. The temperature of the tray has little relevance. Several thermocouples embedded in the material being dried give a good indication unless the material is inhomogeneous. Then only experience can be used as a guide. If material is being dried in a transparent container with a metal stirrer in it [18], a thermometer in good thermal contact with the stirrer is useful. After a rearrangement of the charge, the stirrer is left in such a position that the thermometer is covered by the charge; 10 minutes later it is brought to the surface and the thermometer read. This gives an indication of the average value throughout the material and so is as good a basis for judging the completeness of drying as several thermocouple readings.

It has been well known since the beginning of the century that proteins and other large molecules lose weight, presumably because of the loss of water, for days or weeks in an oven or vacuum desiccator. This phenomenon is of little importance in the primary phase of freeze-drying, partly because the open-textured felt comes to equilibrium quickly, but mainly because the water that has been so slowly lost is regained in a few minutes unless special precautions are taken to protect the dried material from air of normal humidity. The material may therefore be removed from the drier within a few hours of its having attained room temperature. If preservation demands more thorough drying, it is then put into vessels that can be sealed while still attached to a manifold containing a desiccant such as phosphorus pentoxide. With some substances there are advantages in very prolonged drying; thus Greaves [35] found that the stability of dried blood-grouping sera toward heating at 100°C increased with the duration of secondary drying up to 108 hours. Differences in the water-binding power of different proteins have been described in several papers [36, 37].

Conclusion

Freeze-drying is now a very important technique, not only for preserving living organisms, foods, and biologically active extracts, but also for preparing materials for examination by optical and electron microscopy. Examples of these uses are amply given in recent symposia [9-12]. It is not, however, a panacea as the use of the unnecessary word "lyophilization" has led many to assume. Traditional farming practice makes use of the changes that freezing brings about in the structure of soil, and Hunter [38] studied the harmful effect of freezing, or subsequent thawing, on organisms. Freezing destroys some viruses [39,40] and lipoproteins [41]. This destruction may not lead to an immediately obvious general breakdown; thus, under certain conditions of freezing, tomato bushy stunt virus loses its infectivity without suffering gross physical change [40]. Much ingenuity has been, and will be, devoted to finding the best rate of freezing, and the best environment, for the preservation of sensitive materials. It is therefore reasonable to assume that the group that can be preserved by this technique will be greatly extended. The main hazard to which properly dried material is exposed is oxidation, for the material has an enormous surface. It is therefore usual to seal freeze-dried sera or bacterial cultures *in vacuo* and to keep foods in nitrogen after drying.

The efficient handling of a freeze-drier is a good refresher course in elementary physics. I have tried in this article to explain what happens at each stage and why some at-first-sight attractive procedures are not used. It is no longer necessary to understand these things; satisfactory results can be obtained with commercial equipment by following the book of instructions religiously. But people who know what they are doing can get results which are just as good much more cheaply.

New information on the use of electrical resistance measurements which indicate the state of the material that is being dried and the time when drying is complete is given in the record of a recent conference on freeze-drying of food [42].

References

1. J. Leslie, *Ann. Chim. Phys.*, **78**, 177 (1811).
2. J. Leslie, *Phil. Mag.*, **51**, 411 (1818).
3. W. H. Wollaston, *Phil. Trans. Roy. Soc. London*, **103**, 71 (1813).
4. H. V. Regnault, *Relation des expériences entreprises pour déterminer les principales lois et les donnees numériques qui entrent dans le calcul des machines a vapeur*, Typographie de Formin Didot Frères. Paris (1847).
5. E. F. V. About, *L'homme a l'oreille cassée* (1862).
6. R. Altmann, *Die Elementarorganismen und ihre Beziehungen zu den Zollen*, Viet, Leipzig (1890).
7. L. F. Shackell, *Am. J. Physiol*, **24**, 325 (1909).
8. W. B. Hamner, *J. Med. Res.*, **24**, 527 (1911).
9. Institute of Biology, *Freezing and Drying*, London (1952).
10. R. J. C. Harris, *Biological Applications of Freezing and Drying*, Academic Press, New York (1954).
11. "Freezing and Drying of Biological Materials," *Ann. N. Y. Acad. Sci.*, **85**, 501 (1960).
12. *Freeze-Drying of Foodstuffs*, D. B. Smith, and S. Cotson, eds., Columbine Press, Manchester (1962).
13. H. Moor, In *Modern Methods of Plant Analysis*, H. F. Linskens and M. V. Tracey, eds., Springer-Verlag, Berlin (1962), **5**, p. 73.
14. N. W. Pirie, In *Modern Methods of Plant Analysis*, Vol. 1, K. Paech, and M. V. Tracey, eds., Springer-Verlag, Berlin (1956), p. 26.
15. H. T. Meryman, *Science*, **130**, 628 (1959).
16. N. W. Pirie, *Biochem. J.*, **25**, 614 (1931).
17. R. I. N. Greaves, *Nature*, **153**, 485 (1944).
18. J. E. Morrison and N. W. Pirie, In *Freeze-Drying of Foodstuffs*, D. B. Smith and S. Cotson, eds., Columbine Press, Manchester (1962).
19. S. O. Levinson and F. Oppenheimer, *The Drying of Ice by Sublimation*, Samuel Deutsch Serum Center, Chicago (1944).
20. R. V. Decareau, In *Freeze-Drying of Foodstuffs*, D. B. Smith and S. Cotson, eds., Columbine Press, Manchester (1962).
21. H. T. Meryman, *Ann. N. Y. Acad. Sci.*, **85**, 630 (1960).
22. A. L. Hopkins, *Ann. N. Y. Acad. Sci.*, **85**, 714 (1960).
23. T. W. G. Rowe, *Ann. N. Y. Acad. Sci.*, **85**, 641 (1960).

24. B. C. Walker, In *Freeze-Drying of Foodstuffs,* D. B. Smith and S. Cotson, eds., Columbine Press, Manchester (1962).
25. R. I. N. Greaves, *Ann. N. Y. Acad. Sci.,* **85**, 682 (1960).
26. J. L. Stephenson, *Bull. Math. Biophys.,* **15**, 411 (1956).
27. J. S. Paterson, N. W. Pirie, and A. W. Stableforth, *Brit. J. Exptl. Pathol.,* **28**, 223 (1947).
28. E. W. Flosdorf, L. W. Hull, and S. Mudd, *J. Immunol.,* **50**, 21 (1945).
29. A. J. Ede, *J. Soc. Chem. Ind.,* **68**, 330, 336 (1949).
30. J. C. Harper and A. L. Tappel, *Advan. Food Res.,* **7**, 172 (1957).
31. P. R. Payne, D. S. Miller, and B. S. Platt, *Proc. Nutr. Soc.,* **20**, xii (1961).
32. J. W. Smith, *Phil. Mag.,* **8**, 380 (1929).
33. L. G. Beckett, In *Biological Applications of Freezing and Drying,* R. J. C. Harris, ed., Academic Press, New York (1954), p. 285.
34. R. J. Heckly, *Science,* **122**, 760 (1955).
35. R. I. N. Greaves, *Brit. Sci. News,* **2**, 173 (1949).
36. H. B. Bull, *J. Am. Chem. Soc.,* **66**, 1499 (1944).
37. H. B. Dunford and J. L. Morrison, *Can. J. Chem.,* **32**, 558 (1954).
38. J. Hunter, *Phil. Trans. Roy. Soc. London,* **65**, 446 (1775).
39. C. Breedis, *J. Exptl. Med.,* **76**, 221 (1942).
40. F. C. Bawden and N. W. Pirie, *Biochem. J.,* **37**, 70 (1943).
41. J. E. Lovelock, *Proc. Roy. Soc. London,* **B**, **147**, 427 (1957).
42. U. S. National Academy of Science and National Research Council, *Freeze-Drying of Foods,* F. R. Fisher, ed., Washington, D.C. (1962).

C H A P T E R   7

Ultracentrifugation

Rodes Trautman

SEPARATION of substances by centrifugation is a very old and well established process. Sedimentation is widely used when spinning down a chemical precipitate or washing red blood cells by pelleting, decanting the supernatant fluid, resuspending and repeating the cycle. Flotation, also, is generally familiar as employed in the cream separator which exploits differences in density between milk and cream rather than size.

Quantitative studies of centrifugation began in the 1920's when Svedberg successfully combined disciplines of mechanics, optics, and mathematics. The work was done mainly at Uppsala, Sweden, having been started at the University of Wisconsin while Svedberg was on sabbatical leave with J. W. Williams. Ten years of instrumentation led to positive proof that proteins were large molecules and could be weighed in the ultracentrifuge—an instrument by means of which sedimentation in a centrifugal field is measured quantitatively. The oil turbine centrifuge with the rotor operated in a hydrogen atmosphere on a rigid horizontal axis was developed (Fig. 7-1 A). At present there are, perhaps, only six such instruments in the world. Henroit and Hugenard, in France, developed the air drive and were the first to spin a mirror at high speed. Beams, at the University of Virginia, was stimulated by their work and together with Pickels, his graduate student, developed machines using either the air turbine or an electric drive, but with a vertical axis and rotors spinning in a vacuum. Pickels entered the virus field with Bauer at the Laboratories of the International Health Division, Rockefeller Foundation, advancing techniques to make possible their goal of a simple instrument for biological research. These early developments are exhaustively covered in the classic treatise by Svedberg and Pedersen [1a].

Pickels' keen business sense and scientific acumen led to formation of Specialized Instruments Company (now, Beckman Instruments, Inc., Spinco Division, Palo Alto, Calif.) and to commercial availability in 1950 of a practical instrument. At present, there are over 3000 Spinco ultracentrifuges throughout the world (Figs. 7-1 B and 7-2 A). Concurrently, Beams continued to develop spinning devices for exotic studies in physics. His magnetically suspended rotor is capable of

Fig. 7-1. Analytical centrifuges. *(A)* Oil turbine ultracentrifuge with rigid horizontal axis operated in H_2 atmosphere. Upper part of protective casing shown in open position above 4 large vertical bolts in center of photograph (for explanation of detail see Figs. 53 and 68 of Svedberg and Pedersen [1a]. Historic and current use is mainly for sedimentation equilibrium (Courtesy, K.O. Pedersen). *(B)* Most widely used analytical ultracentrifuge for observation and registration with almost every method of centrifugation. This Model E has an electric drive, vertical, flexible axis with rotor operated in a vacuum for reduced air friction. At left, analytical rotor in place before vacuum chamber

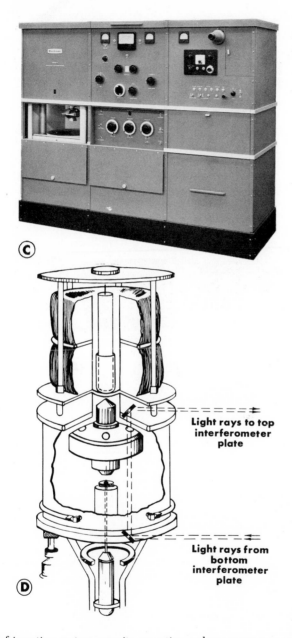

Light rays to top
interferometer
plate

Light rays from
bottom
interferometer
plate

is closed. Refrigeration system permits operation at low temperature and is used to balance cycling heater unit operated by remote temperature indicator and control units (Courtesy, Beckman Instruments, Inc., Spinco Division). (C) Early version of magnetically suspended rotor for long, frictionless operation. Solenoid is above rotor. The accelerating unit below is shown disengaged. (Courtesy, *Review of Scientific Instruments*). (D) Modern instruments [5] have a vacuum chamber and precise optical systems (Courtesy, J.W. Beams and F.N. Weber, University of Virginia).

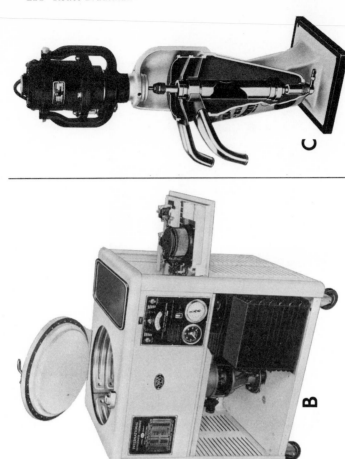

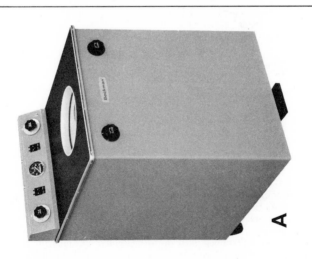

Fig. 7-2. Preparative centrifuges. (*A*) Refrigerated Model L vacuum preparative ultracentrifuge used for concentration, purification, and determination of physical properties of biologically active agents (Courtesy, Beckman Instruments, Inc., Spinco Division). (*B*) Low speed refrigerated centrifuge for routine concentration and clarification of research samples. Speed controller on right is shown hinged open (Courtesy, International Equipment Company). (*C*) Supercentrifuge for continuous recovery of solids from liquids, clarification of liquids, and separation of two immiscible liquids. Liquid is introduced into the rotor through the feed nozzle shown at the bottom. Liquid of greater specific gravity forms the outer layer and the lighter liquid forms the inner layer, both being discharged through separate ports located in the top of the rotor as shown. Solids present in the liquid are deposited against the wall of the rotor and removed periodically (Courtesy, The Sharples Corporation). (*D*) Swinging bucket rotor with

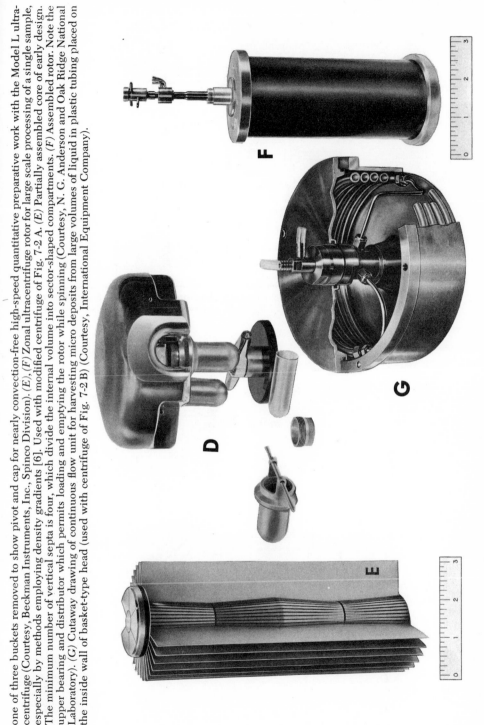

one of three buckets removed to show pivot and cap for nearly convection-free high-speed quantitative preparative work with the Model L ultracentrifuge (Courtesy, Beckman Instruments, Inc., Spinco Division). (E), (F) Zonal ultracentrifuge rotor for large scale processing of a single sample, especially by methods employing density gradients [6]. Used with modified centrifuge of Fig. 7-2 A. (E) Partially assembled core of early design. The minimum number of vertical septa is four, which divide the internal volume into sector-shaped compartments. (F) Assembled rotor. Note the upper bearing and distributor which permits loading and emptying the rotor while spinning (Courtesy, N. G. Anderson and Oak Ridge National Laboratory). (G) Cutaway drawing of continuous flow unit for harvesting micro deposits from large volumes of liquid in plastic tubing placed on the inside wall of basket-type head (used with centrifuge of Fig. 7-2 B) (Courtesy, International Equipment Company).

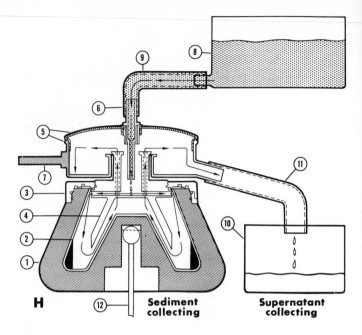

Sediment
collecting

Supernatant
collecting

H

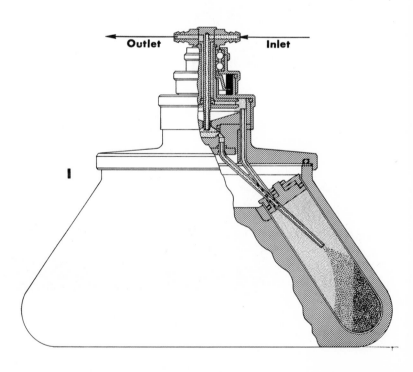

Outlet   Inlet

I

Fig. 7-2 con't. *(H)* Schematic of continuous flow system using an angle rotor. The basic operating procedure is: *(a)* insert polyethylene liner 2 into rotor 1 and tighten cover 3; *(b)* lower collector assembly 5 over discharge cap 4 (assembly supported by collector support rod 7); *(c)* introduce material from reservoir 8 to rotor via inlet plastic tubing 9 and stainless-steel inlet tube 6; *(d)* accelerate rotor (drive shaft 12 supplies power from motor) adjusting input flow rate and rotor speed to provide desired separation. Solids collect in polyethylene liner 2 while liquids are continuously ejected from the discharge cap 4 to the collector 5 from whence they flow to the collection chamber 10 via outlet plastic tubing 11 (Courtesy, Lourdes Instrument Corp.). *(I)* Schematic of continuous flow system for small amounts of precipitate to be collected in separate standard centrifuge tubes in an angle rotor. Angle rotors provide many tubes of moderate volume with a short centrifugation path which uses convection by gravity favorably (Courtesy, Ivan Sorvall, Inc.).

extremely long, stable, coasting operation in a vacuum chamber because of no mechanical contact after the acceleration to operating speed (Fig. 7-1 C). Prior to 1960 the only such instruments were in Beams' laboratory; now there are several individually built to replace the oil turbine machines and they will certainly be made commercially by 1965.

In the last decade the enormous advances in ultracentrifugation [1] have been the result of *(a)* the availability of a routine laboratory instrument (mainly Spinco); *(b)* theoretical stimulation; *(c)* the large number of scientists working in the field; and *(d)* the general realization that the phenomenon of centrifugation not only permits concentration and mild purification of biologically or chemically active agents but determination of fundamental molecular parameters as well. *Ultracentrifugation* now implies quantitative application of centrifugal force to solutions or suspensions of molecules or particles. This does not necessarily mean using high-speed, elaborate optical systems or only sedimentation.

Figures 7-1 to 7-3 show typical centrifugation equipment. The various rotors and cells of Figs. 7-2 and 7-3 indicate the diversity and complexity being exploited. The usable temperature range extends from 0°C for labile biologicals to 150°C for natural or synthetic polymers. The forces employed in routine applications can be as high as 300,000 times that of gravity and pressures developed may reach 400 atmospheres.

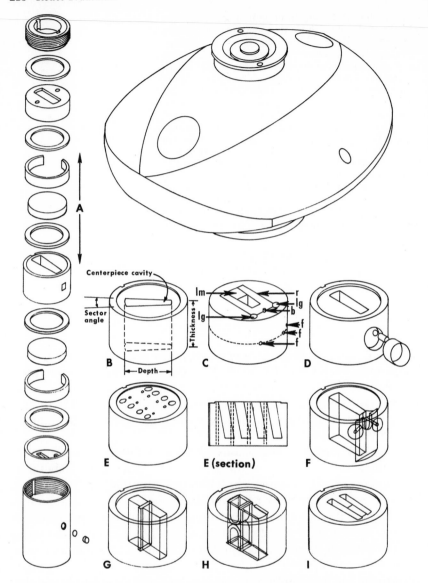

Fig. 7-3. Analytical cells. (*A*) Exploded view of typical analytical cell which fits on shoulder in either or both holes in analytical rotor shown at top and which permits light to pass through centerpiece while spinning. The small hole in the thin edge of the rotor provides a radial reference mark. From top to bottom cell parts are screw ring; screw ring gasket; upper window holder; gasket; window liner; quartz or sapphire window; gasket; centerpiece; gasket; quartz or sapphire window; window liner; gasket; lower window holder, cell housing with filling hole accommodating gasket; and screw plug. (*B*) Standard centerpiece. Thickness in the optical direction is from 1.5 mm for concentrated solutions to 30 mm for dilute solutions, and volumes can be as low as 0.1 ml. (*C*) Capillary type synthetic boundary cell with flow from underneath [7]. (Courtesy, *Makromolecular Chemic*). (*D*) Valve type synthetic boundary cell with solvent initially in cup, solution in sector cavity. (*E*) Multi channel, short column equilib-

rium cell, blind holes shown in section are filled before assembly. *(F)* Capillary type synthetic boundary cell with flow of solvent from chamber above sector cavity. Filled after assembly. *(G), (H)* Partition cells for fractionation after analytical run. *(G)* Fixed, perforated partition. *(H)* Moving solid partition supported by rubber loops. *(I)* Capillary type, double-sector, synthetic boundary cell. Larger volume of solvent is placed in one side, and part flows through central capillary on top of solution. Filled after assembly. Without the capillaries, this same centerpiece forms the standard centerpiece used when baselines are desired simultaneously with solution patterns. (Except for *(D)*, these special cells have been redrawn from technical literature. Courtesy, Beckman Instruments, Inc., Spinco Division.)

Physical Properties of Biological Particles*

Ultracentrifugation can be used without understanding detailed theory; in fact, theory is not available for many of the complex arrangements and materials used. It is necessary to realize only *(a)* that centrifugal force causes particles in solution to attain a terminal velocity increasing with their size, weight, or density and decreasing with the viscosity of the medium and deviations from spherical shape, and *(b)* that movement by centrifugal force, either as sedimentation or flotation, is opposed by diffusion, which increases with the abruptness of concentration changes and decreases both with the size and deviation from spherical shape of the particles and the viscosity of the medium. The sedimentation coefficient s is merely the observed terminal velocity divided by the field strength, and is generally called "s-rate." Practical units are in Svedbergs, 10^{-13} sec, and values are frequently converted to the standard conditions of water at 20°C, $s_{20,w}$. The diffusion coefficient D is merely the spread of particles by Brownian motion divided by the time. Practical units are in Ficks, 10^{-7} cm²/sec, with values also converted to standard conditions, $D_{20,w}$.

The range of size, shape, and density of molecules and particles of biological interest is truly enormous. Figure 7-4 can serve as a rough guide. First, consider in the upper left the density of some particles in aqueous solutions starting with lipids at about 0.9 and going to nucleic acid at 2.2 g/cm³. The range of density that can be obtained with D_2O, sucrose, or salts in H_2O is given below the solution density scale. As indicated along the diagonal dashed line, sedimentation occurs if the solution is less dense than the macromolecule, but above the isodensity value, flotation results. For cream or chylomicrons, flotation occurs in milk or serum as harvested. For lipoproteins, moderate salt concentrations are required, but for proteins, viruses, and nucleic acids, strong solutions of heavy metal salts, typically CsCl, are needed to cause flotation. Fortunately, the biological activity of most macromolecules is retained in CsCl and the tendency to work only with physiological solutions is obsolete.

---

* See Glossary of Symbols at end of Chapter.

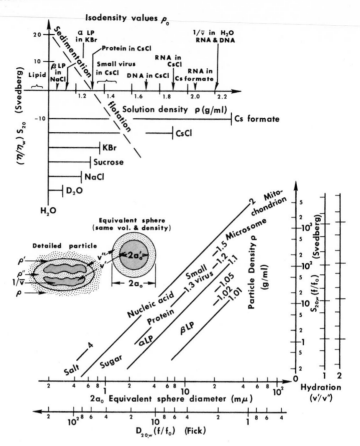

Fig. 7-4. Physical properties of biological materials. The sedimentation coefficient is a measure of terminal velocity per unit centrifugal field in a solution with approximately a constant density that is different from the particle density. The diffusion coefficient is a measure of rapidity of spread by Brownian motion. Coefficients important in design of ultra-centrifugal experiments have been expressed in the lower graph as $s_{20,w}$ (f/f_0), on the right, and $D_{20,w}$ (f/f_0), below, and represent conversion to water at 20°C and multiplication by the friction factor that accounts for deviation from spherical shape. There is an unambiguous relationship between $D_{20,w}$ (f/f_0) and the diameter of the equivalent sphere shown in the lower two scales. The particle density scale, ρ', interior and to the right, refers to the hydrodynamic particle including its solvation mantle. (If the dry particle diameter is desired, the dry density must be used and a slight correction for hydration made by entering on the appropriate vertical scale at the right). The diversity of properties of biological particles is shown by the display of the generic names on the graph (*LP* is lipoprotein).

Inspection of the schematic particles in the middle and the graph at the top reveals three particle densities of practical importance: (*a*) the reciprocal of the partial specific volume ($1/\bar{v}$) which is essentially the dry density; (*b*) the solvated particle density (ρ') which is the wet density; and (*c*) the isodensity (ρ_0) which is the wet density when buoyant in a particular solution. The range of ρ_0 values is shown in the graph. For solution densities above the isodensity value, flotation occurs as indicated along the (η/η_w) s vs. ρ line made linear by use of the viscosity factor. Solution densities (and wet particle densities) can be increased with D_2O, sucrose, or salts as indicated.

The ranges of diffusion coefficients and s-rates, corrected to water at 20°C, are indicated, respectively, along the horizontal axis and vertical axis at the right, with substances displayed in this plane on the basis of particle density. The s and D coordinates have been multiplied by f/f_o, the friction factor, to make the graph general. This factor ranges from unity for spheres to 4 for rodlike particles of 100 to 1 ratio of length to diameter. Note that the sequence of substances is different along any axis. The molecular weight of the biological materials can be determined from the ratio of s and D (for which the friction factor cancels out) provided attention is paid to the density. As indicated in the insert in the lower right, there are several particle densities of importance. Considerable confusion and misinterpretation of centrifugation experiments have resulted from failure to realize that: (a) for (dry) molecular weight, the reciprocal of the partial specific volume is required; (b) for velocity centrifugation or penetration through an immiscible interface, the density of the complete particle is involved; and (c) for combining flotation and sedimentation in the same tube, the density of the net solvated particle is applicable at the buoyant level.

Ultracentrifugation is one of the key techniques available to the biologist for causing different types of particles to move with respect to each other *in vitro*, with all the implications this systematic relative motion may have for separation or characterization. The instrumentation and techniques required to encompass the heterogeneity depicted in Fig. 7-4 will evidently be exacting and varied, and all standard methods cannot be expected to work for all particles.

Scope of Chapter

Basic arrangements of ultracentrifugation experiments or processes are given in the next section. A rapid survey of equipment, methods, theory, and applications can be made from the tables and figures, which purposely have detailed legends not requiring reference to the text.

The physical basis of ultracentrifugation is then considered from an abbreviated but fundamental viewpoint with descriptions, in regular type, preceeding mathematical summaries in small print. An attempt has been made to give the reasoning behind the most exact formulas available. With the advent of analog and digital computers it is no longer necessary to oversimplify exact differential equations, either for developing theory or for data processing. Also, many biologists who use the centrifuge only as their problems require can take advantage of programs which incorporate detailed computations not previously considered, and which they don't need at their fingertips.

As with other complex instruments, the intermediate products such as dial readings, photographic plates, or microcomparator measurements may soon be properly relegated as artifacts, with only significant quantities appearing on computer tabulations.

Finally, detailed experimental procedures are given from the viewpoint of a biologist who has discovered a specific biological activity and who desires to characterize and purify a specific component or causative agent. Since heterogeneity is implicitly involved in all centrifugal experiments it is considered in these sections rather than with the theory, which section may be omitted by most readers.

Methods of Ultracentrifugation

EQUIPMENT

The Spinco ultracentrifuges, Figs. 7-1 B and 7-2 A, are widely distributed and are those most likely to be used by biologists. Basically, both have a drive unit, which is an appropriately geared-up electric motor. It is usually rented and exchanged by the manufacturer after 1.8×10^9 revolutions for the Model L drive and 2.7×10^9 for the Model E drive. The shaft is flexible, which obviates concern for imbalance either initially, or accidentally in case of leakage during a run. The rotors of other manufacturers as well as Spinco, are of four basic types: angle preparative, swinging bucket, analytical, and special. These are explained in the legends. In order to reach the higher speeds frequently required, the rotors have only a small overspeed factor of safety. The maximum speed is reduced 10 per cent after 1000 runs or after 1000 hours at maximum speed, whichever comes first. Pitting or corrosion seriously weakens rotors and is cause for premature derating. Rotors should be coated with silicon grease and stored dry and upside down after rinsing with distilled water. Many centrifuges have refrigeration and heating equipment. In some, provision is made to indicate as well as to control rotor temperature during operation.

The analytical machine (Model E) differs from the preparative (Model L) only in having optical systems for viewing certain experiments during centrifugation. Cells (Fig. 7-3) having either optical quartz or sapphire windows on either side of a centerpiece are tightened precisely with a torque wrench. The simplest centerpiece shown in Fig. 7-3 has merely a single sector opening. The most complicated consists of multiple chambers, some of which are capillary connected. Materials range from gold-plated aluminum to plastic, the latter obtainable in blanks for individual design and machining.

For lower speed preparative work there are numerous commercial centrifuges. A common refrigerated one is shown in Fig. 7-2 B.

Various swinging tube "heads" accommodate tubes or bottles up to 250 ml. A useful chart of maximum head speed and the number of times gravity developed at the tip is given on the nameplate. A high-speed attachment can be added for smaller rotors producing up to 25,000g. Convenient desk-top centrifuges are used in clinical work, for packing chemical precipitates, or for clarifying research samples. Continuous flow heads are made by several companies, and some of the types are shown in Fig. 7-2.

Detailed operating procedure can be found in the manufacturers' manuals. With Spinco equipment, individual instruction can be obtained from the field engineer.

METHODS

There are many ways an experiment may be designed to utilize the systematic relative motion caused by the centrifugal field in the presence of diffusion. Some correspond to types used in electrophoresis, and others have unique features stemming from the presence of the impermeable top and bottom of the cell. The three basic physical concepts employed are *velocity*, which exploits size, or shape differences; *isodensity*, which exploits density differences; and *equilibrium*, which exploits mass differences. Use of combinations of these as well as obsolescence of some variations are expected to continue in this ever expanding branch of molecular biology. This makes detailed classification difficult, and there is no general acceptance of any particular scheme [1].

The basic methods will be described in conjunction with Fig. 7-5, which depicts tubes with an initial loading t_0, appearance after two selected periods of centrifugation t_1, t_2, and after a very long time t_∞. Either the transient t_0, t_1, t_2, or the equilibrium t_∞, or both may be of interest. Other shapes of "cells" or tubes can be used and no distinction need be made between gravitational or centrifugal fields, analytical or preparative, or low- or high-speed applications. If the contents are analyzed after the centrifuge stops, the experiment is called *preparative;* if the tube or cell is observed optically during centrifugation, it is called *analytical.* Both procedures can be quantitative, and under certain conditions even an analytical experiment can yield fractions for other purposes. There are four major types of assay: *analytical* (i.e., chemical or biological) on fractions, *schlieren, interferometric*, and *absorption* optical. Some of the numerous methods for fractionation before analytical assay are shown schematically in Fig. 7-6. Other than simple pouring-off of the supernatant fluid (Fig. 7-6 A), all require considerable skill and attention to the details indicated in the legend to minimize destruction of the resolution obtained by the end of the centrifugation period. Typical patterns from the three optical assays are shown in Fig. 7-7. For detailed

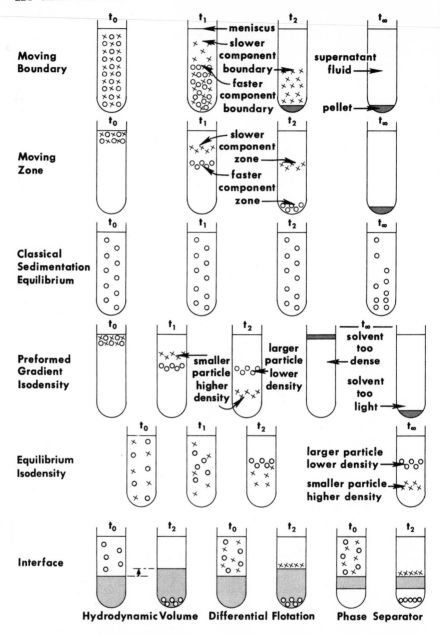

Fig. 7-5. Methods of centrifugation. Shown are basic arrangements to utilize systematic relative motion of particles with respect to solvent in the presence of diffusion, exploiting size, mass, or density differences. Either preparative or analytical centrifuges can be used and tubes or cells can have various shapes. In all figures circles represent particles faster (i.e., larger or more symmetrical) but less dense than particles of opposite characteristics marked as crosses. t_0, schematic representation of initial loading; t_1, t_2, two times during centrifugation; t_∞, equilibrium. Continuous flow arrangements utilize one or more of these basic types (see Fig. 7-2).

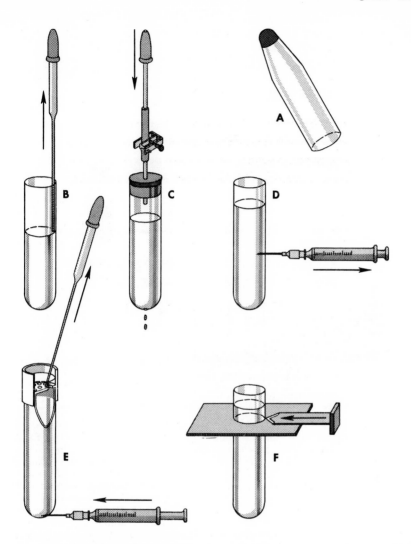

Fig. 7-6. Fractionation methods after preparative centrifugation. Fractionation should be done at temperature of run to avoid convection. Arrows show direction of fluid or air flow. All except *(F)* do not require special equipment [1]. *(A)* Decantation. *(B)* Removal with a Pasteur pipette whose tip must be kept in meniscus so that a mixture of air bubbles and solution is withdrawn. Foam is broken, after transfer to calibrated tube, in desk-top clinical centrifuge for accurate measurement of volume (for application see Fig. 7-16). *(C)* Drip-out method. Tube must be sealed at top before puncture with needle. Speed of drops is governed by the screw clamp, and final emptying or freeing clogged puncture is done by squeezing bulb after closing hole at top with finger (for application see Fig. 7-17). *(D)* Syringe withdrawal method after puncture. *(E)* Flow-out top method, accomplished by slow injection of dense sucrose in bottom. *(F)* Tube slicer method useful for separation into two fractions with large numbers of tubes (schematic, only)(Commercially available from Beckman Instruments, Inc., Spinco Division). Freezing and slicing are not generally useful because of convection during freezing.

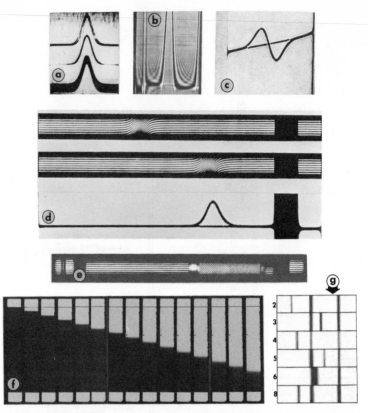

Fig. 7-7. Major optical registrations. (a to c) Widely used phaseplate schlieren optics are the most rugged, most versatile, and most sensitive to heterogeneity (see Fig. 7-18 for operator's adjustments). *(a)* Moving boundary method. Comparison of three schlieren diaphragms: wire, phaseplate, and bar, respectively, from top to bottom. *(b)* Phaseplate at high magnification in vertical dimension (15° angle)(Courtesy, [8] *Biochemica et Biophysica Acta). (c)* Isodensity equilibrium method for bovine serum albumin initially at 1 mg/ml in ρ 1.28 CsCl; double sector cell; 56,100 R.P.M. for 24 hours at 25°C (Courtesy, [9] authors and *The Journal of Physical Chemistry). (d) (e)* Rayleigh (and other types of) interference optics are the most precise for concentration measurements, but are complicated to use and are limited in application. *(d)* Moving boundary method for bushy stunt virus at 5 mg/ml, 14,290 R.P.M. From top to bottom the frames correspond to 96 and 128 min. The bottom comparison phaseplate schlieren pattern is at 130 min 80° angle. Double sector cell has to be used (Courtesy, [10] authors and *The Journal of Physical Chemistry). (e)* Classical sedimentation equilibrium method for sucrose at 54 mg/ml, 35,600 R.P.M. (sapphire windows) in short column (4.5 mm) (Courtesy, [11] authors and *The Journal of Physical Chemistry). (f) (g)* Absorption optics are most easily automated with a scanning photocell [12] and are most promising for specificity [13]. Densitometer tracings of absorption films, if used, are required for accurate measurements. *(f)* Moving boundary method at successive times during run showing single component: purified poliomyelitis virus at 0.2 mg/ml; 23,150 R.P.M.; 2 min between exposures (154S) (Courtesy [14] authors and *New York Academy of Sciences). (g)* Isodensity equilibrium method for bacteriophage in ρ 1.50 CsCl at 27,690 R.P.M. for 12 hours at 20°C. The dense phage in the right-hand band was added as a marker in the several runs shown. The middle common band is normal λ-bacteriophage, whereas the third band in each photograph is a transducing phage which has a variable density in the series of lysates (Courtesy, [15] *The Journal of Molecular Biology).*

optical alignment and theory the reader should consult the manuals and general references. Figure 7-7 will be referred to throughout the description of methods below and in later sections.

Separation of solutes from each other as well as from the solvent is an important feature of centrifugation processes; consequently, Fig. 7-5 has been drawn for two classes of particles on the basis of size and density, choosing, arbitrarily, the larger particle to be less dense. The purpose of each method is given after its name.

INDIVIDUAL PARTICLE. To obtain and observe systematic relative motion of single particles with respect to solvent. In principle this process corresponds to the microscope method of electrophoresis, but is not used at present in the laboratory.

VELOCITY METHODS. To utilize the terminal velocity of particles such that transport by sedimentation or flotation is large in comparison with that of diffusion, which, however, cannot be ignored completely. There are two main velocity subtypes, each having electrophoretic counterparts.

Moving Boundary. To utilize concentration changes to follow a boundary region whose movement is characteristic of (invisible) particles in the bulk solution (plateau) ahead. This corresponds to moving boundary electrophoresis with the major technical difference of having a top and bottom to the cell. The initial boundary is formed by the meniscus as the centrifugal field sediments particles away; or, correspondingly, the bottom forms the initial boundary in flotation. In both cases the pattern is of the descending type, but with the further property that the tube bottom in sedimentation or meniscus in flotation permits packing into a pellet. As seen in Fig. 7-5, centrifuging too long destroys the relative separation of two components. The slower component can be obtained free of the faster component, but in poor yield, by stopping at time t_2. The pellet, correspondingly, is relatively depleted in the slower component. A subsequent short clarification run of the dispersed (and usually diluted) pellet sediments even faster components and debris as well as incompletely resuspended material. Alternate cycles of high and low speed are called differential centrifugation [1b].

The moving boundary method is by far the most common application of centrifugation. It can be used for concentration and purification. If analyzed before the plateau is gone, it is used for precise measurement of sedimentation coefficients. If analyzed before the boundary region even clears the meniscus, it also yields molecular weight information (Archibald method). Since the initial boundary is developed by the centrifugation process, the moving boundary method can be used for concentration measurements as well as homogeneity. For certain systems, the initial boundary can be formed at an intermediate position in the cell by layering at rest or using the centrifugal field during acceleration to empty one chamber of complex cells, as shown in Fig. 7-3.

Moving boundary methodology will be given in later sections. For examples of applications refer also to Figs. 7-7 A,B,D, and F and 7-16 D.

Moving Zone.   To utilize movement of a zone or band of particles. The initial zone must be inserted either at rest or by the emptying of a chamber by the centrifugal field. Centrifugation must be terminated before the separated zones are superimposed in the pellet.

Since sedimenting particles increase the solution density, the leading edge of the zone tends to create a density inversion as it moves into fresh solvent. This is stabilized by providing, initially, a continuously increasing solvent density down the tube. Unfortunately, the moving zone method has been called "density gradient centrifugation" because of the stabilizing density gradient, which is actually incidental to the velocity method. Methods of forming the density gradient are given on page 275. The porous media used in zone electrophoresis will not stabilize, on theoretical grounds, and have been tried numerous times without success.

Preparatively, the moving zone method is used most significantly to separate, in one cycle, faster components from slower ones without pelleting. One cycle of moving zone centrifugation yields a faster component with a purity equivalent to 10 to 20 cycles of differential centrifugation. However, less starting material can be used and the fraction is diluted from the original. The method can also be used to measure sedimentation coefficients, commonly in a relative manner against marker substances. It should be noted for s-rate measurements on labile biologicals that the moving boundary method leaves the active agent in its original environment whereas the moving zone method moves it through an arbitary solvent. On the other hand, with crude or qualitative assays, detection of a zone is easier than location of a boundary and requires far less material.

Analytically, the moving zone method may reveal heterogeneity better than the moving boundary method in strongly concentration-dependent systems, and uses an order of magnitude less material.

Classical Sedimentation Equilibrium.   To redistribute particles so that *either* sedimentation *or* flotation is balanced by diffusion. It is used for molecular weight and activity coefficient determinations, and to obtain a density gradient for other purposes. In itself, it results in no purification, is not used preparatively, and has no electrophoretic counterpart. The transient is used to measure the diffusion coefficient.

ISODENSITY. To combine sedimentation *and* flotation in the same tube by using a density gradient straddling the buoyant density. There are two main subtypes. The preformed gradient type has its counterpart in electrophoresis where a pH gradient straddling the isoelectric point is utilized. The field-formed gradient equilibrium type has no electrophoretic equivalent.

Preformed Gradient Isodensity. To utilize fast movement of particles to a position corresponding to their density. Particles with differing properties may cross during the transient approach to their own isodensity level as shown at t_1 and t_2, in Fig. 7-5. The method is transient because material used to form the density gradient will redistribute in the field and, eventually, separated zones may migrate to bottom or top. This is actually a long time compared to t_2; therefore, the time to stop centrifugation is not critical and the method is not of the velocity type.

The preformed gradient isodensity method can have the macromolecular material present in all layers initially. A larger yield will be obtained, but the particles cannot move to a region never occupied by slower moving particles of the same or different density. As depicted in Fig. 7-5, the method is used *(a)* for isolation of mitochondria, microsomes, and other cellular components; *(b)* for isolation of viruses; and *(c)* for assay of unknown biological solutions. Note that concentration as well as purification without pellet formation can be achieved and that isodensity values can be measured. Methods for preforming the density gradient are similar to those for the moving zone method.

Isodensity Equilibrium. To utilize classical sedimentation equilibrium of small substances or mixed solvents to form a density gradient in which large particles band at their isodensity levels. In contrast to the preformed gradient this is a field-formed gradient which requires no elaborate initial layering but merely that the nominal density be close to the isodensity value. In contrast to classical sedimentation equilibrium, *both* sedimentation *and* flotation are balanced by diffusion in the macromolecular band, but either for the gradient substance. This method can be used for slow particles as well as fast ones, and is used preparatively to concentrate and purify nucleic acids and viruses. Its analytical use is for assay and precise measurement of isodensity, homogeneity, or molecular weight.

INTERFACE CENTRIFUGATION. To cause selective transfer of particles from one immiscible phase to another. There is no electrophoretic counterpart. References to the literature will be given for the subtypes as the method has not been reviewed in general and will not be discussed further in this chapter.

Backward Flow Interface. To displace an interface according to the hydrodynamic volume of penetrating particles. It is used for cells, bacteria, and viruses [16].

Differential Flotation. To separate particles according to differences in density not using aqueous isodense solutions. It is used for tissue culture cells with the separated denser cells retaining viability and free from growth medium [17].

Aqueous Phase Separator. To permit selective transfer of particles from a crude aqueous solution to a short isodensity column. It is used for viruses to effect a final purification from tissue components or degradation debris [18].

CONTINUOUS FLOW. To separate particles from enormous volumes of harvest fluids or partially purified solutions. Moderate increase of yield in any of the foregoing methods can be obtained with swinging bucket or angle rotors having either multiple or larger tubes (Fig. 7-2). In angle rotors collision with the walls and subsequent convection across the field promoted by gravity are used advantageously. But, for pilot plant or large-scale laboratory work, continuous input of starting fluid is required. The most common application is the cream separator, a laboratory version of which is shown in Fig. 7-2. Numerous modifications for special purposes are also shown; none has a continuous output of sediment, but one permits fractionation of sedimentable material from a continuous input. The continuous flow processes are complex and empirical, and manufacturers' instruction books should be consulted for details of operation.

Physical Basis of Ultracentrifugation

GENERAL

It is now possible to determine by ultracentrifugal means almost a dozen parameters for systems ranging in molecular weight from a few hundred to many millions. These include the sedimentation coefficient, diffusion coefficient, molecular weight, particle density, shape, and hydration, as well as colligative properties such as concentration, activity coefficient, homogeneity, and chemical equilibrium constants. In addition, it is possible to concentrate and purify solutes by using their systematic relative motion in the centrifugal field in a variety of preparative procedures. At least five geometrical arrangements are employed: (a) a tube of constant cross-sectional area in a uniform field; (b) a cylindrical tube in an angle rotor; or (c) a cylindrical tube in a swinging bucket rotor; (d) a sector shaped centrifuge cell; or (e) a cell which narrows with increasing distance, such as a reversed sector or conical centrifuge tube. Detailed theory, experimental design, and methods of computation for such a broad subject must of necessity be quite involved and require mathematical exposition. Here, only underlying concepts will be sketched with mathematical exposition given in small print. Symbols are summarized in the glossary. The choice of topics reflects the author's opinion as to points of view anticipated to remain important. For details, the reader can consult the treatises by Svedberg and Pedersen [1a], Schachman [1f], and Fujita [1j]; the monographs by Williams *et al.* [1d], Baldwin and Van Holde [1g], and Vinograd and Hearst [1l]; the excellent chapters from a computational viewpoint by Schachman [1c], the Claessons [1i], and Markham [1k]; and the proceedings of a conference on the ultracentrifuge [1m]. Research literature references will be given only where the topic is not covered in the general references.

BROWNIAN MOTION AND DIFFUSION

FREE DIFFUSION.   Particles differing in density from the solution that do not settle under gravity alone, are kept in suspension by Brownian motion. When such random molecular motions result in transport of matter from one part of a system to another, the process is called diffusion. In a dilute solution each particle behaves independently of the others, which it seldom meets, and, as a result of collision with solvent molecules, moves sometimes toward a region of higher, and sometimes of lower, concentration, with no preferred direction towards either. Consider two thin, equal elements of volume on either side of any horizontal section in a solution that has a lower concentration layered over a higher concentration. Although it is not possible to say which way any particular solute particle will move in a given interval of time, it can be said that, on the average, a definite fraction of particles initially in the lower element of volume will cross the section from below and the same fraction of molecules in the upper element will cross from above. Thus, simply because there are more particles in the lower element than in the upper, there is a net transfer from the lower to the upper side of the section due to independent random molecular motions.

FICK'S FIRST LAW OF DIFFUSION.   Fick's first law states that the mass of solute diffusing across a plane per unit area per unit time is proportional to, and in a direction to diminish, the concentration gradient. Application of this differential equation has been especially rewarding in determining the effects of diffusion in nature and in experimental arrangements designed to measure the diffusion coefficient [2]. Fick's phenomenological description of the process does not mean the concentration gradient drives particles, as will be seen by quantitating the statistical picture presented above, which, incidentally, has been programed for a computer using the Monte Carlo method [2a].

Consider one-dimensional movement of particles in a uniform tube of unit cross section [2b, 3b]. Let n displacements $\delta_1, \cdots, \delta_n$ in time t be of the same absolute magnitude δ but completely independent and at random regarding their positive or negative direction. The mean square displacement $\overline{\Delta x^2}$ over all particles can be represented as

$$\overline{\Delta x^2} = \sum_1^n \delta_i^2 = n\delta^2 \tag{1}$$

Let $\tau = t/n$ be the time for any one displacement; then

$$\overline{\Delta x^2} = (\delta^2/\tau)t \tag{2}$$

In principle, experimental determination of $\overline{\Delta x^2}$ involves observation of net displacements of a large number of particles over the same time interval, or the net displacement of a single particle in many repeated equal time intervals. It has been found experimentally that $\overline{\Delta x^2}/t$ is essentially constant for any one system, hence δ^2/τ is constant in this oversimplified model of equal-length elementary displacements.

Referring to Fig. 7-8, let c and $c + (\partial c/\partial x)\,dx$ represent the average concentration (w/v) in each of two hypothetical compartments on either side of a plane Q. Now choose a time interval dt in accordance with Equation (2) so that $dt = \tau$ and

$$dx = [(\delta^2/\tau)dt]^{1/2} = \delta \tag{3}$$

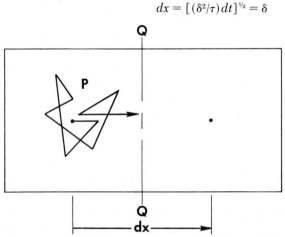

Fig. 7-8. Schematic Brownian motion. Particle initially at point P takes random motions due to collisions with solvent molecules. On magnified scale, for theoretical deductions, dx corresponds to the average distance of each displacement.

Then, all particles in the left-hand compartment will move out; half go to the left and half cross plane Q to the right. Similarly, all particles in the right-hand compartment will also move out, half going to the right and half crossing plane Q to the left. The net mass crossing the plane per unit area to the right is

$$\frac{c\,dx}{2} - \frac{[c + (\partial c/\partial x)\,dx]\,dx}{2} = -\frac{\partial c}{\partial x} \cdot \frac{(dx)^2}{2} \tag{4}$$

The net weight per unit area per unit time $(\delta m'/\delta t)_D$ is then

$$\left(\frac{\partial m'}{\partial t}\right)_D = -\left[\frac{\partial c}{\partial x} \cdot \frac{(dx)^2}{2}\right]/dt \tag{5}$$

Substituting for dt from Equation (3) gives Fick's first law

$$\left(\frac{\partial m'}{\partial t}\right)_D = -D\frac{\partial c}{\partial x} \tag{6}$$

where

$$D \equiv \delta^2/(2\tau) \tag{7}$$

The coefficient of proportionality D in Equation (6) is the diffusion coefficient with the unit 10^{-7} cm²/sec called a Fick and denoted F.

EINSTEIN-SUTHERLAND EQUATION.   The relationship between Brownian motion, diffusion coefficient, and friction factor is extremely important. The frictional force f_f exerted by viscous solutions increases with the velocity dx'/dt of a particle whose distance x' from some origin is a function of time.

$$f_f = f\, dx'/dt \tag{8}$$

Referring to Fig. 7-8, half the particles at P were considered to move to the right an average distance dx in the time dt selected according to Equation (3). The end of this time interval can be considered the start of the next, with each particle recovering on the average its original kinetic energy E given by

$$E = (1/2)\ (R/N)T \tag{9}$$

where $R = 8.314 \times 10^7$ erg/°C/mole is the gas constant; $N = 6.023 \times 10^{23}$ molecules/mole, Avogadro's number; and T, absolute temperature. During the first interval each particle, on the average, transferred this energy back and forth with the solvent by collisions. Considering that both those particles which moved to the left as well as those to the right lost and gained this energy E once, 4 E units of energy per particle were involved on the average. This energy is equal to the work done by the friction force moving the distance dx. Thus

$$f(dx'/dt)\ dx = 4\ [(1/2)\ (R/N)T] \tag{10}$$

Use Equations (3), (7), and (10) and $dx' = dx$ to give

$$D = RT/(fN) \tag{11}$$

This is the Einstein-Sutherland equation.

Separation of the friction coefficient f into the three factors of viscosity, size, and shape can be accomplished by defining an equivalent sphere of the same volume and density as the particle. The value of f for the equivalent sphere of radius a_0 is denoted f_0 and given by Stokes' law as

$$f_0 = 6\pi\eta a_0 \tag{12}$$

with

$$(4/3)\pi a_0^3 = M'/\rho' \tag{13}$$

where M' is the mass and ρ' the density of the complete particle. The friction coefficient can then be written as

$$f = 6\pi\eta a_0 (f/f_0) \tag{14}$$

where (f/f_0) is called the friction factor and represents the hypothetical velocity of the equivalent sphere compared with the actual particle.

Equations (11) and (14) were used for the conversion between $D(f/f_0)$ and a_0 in Fig. 7-4.

SEDIMENTATION OR FLOTATION

CENTRIFUGAL FORCE.   This is the reaction to change of direction in the rotational motion of a mass element. Referring to Fig. 7-9, the force registered by the hypothetical mass-less spring indicator will be

$$f_c = M'\omega^2 r \tag{15}$$

where f_c is the centrifugal force on mass M' rotating at an angular velocity ω at a distance r from the axis, and where $\omega^2 r$ is the angular acceleration. The force exerted by the spring on M' when the radius is constant is equal and opposite to centrifugal force and is termed centripetal force since it is directed toward the center of rotation. The force due to gravity is

$$f_g = M'g \tag{16}$$

where g is the acceleration of gravity. Comparison of Equations (15) and (16) shows why centrifugal force is considered gravitation-like —both forces depend on mass and acceleration. The magnitude of centrifugal force compared to gravitational force is called relative centrifugal force RCF where

$$RCF \equiv \omega^2 r/g = 1.119(10^{-5})r(rpm)^2 \tag{17}$$

In this expression, the symbol (rpm) is used for speed when expressed in revolutions per minute (*R.P.M.*). This conversion of angular velocity from radians per second is

$$(rpm) = [60/(2\pi)]\omega \tag{18}$$

SEDIMENTATION COEFFICIENT. The systematic relative velocity of a particle per unit centrifugal field strength is such a useful quantity that it is formally called the sedimentation coefficient s. Thus

$$s \equiv [1/(\omega^2 r')]dr'/dt = (1/\omega^2)d\ln r'/dt \tag{19}$$

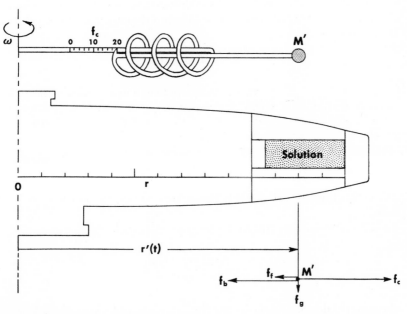

Fig. 7-9. Schematic centrifugal force. The hypothetical mass-less spring indicator demonstrates the force exerted by the mass M' when restrained to circular motion. A distinction is made between a radial coordinate r on the rotor and the distance r' from the axis of a particle moving in solution. Four external forces superimposed on a particle undergoing Brownian motion are: f_c, centrifugal; f_b, buoyant; f_f, friction; f_g, gravity. A fifth, not shown, for charged particles is due to possible electrical fields.

with $\omega^2 r'$ from Equation (15) representing the centrifugal force per unit mass where r' is the distance from the center of rotation of the particle moving with radial velocity dr'/dt. The sedimentation coefficient is commonly referred to as s-rate s and is expressed in units of 10^{-13} sec called a Svedberg S.

The s-rate depends directly on the size and difference in density between particle and medium but inversely on the viscosity and deviation from spherical shape. The reason the centrifuging particle reaches a terminal velocity is shown below. Even though sedimentation or flotation is superimposed on Brownian motion, it is possible to measure s-rates in the presence of diffusion, basically, by operating at high speed using the moving boundary or moving zone methods. A new method uses the transient approach to isodensity equilibrium [19].

Consider a (large) rigid particle of mass M' and density ρ' suspended in a liquid of density ρ. Under gravity alone, the net force is equal to its weight diminished by a buoyant force equal to the weight of fluid displaced (Archimedes' principle). If the solution is contained in a cell and is rotated, the forces acting on the particles will be as indicated in Fig. 7-9. If the densities of particle and liquid are identical, the particle will remain at the same level (same r) regardless of level or speed because the buoyant force f_b is also magnified. It is the centrifugal force on the displaced liquid of volume M'/ρ'; thus

$$f_b = (M'/\rho')\rho\,\omega^2 r' \tag{20}$$

If the density ρ' is greater than ρ, the particle will move radially encountering frictional resistance f_f which increases with the velocity of the particle and is given by Equations (8) and (14). The velocity will thus reach a terminal value for which

$$f_f = f_c - f_b = 6\pi\eta a_0 (f/f_0)\,dr'/dt \tag{21}$$

(neglecting linear acceleration of the particle's radial motion and the Coriolis force).

Combine Equations (15), (19), (20), and (21) to give

$$s = \frac{(2a_0)^2(\rho' - \rho)}{18\eta\,(f/f_0)} \tag{22}$$

The independence of s on ω^2 or r' but on molecular parameters shows why this quantity is so useful. If $\rho' < \rho$, s is negative, and the process is called flotation.

Note that the s-rate is defined here from velocity, not from Equation (22). As such, the transport of mass per unit time per unit area due to sedimentation $(\partial m'/\partial t)_s$ can be expressed as

$$\left(\frac{\partial m'}{\partial t}\right)_s = \omega^2\,rsc \tag{23}$$

Definition of s by flow expressions [1d] equivalent to Equation (23) avoids the implicit assumption of Equation (22) that an individual particle's velocity can be measured.

A distinction has been made between the coordinate r and the moving position r'. An s-rate scale can be made by converting r as though each point represents a particle having moved from r_a in the time t with an average (or "apparent") s-rate s^*. Thus

$$s^* \equiv [1/(\omega^2 t)] \ln (r/r_a) = (1/t) \int_0^t s\,dt \tag{24}$$

where the right-hand member can be shown from Equation (19), without assuming s constant.

COMBINATION OF CENTRIFUGATION AND DIFFUSION PROCESSES

It is quite important to realize that both transport processes of sedimentation (or flotation) and diffusion take place together in most experiments in the ultracentrifuge. Both are involved with Brownian motion. The systematic relative velocity of solute with respect to solution caused by the centrifuge, in general, is very small compared to the random motion in its shortest increments. This is known as the average drift velocity concept of centrifugation and explains five often-discussed points. First, at present no biological particle has been shown to be oriented by sedimentation. Second, no conjugated particle has been shown to be broken by the centrifugal field even though its parts have differing density or size. Third, any one particle may move for a time in a direction opposite to the centrifugal force. Fourth, the friction factor for movement in a centrifugal field is the same as for diffusion. Fifth, wherever there is a concentration gradient in the centrifuge cell, whether it is set up initially or develops as a result of the field, transfer of mass by centrifugation and diffusion will be superimposed.

Combination of the two processes will be considered below when: (a) sedimentation and diffusion coefficients of a particular solute are measured in separate experiments; (b) diffusion spreads a moving boundary; (c) the two processes are balanced in the ultracentrifuge either with (1) solute tending to move by centrifugation only in one direction, classical sedimentation equilibrium, or (2) solute undergoing both sedimentation and flotation in the same cell, isodensity equilibrium.

CALCULATIONS FROM SEDIMENTATION AND DIFFUSION COEFFICIENTS

SVEDBERG EQUATION.   If both the s-rate and diffusion coefficient are determined by separate experiments, the two can be combined by simultaneous solution of Equations (11) and (22).

Eliminating f/f_0 yields the Svedberg equation for molecular weight M

$$N\left(\frac{4}{3}\pi\ a_0^3\right)\rho' = M = \frac{10^{-6}RTs}{D(1-\rho/\rho')} \qquad (25)$$

with s in Svedbergs and D in Ficks and where M is the weight of N particles. Actually, the Svedberg equation has $1/\rho'$ replaced by the partial specific volume and M considered the anhydrous molecular weight. The complications of finite concentration, electrical charge, hydration, and partial specific volume will be treated in other sections.

FRICTION FACTOR. Instead of eliminating f/f_0 in Equations (11) and (22), a_0 can be eliminated to give

$$(f/f_0)^3 = \left[\frac{10^{27}R^2T^2}{162\pi^2N^2\eta^3}\right]\left(\frac{\rho'-\rho}{D^2s}\right) \qquad (26)$$

with s in Svedbergs and D in Ficks. For water at 20°C the factor in brackets is 1009. This relation is plotted in Fig. 7-4 and can be used to check for deviations from spherical shape when D, s, and ρ' are accurately known. The effect of shape on f/f_0 has been calculated theoretically for various models. Consider here only ellipsoids of revolution and various dimers indicated in Table 7-1. The second column gives the reciprocal of the friction factor expressed as the s-rate of the particle compared to a sphere of the same

TABLE 7-1.

FRICTION FACTORS [1f,20] FOR ELLIPSOIDS OF REVOLUTION EXPRESSED AS
THEIR S-RATE COMPARED TO THAT OF VARIOUS MODELS

s-Rate Ratios					
Prolate Ellipsoid				Oblate	
Monomer axial ratio	Monomer to equivalent sphere (f_0/f)	End-to-end dimer to monomer	Side-to-side dimer to monomer	Monomer axial ratio	Monomer to equivalent sphere (f_0/f)
1000	0.07601	1.10	1.82	1/1000	0.1570
300	0.1428	1.11	1.77	1/300	0.2341
100	0.2460	1.14	1.74	1/100	0.3363
30	0.4243	1.17	1.66	1/30	0.4951
10	0.6481	1.23	1.56	1/10	0.6861
8	0.6978	1.24	1.53	1/8	0.7278
6	0.7610	1.27	1.49	1/6	0.7831
5	0.7968	1.29	1.46	1/5	0.8170
4	0.8460	1.30	1.43	1/4	0.8584
3	0.8988	1.32	1.40	1/3	0.9053
2	0.9579	1.33	1.37	1/2	0.9597
1	1.0000	1.34	1.34	1	1.0000

volume and density. The end-to-end dimer of prolate ellipsoids can be represented by a particle of double (or triple, for small axial ratios) the volume and double the axial ratio, and can be calculated from the factors of the second column to have an increased s-rate given by the ratios in the fourth column. The side-to-side dimer sweeps out a volume four times that of the monomer as it takes random orientation. With half the axial ratio of the monomer, it would have the s-rate ratios indicated in the last column. Note that doubling the volume of a sphere multiplies the s-rate by $2^{2/3} = 1.59$ from Equation (22). Doubling the volume by side-to-side aggregation has a corresponding factor of only 1.34, from Table 7-1. Another property evident from Table 7-1 is that for very asymmetric particles the s-rate is determined more by diameter squared than by length [1f].

SIMULTANEOUS TRANSPORT BY SEDIMENTATION AND DIFFUSION

CONVECTION.   Bulk movement of fluid, both solvent and solute together, is known as convection. It is generally caused by density inversions that result from temperature variations or local concentration changes in cells with sides not parallel to the field vector (Fig. 7-10). Hydrodynamic circulation resulting from particles colliding with or being depleted at the wall may extend an appreciable radial distance, and is deleterious (Fig. 7-10 C).

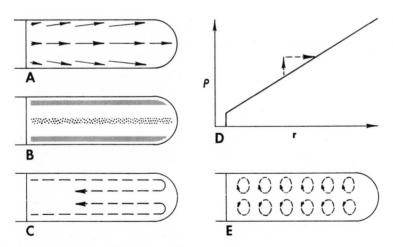

Fig. 7-10. Convection in centrifuge tube or cell without radial walls. (A) Swinging bucket cylindrical tube, solid arrows indicate direction of sedimentation of particles with respect to solvent. (B) Solute concentration changes give density increase at walls and decrease in center. (C) Resulting radial convection, if not prevented. (D) Preformed solution density gradient. As element of solution increases its density at any r, it sinks only slightly until it no longer exceeds the solution density ρ. (E) Resulting desirable eddy-type convection.

A preventive procedure, which directs convection *across* the field for situations in which sector-shaped cells or tubes are not feasible, is to use a slight density gradient of solvent (Fig. 7-10 D). Then the region of increased density at the wall cannot sink along the field but is turned by the magnified hydrostatic leveling forces toward the center, where the density has tended to drop (Fig. 7-10 E). The average component of flow along the field vector in the center of the cell then represents only systematic relative motion of particles with respect to fluid. A slight density gradient is also valuable in angle rotors where convection across the field is essential to the operation (Fig. 7-11 E). Theoretical application of the law of conservation of mass has been limited to systems free from radial convection, but complicated because of nonuniform cells and the nonuniform centrifugal field (Fig. 7-11). Three choices can be made to handle these geometrical complications: (*a*) consider the process rectangular (i.e., uniform field in uniform cell) and apply a correction factor; (*b*) use appropriate mathematical functions for the actual geometrical case; or (*c*) shorten the column (Fig. 7-11 G) so that nonuniformity is negligible in comparison with the distance from the axis of rotation (rectangular approximation). It is worthwhile to distinguish in formulas functional relationships which quantitate the principle being used from those necessitated by the geometrical complications [21]. (see page 280).

Fig. 7-11. Effect of geometry of field and cells used in moving boundary method. (*A*) Radial dilution; t_0, hypothetical cell at axis with initially uniform distribution of particles; t_1, time interval chosen so that if particle at 1 moved to 2, particle at 2 would have moved to 4, since field is proportional to distance. Distribution of particles remains uniform, though diluted. (*B*) In cell not going to axis, a diluting plateau exists ahead of the boundary region. (C to G) Nomenclature using special volume coordinates from meniscus: u to boundary, u' to marked particles in plateau, U to center of rotation (extended cell volume). (*C*) Sector cell. (*D*) Swinging bucket tube. (*E*) Angle tube, equivalent to a swinging bucket tube of greater cross-sectional area; convection downward across centrifugal field caused by gravity does not affect radial movement. (*F*) Cell narrowing with distance; if hyperbolic, $U = \infty$ and there is no radial dilution. (*G*) Uniform field in uniform cell: the rectangular approximation to sector centrifugation, or settling in cylinder under gravity alone.

The law of conservation of mass as applied to transport problems is called the equation of continuity [3a] and states that the flow with respect to solvent into a volume element less the flow out is equal to the time rate of increase of mass in that element. In general vector notation, the equation of continuity is

$$-\frac{\partial c}{\partial t} = \nabla \cdot c\vec{v} \tag{27}$$

where $\vec{v}$ is the velocity of the particles of mass concentration c. Consider a binary, neutral, ideal solution in a sector shaped cell with no transport through either the meniscus at $r = r_a$ or the bottom at $r = r_b$. Equations (23)

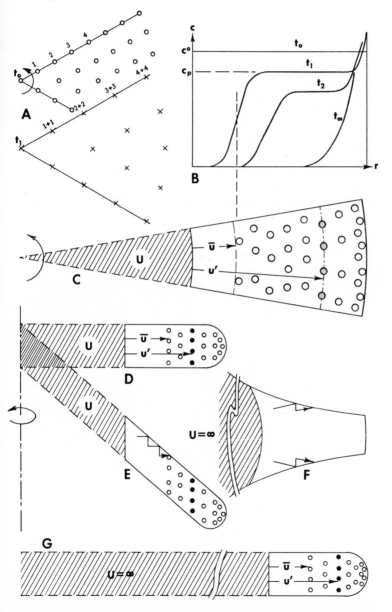

and (6) give the magnitude of the mass transported per unit area per unit time by sedimentation and diffusion, respectively. Thus

$$| \vec{cv} | = \left(\frac{\partial m'}{\partial t}\right)_s + \left(\frac{\partial m'}{\partial t}\right)_D = \omega^2 rsc - D\frac{\partial c}{\partial r} \tag{28}$$

In cylindrical coordinates $\nabla \cdot c\vec{v}$ becomes $(1/r) \, \partial \, (r | c\vec{v} |)/\partial r$ and Equation (28) becomes

$$\frac{\partial c}{\partial t} = \left(\frac{1}{r}\right) \frac{\partial}{\partial r} \left[r\left(D\frac{\partial c}{\partial r} - \omega^2 rsc\right) \right] \tag{29}$$

This is the Lamm differential equation of the centrifuge. A detailed review of a more general form derived from the thermodynamics of irreversible processes is given by Williams *et al.* [1d]. Of great importance is the fact that the solution of this equation involves a transient and an equilibrium distribution of concentration.

MOVING BOUNDARY THEORY.

Plateau. With numerous important systems where the initial concentration is uniform throughout the cell a region will exist of limited radial extent in which the concentration remains uniform but changes with time. Whether increasing in flotation or decreasing in sedimentation, the region is called a plateau and corresponds to the phase between boundaries of electrophoresis moving boundary theory. The existence of a plateau can be predicted [1j] by complicated mathematics from the Lamm Equation (29) for systems with s-rates independent of pressure. Reasoning backwards from its known existence, consider the processes in that region which might disturb the initial plateau [22]. If they are independent of radius, the plateau will not be destroyed even though its magnitude and extent are time dependent. It may seem paradoxical that those particles further from the axis of rotation under a greater centrifugal force do not dilute more than those in closer. An arrangement of coins as in Fig. 11A for a cell extending to the axis readily demonstrates that if each particle moves a distance proportional to its original distance from the center, the particles remain uniformly distributed.

In the plateau, $\partial c/\partial r = 0$ and there will be no net flow by diffusion. Hence Equation (27) can be reduced to [22]

$$\frac{\partial c}{\partial t} = -\left(\frac{1}{y}\right) \frac{\partial}{\partial r} \left[(RCF)g \, c \, s'y \right] \tag{30}$$

where s' is the s-rate of particles in the plateau and (RCF) g is the field strength in general, and is given by Equation (17) in particular. In any cell with a transverse section having y proportional to any power of the radius and s' a function only of c, Equation (30) yields $\partial c/\partial t$ independent of r. This can be expressed as

$$d\ c_p/dt = -2\omega^2 c_p s' \tag{31C}$$

$$d\ c_p/dt = -\omega^2 c_p s' \tag{31D,E}$$

$$d\ c_p/dt = 0 \tag{31F,G}$$

where c_p refers to the plateau, and the letter in the equation number refers to the geometry of the corresponding part of Fig. 7-11. The fact that dimensions do not appear means that cell sections perpendicular to the axis need be only of the same shape, but not necessarily the same size. Hence, these equations apply to angle centrifuge tubes, provided there is a slight density gradient, as already postulated for convective systems.

Moving Boundary Condition. Since particles in the plateau are not directly visible, the moving boundary method relies on observing a boundary between supernatant fluid and plateau by some colligative property of the solution. In the boundary region there will be other processes besides centrifugation taking place, e.g., diffusion and chemical reaction, and individual particles may move opposite to the centrifugal field, or may convert from one complex form to another. Even so, it is possible to measure a property of the concentration distribution in the boundary region which has the same s-rate as do particles ahead in the plateau. In the simplest system this is the radius of gyration of the concentration gradient distribution about the center of rotation and is approximated by the position of the maximum in the peak.

Let $\bar{r}$, a function of time, be the distance (of the property) of the boundary which has the same s-rate s' as do plateau particles. Thus, set

$$s = \left(\frac{1}{\omega^2 \bar{r}}\right) \frac{d\bar{r}}{dt} \equiv \left(\frac{1}{\omega^2 r'}\right) \frac{dr'}{dt} = s' \tag{32}$$

where s is the measured or observed s-rate and which, by convention, is not written with a bar, as would be expected from symmetry.

General Solution. Equations (31) and (32) are the basic differential equations of the moving boundary method. The geometrical complications of both the nonuniform field and cell cross-section can be handled mathematically by converting to volume coordinates. Let U be the volume between center of rotation and starting level if the sides of the cell were extended to the center of rotation as in Fig. 7-11 C to G. With this change in variable and considerable rearrangement, Equations (31) and (32) can be generalized to [22]

$$\left. \begin{array}{c} d[c_p(u'-\bar{u})]/dt = 0 \\ d[c_p(1+\bar{u}/U)]/dt = 0 \end{array} \right\} \tag{33}$$

The solution to these equations is

$$c^0 = c_p + \frac{1}{U}\int_{c_a}^{c_p} u\,dc = c_a + \int_{c_a}^{c_p}\left(1+\frac{u}{U}\right)dc = c_a + \int_{r_a}^{r_p}\left(1+\frac{u}{U}\right)\left(\frac{\partial c}{\partial r}\right)dr \tag{34}$$

$$\bar{u} = u_p - \frac{1}{c_p}\int_0^{u_p} c\,du = \frac{1}{c_p}\int_{c_a}^{c_p} u\,dc = \frac{\displaystyle\int_{c_a}^{r_p} u\left(\frac{\partial c}{\partial r}\right)dr}{\displaystyle c_a + \int_{r_a}^{r_p}\left(\frac{\partial c}{\partial r}\right)dr} \tag{35}$$

where c^0 is the initially uniform concentration, and integration by parts has been used, as well as the relation for the concentration at any point, if known at one point

$$c_p = c_a + \int_{r_a}^{r_p}\left(\frac{\partial c}{\partial r}\right)dr \tag{36}$$

Several deductions can be made from Equations (34) and (35).

1. The relationships are valid for sedimentation or flotation and are independent of assumptions about uniformity of the field, boundary spreading, concentration dependence of s, concentration remaining at the meniscus, or temperature, speed, and time involved.

2. Since $\int_0^u c\,du$ is the total mass between c_a and c_p and is equal to $c_p(u_p - \bar{u})$ from Equation (35), the boundary position is the equivalent, infinitely sharp position obtained either with no diffusion or by conceptually rearranging particles in the boundary region to a step function.

3. If $c_a = 0$, the right-hand member of Equation (35) in the rectangular case specifies a first moment for the boundary position, a well-known relation in electrophoresis. However, in a sector cell, Equation (35) specifies the square root of the second moment, which is also known as the radius of gyration.

$$\bar{r} = \left[\int_{r_a}^{r_p} r^2(\partial c/\partial r)\,dr \bigg/ \int_{r_a}^{r_p}(\partial c/\partial r)\,dr\right]^{1/2} \tag{37}$$

4. The relation between plateau concentration and boundary position is

$$c_p = c^0/(1+\bar{u}/U) \tag{38}$$

This is the general radial dilution rule that for a sector cell with volumes proportional to r^2 becomes the square law

$$c^0 = c_p(\bar{r}/r_a)^2 = \int_{r_a}^{r_p} (r/r_a)^2 (\partial c/\partial r)\,dr + c_a \tag{39}$$

5. A moving boundary experiment basically yields both the initial concentration and the boundary position. In the centrifuge, changes in concentration are related to boundary positions because of the radial dilution, and boundary positions are involved with initial concentrations at early times because the starting boundary is formed by the field at the meniscus (or cell bottom, in flotation). Determination of c^0 from c_p follows from Equation (39), and will be discussed on page 255 for early times when $c_a \neq 0$. Table 7-2 gives specific formulas deduced from Equation (35) for the boundary position, depending upon which concentrations are known, if any, and the form of the primary data [21]. For example, there could be observation of: (a) the total amount of solute in a finite volume by chemical or biological activity; (b) concentration from blackening of a film in absorption optics; (c) concentration differences from interference fringes; or (d) concentration gradients in schlieren optics.

Concentration and Pressure Dependence.   The fact that particles not involved in boundary regions move under ever-changing concentration and pressure means that their sedimentation coefficient s' will not be constant, in general, during a run. Both effects are very complex and have not yet been adequately derived in terms of fundamental molecular processes. Instead, empirical relations are chosen.

Two forms of the concentration dependence

$$s' \approx s^0/(1+kc) \tag{40a}$$

$$s' \approx s^0(1-k'c) \tag{40b}$$

are used, depending on which fits over the larger concentration interval. Here s^0 is the s-rate at infinite dilution. The dependence on elevated pressure P is written

$$s' \approx s_0(1-k''P) \tag{41}$$

where s_0 is the s-rate at 1 atmosphere. The pressure at any level is related to the density and field by

$$dP/dr = \omega^2 r\rho \tag{42}$$

where the density ρ may vary with pressure empirically by

$$\rho \approx \rho_a(1+k'''P) \tag{43}$$

TABLE 7-2

COMPUTATION OF S-RATE BY MOVING BOUNDARY METHOD
(Reprinted [21] by permission of Academic Press)

Assay: Method	Assay: Variable	Variable along field, cell	Boundary Position: Formula	Boundary Position: Approx. location at	Concentration conditions	c^0	c_a	c_p
General	Conc. c	Volume u, any cell	$\bar{u} = \dfrac{1}{c_p}\int_{c_a}^{c_p} u\,dc$		$c^0 = c_p + \dfrac{1}{U}\int_{c_a}^{c_p} u\,dc$			
Chemical or biological activity	Quantity $c\Delta u$	u, any cell	$\dfrac{U}{U+\bar{u}} = \dfrac{U + \Sigma c\Delta u/c^0}{U + \Sigma\Delta u}$	Largest change in $c\Delta u$		Known	Any	Unknown
	c	du, any cell	$\bar{u} = u_p - \dfrac{1}{c_p}\int_0^{u_p} c\,du$	$1/2\,c_p$ level if $c_a = 0$		Unknown	Any	Known
Phaseplate schlieren optics or differentiated absorption optics	Conc. gradient $\partial c/\partial r$	Radius r, sector cell	$\left(\dfrac{r_a}{r}\right)^2 = 1 - \dfrac{1}{c^0}\left[\int_{r_a}^{r_p}\left(\dfrac{r}{r_a}\right)^2\left(\dfrac{\partial c}{\partial r}\right)dr - \int_{r_a}^{r_p}\left(\dfrac{\partial c}{\partial r}\right)dr\right]$ $\bar{r}^2 = \dfrac{\int_{r_a}^{r_p} r^2(\partial c/\partial r)\,dr}{\int_{r_a}^{r_p}(\partial c/\partial r)\,dr}$	Maximum ordinate		Known / Unknown	Any / Zero	Unknown / Unknown

Method			Equation			
	c	dr, sector cell	$\bar{r}^2 = r_p^2 - \dfrac{2}{c_p}\displaystyle\int_{r_a}^{r_p} cr\, dr$	Unknown	Any	Known
	dc	r, sector cell	$\bar{r}^2 = \dfrac{1}{c_p}\left(r_a^2 c_a + \displaystyle\int_{c_a}^{c_p} r^2\, dc\right)$			
Absorption optics with scanning densitometer or Rayleigh interference optics	c	dr, sector cell	$\left(\dfrac{r_a}{r}\right)^2 = \left(\dfrac{r_a}{r_p}\right)^2 + \dfrac{2}{c^0 r_p^2}\displaystyle\int_{r_a}^{r_p} cr\, dr$	Known	Any	Known
	dc	r, sector cell	$\left(\dfrac{r_a}{r}\right)^2 = 1 + \dfrac{c_p - c_a}{c^0} - \dfrac{\displaystyle\int_{c_a}^{c_p} r^2\, dc}{r_a^2 c^0}$	Known	Any	Unknown
	c	dr, sector cell	$\bar{r}^2 = r_p^2 - \dfrac{2}{c_p}\displaystyle\int_{r_a}^{r_p} cr\, dr$	Unknown	Zero	Known
	dc	r, sector cell	$\bar{r}^2 = \dfrac{1}{c_p}\displaystyle\int_{0}^{c_p} r^2\, dc$			

(brace, last two rows) $1/2\ c_p$ level, minimum fringe spacing

The solution of Equations (42) and (43) is

$$P = (1/k''') \exp \{(k'''/2)\rho_a\omega^2 r_a^2 [(r/r_a)^2 - 1] - 1\} \tag{44}$$

Even though P may reach 300 atmospheres in slightly compressible fluids

$$P \approx (1/2)\omega^2 r_a^2 \rho_a [(r/r_a)^2 - 1] \tag{45}$$

Combination of Equations (40a), (41), and (44) gives

$$s' \approx \frac{1 - b[(r/r_a)^2 - 1]}{1 + a\ c/c^0} s_0^0 \tag{46}$$

where

$$\left.\begin{aligned} a &= k\ c^0 \\ b &= (1/2)k''\omega^2 r_a^2 \rho_a \end{aligned}\right\} \tag{47}$$

are concentration and pressure dependence parameters, respectively, and s_0^0 is the s-rate at both infinite dilution and atmospheric pressure.

The Lamm Equation (29), with s replaced by s' of Equation (46), shows that a plateau cannot exist if $b \neq 0$, but can for any a if $b = 0$ [as already implied in Equation (31b)]. The complete solution of Equation (29) with both concentration and pressure dependence is not available. However, experience with the moving boundary method indicates that for reasonably sharp peaks the assumption of $D \approx 0$ is adequate. Let $\bar{r}$ be the boundary position and $\bar{c}$ the concentration at $\bar{r}$. The moving boundary condition is to be applied to particles at concentration $\bar{c}$ with s-rate given by Equation (46). For convenience, change the variables to

$$\begin{aligned} u_* &\equiv (\bar{r}/r_a)^2 \\ \beta_* &\equiv \bar{c}/c^0 \\ t_* &\equiv 2\ \omega^2\ s_0^0 t \end{aligned} \tag{48}$$

Equation (32) can then be written [1j]

$$\frac{du_*}{dt_*} = \frac{u_*}{1 + a\beta_*} [1 - b(u_* - 1)] \tag{49}$$

An expression for β_* must be found before this can be solved.

If $b = 0$, Equation (39) shows $\beta_* = 1/u_*$ even if $a \neq 0$. Now, with $b \neq 0$, the s-rate is slowed differently at different levels. Assume that $\bar{c}$ is increased by the same factor that the s-rate is slowed at that level by the pressure effect, i.e., the numerator of Equation (46), to give

$$\beta_* \approx 1/\{u_*[1 - b(u_* - 1)]\} \tag{50}$$

By using Equation (50) and Taylor expansion of $u_\circ$ about unity, Billick [23] showed that the solution to Equation (49) can be written

$$\frac{\ln u_\circ}{t_\circ} = \frac{1}{1+a}\left\{1-\frac{1}{2}\left[\frac{b(2a+1)-a}{1+a}\right]\frac{t_\circ}{1+a}+\cdots\right\} \tag{51}$$

Conversion back to $\bar{r}$, t, and the initial s-rate $s_0 = s_0^0/(1+a)$ yields the basic relation

$$\ln \bar{r} = \ln r_a + s_0\omega^2 t - \left[\frac{b(2a+1)-a}{1+a}\right](s_0\omega^2 t)^2 + \cdots \tag{52}$$

The coefficient of the square term depends on the form of concentration and pressure dependence relations [chosen here as Equations (40a) and (41)].

The conversion of boundary position to s-rate is a completely separate operation from locating the boundary. Graphically, the s-rate at any time is the slope of $\ln \bar{r}$ vs. t according to Equations (19) and (32). The initial slope is most useful. Equation (52) gives this and the combined pressure and concentration coefficient when least squares computer data processing is used [23]. If only two points are available, the average (or apparent) s-rate s^* is computed from Equation (24).

Johnston-Ogston Effect. Another phenomenon taking place in the boundary region but absent in the (all-component) plateau is the Johnston-Ogston effect (Fig. 7-12 A). As faster component particles move away from the initial boundary position, they overtake particles of the slower component. These uncovered slower particles are left in a lower viscosity medium (since they are devoid of the faster component) and they speed up. This increases their concentration in the slower boundary region and thereby gives a superimposed negative gradient of slower component in the faster boundary region. The Johnston-Ogston correction converts observed concentrations in intervening phases to initial concentrations.

Figure 7-12 shows notation for the two component analysis. A sector cell complication is that radial dilution in the γ plateau continuously decreases the factor by which the slower component speeds (and, hence, builds) up. This leads to a convective situation in the β region. Assume that: (*a*) there is no ambiguity in distinguishing a dividing level r_1 between slower and faster boundary regions; (*b*) the concentration at the starting level is zero; (*c*) boundary positions are located by second moments, as in Equation (37); and (*d*) the superimposed boundary of slower component does not shift the faster boundary position. Then the following can be written from Equation (39) by dividing the interval from r_a to r_p at r_1 [24]

$$c_s^0 + c_f^0 = \int_{r_a}^{r_1} (r/r_a)^2(\partial c/\partial r)\ dr + \int_{r_1}^{r_p} (r/r_a)^2(\partial c/\partial r)\ dr \tag{53}$$

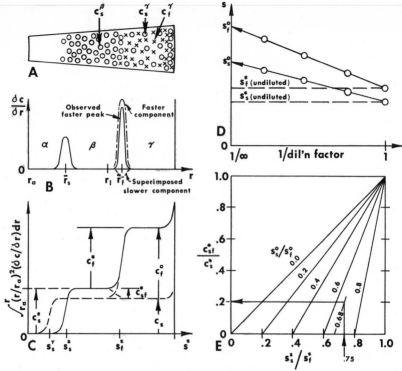

Fig. 7-12. Johnston-Ogston effect in moving boundary method. *(A) Distribution of particles in a two-component mixture; the slower component concentration* c_s^β *is greater than* c_s^γ *ahead of the faster boundary.* (B) Gradient pattern showing faster peak diminished by superimposed slow-component gradient. (C) Notation using square law corrected measurements and apparent s-rates. Both c_s^* and c_f^* are measurable, but do not equal true initial concentrations c_s^0 and c_f^0. (D) Additional information needed to make the correction comes from a dilution series. (E) Correction c_{sf}^* depends on the amount the ratio of s-rates is diminished from its infinite dilution value. Entering with ratio of s_s^*/s_f^* for the undiluted run of D, for example, the correction is read from the ordinate at the s_s^0/s_f^0 line (modified from references [24] and [25]).

The observable quantities for slower and faster boundary regions (peaks) are

$$\left. \begin{aligned} c_s^* &\equiv \int_{r_a}^{r_1} (r/r_a)^2 (\partial c/\partial r) \ dr = (\bar{r}_s/r_a)^2 c_s \\ c_f^* &\equiv \int_{r_1}^{r_p} (r/r_a)^2 (\partial c/\partial r) \ dr = (\bar{r}_f/r_a)^2 c_f \end{aligned} \right\} \tag{54}$$

$$\left. \begin{aligned} s_s^* &\equiv [1/(\omega^2 t)] \ln (\bar{r}_s/r_a) \\ s_f^* &\equiv [1/(\omega^2 t)] \ln (\bar{r}_f/r_a) \end{aligned} \right\} \tag{55}$$

using Equations (24) and (37) and letting c_s and c_f refer to total concentration changes across each boundary, respectively. Let

$$\chi \equiv \int_0^t s_s^\gamma \, dt \Big/ \int_0^t s_f^\gamma \, dt \tag{56}$$

This is not measurable in a conventional run since there is no boundary moving at s_s^γ indicated by the dashed line in Fig. 7-12 C. In very limited situations a synthetic boundary cell run can be made. With considerable rearrangement, using Equations (31C), (32), (54), (55), and (56) and the relationship from Fig. 7-12 that $c_f = c_f^\gamma + c_s^\gamma - c_s^\beta$, Equation (53) yields

$$\beta \equiv \frac{c_s^*}{c_s^0} = \frac{(\bar{r}_f/r_a)^{2(1-\chi)}-1}{(r_f/r_s)^2-1} \tag{57}$$

Here β is the factor by which the square law corrected slower peak area exceeds the initial concentration of slower component.

If c_s^0 is known, β can be computed and then χ, using Equation (57) rewritten as

$$X = \frac{-\log\{(r_a/\bar{r}_f)^2 + \beta[(r_a/\bar{r}_s)^2 - (r_a/\bar{r}_f)^2]\}}{\log[(r_f/r_a)^2]} \tag{58}$$

In many cases it will be found that

$$\chi \approx s_s^0/s_f^0 \tag{59}$$

where the superscript zero indicates infinite dilution and where this relation would be expected from Equation (56) if the γ solution, quite reasonably, slows both faster and slower components by the same factor.

In practice, c_s^0 is usually to be determined. A dilution series can yield s_s^0 / s_f^0. Then, in any run of that series or in subsequent assays, c_s^0 is computed for each frame from Equations (57) and (59). The values from several frames should agree and can be averaged. The faster component's initial concentration is computed from Equation (53).

The relationship between observed square law corrected areas and initial concentration can be written from Equations (53) and (57) as

$$\left. \begin{array}{l} c_s^0 = c_s^* - [c_s^*(\beta-1)/\beta] = c_s^* - c_{sf}^* \\ c_f^0 = c_f^* + [c_s^*(\beta-1)/\beta] = c_f^* + c_{sf}^* \end{array} \right\} \tag{60}$$

where c_{sf}^* is the absolute value of the correction and which is seen to be the same for both square law corrected peaks. In extreme cases the faster boundary can be annihilated.

If β is constant from frame to frame, the *change* in the Johnston-Ogston effect during the run must have been within plate reading error and the approximation $_a{}^x \approx 1 + x \ln a$ will be adequate to express Equations (57), (59), and (60) as

$$\frac{\beta-1}{\beta} = \frac{s_s^*/s_f^* - s_s^0/s_f^0}{1 - s_s^0/s_f^0} = \frac{c_{sf}^*}{c_s^*} \tag{61}$$

A chart for ready estimation of corrections can be constructed from β [1j] or $(\beta-1)/\beta$ [25] (Fig. 7-12 E). The latter is linear and is convenient with square-law corrected area measurements. Referring to the example of Fig. 7-12 D, the dilution series yields $s_s^0/s_f^0 = 0.68$. If $s_s^*/s_f^* = 0.75$ in the undiluted run, the correction is 20 per cent of the observed square-law corrected slow peak (Fig. 7-12 E).

EFFECT OF TIME AND DIFFUSION.   Diffusion is involved in three main considerations of centrifugation experiments starting with a uniformly filled cell or tube. First, moving boundary patterns, especially from large particles in long cells, can be mathematically extrapolated to infinite time as if the plateau never disappeared to increase the resolution. Second, the impervious top and bottom cause the concentration gradient to adjust so that the combination of sedimentation and diffusion yield no net transport through these interfaces for all times during the run. This will be treated as the Archibald method, which can yield a molecular weight as well as the initial concentration from data taken before the plateau is gone. Third, later, the transient approach to classical sedimentation equilibrium can be used to determine the diffusion coefficient.

Resolution of Components.   The fact that the boundary region does not remain infinitely sharp means that two components of slightly different s-rates will have overlapping boundary regions. Extensive investigation into ways of exploiting precise measurement of the spreading with time are based on a fundamental concept: the spreading of a single component due to diffusion is related to the square root of the time [cf. Equation (7)], whereas the separation between peaks of different s-rates is proportional to the first power [cf. Equation (24)]. Observed patterns (Fig. 7-13 A) grow broader with time, but normalized ones grow narrower (Fig. 7-13 B) [1d]. Thus, at long times in a cell of great length the width of a normalized boundary region will reflect differences in s-rate of components in the all component plateau.

Treat each element of area of the concentration gradient pattern as representing the boundary of a separate component. In order to determine the proper normalizing function, make a change of variable in Equation (39) to s^* using Equation (24) and $dr = \omega^2 rt\, ds^*$. This gives for $c_a = 0$

$$1 = \int_0^\infty \left[\left(\frac{\omega^2 r^3 t}{c^0 r_a^2} \right) \frac{\partial c}{\partial r} \right] ds^* = \int_0^\infty g^*(s^*)\, ds^* \tag{62}$$

Hence, $g^*(s^*)$, the "apparent distribution function" with respect to apparent s-rate, is the appropriate function given in square brackets.

The best resolution is obtained by extrapolating $g^*(s^*)$ to infinite time, illustrated in Fig. 7-13 C and D. This is the proper way to analyze overlapping moving boundary patterns in lieu of dropping perpendiculars at the minima for any particular frame during the run, even though the infinite time pattern is not precise because of too long an extrapolation.

Archibald Method. With synthetic boundary cells in the centrifuge for which solvent is layered above solution (as in electrophoresis)

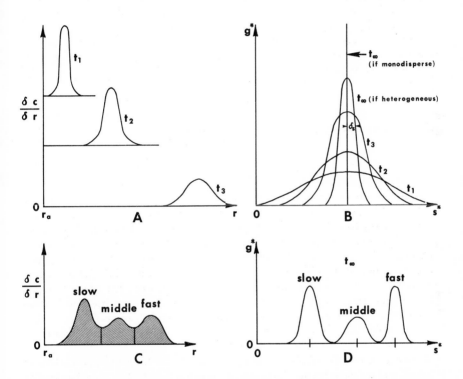

Fig. 7-13. Conversion of moving boundary patterns to apparent distribution function with respect to apparant s-rate, $g^*(s^\circ)$. (A) Gradient patterns for successive times. (B) Superimposed plot of distribution function for patterns of A. The trend in spreading is opposite to A, and extrapolation to infinite time yields a curve with standard deviation σ_s due to heterogeneity in s-rate classes. (C) Overlapping paucidisperse gradient pattern because of diffusion. (D) Extrapolated distribution function for C shows greatly improved resolution. An application is given in Fig. 7-21 A.

the starting boundary area represents the initial concentration difference. In conventional cells, there will be a period during which the boundary region touches the meniscus. Similarly, at the bottom of the cell there will be concentration gradients as solute sediments. Archibald [26] realized that, since no mass could be transported out of the cell, the net flow given by Equation (28) must be zero at r_a and r_b. This meant that $\partial c/\partial r$ would adjust itself so that

$$s/D = [(1/c)(\partial c/\partial r)/(\omega^2 r)]_{r=r_a,r_b} \tag{63}$$

If both $\partial c/\partial r$ and c could be determined for either, or both, the top and bottom of the cell, the ratio s/D could be calculated. To determine c_a or c_b, it is merely necessary to know c^0 and use Equation (39).

Because of steep gradients, the method is extremely sensitive to errors in r_a and/or r_b. Location of these surfaces by bisecting flanking fringes from a meniscus has been proposed [27]. Because of optical effects, the gradient cannot actually be measured at the true meniscus and must be obtained by extrapolation. This is frequently done right on the comparator screen, but linearity can be achieved [28] by plotting $(\partial c/\partial r)/(rc)$ vs. $(r-r_a)/(rc)$. This is shown from Equation (28) by approximating the flow near the meniscus by

$$\omega^2 rsc - D\partial c/\partial r = 0 + \ell\,(r-r_a) + \cdots \tag{64}$$

where ℓ is an unknown constant. Rearrangement gives

$$(\partial c/\partial r)/(rc) = \omega^2 s/D - (\ell/D)(r-r_a)/(rc) + \cdots \tag{65}$$

A similar expression would be used for the cell bottom, which is frequently made visible as a second meniscus with a transparent dense immiscible fluid. An attractive suggestion [29] is to use speeds sufficient to develop an almost horizontal gradient at the meniscus, and to perform a duplicate run in a synthetic boundary cell to give the plateau concentration, so that c_a can be determined from Equation (36) instead of Equation (39). Actually, this effects no increase in precision (since the denominator in Equation (63) now has a larger percentage error), precludes use of data from the cell bottom (since gradients there at the higher speed are too steep), and is not applicable to very small molecules (since they cannot be dialyzed in order to obtain the solvent for the synthetic boundary cell run).

Conversion of s/D values to molecular weight for both top and bottom of the cell and for each frame is done with Equation (25). Corrections for activity coefficient variation with concentration, if infinite dilution values are not used, and net solvation are the same as required in classical sedimentation equilibrium [cf. Equation (83) or (94)]. If the Archibald method is used to demonstrate homogeneity by claiming no trend in successive values, then the primary data should be analyzed in a different way. Rewrite Equation (63) by adding and subtracting c^0 as [25,30]

$$[(\partial c/\partial r)/(\omega^2 r)]_{r_a} = (s/D)[-(c^0-c_a) + c^0] \tag{66}$$

A graph of the left-hand side against $-(c_0 - c_a)$, which is measureable without knowing c^0 by Equation (39), gives a straight line with slope s/D and intercept c^0. A corresponding equation for the bottom of the cell can be written and the data plotted on the same graph. If there is heterogeneity, the line will be curved [31] with: (a) the final slope (at the meniscus) giving s/D for the slowest component; (b) the initial slope giving the z-average s/D; and (c) the chord giving the weight average s/D. Alternatively, such a plot can be used to determine c^0 for moving boundary patterns that do not clear the meniscus regardless of any interpretation of the slopes [25,30].

Transient Approach to Sedimentation Equilibrium. Moving boundary theory represents one form of the transient solution of the combined transport problem prior to the plateau being shortened to zero. As time further increases, the transport by diffusion increases to balance that by centrifugation, and equilibrium is attained at every level in the cell. To understand the entire transient it is necessary to consider solutions valid for long times in a cell of finite length.

Van Holde and Baldwin [32] succeeded in reducing an approximate solution of the Lamm Equation (29) to a very simple relationship of significant value, practically, and conceptually. This superseded the application of the Mason-Weaver solution for a gravitational field by Svedberg and Pedersen [1a]. LaBar and Baldwin [11] examined the exact solution of Nazarian [33] in great detail and put the relationship into still more precise form. Basically, the notion is that the time to reach within ϵ of equilibrium is independent of speed but proportional directly to the square of the column depth and inversely to the diffusion coefficient. Thus, the transient in low-speed centrifugation experiments depends on and can be used to measure D, whereas the transient in high speed runs depends on and can be used to measure s. The criterion as to high or low speed depends on the particle; for very small or asymmetric ones existing centrifuges cannot go fast enough for the s measurement, and for very large or compact particles they cannot go slow enough for stability. These instrumentation problems are always under active development, as are theoretical ones involved in the opposite calculation of s at low and D at high speed.

The tractability of the transient solution depends on selection of certain parameters [32] (Fig. 7-14 A). Let c_a and c_b be the (w/v) concentration at r_a and r_b, respectively. Let the subscript *eq* refer to values at equilibrium. Define α, ϵ, and λ as

$$\left.\begin{aligned}
\alpha &\equiv c^0/(c_b - c_a)_{eq} \\
\epsilon &\equiv [(c_b - c_a)_{eq} - (c_b - c_a)]/(c_b - c_a)_{eq} \\
\lambda &\equiv (r_b - r_a)/(r_b + r_a)
\end{aligned}\right\} \tag{67}$$

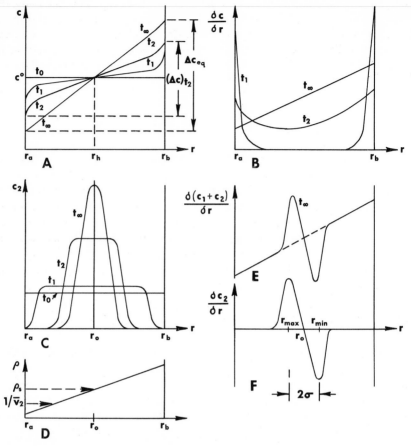

Fig. 7-14. Equilibrium in centrifugal field. *(A)* Classical sedimentation equilibrium method starting with uniform distribution at t_0 gives continuously increasing concentration with distance at t_∞. Fig. 7-22 illustrates method of plotting data from the transient for diffusion coefficient determination. *(B)* Corresponding gradient pattern to A starts very steep at ends and progressively raises in center and tilts. Fig. 7-23 illustrates method of plotting data from the equilibrium pattern for z-average molecular weight determination. *(C)* Isodensity equilibrium method for macromolecule in density gradient produced by classical sedimentation equilibrium of small molecular solute. Both flotation and sedimentation occur, resulting in a zone with band center at r_0. *(D)* The density at r_0 corresponds to that of the net solvated particle which may be greater or less than the reciprocal of partial specific volume. *(E)* Corresponding gradient pattern to C is a biphasic curve superimposed on the equilibrium gradient of smaller molecule as in B. *(F)* Replotted gradient of macromolecule has separation between r_{min} and r_{max} twice the standard deviation of a Gaussian function (for application see Fig. 7-7 C and G).

and t_ϵ as the time for the solute, originally of c^0 throughout, to redistribute to the value ϵ. Then, the Nazarian solution of Equation (29) yields [11]

$$t_\epsilon = F(\alpha, \epsilon, \lambda) \ (r_b - r_a)^2 / D \qquad (68)$$

where

$$F(\alpha,\epsilon,\lambda) \equiv (1/\pi^2)[\ln(1/\epsilon) + \ln K + \ln(K'/K)]/\Omega$$

$$\Omega \equiv 1 + 1/(4\pi^2\alpha^2)$$

$$K \equiv (4/\pi^2)\{1+\cosh[1/(2\alpha)]\}/\Omega^2 \tag{69}$$

$$K'/K \equiv 1 - (\lambda/\alpha)(9.472 \quad 10^{-2}-1.51 \quad 10^{-4}/\alpha^2)$$

Table 7-3 shows that $F(\alpha, \epsilon, \lambda)$ depends very little on λ, which takes into account the sector shape and centrifugal field (a rectangular cell in a uniform field has $\lambda = 0$) and that $F(\alpha, \epsilon, \lambda)$ is a function of ϵ only, if $\epsilon \leqslant 0.5$ and $\alpha \geqslant 1$. This is the range for which the higher order terms omitted in deriving the expression for $F(\alpha, \epsilon, \lambda)$ can be neglected. Even though the original Lamm equation was used, the fact that $F(\alpha, \epsilon, \lambda)$ is essentially a function of ϵ only suggests that the above considerations are applicable to any system whether concentrated, nonideal, or charged, provided that only $\alpha \geqslant 1$. In other words, if at the highest speed the concentration at the bottom is no more than about three times the concentration at the meniscus at equilibrium, the time to reach equilibrium is given by Equation (68) and is independent of speed or distance from center of rotation. At the higher speed, more mass must be redistributed, but it takes the same time to do so. Overspeeding for a precise time shortens the time [34] as does use of a precise preformed concentration step [35].

SEDIMENTATION EQUILIBRIUM

Classical sedimentation equilibrium considers transport by diffusion balanced by transport by sedimentation. Similarly, there could

TABLE 7-3

FACTORS FOR TRANSIENT APPROACH TO CLASSICAL SEDIMENTATION EQUILIBRIUM[*]

α	Ω	$u_h^\dagger$	$F(\alpha,\epsilon,\lambda)$					
			$\epsilon = 0.1$		$\epsilon = 0.01$		$\epsilon = 0.001$	
			$\lambda = 0$	$\lambda = 0.1$	$\lambda = 0$	$\lambda = 0.1$	$\lambda = 0$	$\lambda = 0.1$
0.2	1.6333	0.677	0.1478	0.1449	0.2907	0.2878	0.4335	0.4306
0.5	1.1013	0.581	0.1969	0.1951	0.4087	0.4069	0.6205	0.6188
1.0	1.0253	0.541	0.2080	0.2070	0.4355	0.4346	0.6630	0.6621
2.0	1.0063	0.521	0.2110	0.2105	0.4428	0.4423	0.6747	0.6742
5.0	1.0010	0.508	0.2119	0.2117	0.4449	0.4447	0.6780	0.6778
10.0	1.0003	0.504	0.2120	0.2119	0.4452	0.4451	0.6785	0.6784

[*] See Equations (68) and (69) for definitions of symbols and functions.

be flotation equilibrium. The concentration continuously increases
or decreases, respectively, with distance in these two cases (except
near the center of rotation in the latter) [36]. However, if there is a
density gradient in the cell which straddles the solute particle density,
there will be sedimentation on one side and flotation on the other.
The result is a band or zone of solute which eventually reaches an
equilibrium width in an equilibrium density gradient. This complex
double equilibrium situation will be denoted isodensity equilibrium.

The mathematical solution of the dynamic balance of transports in
either case becomes unwieldy for the nonideal concentrated electrolytes encountered. It will be illustrated for the practical location of
the hinge point in classical sedimentation equilibrium. For more general treatment of equilibrium, thermodynamic description has been
required and is outlined here for binary and ternary systems.

HINGE POINT.   The level in the cell where the concentration in classical
sedimentation equilibrium is equal to the initial concentration is called the
hinge point (Fig. 7-14 A). At $\partial c/\partial t = 0$ Equation (29) becomes for all r

$$D \frac{\partial c}{\partial r} - \omega^2 rsc = 0 \tag{70}$$

The solution of this equation for constant s and D is

$$\frac{c}{c^0} = \frac{e^{u^\dagger/\alpha}}{\alpha(e^{1/\alpha}-1)} \tag{71}$$

where c^0 is the average concentration (initial concentration, if uniform between the cell limits r_a and r_b), α of Equation (67) is

$$\alpha \equiv \frac{c^0}{c_b - c_a} = \frac{2D}{\omega^2 s(r_b^2-r_a^2)} = \frac{1}{\ln(c_b/c_a)} \tag{72}$$

and

$$u^\dagger \equiv (r^2-r_a^2)/(r_b^2-r_a^2) \tag{73}$$

is the fluid volume fraction above r. Equation (71) shows c to be an increasing
function from $c_a < c^0$ to $c_b > c^0$. The hinge point level in the cell r_h, corresponding to $u_h\dagger$, is given implicity by

$$u_h\dagger \equiv (r_h^2-r_a^2)/(r_b^2-r_a^2) = \alpha \ln\left[\alpha(e^{1/\alpha}-1)\right] \tag{74}$$

Values of $u_h^\dagger$ as a function of α are given in Table 7-3.

THERMODYNAMIC DESCRIPTION IN BINARY SOLUTION.   For an
electrolyte in water and a test solute particle moved from r to $r+dr$ thermodynamic equilibrium means

$$d\bar{\mu} = \left(\frac{\partial\bar{\mu}}{\partial r}\right)_{P,m} dr + \left(\frac{\partial\bar{\mu}}{\partial P}\right)_{r,m} dP + \left(\frac{\partial\bar{\mu}}{\partial m}\right)_{r,P} dm = 0 \qquad (75)$$

where $d\bar{\mu}$ is the change in total chemical potential $\bar{\mu}$ of the test particle; m, molal concentration.

The chemical potential μ due to composition under no external field or elevated pressure is

$$\mu = \mu_0 + \nu\,RT\,\ln\,\gamma m \qquad (76)$$

where μ_0 is the potential in a standard state; γ, activity coefficient; ν, number of ions dissociated per molecule. Thus, the last partial derivative is

$$\left(\frac{\partial\bar{\mu}}{\partial m}\right)_{r,P} = \frac{\partial\mu}{\partial m} = \nu RT\,d\ln\,\gamma m \qquad (77)$$

The per cent composition by weight p is related to molality m by

$$m = (1000/M)\,p/(100\text{-}p) \qquad (78)$$

The change in volume of solution per unit weight of solute is called the apparent specific volume ϕ. A convenient form for computation using densities follows from this definition as

$$\left.\begin{array}{c} \phi \equiv (V-V^0)/w \\[6pt] 1 - \phi\,\rho^0 = 100(\rho-\rho^0)/(p\rho) \end{array}\right\} \qquad (79)$$

where V, V^0 are volume of solution and solvent, respectively; w, the weight of solute; ρ^0, density of solvent alone. The partial specific volume $\bar{v}$ is the change in volume per infinitesimal change in weight of solute at constant weight of solvent w^0. This partial derivative can be written in a form for computation as

$$\left(\frac{\partial V}{\partial w}\right)_{w^0} \equiv \bar{v} = \phi + \frac{d\,\phi}{d\,\ln[p/(100-p)]} \qquad (80)$$

From thermodynamic considerations

$$\left(\frac{\partial\bar{\mu}}{\partial P}\right)_{r,M} = M\bar{v} \qquad (81)$$

with the pressure gradient dP/dr given by Equation (42).

Substitution of the partial derivatives in Equation (75) gives

$$\partial\mu/\partial r = \nu\,RT\,d(\ln\,\gamma m\,)/dr = M(1-\bar{v}\rho)\omega^2 r \qquad (82)$$

This shows that both (anhydrous) molecular weight and partial specific volume enter without specifying the actual kinetic unit; even so, $M(1-\bar{v}\rho)$ is called the effective mass.

For determining molecular weights, Equation (82) can be rewritten as

$$\frac{(1/m)\,dm/dr}{\omega^2 r} = \frac{M(1-\bar{v}\,\rho)}{\nu RT(1+m\,d\ln\gamma/dm)} \tag{83}$$

For determining activity coefficients, integral expressions taking pressure effects into account are used [37].

THERMODYNAMIC DESCRIPTION IN TERNARY SOLUTION. Consider a mixed solvent whose components are labeled 0, 1, and a macromolecular solute labeled 2. The solvent could be $CsCl_{(1)}$ in $H_2O_{(0)}$ or two organic liquids for polymer studies. For the ternary system at constant temperature, two equations corresponding to Equation (75) will apply.

$$\left(\frac{\partial\bar{\mu}_1}{\partial r}\right)_{P,m_1,m_2} dr + \left(\frac{\partial\bar{\mu}_1}{\partial P}\right)_{r,m_1,m_2} dP + \left(\frac{\partial\bar{\mu}_1}{\partial m_1}\right)_{r,P,m_2} dm_1 + \left(\frac{\partial\bar{\mu}_1}{\partial m_2}\right)_{r,P,m_1} dm_2 = 0 \tag{84}$$

$$\left(\frac{\partial\bar{\mu}_2}{\partial r}\right)_{P,m_1,m_2} dr + \left(\frac{\partial\bar{\mu}_2}{\partial P}\right)_{r,m_1,m_2} dP + \left(\frac{\partial\bar{\mu}_2}{\partial m_1}\right)_{r,P,m_2} dm_1 + \left(\frac{\partial\bar{\mu}_2}{\partial m_2}\right)_{r,P,m_1} dm_2 = 0 \tag{85}$$

As before, these can be reduced to

$$M_1(1-\bar{v}_1\rho)\omega^2 r\,dr = \left(\frac{\partial\mu_1}{\partial m_1}\right)_{r,P,m_2} dm_1 + \left(\frac{\partial\mu_1}{\partial m_2}\right)_{r,P,m_1} dm_2 \tag{86}$$

$$M_2(1-\bar{v}_2\rho)\omega^2 r\,dr = \left(\frac{\partial\mu_2}{\partial m_1}\right)_{r,P,m_2} dm_1 + \left(\frac{\partial\mu_2}{\partial m_2}\right)_{r,P,m_1} dm_2 \tag{87}$$

Let Γ_1' be the thermodynamic binding coefficient expressed as the net grams of component 1 bound per gram of macromolecule 2

$$\Gamma_1' \equiv \frac{M_1}{M_2}\left(\frac{\partial m_1}{\partial m_2}\right)_{\mu_1} = -\left(\frac{M_1}{M_2}\right)\frac{(\partial\mu_1/\partial m_2)_{m_1}}{(\partial\mu_1/\partial m_1)_{m_2}} \tag{88}$$

where the triple product rule is used to obtain the right-hand member. Define an analogous parameter (without name to imply physical interpretation) as

$$\gamma' \equiv \left(\frac{M_2}{M_1}\right)\frac{(\partial\mu_1/\partial m_1)_{m_2}}{(\partial\mu_2/\partial m_2)_{m_1}} \tag{89}$$

which approaches zero as $m_2 \to 0$. The simultaneous solution of Equations (86) and (87), first eliminating dm_1 and then dm_2, after considerable algebra, is

$$\frac{dm_1}{dr} = \frac{[M_1(1-\bar{v}_1\rho)+M_2\gamma'\Gamma_1'(1-\bar{v}_2\rho)]\omega^2 r}{(\partial\mu_1/\partial m_1)_{m_2}(1-\gamma'\Gamma_1'^2 M_2/M_1)} \tag{90}$$

$$\frac{dm_2}{dr} = \frac{M_2[(1+\Gamma_1')-\rho(\bar{v}_2+\Gamma_1'\bar{v}_1)]\omega^2 r}{(\partial\mu_2/\partial m_2)_{m_1}(1-\gamma'\Gamma_1'^2 M_2/M_1)} \tag{91}$$

SOLVATION AND BUOYANT FORCE. Consider N macromolecules of weight M_2 which have a dry volume of V' ml/g, and have a solvation mantle of volume V'' ml/g and density ρ'' (Fig. 7-4). The weight and density of the composite particle, $M_2(1+V''\rho'')$ and $(1+V''\rho'')/(V'+V'')$, respectively, can be substituted for M and ρ' of Equation (25), which can then be rearranged to

$$10^{-6}RTs/D = M_2[1-V'\rho+V''(\rho''-\rho)] \tag{92}$$

where s and D are in Svedbergs and Ficks, respectively. The density ρ'' of the solvation mantle which migrates with the macromolecule could be: (a) the same as ρ; (b) less than ρ, if the solvent contains inorganic salts, sucrose, or other inert molecules which cannot fit as close to the particles as can water; or (c) greater than ρ, if there is selective binding of a dense component of the solvent such as ionically bound heavy metal ions.

Dynamically, if $\rho'' = \rho$, any amount of solvent bound does not affect the calculation of the anhydrous molecular weight M_2 of Equation (92). The additional centrifugal force due to increased mass is cancelled by increased buoyancy, and both s and D are affected to the same degree by a change in V'' through the change in friction.

Whether or not both components 0 and 1 are bound in the same proportion as present in the bulk solution, the thermodynamic expression $M_2(1+\Gamma_1')$ is not the same as $M_2(1+V''\rho'')$. Equation (91) can be put in a form similar to Equation (83) as

$$\frac{(1/m_2)dm_2/dr}{\omega^2 r} = \frac{M_2(1+\Gamma_1')\{1-\rho[(\bar{v}_2+\Gamma_1'\bar{v}_1)/(1+\Gamma_1')]\}}{\nu RT(1+m_2 d \ln \gamma_2/dm_2)(1-\gamma'\Gamma_1'^2 M_2/M_1)} \tag{93}$$

$$= \frac{M_2\{1-\bar{v}_2\rho+[\Gamma_1'(1-\bar{v}_1\rho)]\}}{\nu RT(1+m_2 d \ln \gamma_2/dm_2)(1-\gamma'\Gamma_1'^2 M_2/M_1)} \tag{94}$$

If the factor in square brackets in Equation (93) is considered the reciprocal of the density of a hypothetical particle with only net solvation, then the net solvated molecular weight, $M_2(1+\Gamma_1')$, will be computed (subject to a correction from the denominator if the data do not refer to infinite dilution). If the partial specific volume $\bar{v}_2$ is used in Equation (83), then comparison with Equation (94) shows that the anhydrous molecular weight M_2 will be calculated whether or not there is solvation only if $\Gamma_1' = 0$.

Comparison of Equation (94) with Equation (63) shows that, if data are not extrapolated to infinite dilution, there will be a correction factor, $1 + m\, d \ln \gamma/dm$, even if $\Gamma_1' = 0$ in the Archibald method and, hence, also in Equation (25), using s and D from separate experiments. In addition, there will be terms involving Γ_1' if anhydrous molecular weight is desired.

It is not true, however, that the dry diameter will be calculated from Equation (22) if the dry density is used, even if the net solvation is zero. To show this, let $2a_0'$ be the equivalent sphere diameter of the dry particle (Fig. 7-4).

Then

$$
\left.
\begin{aligned}
(a_0/a_0')^3 &= 1 + V''/V' \\[4pt]
\frac{\rho'-\rho}{1/V'-\rho} &= 1 - \frac{V''(1-V'\rho'')}{(V'+V'')(1-V'\rho)}
\end{aligned}
\right\}
\tag{95}
$$

If there is no selective solvation ($\rho''=\rho$), Equation (22) can be written using Equation (95) as

$$
\frac{s}{(1+V''/V')^{2/3}[1-(V''/V')/(1+V''/V')]} = \frac{(2a_0')^2(1/V'-\rho)}{18\eta\,(f/f_0)}
\tag{96}
$$

For a hydration, V''/V', of 1 and 2 the denominator on the left-hand side is 0.7937 and 0.6934, respectively. If the hydration can be estimated, the observed s-rate can be corrected so that the dry diameter can be calculated on the right using the reciprocal of the partial specific volume for $1/V'$. This is the equation used for the hydration scales on the right of Fig. 7-4.

EQUILIBRIUM DENSITY GRADIENT.   In the absence of net binding, ($\Gamma_1'=0$) the equilibrium distribution of component 1 (salt) from Equation (90) is independent of component 2 (macromolecule). At infinite dilution of component 2 the density at each level is determined by m_1 according to Equations (78) and (79) (Fig. 7-14 D). In this case Equation (90) can be rewritten using Equation (76) as

$$
\frac{d\rho}{dr} = \frac{M(1-\bar{v}\rho)\omega^2 r}{\nu RT\partial(\ln \gamma m)/\partial\rho}
\tag{97}
$$

Hearst *et al.* [38] found that the effects of pressure in aqueous CsCl solutions are negligible in changing the solute molality or its redistribution. They were able to separate Equation (97) into two main terms

$$
\frac{d\rho}{dr} = \frac{d\rho_c}{dr} + \kappa(\rho_c)^2\omega^2 r
\tag{98}
$$

where

$$
\frac{d\rho_c}{dr} = \left[\frac{M(1-\bar{v}\rho)\omega^2 r}{\nu RT\partial(\ln \gamma m)/\partial\rho}\right]_{P=0}
\tag{99}
$$

Here $d\rho/dr$, the physical density gradient, is a linear summation of the composition density gradient at atmospheric pressure $d\rho_c/dr$ and the compression gradient given by the last term in which ρ_c is the density calculated from composition alone at $P=0$ and κ is the isothermal compressibility coefficient of the solution $(1/\rho)d\rho/dP$. Values of m, ρ, and γ at atmospheric pressure are available for many solutes of interest. They have been used in numerical evaluations of the composition density gradient [39,40], some values of which are given in Table 7-4.

TABLE 7-4

DENSITY GRADIENT [39, 40] PRODUCED WITH CLASSICAL SEDIMENTATION
EQUILIBRIUM AT HIGH CONCENTRATIONS (25°C)*

p	ρ	CsCl	ρ	KBr	ρ	Urea
30	1.2858	6.25	1.2566	2.94	1.0795	0.348
35	1.3496	6.91	1.3117	3.18		
40	1.4196	7.46	1.3715	3.30	1.1084	0.356
45	1.4969	7.90				
50	1.5825	8.19			1.1381	0.325
55	1.6778	8.28				
60	1.7846	8.25				
65	1.9052	8.01				

m	ρ	Sucrose	ρ	RbCl	RbBr
0.2	1.0223	1.17	1.05	1.02	1.49
0.4	1.0453	2.01	1.10	1.81	2.74
0.6	1.0665	2.58	1.15	2.43	3.94
0.8	1.0861	2.94	1.20	2.90	4.71
1.0	1.1042	3.14	1.25	3.15	5.64
1.2	1.1210	3.25	1.30	3.24	6.11
1.4	1.1367	3.31	1.35	3.60	6.54
1.6	1.1512	3.27	1.40	4.28	6.97
1.8	1.1649	3.19	1.45		7.29
2.0	1.1776	3.11			
3.0	1.2310	2.70			
4.0	1.2712	2.22			
5.0	1.3025	1.78			
6.0	1.3276	1.34			

* Entry under substance name is $[10^{10}/(\omega^2 r)]\,d\rho/dr$.

DETERMINATION OF CONCENTRATION IN CLASSICAL AND ISO-
DENSITY EQUILIBRIUM.   Let Q be the quantity of solute in a sector cell.
At any time

$$Q = 2\,\Theta\,a'\int_{r_a}^{r_b} rc\,dr \qquad (100)$$

where 2Θ is the sector angle and a' the cell thickness, and so initially

$$Q = \Theta\,a'\,(r_b^2 - r_a^2)c^0 \qquad (101)$$

Eliminating Q gives for both classical and isodensity equilibrium

$$c^0 = [2/(r_b^2 - r_a^2)]\int_{r_a}^{r_b} rc\,dr \qquad (102)$$

By integration by parts Equation (102) can be expressed as

$$c^0 = -[1/(r_b^2-r_a^2)] \int_{r_a}^{r_b} r^2(\partial c/\partial r)\,dr \qquad (103)$$

for measurements of $\partial c/\partial r$ instead of c with a zone or band having $\partial c/\partial r = 0$ at r_a and r_b.

If the concentration gradient in isodensity equilibrium is symmetrical about a point r_0, Equation (103) can also be written

$$c^0 = -[2r_0/(r_b^2-r_a^2)] \int_{r_a}^{r_b} (r-r_0)(\partial c/\partial r)\,dr \qquad (104)$$

which is a first moment of the gradient pattern about band center [41]. If $c(r)$ in addition is Gaussian, it can be described by

$$\left.\begin{aligned}
c &= c_{max} \exp\,[-(r-r_0)^2/(2\sigma^2)] \\[4pt]
c_{max} &= (Q/A)/[\sigma(2\pi)^{1/2}] \\[4pt]
(\partial c/\partial r)_{max} &= -(\partial c/\partial r)_{min} = (Q/A)/[\sigma^2(2\pi e)^{1/2}]
\end{aligned}\right\} \qquad (105)$$

where A is the cross-sectional area of the cell at band center r_0 and the maximum and minimum gradients, respectively, occur at $\mp\,\sigma$, the standard deviation. For the sector cell

$$Q/A = c^0(r_b^2-r_a^2)/(2r_0) \qquad (106)$$

and Equation (105) yields

$$c^0 = (\pi e/8)^{1/2}[r_0/(r_b^2-r_a^2)](r_{min}-r_{max})^2[(\partial c/\partial r)_{max} - (\partial c/\partial r)_{min}] \qquad (107)$$

ISODENSITY EQUILIBRIUM IN TERNARY SYSTEM.

Density of Band Center.   For isodensity equilibrium systems commonly studied (Fig. 7-14 C and D) the maximum macromolecular concentration will occur at the same level in the cell for both w/v and w/w concentration scales [1d]. At band center r_0, $dm_2/dr = 0$ and Equation (91) yields for the value of isodensity ρ_0

$$\rho_0 = \left[\frac{1+\Gamma_1'}{\bar{v}_2+\Gamma_1'\bar{v}_1}\right]_{r_0} \qquad (108)$$

Band Shape at Infinite Dilution.   When sufficiently dilute, the macromolecular particles, even though solvated, behave independently [42] with

$$(\partial\mu_2/\partial m_2)_{m_1}[1-\gamma'\,\Gamma_1'^2 M_2/M_1] \approx RT/m_2 \qquad (109)$$

With this approximation, Equation (91) becomes

$$RT\, d \ln m_2/dr = \omega^2 r M_2 [1 - \bar{v}_2 \rho) + \Gamma_1'(1 - \bar{v}_1 \rho)] \qquad (110)$$

Assume variation about band center due to the equilibrium distribution of solute 1 to be given by linear relations [43]

$$\rho = \rho_0 + (d\rho/dr)_{r_0}(r - r_0)$$
$$\bar{v}_1 = \bar{v}_{1,0} + (d\bar{v}_1/dr)_{r_0}(r - r_0)$$
$$\bar{v}_2 = \bar{v}_{2,0} + (d\bar{v}_2/dr)_{r_0}(r - r_0) \qquad (111)$$
$$\Gamma_1' = \Gamma_{1,0}' + (d\Gamma_1'/dr)_{r_0} (r - r_0)$$

Substitution into Equation (110), discarding all terms of the order of $(r - r_0)^2$, gives

$$d \ln m_2/dr = -(r - r_0)/\sigma^2 \qquad (112)$$

where σ^2 is defined by

$$\frac{RT}{\omega^2 r_0 \sigma^2} = M_2 \left[\bar{v}_2 \frac{-d\rho}{dr} + \rho \frac{d\bar{v}_2}{dr} - \frac{d\Gamma_1'}{dr}(1 - \bar{v}_1 \rho) + \Gamma_1' \left(\bar{v}_1 \frac{-d\rho}{dr} + \rho \frac{d\bar{v}_1}{dr} \right) \right]_{r_0} \qquad (113)$$

Equation (112) integrates to a Gaussian function centered at r_0

$$m_2 = (m_2)_{r_0} \exp \left[-(r - r_0)^2/(2\sigma^2) \right] \qquad (114)$$

where σ is seen to be its standard deviation (Fig. 7-14 E).

Band Width at Infinite Dilution. The rather formidable expression of Equation (113) for σ^2 can be simplified using M_s and ρ_s as the molecular weight and density of the hypothetical effective solvated macromolecule considered on page 261 for classical sedimentation equilibrium and defined by [42]

$$\left. \begin{array}{l} M_s \equiv M_2(1 + \Gamma_1') \\[2mm] \rho_s \equiv (1 + \Gamma_1')/(\bar{v}_2 + \Gamma_1' \bar{v}_1) \end{array} \right\} \qquad (115)$$

where $(\rho_s)_{r_0} = \rho_0$ by Equation (108). Differentiation of Equation (115), substitution, and extensive rearrangement without discarding any terms yields from Equation (113)

$$\sigma^2 = \left[\frac{RT\rho}{M_s (d\rho/dr)_{eff} \omega^2 r} \right]_{r_0} \qquad (116)$$

where

$$\left(\frac{d\rho}{dr}\right)_{eff} \equiv \left[\frac{d\rho}{dr} + \rho^2\frac{d(1/\rho_s)}{dr}\right]_{r_0} \tag{117}$$

These equations show that the *net* solvated particle determines the band width. This, of course, is related to the similar situation with classical sedimentation equilibrium using Equation (93). The equivalent Equations (113) and (116) give the Meselson et al. [44] relation in the absence of solvation. Equation (113) has the advantage of expression in terms of thermodynamic quantities, even though unknown.

Study of the pressure dependence of ρ_s shows that quantities calculated at atmospheric pressure need be augmented by a compressibility term [42]

$$\rho^2 \, d(1/\rho_s)/dr \approx -[d\rho_s/dr]_{r_0} - \kappa_s\rho_c^2\omega^2r \tag{118}$$

where ρ_c is the density calculated from composition of solute 1 at atmospheric pressure and κ_s is the compressibility of the solvated macromolecular particle. Using Equations (98) and (118), Equation (117) becomes

$$\left(\frac{d\rho}{dr}\right)_{eff} = \frac{d\rho_c}{dr} - \left(\frac{d\rho_s}{dr}\right)_{P=0} + (\rho_c)_0^2\omega^2r\,(\kappa-\kappa_s) \tag{119}$$

which shows that the effective density gradient is the composition gradient diminished by a solvation gradient and enhanced by a net compression gradient due to differences in compressibilities of solvent and solvated macromolecules. The first term is by far the dominant one in aqueous systems (Table 7-4) and the second can be estimated from variation of ρ_0 with slight changes in chemical nature of solute 1 [42].

Band Width at Finite Concentration. If concentrations are expressed on the (w/v) scale and $\Gamma_1' = 0$, Equation (91) can be rewritten [45]

$$d\mu_2/dc_2 = M_2(1-\bar{v}_2\rho)\omega^2r \, dr/dc_2 \tag{120}$$

Let the nonideality of the macromolecule be such that

$$d\mu_2/dc_2 \approx RT(1/c_2 + 2BM_2) \tag{121}$$

where B is related to the second virial coefficient. Substitution of Equation (121) and applicable parts of Equation (111) and integration yields

$$\ln[c_2/(c_2)_{r_0}] = -(r-r_0)^2/(2\sigma^2) - 2BM[c_2-(c_2)_{r_0}] \tag{122}$$

instead of Equation (114), where σ is the standard deviation when $B = 0$. If $r_{min} - r_{max}$ is the distance between (observed) inflection points of Equation (122), it can be shown that

$$(r_{min} - r_{max})^2 = 4\sigma^2[1+4e^{-1/2}BM_2(c_2)_{r_0}] \tag{123}$$

Nonideality of the usual type, $B > 0$, makes the band broader. After σ^2 is obtained by correcting for concentration from Equation (123) or by extrapolation, it can be used in Equation (116) to compute M_s.

CHARGE EFFECTS

Most substances of biological interest have an electrical charge which complicates their behavior in centrifugal fields [46, 47]. Let M refer to the molecular weight of the neutral constituent which has $\nu-1$ counterions for each ionized primary particle. Evidently, the mass of the particles in solution is less than M and one would expect at least the factor ν on the right of Equation (25) [cf. Equation (83)]. For example, D and s for KCl at 25°C are 176 F and 0.193 S, respectively [2, 47]. In Equation (25), as written, these yield $M = 35.7$, approximately half the correct value $39 + 35.5$. A macroion will tend to precede its counterions and generate an electrical field which causes an opposing electrophoretic movement. This is known as the primary charge effect. In diffusion, the opposite situation exists because the counterions have a larger diffusion rate and an augmenting electrophoretic movement results. Thus, these primary charge effects, also, do not cancel when sedimentation and diffusion are combined.

The presence of a supporting electrolyte reduces the electric field strength produced by separated charges. However, the supporting electrolyte can itself have a primary charge effect with its field causing electrophoretic migration of the macroion, either enhancing or diminishing its sedimentation. This is known as the secondary charge effect.

SEDIMENTATION VELOCITY.   Consider a solution containing a macroion, 2, its counterion, 1, and other ions having charges q_i, molal concentrations m_i, s-rates s_i, and signed electrophoretic mobilities u_i. Let the composite of all the primary charge effects cause a field $d\psi/dr$. The net velocity in the plateau can be written [47]

$$
\left.
\begin{aligned}
dr'_0/dt &= s_0\omega^2 r' - u_0 d\psi/dr \\
&\ \bullet \\
&\ \bullet \\
&\ \bullet \\
dr'_n/dt &= s_n\omega^2 r' - u_n d\psi/dr
\end{aligned}
\right\} \tag{124}
$$

As in electrophoresis alone, the electroneutrality condition means that in any lamina there can be no net movement of charge, hence

$$\sum_0^n q_i m_i dr'_i/dt = 0 \tag{125}$$

Simultaneous solution of Equations (124) and (125) gives for the macroion

$$s_2' \equiv (dr_2'/dt)/(\omega^2 r_2') = s_2 - u_2 \sum_0^n q_i m_i s_i \Big/ \sum_0^n q_i m_i u_i \qquad (126)$$

where s_2' is the net velocity expressed as an s-rate.

If the solution contains only the macroion and its counterion, $q_2 m_2 = -q_1 m_1$ and Equation (126) becomes

$$s_2'/s_2 = 1 - (1-s_1/s_2) T_2 \qquad (127)$$

where

$$T_2 \equiv q_2 m_2 u_2/(q_2 m_2 u_2 + q_1 m_1 u_1) = |u_2| \Big/ (|u_2|+|u_1|) \qquad (128)$$

is the transference number of the macroion. As the charge on the macroion is increased (by changing pH away from isoelectric point), $|u_2| \to |u_1|$. Also, since the counterion is small $s_1 \ll s_2$. Hence, from Equations (127) and (128) the primary charge effect, in the limit, could cut the observed s-rate of the macroion in half.

With a supporting electrolyte with common counterion Equation (126) can be written

$$\frac{s_2'}{s_2} = 1 - T_2 + \frac{u_2}{s_2}\left[s_1+\left(\frac{q_3 m_3}{q_1 m_1}\right)s_3\right]\Big/\left[u_1+\left(\frac{q_3 m_3}{q_1 m_1}\right)u_3+\left(\frac{q_2 m_2}{q_1 m_1}\right)u_2\right] \qquad (129)$$

As the concentration of supporting electrolyte is increased $T_2 \to 0$ which reduces the primary charge effect, but, with $-q_1 m_1 \to q_3 m_3 > q_2 m_2$ the secondary charge effect approaches

$$\frac{s_2'}{s_2} \to 1 - \left(\frac{s_1-s_3}{s_2}\right)\left(\frac{u_2}{|u_1|+|u_3|}\right) \qquad (130)$$

EQUILIBRIUM. The charge term to be added to Equation (75) is

$$(\partial\bar{\mu}/\partial\psi)_{r,P,m}\, d\psi = q\, \mathcal{F}\, d\psi \qquad (131)$$

where q is the charge, $\mathcal{F}$ the Faraday. For classical sedimentation equilibrium, assume $\Gamma_1' = 0$, infinite dilution, include a term like Equation (131) in both Equations (86) and (87), and solve simultaneously eliminating $d\psi$. This yields [37]

$$\frac{RT\, d\ln m_2}{\omega^2 r\, dr} = M_{PA_q}(1-\bar{v}_{PA_q}\rho) - \left(\frac{q}{2}\right)M_{BA}(1-\bar{v}_{BA}\rho) \qquad (132)$$

Here constituent 2 is considered a macromolecule PA_q and constituent 1 the supporting electrolyte BA. Comparison of Equations (94) and (132) indicates that the charge effect is the same as a net binding per gram Γ'' of

$$\Gamma'' \equiv (q/2)M_{BA}/M_{PA_q} \qquad (133)$$

For isodensity equilibrium the electric field is determined mainly by the salt redistribution [48]. Its magnitude can be determined by writing Equation (75) with the term from Equation (131) for both the salt anion, subscript a, and cation, subscript c, and solving simultaneously for $d\psi/dr$. Then write Equation (75) for the charged macromolecule with this $d\psi/dr$ and assume no interaction ($\Gamma_1' = 0$). With linear assumptions about the gradient, Equation (114) results again with band center at [48]

$$\rho_0 = \frac{1 + q(M_a - M_c)/(2M_2)}{\bar{v}_2 + \dfrac{q(M_a - M_c)}{2M_2}\left(\dfrac{M_a\bar{v}_a - M_c\bar{v}_c}{M_a - M_c}\right)} \tag{134}$$

and width

$$\sigma^2 = \left\{\frac{RT\rho}{[M_2 + q(M_a - M_c)/2](d\rho/dr)\omega^2 r}\right\}_{r_0} \tag{135}$$

Comparison of Equations (97), (115), (116), (134), and (135) indicates that if $\bar{v}_a \approx \bar{v}_c$ the charge effect is the same as a net binding per gram of

$$\Gamma''' \equiv (q/2)(M_a - M_c)/M_2 \tag{136}$$

Determination of s-Rate and Density of Biologically Active Agent (Preparative Ultracentrifugation)

Suppose a new biological activity is discovered and an assay can be developed that is an approximate measure of concentration of the active agent. One of the first physical quantities that should be determined is the s-rate of the activity. This is done by assaying swinging tube fractions in order to locate the boundary between supernatant fluid and bulk suspension, after centrifugation at a known speed, time, and temperature (moving boundary method). Once the s-rate is known: (a) the proper conditions can be selected for clarifying or pelleting the agent; and (b) optical centrifuge patterns on crude or partially purified material can be interpreted; and, if the particle density is assumed or measured: (c) an estimate of the particle size can be made; (d) moving zone preparative procedures can be designed.

Rough determination of s-rate and selection of rotor, speed, and time for pelleting are interrelated, so they will be considered together using an $\overline{ST}$ [s-t-bar] chart for rapid calculation. A more precise method will be given using a boundary locator function u^* (u-star). Then moving zone methods, including procedures for making density gradients, will be treated. Finally, particle density determinations are covered. Reference to the general description in the section Methods of Ultracentrifugation will be required.

SEDIMENTATION COEFFICIENT

$\overline{ST}$ CHART METHOD.   The time required for a boundary, starting at the meniscus, to sediment to a given level is called the precipitation time t''. Two factors are involved: (a) s^*, the average s-rate, embodying the nature of solute, solvent, and temperature; and (b) P_i, the performance index, which includes operating details of tube size, its location in rotor, and speed used. Formally,

$$t'' = \left(\frac{10^{13}}{4\,\pi^2}\right)\frac{1}{s^*P_i} \tag{137}$$

where

$$P_i \equiv (rpm)^2/\ln(r/r_a) \tag{138}$$

with r_a, the radius to the meniscus; (rpm), speed in R.P.M.; s^*, in Svedbergs; and t'', in hours [Equation (137) follows from Equations (18) and (24)]. Values of P_i are available in instruction manuals, usually for maximum fill of tube. A convenient monogram has been published by Giebler [49] for other volumes for both Spinco and Phywe machines.

The equivalent time of the accelerating or decelerating periods can be shown to be one-third of their duration if the acceleration is constant, that is, if the speed is changed linearly with time. Under these conditions, the true centrifugation time is merely the elapsed time between reaching two-thirds operating speed on the way up and again on the way down.

A further simplification can be made for rapid laboratory calculations with a function [21]

$$\overline{ST} \equiv \left(\frac{10^{13}}{4\,\pi^2}\right)\frac{\ln(r_b/r)}{(rpm)^2_{\max}} \tag{139}$$

where r_b is the radius to the bottom. This has a minor advantage over P_i in that tabulation only as function of volume and not as speed is necessary (Fig. 7-15), but more significantly, simple difference in $\overline{ST}$ values gives the product of average s-rate and time for a particle to sediment through the volume under consideration. Analogous to Equation (137)

$$s^*t'' = \Delta\overline{ST}(rpm)^2_{\max}/(rpm)^2 \tag{140}$$

where $\Delta\overline{ST}$ is the difference in $\overline{ST}$.

As an example, consider Table 7-5 which represents data on just two fractions from three swinging bucket runs on a biologically active agent. The top 4-ml fraction extends from 5 ml to 1 ml. Using a tabulation equivalent to Fig. 7-15, the corresponding $\overline{ST}$ values are 94 and 17. Thus the s-rate is 16 S from Equation (140). Suppose it is desired to concentrate this agent from about 100 ml of crude harvest fluid. In a Spinco #40 rotor with 12 ml per tube, sedimentation from meniscus to pellet corresponds to $\Delta\overline{ST} = 108 - 0$. At top speed (40,000 R.P.M.) Equation (140) gives $t'' = 108/16 = 6.75$ hr. Determine now the speed to use for an 18 hr overnight run. Equation (140) rewritten is

$$(rpm) = (rpm)_{max}[\Delta\overline{ST}/(s^*t'')]^{1/2} \tag{141}$$

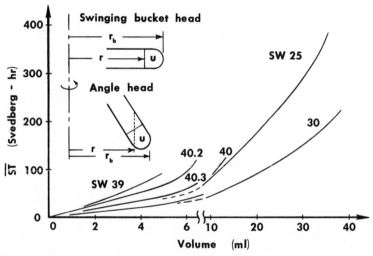

Fig. 7-15. Rotor characteristics for rapid computation of minimum apparent s-rate of particles traversing any volume in preparative ultracentrifugation. Numbers on curves refer to Spinco rotors. The ordinate $\overline{ST}$ is the product of s-rate and time, corrected for speed. Inserts show measurements required to compute $\overline{ST}$ for any rotor-tube combination not given. An application is given in Table 7-5 ([21] Courtesy, Academic Press, Inc.).

which gives 24,500 R.P.M. Another possibility is to run at 4°C. For practical purposes, the variation in s-rate with temperature depends mainly on the viscosity change of water [cf. Equation (22)]. The 16 S at 20°C becomes 16(1.0050/1.5674) = 10.3 S at 4°C. The speed to use for 18 hr, then, would be 30,500 R.P.M.

The above concentration procedure is normally reported as: "...centrifugation in the cold at 60,000g for 18 hr." However, this does not give enough information to enable another worker to perform an equivalent centrifugation. Instead, the report should state: "...centrifugation sufficient to pellet particles of 10 S at 4°C." If the other worker had only a Spinco #30 rotor and 20 ml of material, he would put 15 ml of mineral oil on top to avoid tube collapse, and, using Fig. 7-15, calculate the time to use as $t'' = 125/10 = 12.5$ hr at 30,000 R.P.M.

BOUNDARY LOCATOR METHOD. A more precise determination of s-rate requires stopping the centrifuge before the boundary reaches the bottom, taking several fractions for assay, establishing that a plateau exists, locating the boundary position, and converting

TABLE 7-5

Sample calculation of s-rate of biologically active agent by precipitation time determination with known rotor-tube characteristics (moving boundary method)

DATA: SW-39 ROTOR; 36,000 R.P.M.; 20°C

Fraction	Per cent activity recovered		
	4 hr	6 hr	8 hr
Top 4 ml	20	1	0.4
Bottom 1 ml	80	99	99.6

CALCULATION:
From table, time to just empty top 4 ml: 6 hr.
From Fig. 7-15 for top 4 ml: $\Delta \overline{ST} = 94 - 17 = 77$.
$$\therefore s^{\circ} = \frac{77}{6} \left(\frac{40,000}{36,000} \right)^2 = 16 \text{ S}$$

its displacement to an s-rate (Fig. 7-16). For relatively purified agents, there is an insufficient density gradient (provided in crude preparations by contaminant boundaries) to prevent radial convection [cf. Fig. 7-10]. Hence, sucrose is used as follows: weigh 150 mg sucrose into two test tubes, and dissolve with 3 ml and 6 ml, respectively, of the sample. Transfer 1 ml of the former to each of 3 centrifuge tubes, layer 2 ml of the latter on each, then layer 2 ml of the sample. Slight agitation with a saw-toothed wire blurs the density steps into a smooth gradient of sucrose but the agent is uniformly distributed. Use slow acceleration (~ 2000 R.P.M./min) and deceleration without brake after the period at operating speed. Compute an apparent boundary location u^* as if each cut were in the plateau. The appropriate formula [22] comes from Table 7-2 by replacing $\overline{u}$ by u^*

$$U + u^* = (U + u)/[1 + \Sigma c \, \Delta u/(c^{\circ}U)] \tag{142}$$

The effect of a fractional error in the assay dc/c is

$$-du^* = (u - u^*)[(U + u^*)/(U + u)]dc/c \tag{143}$$

Table 7-6 shows a sample calculation for an agent titrated using doubling dilutions [50]. The boundary position corresponds to the intersection of the best plateau line (vertical) and the $u = u^*$ line [cf. Fig. 7-16 C].

CONVERSION TO STANDARD CONDITIONS. First convert the boundary position to an observed s-rate using Equation (140), if volumes are used, or using

$$s^* = F_s(\log \bar{r} - \log r_a)/t' \tag{144}$$

where s^* is in Svedbergs; t', in min; and r_a and $\bar{r}$, radii corresponding to starting level and boundary location, respectively [cf. Equation (24)]. The speed factor F_s, defined later in Table 7-7, can be tabulated for speeds commonly used.

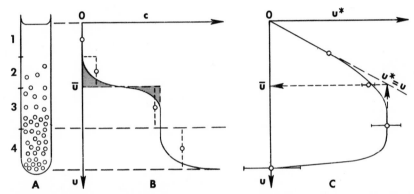

Fig. 7-16. Location of boundary in preparative ultracentrifugation by biological assay of relatively large fractions. (A) Schematic distribution of broad boundary having moved part way down the tube. (B) If precise concentration curve were obtainable, the boundary would be located by matching cross-hatched areas. With only four fractions indicated by circled numbers, the dashed histogram of average concentrations would not locate boundary. (C) Plotting the average concentration times the volume as a special boundary locator function u° gives a curve demonstrating a plateau, which when extended to the diagonal $u^* = u$ locates the boundary $\bar{u}$. The effect of the assay error increases with distance from the $u^\circ = u$ line, as indicated by the horizontal extent at each plotted point. See Table 7-6 for data for an actual agent (modified from references [22] and [50]).

By convention, conversion to 20°C and water is done as though the s-rate depends only on the factors given in

$$s = \frac{M(1-\bar{v}\rho)}{6\pi\eta a_0(f/f_0)N} \tag{145}$$

where M is molecular weight; $\bar{v}$, partial specific volume; ρ, η, solution density and viscosity, respectively; $2a_0$, equivalent sphere diameter (Fig. 7-4); and f/f_0, the friction factor. [This relation follows

TABLE 7-6

Sample Calculation of s-rate of Biologically Active Agent by Moving Boundary Method in Swinging Bucket Rotor [50]

	Data				Calculations							
						Boundary Locator Function				Error		
Fraction	r	Δu	c	$u=\Sigma\Delta u$	$c\Delta u$	$\Sigma c\Delta u$	$\Sigma c\Delta u/(c^\circ U)$	$U+u^\circ$	u°	$u-u^\circ$	$(U+u^\circ)/(U+u)$	$-du^\circ$
Meniscus	5.40											
Tube 1 ①	7.10	2.0	1	2.0	2.0	2.0	0.0197	8.189	1.839	0.161	0.98072	0.0395
②	7.95	1.0	4	3.0	4.0	6.0	0.0591	8.828	2.478	0.522	0.94417	0.1232
③	8.80	1.0	8	4.0	8.0	14.0	0.1378	9.097	2.747	1.253	0.87894	0.2753
④	9.80	1.0 (0.7)	64	5.0	64.0	78.0	0.7677	6.421	0.071	4.929	0.56573	0.6971
Meniscus	5.40											
Tube 2 ①	7.35	2.3	1	2.3	2.3	2.3	0.0226	8.459	2.109	0.191	0.97792	0.0467
②	8.20	1.0	8	3.3	8.0	10.3	0.1014	8.762	2.412	0.888	0.90798	0.2016
③	9.15	1.0	16	4.3	16.0	26.3	0.2589	8.460	2.110	2.190	0.79437	0.4349
④	9.80	2.0 (0.7)	32	5.0	64.0	90.3	0.8888	6.009	−0.341	5.341	0.52943	0.7069
Meniscus	5.40											
Tube 3 ①	7.75	2.7	2	2.7	5.4	5.4	0.0531	8.594	2.244	0.456	0.94961	0.1083
②	8.65	1.0	8	3.7	8.0	13.4	0.1319	8.879	2.529	1.171	0.88348	0.2586
③	9.50	1.0	16	4.7	16.0	29.4	0.2894	8.570	2.220	2.480	0.77557	0.4809
④	9.80	1.6 (0.3)	32	5.0	51.2	80.6	0.7933	6.329	−0.021	5.021	0.55762	0.7000

SW-39 lusteroid tube 0.85 cm/ml

∴ $U = 5.40/0.85 = 6.35$ ml

35,000 R.P.M. 350.3 min, 17.5°C

Initial complement-fixing titer 16

Assay error ± 25%

Assume $\bar{v} = 0.75$ ml/g and independent of temperature

s-RATE

From graph of $(u^\circ \pm du^\circ)$ vs. u, $\bar{u} = 2.50$ ml; $s^\circ = \dfrac{2.303 \cdot 10^{13}}{\omega^2 t} \log \dfrac{U+\bar{u}}{U} = 11.37$ S

Corrections for average of 25 mg/ml sucrose:

$\rho_4^{17.5} = 1.0084$; $(\eta/\eta_w)_{20} = 1.067$; $(\eta_{17.5}/\eta_{20})_w = 1.064$; $(1-\bar{v})/(1-\bar{v}\rho) = 1.026$;

$\therefore s_{20,w} = \left(\dfrac{1-\bar{v}}{1-\bar{v}\rho}\right)\left(\dfrac{\eta_T}{\eta_{20\,w}}\right)\left(\dfrac{\eta}{\eta_{w'T'}}\right)s^\circ = 13.2$ S from Equations (11), (14), and (92) if infinite dilution and no selective solvation are assumed]. Then

$$s_{20,w} = \left(\frac{1-\overline{v}}{1-\overline{v}\rho}\right)\left(\frac{\eta_T}{\eta_{20}}\right)_w\left(\frac{\eta_{soln}}{\eta_w}\right)_{T'} s \tag{146}$$

where the temperature T' of the viscosity measurement need be only approximately equal to T, the temperature of the run. [To derive Equation (146), write Equation (145) for $s_{20,w}$ and divide by Equation (145) assuming M, a_0 and f/f_0 are constant].

MOVING ZONE METHOD. The preformed density gradient, incidental to the moving zone process, must be used for stabilization against convection, but prevents the s-rate from being constant during the run. Methods for formation of the gradient can also be used at the higher densities required for preformed isodensity centrifugation as well. One requiring no special equipment consists of an initial layering of a few discrete density steps which are blurred: (a) by stirring with a saw-toothed wire as mentioned above; (b) by tilting the tube and rotating; or (c) by diffusion or standing over night. A gradient engine [1e, 1h] mixes two solutions of different density progressively and fills the centrifuge tube with a precisely linear gradient. Theory for various types of mixers, some easily assembled, is given by Bock and Ling [51].

Convenient formulas for calculating the density of a mixture of two stock solutions are

$$\overline{v} = (p_1\overline{v}_1 + p_2\overline{v}_2)/100 \tag{147}$$

$$\rho = (V_1\rho_1 + V_2\rho_2)/(V_1 + V_2) \tag{148}$$

where $\overline{v}$ is partial specific volume; p, weight per cent; and V, volume. The first equation is rigorous, but the second assumes additivity of volume.

Consider now what happens when the sample is layered on top of the preformed gradient. Because of the appreciable difference in diffusion rates, the initial zone will receive more sucrose from below than it loses protein. The density may increase to values higher than the local density just below the zone, and convection in the form of small droplets develops. The raining-down of visible droplets is quite dramatic, as well as disastrous. The most successful way to reduce the effect is to use only a very dilute initial sample, blurring the lower boundary as it is applied. Additives with compensating properties as well as inverse gradients of protein in the initial sample may be practical in some cases, and have been considered theoretically by Svensson et al. [52].

The droplet sedimentation and the dilution of the migrating zones are the major limitations of the moving zone method. The s-rate can be determined by locating the center of the initial and final zones (by biological assay of fractions). After conversion to s^*, corrections to water at 20°C can be made as in Equation (146), selecting the average concentration of the gradient as the effective solvent. More sophisticated treatments are available [1h].

ISODENSITY

For an isodensity measurement it is essential to be able to increase the density of the harvest fluid without inactivating the agent. First try CsCl and sucrose as diluents. Note that the density range for various solutes is definitely limited (Fig. 7-4). Set up a preformed gradient isodensity run, using any of the methods for making a gradient given above. Measure the density and activity of fractions. Repeat the run narrowing the density range for more precision.

For the slightest gradient, the centrifugal field itself can be used to develop the density difference between top and bottom of the tube. Fill the tube full at a density equal to the best estimate for the particle. Operate at top speed for successive periods of time, starting with at least 8 hr. An example of the resolution obtainable is given in Fig. 7-17.

Determination of Optical s-Rate, Isodensity and Purity (Analytical Ultracentrifugation)

OPTICAL SYSTEMS AND COMPARATORS

It is not necessary to study detailed optical theory [2c] before using the analytical ultracentrifuge. It is well, though, to understand a few general principles about the schlieren, Rayleigh interferometric, and absorption optics commonly used [1f, 54] (Figs. 7-7 and 7-18).

ALL SOLUTES PRESENT CONTRIBUTE TO THE PATTERN. The refractometric methods depend upon the specific refractive increment R_1

$$n - n^0 = R_1 c + R_{11} c^2 + \cdots \qquad (149)$$

where n and n^0 are the index of refraction at concentration c(w/v) and infinite dilution, respectively. Quite amazingly, R_1 is relatively constant from the smallest to the largest substance. This makes mass calculations easier (using a nominal value of 0.000186/mg/ml) but means that specificity is lacking. In contrast, with absorption optics the extinction coefficient is quite selective with wavelength. Monochromators covering ultraviolet and visible ranges are available and have been especially useful in nucleic acid studies.

OPTICAL SYSTEMS MUST BE FOCUSED. Alignment is usually done by the manufacturer or the field engineer. One should decide on the primary reference and have an agreement whereby the optics are not adjusted without prior approval.

There is still considerable controversy as to the proper place for focus, since the cell is a thick object and the depth of focus of the system is rather shallow. A practical solution is to focus on the rotor reference edges, since they need to be sharp for accurate alignment of photographic records, and the focus cannot conveniently be changed for each solvent or thickness of cell used (Fig. 7-3).

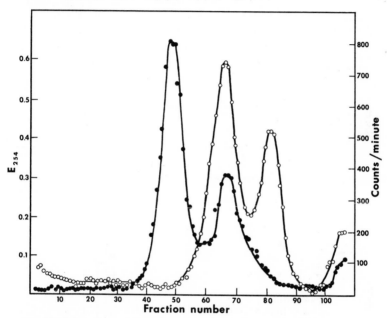

Fig. 7-17. Location of zones in preparative isodensity equilibrium method. Ribosome fractions collected by drip-out after centrifugation for 35 hr at 37,000 *R.P.M.* Density decreases from left to right, initial value 1.686. The isotopically denser ribosomes, revealed by P^{32} counts, solid circles, were from cells grown in N^{15}, C^{13}, P^{32} media and added at high dilution to normal cell extracts. They are not detected by the extinction coefficient measurements (E_{254}) which locate the heavy and light normal ribosome bands, open circles ([53] Courtesy, authors and *Nature*).

Both refractometric methods are astigmatic, with the second focus (for ordinates) at the schlieren diaphragm (Figs. 7-7 and 7-18). They do not, therefore, reveal rotor motion.

LIGHT RAYS ARE DEVIATED BY PASSING THROUGH AN INDEX OF REFRACTION GRADIENT. This is the basis of schlieren, but complicates interference and absorption optical systems.

NONPARALLEL ILLUMINATION FORESHORTENS THE SOLUTION. The true length can be measured between meniscus fine structure patterns [27] if a dense immiscible fluid is used to make a bottom interface.

ADJUSTMENTS DURING RUN.   In only schlieren optics can the magnification and pattern centering be changed at will. This is done with the schlieren diaphragm (Fig. 7-18). Fringes can be sharpened by light source adjustments in interference optics, but no adjustments can be made with the absorption system.

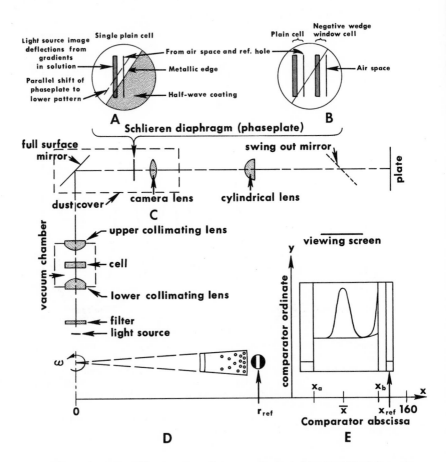

Fig. 7-18. Schematic schlieren optics showing operator adjustments and comparator alignment. (A), (B) Light source images as seen looking toward camera at schlieren diaphragm, which is adjustable in rotation and cross-optical axis position and gives the optical shadows (schlieren). Half-wave coating is actually transparent, as indicated in B. (C) Schematic arrangement of components. (D), (E) Cell and reference hole in rotor are magnified radially as in E, which shows schlieren pattern visible on viewing screen or plate. The axis of rotation on comparator scale is located to the left from the center of the image of the rotor reference a distance $M_oM_e r_{ref} = x_{ref}$. The 160 mm is a convenient value of x_r for normalizing radius cubed scale measurements [21, 25].

THE PHASEPLATE IS THE MOST COMMON SCHLIEREN DIAPHRAGM. Its fine metallic edge (Fig. 7-18) casts a shadow for parts of the pattern with no deflection, and the transmission half-wave coating casts an interference shadow for deflected rays, which rays, incidentally, produce light source images defocused by the lens action of the gradient.

COMPARATORS. The simplest form of a one-dimensional comparator is a ruler or scale. Graph paper is a two-dimensional comparator

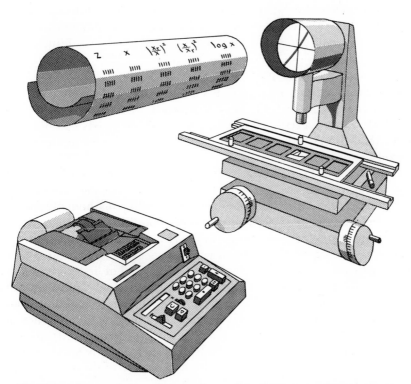

Fig. 7-19. Plate reading equipment for analytical ultracentrifugation. For schlieren or interference optics plates a two-dimensional comparator, at the right, should have projection-viewing; holder that permits sliding movement of the plate on the carriage parallel to itself; angular movement of carriage for alignment; sufficient travel to cover a frame without guage blocks; easily read scales; and rugged enough construction with proper lead screw pitch so that digital read-out converters can be attached (Courtesy, Gaertner Scientific Corporation).

The calculator at the left should print and handle multiplication with storage separately from the arithmetic register (Commercial equipment especially suited for plate reading shown schematically here is obtainable from Underwood Corporation − Tetractys − CR − and Gaertner Scientific Corporation − Coordinate Plate and Film Comparator).

The mathematical table indicated schematically in the center is to facilitate plate analysis when using the desk calculator. Some of the functions and formulas needed are indicated in Table 7-7.

and is used commonly for enlarger or densitometer tracings. Complex patterns of analytical ultracentrifugation are sufficiently stable and theoretically interpretable to warrant more elaborate measurement. Toolmakers' microscopes and optical comparators have the desired precision (within ±0.002 mm) and range (50 × 50 mm) (Fig. 7-19). However, since such instruments were not designed for plate analysis, there has been considerable confusion in making the adaptation. Those instruments with a precise projector frequently do not permit adequate plate alignment and provide an unneeded feature, since tracings and measurements on the image are not done. Rugged instruments with a carriage designed for precise alignment and two-dimensional calibrated movement can be adapted by adding a convenient plate holder, revolution counters, or digital read-out for automatic card or tape punching.

PHOTOGRAPHIC PLATES, ENLARGER, OR DENSITOMETER TRACINGS REPRESENT MAGNIFIED CELL IMAGES IN THE RADIAL DIRECTION. The comparator abscissa axis can be set so as to read directly the distance from the axis on such optically enlarged patterns (Fig. 7-18).

GEOMETRICAL CORRECTIONS. The sector-shaped cell and the increasing centrifugal field with radius introduce geometrical complexity into formulas. This requires higher mathematical functions than would be used for rectangular conditions (uniform field in a uniform cell). These include [21]: (*a*) logarithm instead of simple difference for s-rate; (*b*) integral with respect to $r^2 \, dr$ instead of dr for initial concentration; (*c*) second moment instead of first for boundary position; (*d*) fourth moment instead of second for boundary spreading; and (*e*) r^3 factor instead of a constant for distribution function. Many of these calculations are greatly simplified [25] in schlieren optics (*a*) by setting the comparator so that it reads the (magnified) distance from the center of rotation and (*b*) by measuring ordinates at selected abscissae from a radius-cubed scale. A summary of these formulas is given in Table 7-7 for reference.

SEDIMENTATION COEFFICIENT

Moving boundary schlieren patterns of crude extracts of the active agent under investigation could look like Fig. 7-20. The method most commonly used to measure the s-rate of these two observed peaks can be cited as: ". . . s-rate determined from the slope of log x_{max} vs. *t* plots." The procedure is to align the plate on the comparator so that the abscissa scale reads the (magnified) distance from the center of rotation (Fig. 7-18). Read for each frame the position of the meniscus, x_a, and of each maximum, x_{max}. Average meniscus readings, checking for any trend which would indicate cell leakage. Plot log x_{max} against

t. (In Fig. 7-20, x_{max} is taken as an approximation to the actual boundary position $\bar{x}$, cf. Table 7-2.) If the automatic camera had been set to take pictures at true centrifugation time (by starting at two-thirds operating speed during linear acceleration), all lines should go through log x_a. Points not on lines represent errors or unresolved

TABLE 7-7

SCHLIEREN OPTICAL METHOD FORMULAS [21, 25]
FOR COMPARATOR USING RADIUS-CUBED SCALE

$F_0 = 1/(M_0 M_e)$	x_r = comparator reference (usually 160 mm)
$F_x = x_r/(3000\ M_0 M_e)$	$Z = (10\ x/x_r)^3$
$F_y \equiv 1/(a'b'M_c M_e R_1)$	$dZ = (3000/x_r^3)x^2\ dx$
$F_s \equiv 10^{13} \ln 10/(60\omega^2)$	$y = y_{soln} - y_{solv}$

MOVING BOUNDARY METHOD WHEN $c_a = 0$

Routine, general use

$c^0 = [F_x F_y (x_r/x_a)^2 \tan \theta]\ \Sigma y \Delta Z$ $\qquad s^0 = F_s(\log x - \log x_a)/t'$

$$\left(\frac{x}{x_r}\right)^2 = \frac{\Sigma y \Delta Z}{\Sigma (x_r/x)^2 y \Delta Z} \qquad g^0 = \left\{\left[\frac{3t'\ \ln 10}{F_s}\right]\left[\frac{F_x F_y (x_r/x_a)^2 \tan \theta}{c^0}\right]\right\} yZ$$

$$s = F_s\ d \log \bar{x}/dt'$$

Special use

$c_p = [F_x F_y \tan \theta]\ \Sigma (x_r/x)^2 y \Delta Z \qquad \dfrac{x_{mean}}{x_r} = \dfrac{\Sigma (x_r/x) y \Delta Z}{\Sigma (x_r/x)^2 y \Delta Z}$

$$(M_0 M_e \sigma)^2 = x_r^2 \left\{\frac{[\Sigma y \Delta Z][\Sigma (x_r/x)^2 y \Delta Z] - [\Sigma (x_r/x) y \Delta Z]^2}{[\Sigma (x_r/x)^2 y \Delta Z]^2}\right\}$$

$$(M_0 M_e \sigma^0)^2 = \frac{x_r^2}{4}\left\{\frac{[\Sigma (x/x_r)^2 y \Delta Z][\Sigma (x_r/x)^2 y \Delta Z] - [\Sigma y \Delta Z]^2}{[\Sigma y \Delta Z][\Sigma (x_r/x)^2 y \Delta Z]}\right\}$$

$$2Dt = \left(\frac{1}{M_0 M_e}\right)^2\left[\frac{2 \ln 10\ (\log \bar{x} - \log x_a)}{(\bar{x}/x_a)^2 - 1}\right](M_0 M_e \sigma^0)^2$$

ISODENSITY METHOD FOR ASSAY, $c_n = c_b = (\partial c/\partial r)_{r_a} = (\partial c/\partial r)_{r_b} = 0$

$c^0 = F_x F_y [x_r^2/(x_b^2 - x_a^2)] \tan \theta\ \Sigma y \Delta Z$

$c^0 = (\pi e/8)^{1/2} F_0^2 F_y \tan \theta\ [x_0/(x_b^2 - x_a^2)](y_{max} - y_{min})(x_{min} - x_{max})^2$

(if Gaussian zone)

peaks, as at t_1. The magnification is not used in the calculation because of the log function [cf. Equations (19) and (144)]. The instantaneous s-rate in Svedbergs is

$$s = F_s(d \log \bar{x}/dt') \qquad (150)$$

If the lines are straight, the calculated s-rate is for the plateau concentration existing at mid-time determined from the boundary position at that time and c^0 by

$$c_p = c^0 (x_a/\bar{x})^2 \qquad (151)$$

[cf. Equation (39)].

A more elaborate method programed for digital computers [23] is a least squares analysis using Equation (52) twice. First, omitting meniscus readings, compute the best quadratic through the points. Then calculate the zero time correction required to make log x_a fall on this curve. Second, use all points with the corrected time. The coefficient of the linear term is the s-rate corresponding to the initial concentration at atmospheric pressure. The square term coefficient gives the order of magnitude of combined pressure and dilution effects during the run.

Procedures for computation of the boundary position $\bar{x}$, when x_{max} is not adequate have been systematized and described elsewhere [21,25] (Table 7-7).

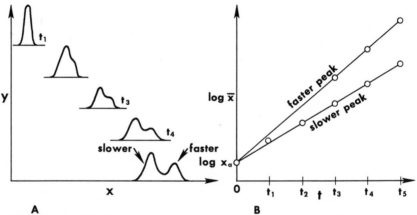

Fig. 7-20. Optical determination of s-rate. *(A)* Schlieren patterns finally resolving into two peaks. *(B)* Plot of log $\bar{x}$ vs. t. The location of maxima in A can be used to approximate $\bar{x}$. The s-rates are proportional to the slopes of the lines, which must intersect at point corresponding to meniscus.

PAUCIDISPERSITY AND HETEROGENEITY IN s-RATE

Compare the s-rate of the biological activity with the s-rates of all the visible peaks. If one corresponds, it presumably represents the active agent and all the rest represent impurities. In this case, the system is said to be paucidisperse, since there are only a few components. With some highly sensitive biological assays it is possible that the active agent is too dilute to see and all peaks are contaminants.

This question can be resolved when the conversion factor between biological activity and mass concentration is known.

A common error is to turn off the centrifuge as soon as a peak clears the meniscus (Fig. 7-20, t_1), and claim homogeneity. Schlieren patterns are not usually accepted for publication anymore; if they are submitted, they should be ones where the peak has moved at least ten times its average width.

Relative purity in paucidisperse systems is afforded by area measurements with schlieren, fringe counts with interference, or pen displacements of densitometer tracings with absorption optics. Radial dilution corrections are necessary to convert measured plateau concentrations c_p to more meaningful initial concentrations c_0 (Fig. 7-11) according to Equation (151). Alternatively, the corrections can be applied automatically using the formulas of Table 7-7 [cf. Equation (39) and Table 7-2].

A dilution series should be made using two double sector cells at once with four different concentrations (Fig. 7-12 D). This gives an idea of s-rates to be expected in various crude preparations, and gives infinite dilution s-rate ratios. These are important in Johnston-Ogston corrections if more precise relative purity calculations are necessary, or if the moving boundary pattern is to be used as an assay. If the s-rate first increases and then decreases as the concentration approaches zero, dissociation is taking place. Other types of interactions are revealed by anomalous area changes on dilution and failure to obtain baseline regions between peaks. For a complete review of the increasingly important study of interacting systems see Gilbert [55].

There is a strong possibility that a distribution of s-rate classes is present under each discernible peak. Thus each component can itself be heterogeneous. This can be determined by extrapolating the pattern to infinite time so that boundary spreading due to heterogeneity will not be masked by spreading by diffusion (Fig. 7-13). With lipid-free human serum such an extrapolation gave a pattern like Fig. 7-21 A [56].

Heterogeneity by sedimentation rate does not necessarily correspond to heterogeneity by electrophoresis, as seen in the pictorial representation of normal human serum (Fig. 7-21 B) [56].

ISODENSITY

Adjust a solution containing the active agent to the isodensity found by biological assay of preparative fractions. Analytical centrifugation for at least 8 hr is required to reach an equilibrium density gradient of the salt. In this time, viruses will also be in equilibrium bands, but DNA (deoxyribonucleic acid) and serum proteins require another 8 to 16 hr [19]. A schlieren pattern of an isodensity zone will look like Fig. 7-7 c, ultraviolet absorption zones like Fig. 7-7 g.

The density at band center ρ_0 is calculated approximately from

$$\rho_0 = \rho_h + (d\rho/dr)_{r_h}(r_0 - r_h) \tag{152}$$

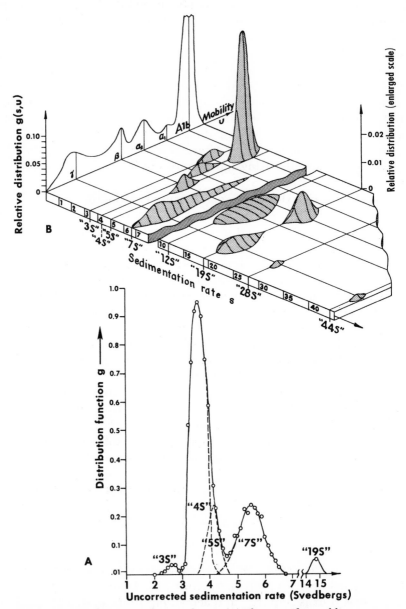

Fig. 7-21. Paucidispersity of s-rate classes. (A) Ultracentrifuge schlieren pattern from normal lipid-free human serum extrapolated to infinite time. (B) Electrophoretic and ultracentrifugal display of major serum proteins (Courtesy, *The Journal of Biological Chemistry*). For paucidispersity in density see Fig. 7-7 G and heterogeneity in molecular weight see Fig. 7-23.

where ρ_h is the density of a marker banded at r_h and $(d\rho/dr)_{r_h}$ is computed from Table 7-4 using

$$\frac{d\rho}{dr} = \frac{\{[10^{10}/(\omega^2 r)]d\rho/dr\}\omega^2 r}{10^{10}} \tag{153}$$

As an example, 40 per cent (w/w) CsCl (56.9 g/100 ml of solution) at equilibrium at 50,740 R.P.M. with r_a and r_b 6.25 and 7.25 cm, respectively, will have $d\rho/dr = 0.142$. In the 1-cm column there will be 0.142 g/ml density difference, which corresponds from a concentration vs. density table to $c_b - c_a$ of 18.8 g/100 ml. Hence α of Equation (67) is 3.0. From Table 7-4 $u_h\ddagger = 0.514$, and $r_h = 6.782$. In the absence of a marker, the initial density 1.4196 is used at r_h.

If the partial specific volume in the isodense solution is known, then the net binding coefficient (w/w), representing the excess salt bound over and above the nominal proportion in the bulk solution, can be calculated from

$$\Gamma_1' = (\rho_0\bar{v}_2 - 1)/(1 - \rho_0\bar{v}_1) \tag{154}$$

[This follows from Equation (108)]. Determination of the partial specific volume requires density measurements on pure solutions of the agent [1c]. The data are plotted in accordance with Equations (79) and (80). This is rarely possible with biological agents, and so values are estimated from composition or from isodensity measurements. Sometimes a plot of ηs vs. ρ for the agent in H_2O-D_2O mixtures can be extrapolated to $\eta s = 0$ (Fig. 7-4). The reciprocal of the corresponding density is chosen for $\bar{v}$. Correction is necessary for deuterium exchange [57], and with many agents the extrapolation is too long for precision.

DENSITY PAUCIDISPERSITY

The presence of several bands in analytical isodensity centrifugation indicates paucidispersity with respect to density (Fig. 7-7 G). Comparison of their densities with that determined biologically helps identify the active agent. Each band may also encompass density heterogeneity. Procedures for separating this from broadening by diffusion have been considered, but are not routine at present [1m].

The field-formed isodensity method has an interesting feature of concentrating all the agent to give the optical pattern. This is in direct contrast to moving boundary patterns which are produced by but a few of the particles present. An isodensity assay is thus a micromethod and attractive for biological studies. The initial concentration is determined by integrating the patterns or by assuming a Gaussian function, Table 7-7 [cf. Equations (102) through (105)].

IMPLICATIONS FOR PURIFICATION AND CONCENTRATION

Knowledge of the s-rate and density of the agent and how close contaminants are to these values is invaluable in designing purification procedures. Combinations of moving boundary, moving zone, isodensity, and interface centrifugation [18] can be made either successively or in the same tube. Moving boundary analytical ultracentrifugation should be used to follow the purification steps. Sometimes fundamental parameters can be obtained intentionally or as a by-product from complex preparative procedures.

Optical Determination of Diffusion Coefficient, Molecular Weight, and Heterogeneity of Partially Purified Agents

After the agent has been purified, at least to exhibiting only a single moving boundary peak and single isodensity band, the diffusion coefficient and molecular weight can be determined. Modern methods exploit the property that the time to reach within any given closeness to classical sedimentation equilibrium depends directly on the square of the column depth and inversely on the diffusion coefficient [1a, 11, 32].

Exceedingly stable, low-speed operation for molecular weights greater than 10^6 is possible with the magnetically suspended ultracentrifuge [5]. Below this, good results can be obtained with standard equipment with or without heavy rotors [58] using small volumes: (*a*) to reduce the time required for equilibrium; (*b*) to enable multiple runs in special centerpieces [58] (cf. Fig. 7-3); and (*c*) to conserve material for rare biological preparations. Such short column centrifugation in which equilibrium is reached for all levels in the cell has largely replaced the Archibald method [1c, 1f, 26], which exploited the no net flow condition only at the top and bottom of the cell, but from the start. It still has application in special cases and historical significance.

Determination of the diffusion coefficient from the transient approach to classical sedimentation equilibrium is replacing methods using the optical system of the ultracentrifuge merely for recording diffusion from a synthetic or sedimenting boundary. These older methods involve large zero time corrections and formidable complications due to concentration dependence and heterogeneity [1j]. Ideally, sufficient stable material should be available for a classical free diffusion experiment [2c].

Brief procedures will be given here first for the diffusion coefficient measurement, then for molecular weights, including recent isodensity equilibrium methods.

DIFFUSION COEFFICIENT

Perform a classical sedimentation equilibrium run to determine the difference in concentration $(c_b-c_a)_{eq}$ between top r_a and bottom r_b. For each frame during the transient approach to equilibrium compute

$$\epsilon = 1 - (c_b-c_a)/(c_b-c_a)_{eq} \qquad (155)$$

Plot $\log (1/\epsilon)$ against t (Fig. 7-22). The equation for this line, if $\alpha \geqslant 1$, $\epsilon \leqslant 0.5$, $\lambda \leqslant 0.1$ [cf. Equation (68)], is

$$\log (1/\epsilon) = -\log K' + \{\pi^2\Omega/[2.303\,(r_b^2-r_a^2)]\}Dt \qquad (156)$$

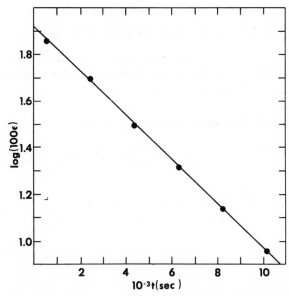

Fig. 7-22. Diffusion coefficient determination using the transient of classical sedimentation equilibrium method. Ribonuclease at 11 mg/ml, 15,220 R.P.M. in 3 mm column. Closeness to equilibrium measured by $\epsilon = 1 - (c_b - c_a)/(c_b - c_a)$ eq of Fig. 7-14 A. Either $\log \epsilon$ or $\log 1/\epsilon$ can be plotted. (Courtesy [32] authors and *The Journal of Physical Chemistry*).

Either the initial concentration c_0 or an absolute scale of concentration must be known to calculate the parameter α according to

$$\alpha = c^0/(c_b-c_a)_{eq} = 1/[\ln(c_b/c_a)] \qquad (157)$$

but, fortunately, α need be only approximated [cf. Equations (67) and (72)]. K' is a complicated approximate relation involving both α and the sector shape parameter

$$\lambda = (r_b - r_a)/(r_b + r_a) \tag{158}$$

but does not have to be evaluated in order to convert the best slope to D, using values of Ω, as a function of α, from Table 7-3. An alternate method which is even less sensitive to α, but depends on λ, is to plot $F(\alpha, \epsilon, \lambda)$ from Table 7-3 for each ϵ against t. Then D is calculated from the slope since [cf. Equation (68)]

$$F(\alpha,\epsilon,\lambda) = [1/(r_b - r_a)^2]Dt \tag{159}$$

Unfortunately, at the time of writing, the effect of heterogeneity with respect to diffusion coefficient has not been treated, so the values obtained represent some unknown sort of average, if the preparation of the agent is not homogeneous.

MOLECULAR WEIGHT HETEROGENEITY

The classical sedimentation equilibrium pattern from the diffusion coefficient experiment, or others, can be analyzed for molecular weight and heterogeneity information. Three successively higher types of averages can be written for any property, but have been especially applied to molecular weight distributions as the number average $\overline{M}_n$

$$\overline{M}_n \equiv \frac{\Sigma n_i M_i}{\Sigma n_i} = \frac{\Sigma c_i}{\Sigma c_i/M_i} \tag{160}$$

where n_i is the number of particles of molecular weight M_i and (w/v) concentration c_i; the weight average $\overline{M}_w$

$$\overline{M}_w \equiv \frac{\Sigma c_i M_i}{\Sigma c_i} \tag{161}$$

and the z-average $\overline{M}_z$

$$\overline{M}_z \equiv \frac{\Sigma c_i M_i^2}{\Sigma c_i M_i} \tag{162}$$

The weight and z-averages are related to the variance σ_M^2 of the molecular weight distribution of c_i vs. M_i by

$$\sigma_M^2 = \frac{\Sigma c_i (M_i)^2 - (\Sigma c_i M_i)^2/\Sigma c_i}{\Sigma c_i} = \overline{M}_w \overline{M}_z - \overline{M}_w^2 \tag{163}$$

If the system is homogeneous $\sigma_M = 0$ and $\overline{M}_n = \overline{M}_w = \overline{M}_z$. Fortunately, the centrifuge data can yield both $\overline{M}_w$ and $\overline{M}_z$.

If c^0 is known, the weight average molecular weight can be determined using

$$\frac{2(c_b - c_a)_{eq}}{c^0(r_b^2 - r_a^2)} = \frac{\omega^2 \overline{M}_w (1 - \overline{v}\rho)}{RT} \tag{164}$$

[This follows from an integral of Equation (83) if all species have the same $\overline{v}$]. Interference optics are best suited for this type of measurement. Whether or not c^0 is known, make a plot of $(1/r)\,(\partial c/\partial r)$ against $(c - c_a)$ (Fig. 7-23). Combined schlieren and interference optics are best suited for this. The slope of the line gives the z-average molecular weight according to

$$\frac{\partial c}{r\,\partial r} = \frac{\overline{M}_z (1 - \overline{v}\rho)\omega^2}{RT} [(c - c_a) + c_a] \tag{165}$$

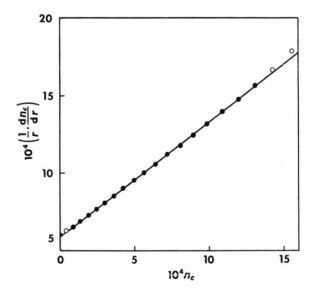

Fig. 7-23. Determination of molecular weight from classical sedimentation equilibrium method. Index of refraction measurements have been used (n_c) for ribonuclease in 3 mm column, 8.4 mg/ml, 20,410 R.P.M., 20°C. For a solute which is heterogeneous with respect to molecular weight, the slope on this plot gives z-average molecular weight. Note the curvature near ends of plot. Open circles show data taken within 0.03 cm of ends of the column (Courtesy, [32] authors and *The Journal of Physical Chemistry*).

If absolute concentrations are known in interference optics, then Equation 165 can be used as

$$\frac{\partial \log c}{\partial r^2} = \frac{\overline{M_z}(1-\bar{v}\rho)\omega^2}{2RT \ln 10} \qquad (166)$$

The slope of a graph of log c vs. r^2 will yield the z-average molecular weight at each point. It is evident that the longer the cell the greater the opportunity for heterogeneity determination. The tendency to use ultrashort columns and claim molecular weight homogeneity parallels the error of turning off a moving boundary run too soon, as mentioned above.

It should be noted that in a binary solution, solvation does not affect the calculation of anhydrous molecular weight. In a ternary solution — solvent $(_0)$, small molecule $(_1)$, macromolecule $(_2)$ — solvation enters only to the extent of the excess of the small component bound over its nominal ratio to solvent in the bulk solution. This is expressed on a weight basis with respect to macromolecule as the net solvation parameter Γ_1', which in the limit becomes the value given by Equation (154) for isodensity equilibrium. If the hypothetical net solvated partial specific volume $\bar{v}_s$ is used according to

$$\bar{v}_s = (\bar{v}_2 + \Gamma_1' \, \bar{v}_1)/(1+\Gamma_1') \qquad (167)$$

the net solvated molecular weight M_s will be determined as

$$M_s = M_2(1+\Gamma_1') \qquad (168)$$

[cf. Equation (93)]. For low densities (dilute solutions of all components) Γ_1' is generally neglected. Corrections for activity coefficient variation and the coefficient R_{11} of Equation (149), when refractometric methods are used are given by Van Holde and Baldwin [32].

DENSITY HETEROGENEITY

Systems dilute in macromolecule, or extrapolated to infinite dilution, yield a molecular weight from the band width. Unlike classical sedimentation equilibrium, a binary system cannot be used, and the net solvation parameter Γ_1' becomes appreciable as does density heterogeneity.

Measure the variance of the concentration distribution in the zone by taking half the distance between inflection points (Fig. 7-14) or from a plot of log c vs. r [40]. Extrapolate data to infinite dilution [cf. Equation (123)] and compute the net solvated molecular weight of Equation (168) from

$$M_s = \left(\frac{RT}{\omega^2}\right)\left[\frac{\rho}{r(d\rho/dr)_{\text{eff}}}\right]_{r_0}\left(\frac{1}{\sigma^2}\right) \qquad (169)$$

For detailed studies $(d\rho/dr)$ from Table 7-4 will not be a good enough approximation to $(d\rho/dr)_{\text{eff}}$ [in which case use Equation (119)].

A Gaussian distribution of density classes with variance σ_ρ^2 will broaden the observed Gaussian zone from that due to a single species (variance σ_1^2) according to [43]

$$\sigma^2 = \sigma_1^2 + \sigma_\rho^2/(d\rho/dr)^2 \qquad (170)$$

Thus density heterogeneity leads to too low a value of molecular weight, and probably explains most of the controversy over DNA molecular weights from CsCl isodensity experiments.

Glossary of Symbols

a — concentration dependence parameter kc^0

a' — cell path length

a_0 — radius of sphere of same volume and density as solvated particle (equivalent sphere)

a_0' — radius of sphere of same volume and density as dry particle

A — cross sectional area

b — pressure dependence parameter

b' — optical lever arm

B — virial coefficient

CONCENTRATION

c — general (w/v)

c^0 — initial of solute

$\bar{c}$ — at $\bar{r}$ if $D = 0$

c^* — square law corrected

c_{sf}^* — Johnston-Ogston correction

d — differential

D — diffusion coefficient

E — energy

exp — exponential function

FORCE

f_b — buoyant

f_c — centrifugal

f_f — friction

f_g — gravitational

FRICTION COEFFICIENTS

f — general, force/velocity

f_0 — of equivalent sphere $6\pi\eta a_0$

f/f_0 — friction factor (Table 7-1)

$F(\alpha,\epsilon,\lambda)$ — closeness to equilibrium function (Table 7-3)

$F - 10^{-7}$ cm²/sec, 1 Fick

F_0, F_s, F_x, F_y — comparation factors (Table 7-7)

$\mathcal{F}$ — Faraday

g — acceleration due to gravity

g^* — distribution function of s-rate

k — concentration parameter $(s^0/s'-1)/c$

k' — concentration parameter $(1-s'/s^0)/c$

k'' — pressure parameter $(s_0/s'-1)/P$

k''' — density parameter $(\rho-\rho_a)/P$

K — transient function (rectangular approximation)

K' — transient function (sector cell correction)

l — Taylor expansion coefficient

ln — natural logarithm

log — logarithm to base 10

WEIGHT MEASURES

m — molal concentration

m' — weight transported per unit area

M' — mass

$M, \overline{M}_n, \overline{M}_w, \overline{M}_z$ — molecular weight in general, number average, weight average, z-average, respectively

MAGNIFICATIONS

M_0 — of camera lens

M_c — of cylindrical lens

M_e — of enlarger or comparator

n — number, in general

n, n^0 — index of refraction of solution, solvent, respectively

N — Avogadro's number

p — concentration in weight percent

P — arbitrary point in cell or pressure above atmospheric

P_i — performance index of preparative rotor

q — charge per ion

Q — weight quantity contained in cell, arbitrary plane

RADIAL COORDINATE ON ROTOR

r — fixed

r' — moving

$\bar{r}$ — boundary position (Table 7-2)

r_0 — isodensity band center

r_1 — dividing level between slower and faster peaks

(rpm) — speed in *R.P.M.*

R — gas constant

R_1 — specific refractive increment

R_{11} — square term correction coefficient for R_1

RCF — relative centrifugal force

R.P.M. — rev/min

SEDIMENTATION COEFFICIENT

s — s-rate, in general

s' — of particles in plateau

s^0, s_0, s_0^0 — at infinite dilution, at atmospheric pressure, at both, respectively

s^* — average s-rate scale

s_2' — net of macromolecule, including charge effects

S — 10^{-13} sec, one Svedberg

$\overline{ST}$ — preparative centrifugation function

TIME

t — in sec

t' — in min

t'' — precipitation time in hrs

t_* — reduced time $2\omega^2 s_0^0 t$

t_ϵ — time to reach within ϵ of equilibrium

t_0, t_1, t_2, t_∞ — selected times during a run

T — absolute temperature

T_2 — transference number of macromolecule

SPECIAL VOLUME COORDINATES

$u, u', \overline{u}$ — between r_a and $r, r', \overline{r}$, respectively

u^* — boundary locator function

$u^\dagger$ — fluid volume fraction in cell $(r^2-r_a^2)/(r_b^2-r_a^2)$

u_* — reduced volume $\overline{r}^2/r_a^2$

u_i — electrophoretic mobility

U — extended cell volume between $r=0$ and r_a

VOLUME OF PARTICLES OR FLUIDS

v — volume, in general

$\overline{v}$ — partial specific volume

$\overline{v}_{i,0}$ — partial specific volume of i-th component at isodensity band center

V — volume of solution

V^0 — volume of solvent

V' — specific volume of dry particle

V'' — volume of solvation mantle per gram of dry particle

WEIGHT

w — of solute

w^0 — of solvent

w/w — weight per weight measure

w/v — weight per volume measure

RADIAL COORDINATE ON PLATE

$x, x', \overline{x}, x_0$ — $M_0 M_e$ times the corresponding r on rotor

x_{mean} — first moment of schlieren pattern

x_r — comparator reference

x_{ref} — rotor reference distance on plate

y — general ordinate

y — ordinate on schlieren pattern $y_{soln} - y_{solv}$

Z — normalized radius cubed scale $(10x/x_r)^3$

SUBSCRIPTS

a, b, p — meniscus, cell bottom, plateau, respectively

a, c — anion, cation, respectively

BA, PA_q — supporting electrolyte constituent, (charged) macromolecular constituent, respectively

eff — effective, taking into account macromolecule

eq — classical sedimentation equilibrium

h — hinge point

max, min — extremes of concentration or gradient distributions

s,f — slower, faster component, respectively

s — net solvated macromolecule

T,T' — temperature of run, temperature of viscosity measurement, respectively

0,1,2 — solvent, small molecule, macromolecule constituents, respectively

20,w — standard conditions of water

α,β,γ — superscripts for supernatant fluid, slower component phase, all-component plateau, respectively

α — classical sedimentation equilibrium parameter

β — build up factor of slower component c_s^*/c_s^0

β_* — reduced concentration $\bar{c}/c^0$

INTERACTION PARAMETERS

γ — activity coefficient on molal scale

γ' — thermodynamic function in ternary system

Γ_1' — net solvation expressed for component 1 bound to 2 (w/w)

Γ'' — net charge effect in classical sedimentation equilibrium

Γ''' — net charge effect in isodensity equilibrium

δ — displacement in Brownian motion

∂ — partial derivative

Δ — difference

ϵ — closeness to classical sedimentation equilibrium

η — coefficient of viscosity

θ — schlieren diaphragm angle

Θ — half-sector angle of cell

κ — compressibility of solution

λ — sector cell parameter $(r_b-r_a)/(r_b+r_a)$

μ — chemical potential

$\bar{\mu}$ — total potential

μ_0 — chemical potential in standard state

ν — number of ions per molecule

$\vec{v}$ — vector velocity

DENSITY

ρ — of solution

ρ^0 — of solvent

ρ' — of hydrodynamic particle

ρ'' — of solvation mantle

ρ_c — of solution due to composition at atmospheric pressure

ρ_0 — isodensity, of solution at r_0

Σ — summation

STANDARD DEVIATION

σ — of isodensity zone or moving boundary, in general

σ_1 — of isodensity zone from single component

σ^* — of moving boundary using fourth moment

σ_M — of molecular weight distribution

σ_s — of s-rate distribution

σ_ρ — of density distribution

τ — Brownian motion time increment

φ — apparent specific volume

χ — s-rate ratio for Johnston-Ogston correction

ψ — electric potential

ω — angular velocity

Ω — special function of α (Table 7-3)

References

GENERAL BOOKS AND REVIEW ARTICLES

1. Centrifugation
   a. T. Svedberg and K. O. Pedersen, *The Ultracentrifuge*, Oxford University Press, London (1940) (Johnson Reprint Corporation, New York).
   b. C. de Duve and J. Berthet, "The Use of Differential Centrifugation in the Study of Tissue Enzymes," *Internt. Rev. Cytol.*, **3**, 225 (1954).
   c. H. K. Schachman, "Ultracentrifugation, Diffusion, and Viscometry," *Methods Enzymol.*, **4**, 32 (1957).
   d. J. W. Williams, K. E. Van Holde, R. L. Baldwin, and H. Fujita, "The Theory of Sedimentation Analysis," *Chem. Rev.*, **58**, 715 (1958).
   e. C. de Duve, J. Berthet and H. Beaufay, "Gradient Centrifugation of Cell Particles: Theory and Application," *Progr. Biophys. Biophys. Chem.*, **9**, 325 (1959).
   f. H. K. Schachman, *Ultracentrifugation in Biochemistry*, Academic Press, New York (1959).
   g. R. L. Baldwin and K. E. Van Holde, "Sedimentation of High Polymers," *Fortschr. Hochpolymer. − Forsch.*, **1**, 451 (1960).
   h. M. K. Brakke, "Density Gradient Centrifugation and Its Application to Plant Viruses," *Advan. Virus Res.*, **7**, 193 (1960).
   i. S. Claesson and I. Moring-Claesson, "Ultracentrifugation," *Lab. Manual Anal. Methods Prot. Chem.*, **3**, 119 (1961).
   j. H. Fujita, *Mathematical Theory of Sedimentation Analysis*, Academic Press, New York (1962).
   k. R. Markham, "The Analytical Ultracentrifuge As a Tool for Investigation of Plant Viruses," *Advan. Virus Res.*, **9**, 241 (1962).
   l. J. Vinograd and J. E. Hearst, "Equilibrium Sedimentation of Macromolecules and Viruses in a Density Gradient," *Fortsch. Chem. Org. Naturstoffe*, **20**, 372 (1962).
   m. J. W. Williams, *Ultracentrifugation Analysis in Theory and Experiments*, Academic Press, New York (1963).
2. Diffusion
   a. J. Crank, *The Mathematics of Diffusion*, Oxford University Press, London (1956).
   b. W. Jost, *Diffusion in Solids, Liquids, Gases*, Academic Press, New York, 2nd ed. (1960).
   c. H. Svensson and T. E. Thompson, "Translational Diffusion Methods in Protein Chemistry," *Lab. Manual Anal. Methods Prot. Chem.*, **3**, 57 (1961).
3. Physical Chemistry
   a. H. Margenau and G. M. Murphy, *The Mathematics of Physics and Chemistry*, D. Van Nostrand, New York (1943).
   b. S. Glasstone, *Textbook of Physical Chemistry*, D. Van Nostrand, New York, 2nd ed. (1946).

RESEARCH LITERATURE

4. J. W. Beams, J. D. Ross, and J. F. Dillon, *Rev. Sci. Instr.*, **22**, 77 (1951).
5. J. W. Beams, R. D. Boyle, and P. E. Hexner, *J. Polymer Sci.*, **57**, 161 (1962).
6. N. G. Anderson, *J. Phys. Chem.*, **66**, 1984 (1962).

7. G. Meyerhoff, *Makromol. Chem.*, **15**, 68 (1955).
8. R. Trautman and V. W. Burns, *Biochim. Biophys. Acta*, **14**, 26 (1954).
9. J. B. Ifft and J. Vinograd, *J. Phys. Chem.*, **66**, 1990 (1962).
10. E. G. Richards and H. K. Schachman, *J. Phys. Chem.*, **63**, 1578 (1959).
11. F. E. LaBar and R. L. Baldwin, *J. Phys. Chem.*, **66**, 1952 (1962).
12. H. K. Schachman, L. Gropper, S. Hanlon, and F. Putney, *Arch. Biochem. Biophys.*, **99**, 175 (1962).
13. S. Hanlon, K. Lamers, G. Lauterbach, R. Johnson, and H. K. Schachman, *Arch. Biochem. Biophys.*, **99**, 157 (1962).
14. C. E. Schwerdt and F. L. Schaffer, *Ann. N. Y. Acad. Sci.*, **61**, 740 (1955).
15. J. Weigle, M. Meselson, and K. Paigen, *J. Mol. Biol.*, **1**, 379 (1959).
16. I. J. Bendet, C. E. Smith, and M. A. Lauffer, *Arch. Biochem. Biophys.*, **88**, 280 (1960).
17. R. Ballentine and D. D. Burford, *Anal. Biochem.*, **1**, 263 (1960).
18. R. Trautman, S. S. Breese, Jr., and H. L. Bachrach, *J. Phys. Chem.*, **66**, 1976 (1962).
19. M. Meselson, chapter in reference 1m.
20. J. L. Oncley, (personal communication).
21. R. Trautman, chapter in reference 1m.
22. R. Trautman and S. S. Breese, Jr., *J. Phys. Chem.*, **63**, 1592 (1959).
23. I. W. Billick, *J. Phys. Chem.*, **66**, 1941 (1962).
24. R. Trautman, V. N. Schumaker, W. F. Harrington, and H. K. Schachman, *J. Chem. Phys.*, **22**, 555 (1954).
25. R. Trautman, *J. Phys. Chem.*, **60**, 1211 (1956).
26. W. J. Archibald, *J. Phys. Colloid Chem.*, **51**, 1204 (1947).
27. R. Trautman, *Biochim. Biophys. Acta*, **28**, 417 (1958).
28. S. E. Allerton, (personal communication).
29. A. Ehrenberg, *Acta Chem. Scand.*, **11**, 1257 (1957).
30. R. Trautman and C. F. Crampton, *J. Am. Chem. Soc.*, **81**, 4036 (1959).
31. D. A. Yphantis, *J. Phys. Chem.*, **63**, 1742 (1959).
32. K. E. Van Holde and R. L. Baldwin, *J. Phys. Chem.*, **62**, 734 (1958).
33. G. M. Nazarian, *J. Phys. Chem.*, **62**, 1607 (1958).
34. P. E. Hexner, L. E. Radford, and J. W. Beams, *Proc. Natl. Acad. Sci., U. S.*, **47**, 1848 (1961).
35. R. A. Pasternak, G. M. Nazarian, and J. Vinograd, *Nature*, **179**, 92 (1957).
36. J. A. Faucher and G. Kegeles, *J. Phys. Chem.*, **66**, 1945 (1962).
37. J. S. Johnson, K. A. Kraus, and G. Scatchard, *J. Phys. Chem.*, **58**, 1034 (1954).
38. J. E. Hearst, J. B. Ifft, and J. Vinograd, *Proc. Natl. Acad. Sci., U. S.*, **47**, 1015 (1961).
39. R. Trautman, *Arch. Biochem. Biophys.*, **87**, 289 (1960).
40. J. B. Ifft, D. H. Voet, and J. Vinograd, *J. Phys. Chem.*, **65**, 1138 (1961).
41. M. Wales, *J. Polymer Sci.*, **77**, 203 (1963).
42. J. E. Hearst and J. Vinograd, *Proc. Natl. Acad. Sci., U. S.*, **47**, 999 (1961).
43. R. L. Baldwin, *Proc. Natl. Acad. Sci., U. S.*, **45**, 939 (1959).
44. M. Meselson, F. W. Stahl, and J. Vinograd, *Proc. Natl. Acad. Sci. U. S.*, **43**, 581 (1957).
45. J. Dayantis and H. Benôit, *Compt. Rend.*, **254**, 2771 (1962).
46. F. Booth, *J. Chem. Phys.*, **22**, 1956 (1954).
47. K. O. Pedersen, *J. Phys. Chem.*, **62**, 1282 (1958).
48. S. Yeandle, *Proc. Natl. Acad. Sci., U. S.*, **45**, 184 (1959).
49. P. Giebler, *Z. Naturforsch.*, **13b**, 238 (1958).
50. R. Trautman, M. Savan, and S. S. Breese, Jr., *J. Am. Chem. Soc.*, **81**, 4040 (1959).

51. R. M. Bock and N. S. Ling, *Anal. Chem.*, **26**, 1543 (1954).
52. H. Svensson, L. Hagdahl, and K.–D. Lerner, *Sci. Tools*, **4**, 1 (1957).
53. S. Brenner, F. Jacob, and M. Meselson, *Nature*, **190**, 576 (1961).
54. H. K. Schachman, chapter in reference 1m.
55. G. A. Gilbert, chapter in reference 1m.
56. G. Wallenius, R. Trautman, H. G. Kunkel, and E. C. Franklin, *J. Biol. Chem.*, **225**, 253 (1957).
57. W. G. Martin, C. A. Winkler, and W. H. Cook, *Can. J. Chem.*, **37**, 1662 (1959).
58. D. A. Yphantis, *Ann. N. Y. Acad. Sci.*, **88**, 586 (1960).

Weighing Devices and Weighing

J. L. Lords

ARCHEMIDES is given credit for establishing the principle of the lever upon which many of our devices for the measurement of mass and weight depend. The proof used by Archemides was one based upon the symmetrical geometrical representation of a lever in equilibrium. First-, second-, and third-class levers can be used to multiply or reduce forces to bring the applied weight within range of the indicator system. In addition to levers with equal arm lengths, unequal arm levers, and cantilevers (levers supported at one end) have been used to compare mass and weight (Fig. 8-1).

The simplest form of the balance is a lever supported on a knife edge at its exact center, with two pans suspended by similar knife edges at each end of the arms. Precision and analytical balances are some of the most important and useful tools in the analytical laboratory. A precision balance may have long arms or short arms and a variety of accessories may be added, including damping devices to reduce the swing time, auxiliary devices to add weights automatically to the pan, and graticules for the optical projection of the scale image. The classical analytical balances are equal arm balances. Recent developments in analytical instruments include one type of apparatus which operates on the principle of a constant load with unequal arms. Further refinements include so-called microbalances operated on a torsion principle, and the electromagnetic balance. Descriptions of the principles of operation and utilization of these instruments will follow in later sections. Devices to weigh masses greater than those encountered in the analytical laboratory include the steelyard scale, spring scale, and pendulum-type scale, all of which are common in production plants. These latter types are not commonly found in the analytical laboratory since their precision is insufficient for quantities of 200 g or less. The principles of design and operation of these devices will not be discussed here.

Before proceeding further, a description of the units and terminology commonly employed is necessary. The original definition of mass depended upon the mass of a volume of pure water at its maximum density. The inherent standard of mass is a platinum-irridium bar called the Kilogram des Archives and is reposited in the International Bureau of Weights and Measures in France. The United States Bureau of Standards maintains a replica of this prototype for use in the United States of America.

The weight of an object is the result of a combination of factors and depends upon its mass and upon the force of gravity exerted upon it. The usefulness of an equal arm balance becomes obvious when one considers that not only the weight but also mass can be compared on such an instrument. The force of gravity varies from point to point on the surface of the earth, but at any one point masses can be compared with great accuracy.

Weighing is one of the most important measurements utilized in modern science. All possible precautions should be taken when weighing an object to maintain accuracy which is consistent with other determinations in a given experiment.

Certain terms are applied to the description and use of balance, and a complete listing may be found in the Report and Recommendations of the Committee on Balances and Weights, Division of Analytical Chemistry, American Chemical Society [1]. Some of the important terms are considered below.

The *sensitivity* is the ratio of the indicator deflection to the change in load. In other words, it is the number of scaler divisions the pointer moves for a 1-mg change in load. The *sensitivity reciprocal* is a measure of the sensitivity and is the change in load required to change the scale by one division. The *precision* of the balance is defined as the variability of replicate weighings, whereas *accuracy* is the limit of variability of measurement of a known weight. The *capacity* of a balance is the maximum weight that can be carried and measured on one pan.

Capacity and sensitivity are the most useful guides in the use of a balance for a particular laboratory problem. The determined weight of objects and substances used should have accuracy consistent with the accuracy of all other phases of an experiment. In making standard solutions, for example, one need not be more accurate than the third decimal point since the volumetric errors will be of this order of magnitude.

Modern Weighing Devices

Modern weighing devices found in most well-equipped laboratories include the following general types.

TRIPLE BEAM DEVICES

Triple beam devices are used for preweighing or preliminary weight determination in analytical work and for rough weighing during autopsies. These devices (Fig. 8-2) are an example of an unequal-arm lever system, and many are equipped with a counterpoise or counterweight to allow the use of containers for repeated sampling. The sensitivity of such devices varies with the construction and is related to the capacity. Some units with capacities of 100 to 300 g have a sensitivity of 0.01 g, while others with capacities to 3000 g may have a sensitivity of 0.1 g.

TORSION BALANCE

Torsion balances minimize the friction of the system by replacing knife edges and plates with fixed plates or rods, and thereby prolong the life and accuracy of the balance. The most common torsion balance construction (Fig. 8-3) includes three metal frames across which taut steel bands are stretched. The upper and lower beams are fastened solidly to the center of these bands, and the center frame is firmly anchored to the base of the instrument. Counterpoises are provided in some models to position the center of gravity over the center of rotation. The advantages of counterpoises include rapid response, constant sensitivity, and freedom from contamination by dirt and dust. Older torsion balances have a beam with a sliding poise to indicate the smallest weight used, generally 1 g in 100 divisions, while some newer models have a dial loading device which replaces this sliding poise. A double dial system using up to 10 g without the addition of external weights has also been produced. The accuracy generally varies from 0.01 to 0.2 g in instruments with 200 to 4500 g capacities. To increase further the speed of weighing, dashpots, that is, damping devices, have been included to stabilize the mechanism and bring the instrument to equilibrium more rapidly.

ANALYTICAL BALANCE

The most common instrument used to measure masses and weights is the equal-arm analytical balance. As with many instruments, the construction and design of various parts of the balance depend upon the manufacturer as well as the use to which the instrument will be put. In essence the description of a simple balance given in the introduction could suffice here except that the refinements constitute an important step forward in accuracy, speed, and utility.

The balance beam is generally constructed of light, rigid, nonmagnetic material. Commonly the beam is an open truss structure, but recently solid beams have been used by some manufacturers. The beam is supported at its exact center by a knife edge working against a plate. In these balances the knife edge and plate are constructed of very hard material such as agate or sapphire. The knife edges are ground to the shape of a prism and are mounted at right angles to the length of the beam. The plate for the central knife edge is supported on a column of considerable mass which gives stability to this plate and in turn to the beam. Carriers, which hold the object being weighed, are suspended from two similar knife and plate systems at the ends of the beam.

The attachment of the pans is generally by means of a stirrup with a loose link to provide for self-positioning of the pan when the beam is released. This allows the pan to swing freely in all directions while coming to rest.

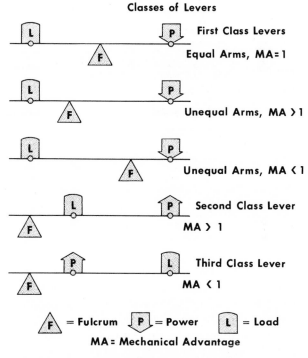

Classes of Levers

First Class Levers
Equal Arms, MA = 1

Unequal Arms, MA > 1

Unequal Arms, MA < 1

Second Class Lever
MA > 1

Third Class Lever
MA < 1

F = Fulcrum P = Power L = Load
MA = Mechanical Advantage

Fig. 8-1. Lever systems. Illustration of the classes and principles of levers. In all three classes the mechanical advantage, i.e., the increase or decrease in power to load ratio, is indicated in a general way. The classical analytical balance, a two-pan three-knife edge balance, is an example of an equal-arm, first-class lever, whereas some single-pan, two-knife edge balances use an unequal-arm, first-class lever. Other lever systems can be, and are used to effect, a balance in massive scale systems used in industry. By combining levers of various classes a reduction in the movement required to indicate the weight of an object can be changed.

302 *J. L. Lords*

The position of the knife edges must be parallel in all planes. Adjustments in the position of the knife edges should always be left to an instrument technician, since misalignment of the knife edges can cause serious wear on the edges and plates and large errors in balance operations.

The arrestment mechanism is a device usually operated from outside the balance case which lowers the balance beam on the knife edges, after which the arrest mechanism releases the stirrups suspending the pans. The arrest mechanism is generally operated by conical points fitting into matching conical receivers or by a cone and groove mechanism. The exact method of releasing the beam and pan may vary with models from different manufacturers. Exact placement of the released beam and pans at the same point in relation one to another on each use is important in order to maintain a parallel position of the knife edges.

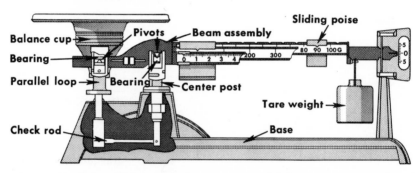

Fig. 8-2. Triple beam balance. The lever system used in this type is an unequal-arm, first-class lever (see Fig. 8-1). The adjustable, sliding weights are on three separate divisions of the long arm of the balance. At the balance point the moments of force about the knife edge are equal. See text for the accuracy of this type of balance and the suggested general uses (Courtesy, OHaus Corporation).

Attached to the center of the beam and perpendicular to it is a long pointer. The pointer generally has a finely drawn end which passes over a scale to indicate the true horizontal position of the beam. Other devices may be used to indicate the beam position; a cross-hair system is attached to the end of the pointer which can be viewed with the aid of a microscope. In others, a magnifying-projection system in which a graticule is attached to the pointer and projected to a screen can be used to evaluate the swing of the balance. Somewhere along the length of the pointer a small poise will be located, which is attached with a small screw or a lock nut system. The purpose of this small weight is to regulate the position of the center of gravity to the beam. As the poise is moved up, the sensitivity and the swing time are increased. Care should be taken in moving this poise since an unstable equilibrium will be formed if the center of gravity of the system is raised too high. The swing time is dependent upon the beam length as well as upon the center of gravity. Sixty seconds has been considered convenient with long beam balances while short beam balances may have this reduced to 10 seconds. Some balances have a poise attached to the beam itself which can be used to regulate the position of the center of gravity.

The rider is the small poise which is placed on a scale and used to indicate smaller weight divisions than those placed on the pan. The rider may weigh up to 0.5 mg, depending upon the balance. The notched scale upon which the rider is placed is generally above the

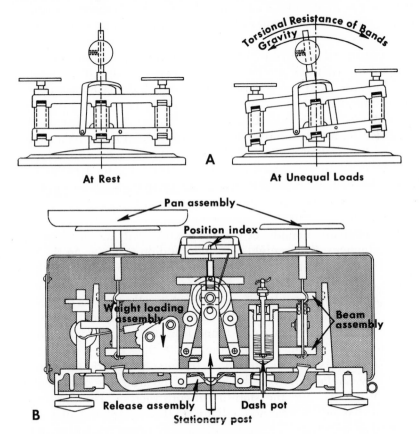

Fig. 8-3. Torsion balance. In this system the problems confronted when knife edges are used to suspend the object weighted and the counterbalancing poise are eliminated by substituting taut metal bands for knife edges. At the balance position there is no torque on the suspending bands. While adjusting to the balanced position the restoring torque, i.e., the forces counteracting the object on the pan, is the sum of the weight added to the opposite pan and of the restoring forces of the bands. This illustration shows a semidetailed view of the loading mechanism used to weigh directly on the balance without the use of added weights. The instrument is loaded mechanically when the calibrated adjusting dial is turned (Courtesy, Torsion Balance Company).

knife edges. When a rider is placed on such a beam the effect is to increase the sensitivity of the machine. Because this beam is parallel to the horizontal plane of the knife edges the sensitivity does not change when the rider is moved from position to position along the notched bar.

In recent times, improvements have been made in balances by the use of a chain to add the small divisions of weight. The chain is generally gold or other noncorrosive material and may be operated by a variety of mechanisms. The chain is attached to the beam and, after being calibrated, the amount of force exerted by the chain is read on a venier scale. The ability to change rapidly the amount of force applied by the chain rather than handle a small rider increases the speed of operation.

To enhance further the speed of weighing operations, devices to dampen the swing of the balance and bring it to equilibrium rapidly have been devised. Air-damping devices include dashpots of various designs and vanes to dampen the swing of the beam. Magnetic damping devices, which may be single or double, are found on many balances and are generally removable from outside the balance case. The withdrawal of the magnetic damping devices will allow the balance to swing freely and is probably preferable for accurate measurements, especially if the rest point method of determining the balance position is used rather than the equilibrium rest point.

To increase still further the speed and convenience of weighing operations many manufacturers have produced automatic weight-loading devices. The weights are mounted on a carrier on the right-hand side of the balance and are placed on the stirrup of the pan by proper mechanical linkages. Some balance manufacturers use a keyboard system to apply the weights while others use a dial system to manipulate the levers which add the weights. Some of these weight loading systems cover a small range from 0.01 to 1 g while others have automatic weight loading from 0 to 99.9 g.

The sensitivity of the analytical balance is a variable quantity. Sensitivity can be varied by the length of the arms, the position of the center of gravity, and the stability of construction. The purpose for which the balance is designed will lead to the construction of balances of different sensitivities. The sensitivity of a good quality analytical balance will be between 0.025 and 0.1 mg for a 200-g capacity. Semi-micro analytical balances and microbalances will have a sensitivity of about 0.01 mg with a capacity of about 20 g.

Some manufacturers supply automatic recording balances. Such balances are adjusted either electromagnetically or photoelectrically and the changes are recorded on a strip chart recorder. These devices may have considerable use in studies involving thermogravimetric analysis and drying to a constant weight.

MICRO AND SEMIMICRO BALANCES

With the increased use of microchemical methods, manufacturers have satisfied the need for accurate measurement of small magnitudes of mass by producing several systems; these include microbalances operated upon the same principles as the analytical balance but with increased sensitivity, spring torsion balances capable of measuring these magnitudes, electromagnetic balances, and ultra microbalances using a constant load lever.

1. The microbalance has a general capacity of 20 g. Most often these instruments are equipped with an optical reading system using a projected graticule. In some microbalances the divisions of the graticule correspond to 1 mg. These microbalances can also be equipped with weight loading devices.

2. Where rapid, repeated weighings are required, a direct reading torsion microbalance can be used to advantage. A method of neutralizing the displacement caused by the application of the weight is accomplished by applying a torque to a finely wound brass spring. The restoring torque is applied until the beam returns to the normal position and the value is read directly from the scale. In some systems the only support of the beam is a coiled spring under tension. The accuracy of these devices is in the range of 0.1 per cent of the scale, and is readable in some models to 0.01 mg.

3. Instruments capable of very high sensitivity have been manufactured using the principle of electromagnetic compensation (Fig. 8-4). The instruments measure the torque produced on a coil suspended in a magnetic field by measuring the electromagnetic torque necessary to restore the beam to the original position. Some instruments are available with several ranges for full-scale movement, for example, 0 to 1, 0 to 5, up to 0 to 100 mg. The precision in the first two ranges is reported by the manufacturer to be 1 μg. Because of the use of an electromagnetic principle these units do not have to be leveled, can be operated over a wide temperature range, and are portable. Some models are adapted for remote control installations and can be equipped to provide a signal for a recorder giving a constant record of weight change.

One of the most recent instruments to come into common usage is the single-pan two-knife edge balance with digital read-out features (Fig. 8-5). Most single-pan two-knife edge balances do not have a complete digital read-out, but have the smallest division on a graticule system. This design was pioneered by the E. Mettler Co. of Switzerland [2, 3]. These instruments operate on a substitution weighing principle. A constant load is on the beam at all times. When the balance is at zero, all weights are applied and are balanced by a fixed counterweight. The equilibrium of the balance is established when weighing an object by the removal of weights until an approximate balance is established. The balance is then completely released and the smallest divisions are measured by a projected graticule system. The weights in some instruments meet the standard set for class S weights by the National Bureau of Standards. The total amount of weight removed is registered on a digital scale and this value, plus the value read from the graticule, is the weight of the object. The sensitivity of these instruments is constant since this is a constant load device. Some such devices have an adjustable counterweight

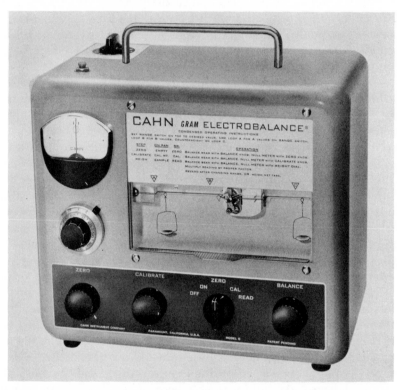

Fig. 8-4. Electrobalance. The method used in this type of microbalance is to measure the restoring force, i.e., the force necessary to restore the lever to the initial position. In this case the energizing current in an electromagnet is measured and is proportional to the deflection of the suspension system. These values can be measured with great accuracy and, coupled with a very delicate suspension system, account for the high degree of accuracy possible in instruments of the design (Courtesy, Cahn Instrument Company).

system to allow taring of containers. The instruments are manufactured in a variety of capacities from 2 mg to 2000 g. The sensitivity of one balance which has a capacity of 2 mg is reported to be 0.1 μg. Instruments with comparable capacities of analytical balances have sensitivities near 0.1 mg.

Single-pan, constant-load instruments may be manipulated very rapidly. The two-position arrest release allows the operator to bring the instrument to approximate balance very quickly. The instrument is then fully released, allowed to come to equilibrium, and the value of the weight recorded. Even those unfamiliar with gravimetric operations can make two weighings per minute.

Some of these instruments can be supplied with automatic recording features. The balance and the recorder are connected photoelectrically which prevents electronic feedback that might occur in instruments connected electronically.

Methods of Weighing on the Analytical Balance

In each of the previous sections concerning design and construction of weighing instruments the methods for use were briefly covered. The analytical, two-pan, precision balance is still the most common weighing device in many laboratories. Two methods for its use will be discussed in some detail.

WEIGHING BY THE METHODS OF OSCILLATION

Weighing by the methods of oscillations is preferred by many users of the analytical balance. Assuming that the precautions necessary to protect the object to be weighed and the balance have been taken, one may proceed as follows.

The rest point of the balance should be determined with no load on the instrument. The rest point is calculated by releasing the balance, and after two or three oscillations, the turning points in both directions on five consecutive swings are determined. One more value in either direction should be taken. The average of these values is then taken and this is the rest point of the instrument without a load. It is sometimes necessary to create a gentle air current to cause the balance to swing. The object to be weighed is then placed on the left pan or suspended from the hook on the stirrup. Weights are then added to the right pan and the release mechanism turned just far enough to see the direction the beam will move. When an approximate balance is obtained by the use of loose weights, the rider is placed at one half the maximum position and the process repeated until equilibrium is obtained. The beam is then released completely and the rest point under load calculated. The difference between the rest point under load and the rest point without a load is then compared. The sensitivity for this particular weight is then determined from a sensitivity curve that should be prepared for every balance used in analytical work. A sensitivity curve is a plot of the sensitivity of the balance under various loads, and can be prepared by determining the change in rest point for various loads from 1 g to the capacity of the balance. The sensitivity represents the scaler division change in the rest point for 1 mg change in load and the amount of change in load for a fractional change in rest point can be calculated. In weighing, if the change in rest point under load is greater than the unloaded rest point the difference should be added. An example may serve to illustrate the method as well as the magnitude of these differences. Suppose the unloaded rest point of a balance is plus 0.5 scaler units and the rest point of this balance is plus 1.2 units with a load of 1.551 g. The sensitivity at 1.0 g read from the previously prepared curve is 2.5 scaler units. The change in rest points is plus 0.7 units. Therefore, if the weight added to cause the deflection 0.001 g multiplied by the

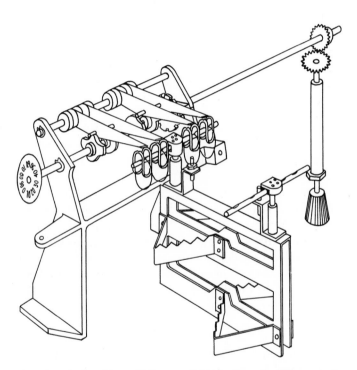

Fig. 8-5. Mettler design. Balances of this design using the constant-load, two-knife edge system have increased the ease and speed of routine weighing operations. In this design the object being weighed is placed on the single pan and weights are mechanically removed from the same stirrup. When the mechanical adjustment has brought the instrument into a sufficiently small deflection of the beam, a graticule system is employed to measure this small deflection. Because there is a constant load on the suspending knife edges the sensitivity is essentially constant (Courtesy, Mettler Instrument Corporation).

difference in scaler units is divided by the sensitivity at that particular weight the result will be the amount of correction to be added to or subtracted from the observed weight.

$$\frac{0.001 \text{ g} \times 0.7}{2.5} = 0.00028 \text{ g}; \ 1.551 + 0.00028 = 1.55128 \text{ g actual weight.}$$

Although the error is not great, for any accurate analytical work the correction should not be neglected.

WEIGHING BY THE METHOD OF SUBSTITUTION

In general, all substances to be weighed should be manipulated in a container if accuracy is to be maintained. Using the previously described method, two weighings would obviously be necessary, one to tare the container and one to weigh the object plus the tare. Weighing by a method of substitution permits some simplification of this process. One method is as follows. The container is placed on the right pan along with enough weights to compensate for the expected substance to be weighed. The instrument is then balanced by adding weights to the left pan. The container is removed and the substance to be weighed placed in the container. When the container plus sample is replaced on the instrument, weights are removed from the right pan until a balance is obtained. The amount of weight removed from this pan is the weight of the sample.

OTHER METHODS

Under certain conditions the use of a double taring system is useful. In this case a pair of containers of approximately the same weight is placed on the pans of the balance. The sample is in the left pan as usual and small weights are added on the right pan to balance. If the sample is to be treated within the container, the tare container is treated in the same manner. Upon completion of the operations the sample and tare are replaced and the change in weight is recorded (this method is referred to as Borda's method of weighing).

For delicate work where extreme accuracy is required the method of double weighing may be employed. In most cases the use of a method using an instrument of greater sensitivity and precision would be preferable to this method. The method of double weighing is merely the weighing of an object first on the left pan and then on the right. The balance must be in exact alignment and the set of weights in good condition. When these conditions are met, the following relationship may be deduced from the moments about the central knife edge. If x and y are the apparent weights on the left and right pans, then the true weight M may be taken as:

$$M = \frac{x + y}{2} \tag{1}$$

This is not strictly accurate unless the lengths of the arms of the balance are exactly the same. Other methods to suit a particular circumstance can be devised if the basic principles and conditions for use of the balance that were discussed previously are considered.

Precautions in Weighing

GENERAL

The temperature of the object to be weighed as well as the temperature conditions near the balance should not be neglected, since temperature gradients, as well as thermal air currents, may cause differential heating of the balance parts. A sensitive instrument should be placed in a constant temperature facility, away from direct sources of heat and sunlight. The object being weighed should be allowed to come to the temperature of the balance before the operations are performed. In cases where the maximum accuracy of the system is required the operator should consider his body as a heat source and operate from a distance. These precautions are probably not necessary for general analytical work.

Both the temperature and the barometric pressure are important considerations in accurate weighing when one considers the buoyant effect of the air. The buoyant effect results from the displacement of a volume of air by the object being manipulated, and also by the weights used to effect a balance. In most cases of analytical measurements this buoyant effect may be disregarded since other errors may be greater by several orders of magnitude. For a detailed description of the correction factors involved, the reader is referred to the United States National Bureau of Standards Circulars [4, 5].

Electrostatic charges can cause some errors in weighing. Quartz and glass vessels build up such charges and when such vessels are used it is well to weigh the object several times to minimize this effect. The use of radioactive devices to dispel the static charges in the balance case may be effective. These devices consist of an ionizing unit containing polonium and a housing to position the unit. Polonium emits alpha particles which are not harmful when used in the units provided. Manufacturers claim a one-year lifetime for the replaceable radioactive units.

One of the most important and most difficult aspects of weighing is the preparation of an object for weighing and/or the state in which the object exists. The nature of the compound or substance to be weighed should be well understood. Volatile and hygroscopic substances should not be weighed in open containers but should lie in weighing vials or other closed containers. Many people disregard this precaution when weighing hygroscopic compounds. The loss of weight of a compound due to water loss can also prove troublesome.

Many difficulties occur in the weighing of biological materials. The state in which these materials are weighed depends on the preference of the user and may be determined by the conditions of the experiment. Published results using wet weight and/or dry weight often do not specify the conditions under which such measurements were made.

The individual may use one or a combination of methods to determine the weight of his experimental materials. Three methods are commonly used to determine the dry weight: (1) heating to a high temperature, (2) removing the water with a desiccant, and (3) freeze-drying or lyophilization.

In using heat to dry biological materials care should be taken to prevent the loss of such substances as CO_2 and to prevent the oxidation of the material. For example, it is possible for biological material to gain weight during drying due to oxidation. In addition, it is difficult to identify the source of small quantities of water in samples. In some cases the water bound as part of the substance weighed cannot be distinguished from the last traces of free water in the system.

Drying materials by using a desiccant, such as sulfuric acid or calcium chloride, generally takes a long time and can lead to troubles, such as loss of CO_2 and oxidation, as noted for drying by heat. In some cases the vapor pressure of the desiccant should be considered since the state of dryness will depend upon the vapor pressure of the desiccant.

Freeze-drying or lyophilization offers one of the better methods for drying biological materials. The principle of this operation is to sublime the water away from the sample in the frozen state. This is usually accomplished by freezing the object in a flask or other container placed in an acetone or alcohol-dry ice mixture and then attaching a trap filled with a similar mixture to the flask and a vacuum pump. By reducing the pressure the rate of drying is increased; an infrared source increases the speed of the operation. Proteins and other biological materials are less likely to be destroyed or, in the case of proteins, to be denatured, with this system than with any of the above methods. (See Ch. 6).

The use of weighing bottles is recommended where great accuracy is required. For general weighing the use of slick, smooth (powder) weighing papers is preferred by many workers. These papers can be handled rapidly and the chemical or substance weighed can be removed easily. The use of rough paper is discouraged for all but very coarse measurements.

The use of desiccants within the balance case is often recommended in humid environments. The best desiccants are those that do not produce any vaporization film.

PRECAUTIONS USING SINGLE-PAN BALANCES

In the use of single-pan balances the operator will find little difficulty. Many models have built-in tare weights and can be loaded and unloaded very rapidly. The obvious precaution in using the half-released position while changing the weights may not need to be mentioned, but serious damage to the machine will result if this is not done. The matter of cleanliness is of great importance as is the case with all fine instruments. An occasional check of the sensitivity and accuracy of any weighing device is necessary. In the author's opinion single-pan, two-knife edge balances can increase the speed of laboratory operation without any appreciable loss of accuracy. Only in cases where extremely small quantities are involved should the use of these instruments with features comparable to two-pan, three-knife edge instruments prove troublesome. In these cases, instruments using the constant-load, two-knife edge system, but with increased sensitivity, may prove useful.

Weights and Weight Classification

Since 1954 the National Bureau of Standards has recognized six classes of weights used in the laboratory. These classes are J, M, S, S-1, P, Q, and T. Class J weights have tolerances starting at 0.003 mg for the small weights and are used to calibrate equipment for ultra-microanalysis. Table 8-1 is a selection of the tolerances for the remainder of the weight classes indicated above. Manufacturers of instruments using self-contained weights refer to these standards in these instruments.

In most laboratories doing analytical work class S-1 weights are most satisfactory. In larger laboratories a set of weights of greater precision should be available for calibration and checking of all weights. For very precise work this set of weights should be checked by the Bureau of Standards and used only as a reference source. In most laboratories the class of weights in any set is marked on the container. In some, however, only the person responsible for the original order can tell the accuracy of a particular set. It is obviously advisable to record the class of a set of weights and make such information available to all who use them.

Weights should be handled carefully and never touched with the fingers. If a weight is damaged by dropping it, it should immediately be noted and recalibrated or replaced.

TABLE 8-1

PARTIAL TABLE OF MG TOLERANCES FOR WEIGHTS OF VARIOUS CLASSES [6]°

Denomination	M	S	S-1	P	Q	T
Grams						
200	1.0	0.050	2.0	4.0	15	160
100	0.50	0.25	1.0	2.0	9.0	100
50	0.25	0.12	0.60	1.2	5.6	62
30	0.15	0.074	0.45	0.90	4.0	44
20	0.10	0.074	0.35	0.70	3.0	33
10	0.050	0.074	0.25	0.50	2.0	21
5	0.034	0.054	0.18	0.36	1.3	13
3	0.034	0.054	0.15	0.30	0.95	9.4
2	0.034	0.054	0.13	0.6	0.75	7.0
1	0.034	0.054	0.10	0.20	0.50	4.5
Milligrams						
500	0.0054	0.025	0.080	0.16	0.38	3.0
300	0.0054	0.025	0.070	0.14	0.30	2.2
200	0.0054	0.025	0.060	0.12	0.26	1.8
100	0.0054	0.025	0.050	0.10	0.20	1.2
50	0.0054	0.014	0.042	0.085	0.16	0.88
30	0.0054	0.014	0.038	0.075	0.14	0.68
20	0.0054	0.014	0.035	0.070	0.12	0.56
10	0.0054	0.014	0.030	0.060	0.10	0.40
5	0.0054	0.014	0.028	0.055	0.080	—
3	0.0054	0.014	0.026	0.052	0.070	—
2	0.0054	0.014	0.025	0.050	0.060	—
1	0.0054	0.014	0.025	0.050	0.050	—

° All tolerances are given in milligrams.

References

1. L. B. Macurdy et al., Anal. Chem., **26**, 1190 (1954).
2. L. B. Macurdy, Rev. Sci. Instr., **19**, 730 (1948).
3. L. Bietry, Chimia, **11**, 92 (1959).
4. Natl. Bur. Std. (U. S.) Circ., **3** (1918).
5. Natl. Bur. Std. (U. S.) Circ., **19** (1924).
6. T. W. Lashof and L. B. Macurdy, Natl. Bur. Std. (U. S.) Circ., **547** (1954).
7. W. G. Brombacker, J. F. Smith, and L. M. Van der Pyl, Natl. Bur. Std. (U. S.) Circ., **567** (1955).
8. J. Reilly and W. N. Rae, Physico-chemical Methods, D. Van Nostrand, New York, 3rd ed. (1939), p. 1.

pH and pH Measuring Devices

J. L. Lords

THE AWARENESS of the value of pH in the control of processes both in industry and in research has accelerated the development of instrumentation to carry out pH determination. Automatic control of pH is commonplace in commercial establishments. Certainly, constant monitoring of pH has extensive application in industry. No one can minimize the importance of pH determination and control in research laboratories; determinations we now consider as common and routine were not simple just a few years ago. We tend to take for granted the operation and design of pH measuring devices, but a basic understanding of the methods employed is of some importance to anyone involved in the use of pH measurements. Some useful references are given at the end of the chapter [1-4].

The value of any individual pH determination of living material or extracts of living material, no matter what system is used to make the determination, is subject to many qualifications. There are many changes within the material that can take place during extraction and during other required manipulations. The problem of the size of the electrodes in relation to the system under study is also important. Even with these complications, a great deal of useful information can be obtained from accurate determinations of the pH values both within living organisms and in extracts of living systems.

Before discussing the devices used to measure pH, a few pertinent statements about what is actually under investigation when pH is measured are necessary. The pH scale in common use was devised by Sørensen in 1909 and has become the most convenient manner in which to express the degree of effective acidity or alkalinity of a particular solution. In contrast to the pH is the total acid content of a solution, which can be determined by titration. The most generally accepted definition is that pH represents the negative logarithm of the hydrogen ion concentration in the solution under consideration.

$$pH = -\log (H) \quad \text{or} \quad H = 10^{-pH} \quad (1)$$

There are, however, discrepancies in the Sørensen pH scale because the activity of the hydrogen ions in solution is not taken into account. From the relationship in Equation (1) it can be seen that the pH scale is inverted. The solutions with the highest concentration of hydrogen ions in a solution have the lowest pH value. The advantage of the pH as a measure of the concentration of the hydrogen ion is that a simple number can be used to express what would otherwise be a cumbersome value to manipulate. A thorough discussion of these problems may be found in the review by Bates [2].

For actual use in biology the Sørensen definition is found to be adequate for most situations. It should be borne in mind that a more accurate statement of pH is that the activity of the H^+ ion in a solution is actually responsible for the electromotive force that is measured, rather than the total concentration of the ion. The definition of the pH of a standard solution is pH_s and may be represented as

$$pH_s = -\log A_H \tag{2}$$

where A_H is the activity of the hydrogen ion in a particular solution. Activity, A_H, is a function of the activity coefficient of the ion as well as the concentration of the ion. Because the activity coefficient cannot be measured for a single ion, the National Bureau of Standards (U.S.A.) has assigned fixed values of pH for various salt mixtures. By using these standard mixtures, pH values can be made more accurate and reproducible from time to time. For critical measurements and where absolute values are required, it is suggested that reported values of pH should be referred to the NBS standards. Where only relative values are required, secondary standards are adequate.

Acid-Base Equilibrium and Buffer Systems

In order to develop concepts of buffer systems from a common basis, there is included at this point a brief summary of the acid-base equilibrium. If one assumes a hypothetical weak acid, HA, which dissociates to a certain amount, then the following equations describe the dissociation of this acid at any degree of dissociation.

$$(HA) \rightleftharpoons (H^+) + (A^-) \tag{3}$$

The degree of ionization or that portion of the acid which dissociates is then measured by the equilibrium constant for the system.

$$K_a = \frac{(H^+)(A^-)}{(HA)} \tag{4}$$

If (A^-) is equal to (HA), then the ratio of (A^-) to (HA) is one. Equation (4) then reduces to:

$$K_a = (H^+) \qquad (5)$$

It follows, then, from the definition of pH, Equation (1), that by taking the logarithm of both sides of Equation (5) we have:

$$pH = -\log (H^+) = -\log K_a = pK_a \qquad (6)$$

The relationship between the amount of the weak acid dissociated in a system to that portion undissociated can be determined if the pH of the system is known. Equation (4) can be rearranged to the following form:

$$K_a(HA) = (H^+)(A^-) \qquad (7)$$

$$(H^+) = K_a \frac{(HA)}{(A^-)} \quad \text{or} \quad K_a = (H^+)\frac{(A^-)}{(HA)} \qquad (8)$$

By taking the logarithm of both sides and using the above definitions, equations in (8) become:

$$pH = pK_a + \log\frac{(A^-)}{(HA)} \quad \text{or} \quad pK_a = pH + \log\frac{(HA)}{(A^-)} \qquad (9)$$

In order to find, then, the approximate pH of a solution of a weak acid and the salt of the same acid, one need only know the pK_a of the acid and the ratio of the salt to the undissociated acid.

This system is especially useful when preparing buffer solutions for use with biological materials. Disregarding for the moment the possible participation of the salt or the undissociated weak acid in the reaction under study, a suitable buffer system for a reaction mixture can be found if the pH of the biological reaction is known.

As can be seen from Equation (9), if the ratio of (A^-) to (HA) is equal to one, the pH of the system becomes equal to pK_a. If one selects an acid with a pK_a close to the required pH and mixes the acid and salt of the acid in equal molar amounts, the resulting pH will be approximately equal to the required pH.

The buffer capacity of such a system is designated by β and is defined as the amount of strong base required to shift the pH by one unit. Further consideration of Equations (4) and (9) will show that the system used for a buffer that has the pK_a nearest the required pH will withstand the greatest addition of either acid or base with the least change in pH. The practical range for pH of any buffer system should be such that the ratio of $(A^-)/(HA)$ in Equation (9) never exceeds 10:1. The maximal limit of this ratio is 100:1 and a buffer with 100:1 ratio will provide only a small buffering capacity.

In addition to the consideration of the ratio of $(A^-)/(HA)$, Equation (9), one must be aware of the effect dilution will have upon the pH of any buffer system. The dilution value is designated as $\Delta pH_{1/2}$ and is defined as the change in pH when the buffer is diluted with pure water to one half the original concentration. The change in pH results from the influence of water on the acid or base, causing a shift toward pH 7 and also from the effect dilution has upon the activities of ionic species in the system.

Many systems available for buffers form ions that may take part in the biological reaction under consideration. If it is at all possible, systems which do not take such a part should be used. In other systems the buffer may not take an active part in the reaction, but by the nature of the ions present may influence the reaction under study. These considerations should not be neglected when selecting a buffer for a particular system.

As a final consideration of buffers in relation to biological systems, the problem of ionic strength should be investigated. The ionic strength of a solution is defined as one half the sum of the product of the concentration and square of the valence of the ions in the solution. The effect of ionic strength is an important consideration when one deals with isolated macromolecular constituents of living systems as well as with a complete cell or organism.

Measurement of pH

Two techniques for the measurement of pH are in general use today. These are colorimetric techniques using visual or optical comparison and techniques using electronic instruments. In the past two decades electronic instruments have almost supplanted the colorimetric systems. The use of impregnated papers for rapid estimation of pH is still useful if time and availability preclude the use of electronic devices. The accuracy of impregnated papers varies with the number of pH units covered and are only accurate to $\pm\frac{1}{2}$ division used in the color chart. Visual or optical comparisons using colored standards and indicators with a limited.range are much more accurate than impregnated papers, and have a wider variety of uses. Electronic equipment can have greater accuracy than either of the above methods. Because colorimetric determinations are not as universally used as in previous times they are not discussed further here.

pH Meters

A pH meter is essentially a voltmeter designed to measure the potential between a reference electrode and a sensing electrode (Fig. 9-1). In most cases the sensing electrode is a glass electrode. The nature of the glass electrode is such that it has a high impedance and is also subject to polarization; the high impedance results from the resistance to current flow through the glass membrane. Polarization is due to the property of the electrode and results from the fact that a small current flowing through the electrode produces a change in the concentration of ions at the surface of the electrode and thereby

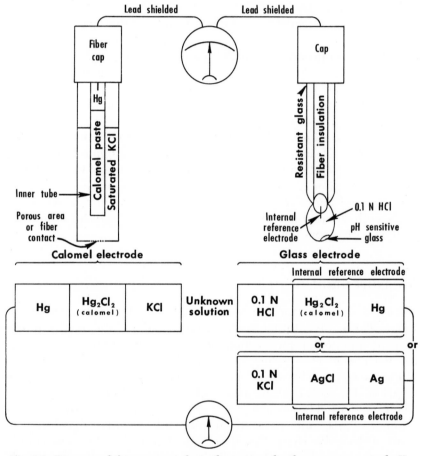

Fig. 9-1. Diagram of the common electrode systems for the measurement of pH. The meter in each case represents a complete potential measuring device of one of several types mentioned in the text. The lower half of the diagram illustrates the several junctions within the completed circuit. Probably the most common glass electrode system in use is the silver-silver chloride system. A thorough discussion of the junction potentials may be found in Bates [2].

a change in the electrode potential. As a result, voltage measuring devices must not draw appreciable current. In general, the resistance of a voltmeter must be above 10^{12} ohms if the accuracy of the determination is to be within 0.1 per cent.

Several circuit designs can achieve this high resistance; the simplest is a potentiometer with a vacuum tube amplifier. Essentially the circuitry for this type of instrument involves matching a potential in the electrode circuit with one in an internal circuit (Fig. 9-2). To increase the sensitivity, the voltage is amplified so that a small change in the potential of matching circuits can be readily detected. This type of instrument does allow some current to flow through the electrode pair while the balance point is being determined and will reduce the accuracy of the determinations to some degree.

Fig. 9-2. Simplified schematic of a common potentiometric amplifier for pH and millivolt measurements. When the slide wire is adjusted to a balance point (B), the grid of the tube is at the same potential as the cathode. The slide wire is then read in millivolts or pH units (Courtesy, Dr. S. Z. Lewin, New York University and the *Journal of Chemical Education*).

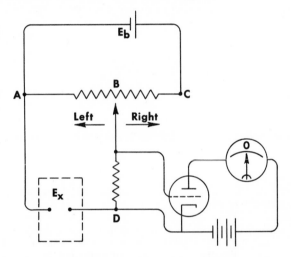

The second type of circuit design used is the electrometer tube. By connecting an electrode pair to the grid and to the cathode of an electrometer tube, the change in potential across the tube can readily be detected (Figs. 9-3 and 9-4). Actually, the cathode-to-plate potential, as detected on the meter, is a measure of the potential in the electrode pair. Based upon the nature of the electrometer tube, certain difficulties are present in this type of instrument. If there is any leakage between the cathode and grid there will be a small current flow in the electrode circuit and this leakage will reduce the accuracy of the instrument markedly. Modern tubes and circuit design have prevented the leakage described above and have produced electrometer tubes with grid currents as low as 10^{-15} amp. With such tubes and circuits the modern pH meter is capable of very accurate measurement without any hindrance from polarization of the electrodes or the high impedance of the circuit.

A third type of circuit design is used to circumvent the difficulties of amplification of a dc signal. In the amplification of a dc signal it is difficult to avoid a drift in the amplifier. The drift may be caused by variations both within the circuit (such as changes in the power supply) and changes in the external environment (such as temperature and humidity). Generally the dc signal is converted to ac and then reconverted to dc and the potential change is then measured. Two systems are in common use for this conversion; they are the electromagnetic chopper and the vibrating reed condenser. An electromagnet on the electromagnetic chopper is used to alternate the direction of current flow in the primary coil of a transformer, and the voltage in the secondary windings of this transformer is then amplified. A vibrating reed condenser accomplishes the same feat by using one fixed condenser plate and a moving plate, which is vibrated

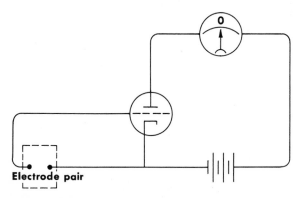

Fig. 9-3. Schematic of essentials of a direct reading circuit employing an electrometer tube. When connected as shown, the difference between the grid and the cathode becomes the same as the electrodes. The plate current indicated on the meter is a measure of this voltage (Courtesy, Dr. S. Z. Lewin, New York University and the *Journal of Chemical Education*).

by an ac-operated electromagnet. In both cases the amplified ac voltage is reconverted by a rectifier to dc and then detected by meter or attenuated by a known voltage in a separate balancing circuit. Stabilization of the amplified circuit is accomplished by what is called negative feedback, by which a portion of the output of the amplifier is fed back into the system in opposition to the input signal. If amplification of the input signal is large and the feedback potential is also an appreciable portion of the output, voltage changes within the instrument circuitry and from stray external sources are minimized. The final voltage depends upon the proportion of input to feedback. If the input drops, more output is introduced to stabilize the voltage.

Final consideration of the type of circuit best suited depends upon the degree of accuracy required and the cost of instrumentation. Potentiometric circuits are very accurate when used in null-balancing instruments. From Fig. 9-1 it is seen that when the balancing circuit is in equilibrium, no current flows in the electrode circuit. During the adjustment to balance there is appreciable current flow in the electrode circuit. Double readings after finding the balance point will allow the electrodes to recover and will overcome some errors. When the maximal accuracy is required, double readings should be used.

Measuring devices using the electrometer tube and the direct-reading meter are rapid and convenient. These types of instruments are easily adapted to operation on 110 v ac current and their stability is established by using feedback circuitry. In terms of accuracy these types are only as accurate as the meter used. Some meters employed have an error of 0.1 per cent at full-scale deflection, but most are only 1.0 per cent accurate for full-scale deflection.

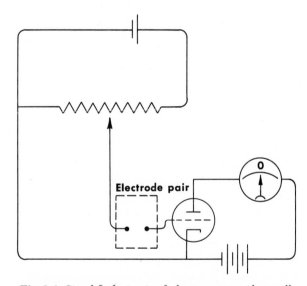

Fig. 9-4. Simplified circuit of electrometer with a null-balance meter. Electrode voltage opposes the voltage of the slide wire. When the slide wire and electrode voltages are equal, the grid and cathode are at the same potential and the meter shows a standard deflection (Courtesy, Dr. S. Z. Lewin, New York University and the *Journal of Chemical Education*).

Temperature Compensation

The voltage generated by a pH shift of one unit at a particular temperature is different from the voltage generated at another temperature. In order to compensate for this, most pH meters are equipped with a manually adjustable resistor to correct the slide wire circuit for the ambient temperature. In other designs temperature compensation is made automatically by the use of a temperature-sensitive resistor or thermistor connected directly to the measuring circuit.

In general, one must select the particular style and design of instrument for his own application. Meters with varying degrees of accuracy and reproducibility are available, and depending upon these variables may cost from $100 to $1,200. In the author's opinion, one does not need an extremely accurate meter for routine measurements, and those models costing from $200 to $400 are adequate for most purposes. The selection of a null- versus a direct-reading instrument depends also upon the considerations mentioned above. In making a large series of measurements, a null-reading instrument is somewhat slower than direct-reading types.

The value of battery operation is twofold. A battery-operated instrument is portable and is less sensitive to extraneous signals. The principal disadvantage is the necessity of continual replacement of batteries with the knowledge that voltage of the battery in the instrument at any one time may not be correct. Line operation assures a constant source of power from time to time but certainly limits the mobility of the instrument.

Operation of the Instruments

Before any pH instrument is used it should be both standardized and calibrated. Standardization of potentiometric instruments involves adjusting the actual potential differences detected within the instrument to coincide with the marking on the scale. In direct-reading instruments the amplification must be adjusted so that a one-unit pH change coincides with a one-unit change in the meter. Calibration means adjusting the absolute value of voltage to equal the voltage indicated upon the meter.

Commercial testing equipment is available to test the circuitry of pH meters. When using these devices one avoids the use of standard buffers with the associated uncertainties as well as the difficulties of possible errors in the electrodes.

No general directions applicable in all situations or with all types of instruments can be given. Each manufacturer suggests a different sequence of operation and use, and because of this it is recommended that anyone using a particular meter become familiar with the manufacturer's instructions. The obvious considerations of cleanliness, both of the meter and the electrodes, need not be expanded upon.

One precaution involving extraneous signals should be mentioned. Since pH meters are high impedance instruments, stray ac signals can be picked up by them. This is a greater problem in ac-operated instruments than in dc-operated ones. Motors and fluorescent lights can produce such signals and cause erroneous measurements. Certainly, then, the electrode leads should be shielded, as they are by most manufacturers. The possibility that observed inaccuracies in measurements may be the result of such stray signals should be borne in mind.

References

1. "Symposium of pH Measurements," *Am. Soc. Testing Mater., Spec. Tech. Publ.*, **73**, 190 (1957).
2. R. G. Bates, *Electrometric pH Determinations*, John Wiley & Sons, New York (1954).
3. S. Z. Lewin, *Chem. Educ.*, **36**, A 477 (1959).
4. H. H. Willard, L. L. Merritt, and J. A. Dean, *Instrumental Methods of Analysis*, D. Van Nostrand, New York (1958).

C H A P T E R 1 0

Ultraviolet and Visible Absorption Spectroscopy

David W. Newman

THE METHODS of spectrophotometry are based on the fact that all chemicals to some extent absorb electromagnetic radiation of specific wavelengths. That is to say, if a beam of light of a specific quality is passed through a chemical, solution, solid, gas, etc., the light transmitted by the chemical is less by the amount of radiation absorbed by the chemical through which it passed. In many cases the light absorbed by the chemical(s) is proportional to the concentration of the chemical(s). Since the light absorbed is proportional to the concentration, a quantitative analysis of the chemical(s) may be made. If one were to prepare a series of known concentrations of a chemical and measure the light absorbed by the material at a known wavelength of light, a standard relationship of the light absorbed with respect to the chemical concentration would be established. Once this standard relationship is known, unknown concentrations may be analyzed quantitatively by preparing the sample, determining the light absorbed at a known and specific wavelength, and referring to the standard graph prepared previously using known concentrations of the chemical.

Since different chemicals may absorb light at different wavelengths, a qualitative analysis of an unknown chemical may be made by determining the absorption spectrum of that chemical. The *absorption spectrum* is the relationship between light absorption and wavelength. It is known that certain kinds of chemicals and chemical bonds absorb light at a specific region of the electromagnetic spectrum. Knowledge of the wavelengths of light absorbed by a chemical will aid in identifying and determining the molecular configuration of the unknown chemical. Very often the material's identity, concentration, and molecular structure can be determined by knowing the absorbance and quality of electromagnetic radiation absorbed.

As a result of the discovery and application of these techniques the chemist and biologist have opened new frontiers of experimentation. Some older types of analytical techniques have been abandoned in favor of spectrophotometry because of the speed and reliability of these methods. The relative range of analyzable concentrations of chemicals has been greatly extended by spectrophotometric techniques. Much lower concentrations of the chemicals may be quantitatively determined. A good example of this is the analysis of chlorophyll solutions. If one were to determine quantitatively the concentration of chlorophyll by titrating for magnesium one would require a much larger sample than is necessary for the colorimetric determination of chlorophyll concentration. The amount of energy spent by the experimenter in order to make a magnesium determination may far exceed the energy spent in determining the chlorophyll concentration colorimetrically. As a result, spectrophotometric methods extend the range of analyzable concentrations, aid in identification of molecules and spatial configurations, and conserve the amount of technical labor required to perform these measurements.

Not only can an analysis of the chemical alone be made, but frequently mixtures of chemicals and even chemicals in intact cells and tissues can be effectively analyzed for single components. If one had a mixture of two or three chemicals which were strikingly different with respect to their absorption spectra, then all that one would have to do is to measure the light absorption by the mixture at several different wavelengths, the number of which depends upon the number of materials in the mixture. A series of simultaneous equations would then be used in order to obtain a quantitative estimation of each of the components in the mixture. These procedures will be defined later.

As mentioned earlier, spectrophotometric procedures can be used to determine quantitatively and qualitatively the content of parts of living cells. Most of these procedures, however, are not used for quantitative analyses. Enzymic reactions can be followed without destroying or interfering with the basic metabolism of the cell. This technique has the advantage of avoiding any artifacts introduced into the system by grinding and fractionating the reaction system.

Since spectrophotometers can be used for quantitative analysis of almost any type of compound, they are widely used for continuously analyzing or monitoring production line chemicals as a measure of quality control. In addition, they are used to monitor the appearance and quantity of noxious and poisonous chemicals which are frequently by-products of many types of industrial operations. For example, colorimeters are used to monitor the presence of mercury vapor in industrial plants which normally produce this chemical. Spectrophotometers are used to monitor the presence and abundance of various types of air pollutants emitted from chemical processing plants. The colorimetric monitoring of the effluent of a chromatographic column is a common practice. It would be difficult to overestimate the usefulness of colorimetric and emission photometric techniques in the diagnosis of disease.

It is little wonder, therefore, that spectrophotometers and colorimeters are being used to a great extent by the investigator of biochemical and chemical reactions. It is not difficult to realize the great applicability of these instruments and methods to the fields of chemistry and biochemistry. It is probably true that no other series of instruments has been more widely used than have spectrophotometers for research and industry in understanding biochemical compounds and reactions. The great usefulness and versatility of these instruments will become more and more evident as research methods improve in the near future. Think of the amazing number of problems that may be studied by coupling spectrophotometric instrumentation with gas-chromatographic instrumentation [1–12].

Nature of Electromagnetic Radiation

DUALISM OF ELECTROMAGNETIC RADIATION

Light, electromagnetic radiation, seems to exhibit properties of both waves and particles. Under certain circumstances light appears to behave as a wave of electromagnetic radiation and will exhibit wave properties, as evidenced by polarization and interference phenomena. On the other hand, the Compton and photoelectric effects of light seem to point to the conclusion that light exhibits properties of particles. As a result of this dualism, it is evident that all types of electromagnetic radiation exhibit properties of waves and of particles. With every wave of electromagnetic radiation there are associated properties which would suggest that this wave is also a particle in space. Also, with particles in space, such as atoms, molecules, cells, etc., there are associated wave properties. Each particle has a certain wavelength associated with it. For example, the moon not only exhibits properties of a particle but also exhibits wave properties and the wavelength associated with it is of a specific nature.

SPECTRUM OF ELECTROMAGNETIC RADIATION

Electromagnetic radiations are identified by their different wavelengths. As mentioned above, each particle has associated with it a wavelength (λ) which may be expressed in cm, millimicrons (mμ) or nanons, Angstrom units $\overset{\circ}{A}$, etc. Consider a source of electromagnetic radiations, such as a hot metal ball; the ball will emit heat and light radiation. The heat radiation will be of an entirely different wavelength from the light radiation. Also, the ball will emit light radiation of different wavelengths (colors when reference is made to the visible portion of the spectrum). Many other types of radiations are also in evidence in the universe. For example, radio waves, microwaves, X-rays, cosmic rays, and gamma rays also are forms of electromagnetic radiation. The wavelengths of electromagnetic radiation will be different for each type of radiation. The wavelength (λ) is mathematically defined as:

$$\lambda = c/v \tag{1}$$

where $c =$ the velocity of light in a vacuum, and, $v =$ the frequency of the radiation.

The velocity of light in a vacuum (c) is a constant for all forms of electromagnetic radiation and therefore the velocity will be the same for all wavelengths of the spectrum—heat, light, X-rays, etc. The velocity (c) in a vacuum is almost equal to 3×10^{10} centimeters per second. The speed of light will vary with different media through which it travels. The ratio of the speed of light through a vacuum to the speed of light through a medium is known as the refractive index:

$$n = c/x \tag{2}$$

where $n =$ refractive index, and $x =$ velocity of light through medium (x).

The refractive index is not constant for different wavelengths. Consequently, refractive indices are always reported at a given wavelength. Consider the example above, when the steel ball emits various forms of radiation, all of the different forms of radiation will be emitted from the ball at the same velocity. If (c) is defined in centimeters per second, the frequency of the wave (v) will be given in waves per second. Since (λ) $= c/v$ then the wavelength of the radiation will be in centimeters. The steel ball will be emitting radiations of various wavelengths traveling at the same speed but of different frequencies. One can easily visualize this by assuming the waves to be similar to the waves of a pond. The frequency of the waves on the pond, being emitted from a point of origin (the place where a rock dropped into the pond), is the number of waves passing a certain point during a specific period of time. For a diagrammatic representation of a spectrum of electromagnetic radiations see Fig. 10-1. The wavelengths of light with which we are concerned here are from 200 mμ to 2 μ-ultraviolet, visible, and near infrared region.

The expression of radiation in wave numbers has many advantages for the theoretical chemist, and as a result this method of expression is more often used by him. However, the majority of investigators in biology using visible and ultraviolet regions still express the region of electromagnetic radiation in wavelength units. The wavenumber is related to wavelength as follows:

$$\nu = 1/\lambda \times 10^4 \qquad \text{(3a)}$$
$$\text{(wavenumber)}$$

where ν = wavenumber in cycles/cm, cm^{-1}, and λ = wavelength in microns (μ).

$$1\mu = 10^3 m\mu = 10^4 \overset{\circ}{A} \text{ units} \qquad \text{(3b)}$$

QUANTIZED NATURE OF LIGHT

Max Planck discovered that waves of electromagnetic radiation are discontinuous. That is, light waves seem to occur in bundles called photons. The energy of each quantum of radiation is given by the equation

$$E = h\nu \qquad \text{(4)}$$

where E = energy of each quantum of radiation in kilocalories; h = Planck's constant which is equal to 6.6×10^{-27} erg-sec; ν = frequency of radiation.

As the frequency of electromagnetic radiation increases, so does the energy per quantum of that radiation. Since the frequency is inversely proportional to the wavelength of radiation, then the higher the frequency the higher the energy and the smaller the wavelength. Conversely, the higher the wavelength of radiation the lower the energy per quantum. Since blue light is of lower wavelength than red light, blue light has more energy per quantum than red light. Visible wavelengths of light have more energy per quantum than infrared light.

Molecular Basis of Light Absorption

Solutions are colored because they absorb specific qualities of light while allowing other colors to be transmitted or reflected. A blue solution may effectively absorb the other colors of visible light such that mostly blue light is transmitted. In general, energy that is absorbed by the solution increases the energy of the atom of the solution. If the solution is absorbing ultraviolet or visible radiation, the absorbed energy will cause some electrons to assume a higher energy state. The atom has thus acquired energy and is said to be excited. Atoms in solution do not, of course, continue to absorb energy without releasing some energy. That is, the electrons are at a higher energy state and the atom is comparatively unstable. Electrons will therefore fall back into orbitals closer to the nucleus and in so doing release energy. This released energy will appear, in general, in other forms—heat and fluorescence. Most absorbing systems will release heat as the electrons fall back into more stable positions. Some systems will fluoresce, some to a greater extent than others.

Absorbed electromagnetic radiation of the infrared region results in a vibration of the absorbing molecules. Vibration that results from the absorption of infrared wavelengths may be of several types. These are discussed in Chapter 11.

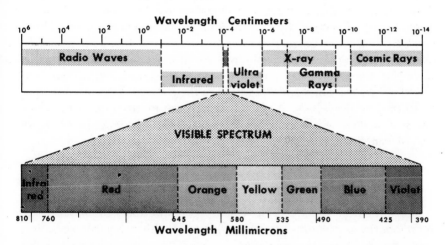

Fig. 10-1. Diagrammatic representation of a spectrum of electromagnetic radiations.

Frequently it is possible to predict the region of maximum absorbance and the absorptivities at these wavelengths of various materials by knowing the molecular structure of the materials. Chemical groups which absorb light are called chromophores [1, 5, 9]. Unsaturated organic compounds, especially, absorb ultraviolet light. A few additional ultraviolet chromophores are—S—, N=N—, and substituted benzene compounds. Many other groups also absorb ultraviolet radiation. As an example, ultraviolet absorption spectroscopy has been used for the identification and quantitative determination of fatty acids. In the fatty acids, two double bonds in conjugation, such as in 9, 11-octadecadienoic acid, show a maximum absorption at approximately 234 mμ. Eleostearic acid which contains three double bonds in conjugation produces absorption maxima at about 300 and 315 mμ. Obviously, colored materials are the subject of study with visible absorption spectroscopy.

Theory of Absorption Spectroscopy

GENERAL

We have briefly considered the physical nature of electromagnetic radiation and the properties of light and particles upon which spectro-photometric measurements depend. Ultraviolet light and visible light are very commonly used for the quantitative determination of biological samples. In addition, certain specific wavelengths are used to identify or verify the identity of the sample.

For quantitative assay the proper wavelength is selected such that a specific chemical absorbs a portion of light impinging upon it. If this occurs, a quantitative analysis may be made by measuring the light energy impinging upon and absorbed by the chemical. Also, the light energy absorbed by the solvent, if the unknown is dissolved, must be known or correction must be made for this. This is usually done by setting the spectrophotometer at a relative zero absorbance with the solvent alone positioned and then measuring the light absorbed by the chemical dissolved in the solvent. The solvent alone is known as the blank. A chemical may be in any one of the three states of matter but most work in experimental biology involves the use of materials in a liquid state.

THEORETICAL CONSIDERATIONS OF LIGHT ABSORPTION

Consider Fig. 10-2. As a light beam (A) penetrates the solution (B) light energy is absorbed by the solution. If this is visible radiation, then the light energy produces an excitation of molecules of the solution causing some electrons to assume a higher energy state. The light that passes through the chemical impinges upon a light trans-ducer — photocell or photomultiplier (C). The transducer then con-verts the light energy into an electrical signal which then is amplified (D) and recorded (E) in some manner. If the content of container (B) is the solvent, the instrument is adjusted to read zero absorbance or 100 per cent transmittance. The blank is probably absorbing some light energy, but the instrument is arbitrarily set to read zero absorb-ance. The probability of light absorption is given by the following equation:

$$dI/I_0 = -a'cdb \qquad (5)$$

where I_0 = intensity of light impinging on the solution or on the solution containing a chemical. In general, this light will be of a specific wavelength or of a few closely associated wavelengths. This light is said to be nearly monochromatic — of a very narrow range of the spectrum. dI = change of light intensity after passing through a solution of concentration (c) and thickness (db). The concentration, of course, may be expressed in milligrams per liter, moles per liter. a' = constant. It is a constant as long as the wavelength and temperature remain the same and only the solution concentration and solution thickness are allowed to vary. If Equation (5) is integrated between the limits I_0 and I, Equation (6) results (at the limit I_0, $b = 0$ and at the limit I, $b = b$);

$$\int_{I_0}^{I} dI/I = -a'c \int_0^b db \qquad (6)$$

The terms $(-a')$ and (c) are constant for each measurement. The term (db) is integrated between the limits (b) and (0) where I = light impinging on the phototransducer.

$$\text{the integral of } 1/I \text{ between the limits} \qquad (7)$$
$$I_0 \text{ and } I = \ln I - \ln I_0 \qquad (8)$$

But,

$$\ln I - \ln I_0 = \ln I/I_0 \qquad (9)$$

Also, the integration of

$$db = b \qquad (10)$$

and

$$\text{the integration of } db \text{ between the limits of } (b) \text{ and } (0) = b. \qquad (11)$$

Therefore, the above integrations result in the following:

$$\ln I/I_0 = -a'cb \qquad (12)$$

But

$$\ln I/I_0 = 2.303 \log I/I_0 \qquad (13)$$

Therefore,

$$2.303 \log I/I_0 = -a'cb \qquad (14)$$

or

$$\log I_0/I = abc = A \qquad (15)$$

where A = the absorbance of the solution as measured with a spectrophotometer or colorimeter, and $a = a'/2.303$, the absorptivity.

It is important to remember here that since the absorbance is linear with respect to the solution concentration, this is often the more useful relationship. However, the per cent transmittance of a solution may be equated to absorbance by the following:

$$A = \log 1/T = -\log T \tag{16}$$

Where

$$T = I/I_0 \tag{17}$$

$$\%T = 100 \times I/I_0 \tag{18}$$

where T = transmittance, and $\%T$ = per cent transmittance.

It is comparatively difficult to measure the real per cent transmittance ($\%T$) of a sample especially if it is housed in a container and as a result the absorption or per cent transmittance of the sample often is made to some arbitrary reference — air, with the sample holder positioned, blank, etc. If the absorbance of a sample is high it may be necessary to measure the absorbance against a blank of some neutral gray filter, wire screen, etc., although the use of wire screen is objectionable since the holes in the screen may act as a slit and cause the dispersion of light. Whatever the reference, it must be so given when reporting spectroscopic data.

GRAPHIC REPRESENTATION OF BOUGUER-BEER LAW

The equation $A = abc$ is known as the Bouguer-Beer law and is sometimes called the Lambert-Beer law or just Beer's law [2]. Since in any one system the absorptivity of the substance and length of the path through the absorbing substance are constants, the absorbance is directly proportional to the concentration. That is, a rectilinear plot of the absorbance (A) with respect to the concentration (c) of the absorbing substance, providing (a) and (b) are constant, will yield a linear relationship. If the length of the path of light through the absorbing substance is 1 cm, the slope of the above relationship is the absorptivity (a).

$$A/c = a \tag{19}$$

A plot of the per cent transmittance of a pure substance with respect to concentration will yield an exponentially declining relationship with a negative slope (Fig. 10-3). Bouguer [3] observed that the intensity of light passing through a medium which absorbs light is reduced, the reduction of which is proportional to the thickness of the absorbing solution. This was his contribution to the Bouguer-Beer law.

If one wishes to determine the concentration of a substance of unknown concentration, then one must prepare a *standard* curve of the absorbance with respect to the concentration of this substance.

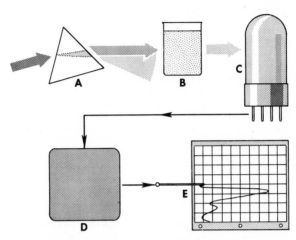

Fig. 10-2. Diagram of spectrophotometer components. (A) prism; (B) sample cell; (C) photocell; (D) amplifier; (E) read-out device.

These measurements must be made at a known, set wavelength and often at a known temperature. Once this standard curve is prepared, the absorbance of the unknown can be determined, and by reference to the standard curve the concentration of the unknown can be established within the limits of the technique, the operator's ability, and the instrument. When a plot of absorbance with respect to concentration of the absorbing substance yields a linear relationship, the relationship is said to have followed Beer's law. The law applies over a limited range of concentrations. In addition, the concentrations at which the law applies are, in general, low concentrations. As a result spectrophotometric measurements are made over a limited range of comparatively low concentrations of the absorbing substance. Many measurements, however, do not follow Beer's law. The following are a few reasons why such deviations occur:

1. Chemical and physical changes may occur to the absorbing particles as the particles increase in concentration. For example, there may be a reaction or interaction between the solvent and solute molecules and the extent of this reaction or interaction may depend upon the concentration of the solute molecules. Further, the concentration of a solute in a solvent may be limited by the solubility of the solute.

2. The temperature of the absorbing substance may markedly change the absorbance of this substance. Temperature may also have an effect on the sensitivity of certain detectors, i.e., lead sulfide detectors. The pH may have an effect on the measured absorbance.

3. Extraneous materials may materially affect the absorbance by the chemical. For example, large particles, molecules, or clusters of molecules may cause an excessive amount of light scattering such that the relationship between absorbance and concentration of the absorbing substance is no longer linear.

4. Difficulties with the instrument, such as light which covers a wide spectral band, may affect the absorbance-concentration relationship so that Beer's law no longer holds. These difficulties will be discussed in more detail later with a discussion of components of the instruments.

INSTRUMENT ERRORS

Consider Fig. 10-4, which is a plot of the absorbance of a solution with respect to wavelength. Consider in particular the region of the curve at a peak maximum. Here, just prior to the peak, the slope is positive and large; in addition, the peak is very sharp. It is easy to understand that errors could result from the following:

1. The wavelength dial might easily be dislocated so that the

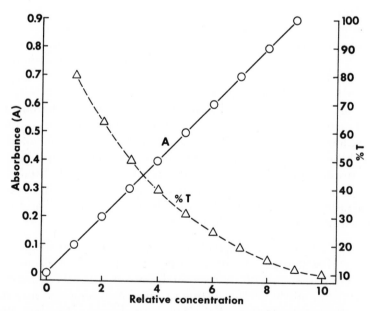

Fig. 10-3. Relationship between absorbance (A) and (%T) and relative concentration of absorbing material. Note the linear relationship between absorbance and concentration.

quality of light selected was not that shown by the wavelength indicator. In addition, the operator may not be able to set the wavelength indicator accurately, and therefore, the quality of light selected might not be that indicated by the dial. The result would be an inaccurate estimate of the absorption peak, especially if automatic scanning of the spectrum were employed. Steps have to be taken to ensure that these errors do not result.

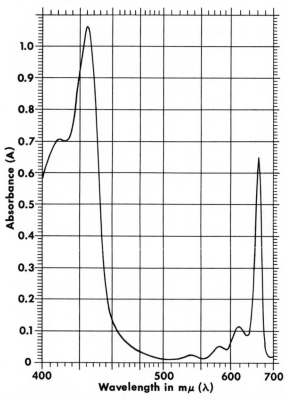

Fig. 10-4. Absorption spectrum of a mixture of chlorophylls in diethyl ether. Note the comparatively sharp absorption peak. The determination of the absorbance of this solution at, say, 650 mμ would be difficult due to the steep slope.

2. The optical system of the spectrophotometer might be such that a very broad band of light, not nearly so monochromatic, would result. This would have a tendency to lower the absorption maximum. There may be no shift of the wavelength of maximum absorption, but the measured absorbance at that wavelength may be less. Consider Fig. 10-5, which is an absorption spectrum of a pigment obtained using two different spectrophotometers. Spectrophotometer (1) had

an excellent optical system so that the light emitted from two prisms was highly monochromatic compared to the light emitted from the optical system of spectrophotometer *(2)*. It will be noticed that the absorption peak obtained with the better instrument is higher and the shoulders are much reduced, whereas the absorption peak obtained with spectrophotometer *(2)* is reduced and the shoulders are heightened. This effect is a result of a wide band of light emitted from the optical system of spectrophotometer *(2)*. It can be easily seen, therefore, that the quality of the components has a tremendous effect on the type of results obtained. A check of the wavelength alignment of recording pen on the paper with the actual quality of light impinging on the sample cell is easily made by using a mercury vapor source. The mercury source emits light of very specific wavelengths and therefore can be used as a means for calibrating these systems. Some instruments have a mercury lamp placed in the housing with other light sources. Further examples and explanations of instrument errors will be given in the sections dealing with various components of spectrophotometers.

QUANTITATIVE ANALYSIS OF COMPOUNDS IN A MIXTURE

GENERAL.   If two or more absorbing solutions are mixed together and if the absorbance of one compound does not interfere in any way with the absorbance of the other compounds of the mixture, then the total absorbance of the solution is:

$$A = a_1b_1c_1 + a_2b_2c_2 + a_3b_3c_3 + \cdots + a_nb_nc_n \tag{20}$$

where A = total absorbance of the solution at some specified wavelength, a_1 = absorptivity of solution [1], b_1, b_2, b_3 = path length of the light beam through the cell, c_1, etc. = concentration (final) of chemicals.

Consider Fig. 10-6. Line *(1)* shows the relationship of the absorbance with respect to wavelength of solution *(1)*. Line *(2)* shows the relationship of the absorbance with respect to wavelength of solution *(2)*. If we mix chemical *(1)* with chemical *(2)* and the final concentrations of chemicals *(1) and (2)* are the same as they were separately, and if both are absorbing at the same wavelengths, then a plot of absorbance of the mixture with respect to wavelength will be obtained. The absorbancies are additive. One could as easily obtain the afore-mentioned graph by adding together the values of the absorbance of each chemical. The result is the same. Also, one could prepare a mixture of three different absorbing compounds and obtain the same result. It is understood, of course, that this additive effect holds true only when no interference of the absorption of one compound by the absorption of the other compound(s) is observed. If this is not true, then the extension of Beer's law may no longer hold. Theoretically, this could be extended for any number of compounds found in a mixture; however, the absorption soon becomes so great that Beer's law no longer holds. Also, the chemicals may interfere and interact.

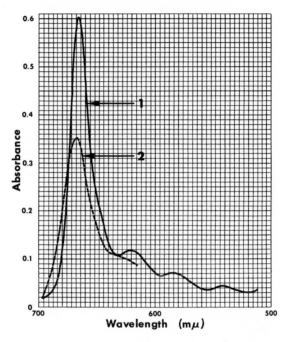

Fig. 10-5. Absorption spectrum of a pigment obtained using two different spectrophotometers.

One cannot obtain a quantitative estimate of the individual chemicals found in a complex mixture merely by measuring the absorbance of the mixture at one wavelength, since the instrument indicates only the absorbance of the total mixture. However, measurement of total absorbance of the mixture at several different wavelengths allows one to determine the amount of each individual chemical found in the mixture. The number of wavelengths which must be considered is determined by the number of individual chemicals found in the mixture. For example, if the mixture contains three individual components (noninterfering), then measurements of the total absorbance of the mixture at three wavelengths are made. Preferably, these measurements should be made at wavelengths that are considerably removed from one another. For example, one may measure the absorbance of the mixture at 425, 450, and 460 mμ. The selection of wavelengths at which the measurements are made is dependent upon the absorption spectra of the individual compounds, the resolution of the instrument, and the skill of the operator. One could not, for example, wish to determine the absorbance of a mixture at 490, 493, and 496 mμ if the optical system of the instrument is such that a wide band of wavelengths is emitted. However, one may logically use these three wavelengths for determining the amounts of three different chemicals found in a mixture, if observation of the absorption spectra would suggest such a procedure. Wavelengths usually should be selected at which the compounds exhibit a comparatively broad absorption band. To determine the amounts, therefore, of three individual chemicals found in a mixture the absorbance at three different wavelengths would be measured. Three different simultaneous equations would result from the extension of Beer's law for the calculation of amounts of the three compounds. It is necessary that the

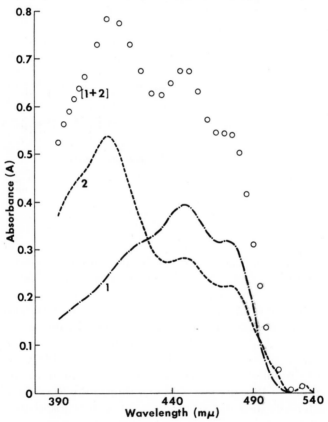

Fig. 10-6. Absorption spectra of two different carotenoids *(1, 2)* and of a mixture of *(1 + 2)*.

selection of wavelengths at which to measure the absorbance of the chemicals be based on the fact that the absorptivities of the three chemicals are different at each wavelength selected.

EXAMPLE OF QUANTITATIVE ANALYSIS OF A BINARY MIXTURE. Chlorophylls *a* and *b* are extracted from green leaf material with an acetone-water mixture in which the final concentration of acetone is 80 per cent [13]. This extract is filtered, the filter washed with 80 per cent acetone, and the solution made to a known volume. The filtered mixture is then placed in an absorption cell, positioned in a spectrophotometer, and the absorbance *(A)* of the solution measured at 645 and 663 mμ wavelengths. These wavelengths are selected for two reasons:

1. The carotenoids, which are present in the extract, do not absorb at these wavelengths.
2. An absorption maximum for chlorophyll b is at 645 mμ and an absorption maximum for chlorophyll a is at 663 mμ when these two pigments are dissolved in 80% aqueous acetone. The absorptivities are given in Table 10-1 [13].

TABLE 10-1

ABSORPTIVITIES OF CHLOROPHYLLS A AND B AT 645 AND 663 mμ
IN 80 PER CENT ACETONE-WATER MIXTURE

| Wavelength (mμ) | Absorptivity | |
	Chlorophyll a	Chlorophyll b
645	16.75	45.6
663	82.04	9.27

Since $A = abc(1) + abc(2)$, then:

$$A645 = 16.75 \text{ Ca} + 45.6 \text{ Cb} \tag{21}$$

$$A663 = 82.04 \text{ Ca} + 9.27 \text{ Cb} \tag{22}$$

Therefore

$$Ca = \frac{A645 - 45.6 \text{ Cb}}{16.75} \tag{23}$$

or:

$$Cb = 0.0229 \text{ A645} - 0.00468 \text{ A663} \tag{24}$$

$$Ca = 0.0127 \text{ A663} - 0.00269 \text{ A645} \tag{25}$$

The concentrations of chlorophyll(s) will be given in grams of chlorophyll per liter extract, where Ca = concentration of chlorophyll a, and Cb = concentration of chlorophyll b.

Spectrophotometers and Colorimeters

COMPONENTS

Several basic components are generally found in most commercial spectrophotometers as well as in custom-built instruments. A brief description of these components and a discussion of functions, as well as the problems involved in the use of these materials, are presented. Each component will be considered in reference to the order in which the light beam strikes the component as well as to the origin and display of the signal. Basic components usually incorporated into commercial colorimeters and spectrophotometers include light source(s), collimator, monochromator, cell compartment, light-sensitive material (photocell, etc.), and read-out device. Many other components are usually found in addition to those mentioned above. Some of these are incorporated into the instrument in order to provide a completely automatic system for determining absorption spectra of samples seated in the sample compartment. Some brief discussion of a few of these components also will be included in this chapter.

LIGHT SOURCES. At least three basic requirements must be met by every light source used, regardless of the spectral region of interest:

1. The source should emit sufficient radiation over the entire spectral region of interest.

2. The source should emit a comparatively even amount of radiation over the range required, although electronic compensation and use of double-beam instrumentation no longer make this requirement essential.

3. The source should be comparatively long-lived and free from excessive changes over a comparatively short period of time.

Frequently used sources for the far and near ultraviolet region (180 to 320 mμ) include the Nestor and Beckman hydrogen lamps. Hydrogen lamps, in general, become comparatively hot and therefore may be isolated from the body of the instrument and/or water-cooled. Ordinary tungsten filament lamps, such as one would see in a slide projector, automobile lamp, or microscope lamp, are the best sources for the visible region of the spectrum for which intense sources are not required. Infrared instruments incorporate, in general, either Globar or Nernst glowers. The Globar is a silicon carbide rod with metal-coated tips provided for making good electrical contact. It is heated to approximately 1200°C and consequently requires a water-cooled jacket in order to avoid overheating the other components. A Globar achieves comparatively good stability. Nernst glowers consist of filaments of zirconium and yttrium oxides and may be somewhat smaller than Globar rods and consequently may be air-cooled.

Starting temperatures are achieved by the use of auxiliary heaters such as a fine gas flame or small platinum wire heater. Greater fluctuations are exhibited by the Nernst glower; therefore, during long periods of scanning time, these fluctuations must be monitored and taken into account.

OPTICAL COMPONENTS.

Windows. The selection of the materials of which the windows in a spectrophotometer are made depends upon the spectral range in which the investigator is interested. Obviously, materials that strongly absorb in a particular wavelength region would not be suitable for windows for that particular region. No one material is entirely satisfactory for the spectral range of the far ultraviolet through the middle infrared. In general, silica glass windows are used in the instrument that covers the ultraviolet region. Glasses such as Pyrex glasses are suitable for the visible, near ultraviolet, and very near infrared (Fig. 10-7). The glasses absorb strongly in the infrared and hence are not suitable for these spectral regions. Halide salts such as NaCl, KBr, KCl, along with other materials such as MgO, are frequently used as window materials for the near infrared and the infrared regions, although only a few of these such as NaCl are suitable for the middle infrared region.

A large variety of cells of various sizes and shapes is available commercially for particular instruments. Many instruments come equipped with standard cell holders enabling cells to be interchangeable from one instrument to another. In addition, many laboratories have sets of cells custom-made and designed for application to specific situations. Commercially made cells for the ultraviolet and visible region of the spectrum are most commonly the standard 1 cm (4 to 5 ml capacity cells), keg-shaped cells, cylindrical cells, short-path length cells for large and small volumes, and the long-path length cells for large and small volumes. Some small-volume cells are prepared from capillary tubing sealed at both ends following introduction of the sample into the tube. Some commercially made cells have a jacket in order that temperature-regulated water may be circulated through the jacket while absorption measurements are being made. These types of cells are frequently used in enzyme kinetic studies; with materials that will not dissolve sufficiently at room temperature in a particular solvent, the temperature must be elevated during the measurement. In addition, the absorption at a particular wavelength of some substances varies greatly with the temperature and consequently absorption measurements must be made under known and controlled temperature conditions for quantitative studies. Some drawings of a few commonly used absorption cells are found in Fig. 10-8.

Care of Cells. Most supply houses provide absorption cells in matched sets of two or more. Care should be taken to prevent contamination of the optical surfaces, since scratches and contaminants may absorb, reflect, and/or scatter light. Special care should be taken to clean properly the cells such that a change in the optical path length does not occur. Only mild cleaning materials, such as methanol (AR) or dilute acid, should be used for glass cells. Never use materials that might etch the surface, such as alkaline detergents, for glass cells. The cells should be handled only on the nonoptical surfaces; perspiration and hand oils will affect the amount of total light absorption.

The path length of cells can usually be determined by preparing a standard solution of a compound of known spectral behavior and measuring the absorption by that sample at a specified wavelength given by the manufacturer. After proper adjustment of the instrument a calculation of the path length of the cell can be made by knowing the expected absorbance by the above-mentioned solution for a particular instrument.

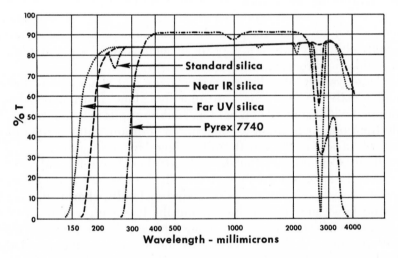

Fig. 10-7. Absorption of ultraviolet, visible, and near infrared light by common types of glass (Courtesy, Beckman Instruments, Inc.).

Very special handling techniques are necessary for work in the far ultraviolet and the infrared. Oxygen and water vapor absorb in the far ultraviolet and hence must be eliminated by purging the optical path with dry nitrogen prior to absorption measurements. Due to the strong absorption of many materials in the ultraviolet, short optical paths must be used.

Isolation of Monochromatic Light. One or a combination of three types of components is generally used for the isolation of narrow spectral regions — filters, prisms, gratings. The exact component used depends upon the spectral region of interest and the narrowness of the spectral band required. Prisms and/or gratings are most commonly used.

1. *Filters.* Less expensive colorimeters still are made which contain a series of optical filters for the isolation of spectral regions. Optical glass filters pass a wider band than do interference filters, and may either contain absorbing materials dissolved or suspended in the glass

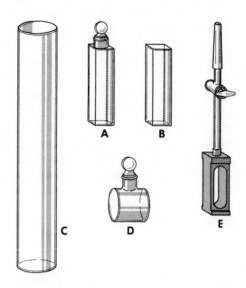

Fig. 10-8. Drawings of some commonly used absorption cells.

or may be a sandwich of a gelatin filter between two glass plates. In many cases Beer's law still applies even though a wide band of radiation has been isolated if the compound absorbs in a very broad spectral region. Widths at half-maximum transmittance are taken as the relative band widths. On the average, the relative band width for interference filters may be approximately 10 mμ whereas for ordinary glass filters it may be approximately 40 mμ. Two or more sharp cut-off filters together are used in some instruments to isolate reasonably narrow bands of radiation.

Monochromators allow a continuous selection of wavelengths, as opposed to filters which do not allow a continuous variation of the quality of light which strikes the sample cell. Some authors prefer to designate colorimeters as instruments with which one cannot continuously vary the monochromatic light, unlike spectrophotometers with which one can vary continuously the monochromatic light. Necessary components of a monochromator system include: the monochromator (device for dispersing the radiation – prism, grating), a slit, and a focusing device.

2. *Prisms.* For the ultraviolet and visible spectral regions prisms are usually crystalline quartz, flint glass, or fused silica. Inexpensive clinical spectrophotometers or colorimeters will frequently use inexpensive, glass prisms. Flint glass prisms are commonly used for the visible region only. Consider Fig. 10-9. As incident light strikes and then travels through the prism (the dispersive medium) the degree of bending is dependent upon the velocity of propagation of a wave through the dispersive medium. The degree of bending of each wavelength of light is dependent upon the index of refraction of each wavelength at the surface B-B'. The refracted rays travel through the prism medium at differential rates and are refracted again at the surface B'-C toward the surface B-C. Again, the degree of bending is dependent upon the index of refraction which is, in turn, dependent upon the wavelength. Employed in many instruments are prisms with aluminized back surfaces such that once the light has been dispersed it strikes the mirror surface and passes back through the prism with a resulting redispersion and a better separation of the spectrum. Quartz has a much greater index of refraction for ultraviolet than for near infrared radiation.

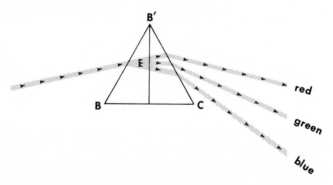

Fig. 10-9. Action of a prism on light. This is a diagram of a 60° prism prepared by placing together two 30° prisms. Angles are not accurately drawn.

3. *Gratings.* Diffraction gratings consist of a support into which are ruled lines. Two general types of gratings may be used: reflection or transmission. Reflection gratings consist of rulings, 400 to 6000 per cm, on a polished reflecting surface. Perhaps a simple description of a transmission grating will illustrate better the use of a grating as a dispersing agent in spectroscopy. If incident radiation strikes a surface containing slits some of the radiation is permitted to pass through the slits and spreads out in waves. The light passing directly through

the slit is focused by a lens system at a focal point and remains as white light. Some of the light is directed toward the lens at an angle Q.

$$\text{Sin } Q = \frac{m\lambda}{d} \qquad (26)$$

where $m=$ an integer, $\lambda=$ the wavelength of light, and $d=$ the distance between slits.

The angle, then, is a function of the wavelength. The greater the wavelength of radiation, the greater the angle in the first order. As a result, red light would be dispersed at a greater angle than would, for example, blue light.

Light from a suitable prism will be dispersed into the various wavelengths of the spectrum. However, some white light impinging upon a grating will be found as white light at the focal point. Further, some higher orders of dispersion will be found; some gratings will concentrate greater than 60 per cent of the incident energy in the band of the first-order spectrum. Gratings are now used to disperse ultraviolet, visible, near infrared, and infrared light. For example, the Cary Model 14 spectrophotometer utilizes a double monochromator consisting of a fused silica prism with a 600 lines/mm echelette grating which gives the monochromator a range from 186 mμ to 3.0 μ. The Bausch and Lomb Spectronic 505 utilizes two gratings instead of the prism-grating combination and may be used from approximately 200 mμ to more than 700 mμ.

DETECTORS.   Light absorption by the material is measured by using a suitable detector. That is, the intensity of the incident light beam without the presence of a sample is measured, followed by measurement of the isolated light beam with the sample between the source and the detector. Selection of suitable detectors for spectrophotometry is made on the basis of:

1. Signal to noise (random electronic fluctuation) level. This level should be in a ratio of 100:1 or greater.
2. Intensity of light impinging upon the detector as well as response of the detector at the wavelength of interest.
3. Suitability of amplification of detector signal.
4. Linearity of response.
5. Response time.

If the signal to noise ratio of the instrument is low, repeatable measurements over a short period of time become almost impossible. A stable electronic system is most important. A voltage regulator is used in most instruments. A common estimate of the minimum requirement of signal to noise is 100:1; however, much higher ratios would be desirable. As the intensity of light impinging upon the detector increases, the ratio, in general, of the signal to noise increases. Further, many detectors, except thermocouples and thermistors, are much more sensitive to certain rather specific wavelengths than others.

It is obvious that comparatively rapid response time and rapid recovery without fatigue would be required for maximum adaptability of a detector for a spectrophotometer, especially automatic scanning systems in which rapid changes in light intensity must be detected.

Common detection systems used for the ultraviolet and visible regions include:

Human Eye.   The human eye is not well adapted for a great number of applications of this sort since: *(a)* response time is slow; *(b)* recovery is slow; *(c)* it is affected by previous environment; *(d)* it is not suitable for amplification; *(e)* it is not equally sensitive from wavelength to wavelength and from eye to eye; and *(f)* it cannot be precisely calibrated—no better than 1 per cent accurate.

Photoemissive Cells.   The photomultiplier is a good example of a photoemissive cell. Light energy impinging upon the sensitive surface within a photoemissive cell causes an emission of electrons, provided the source is of high enough intensity. The electrons are attracted by a potential difference to a second sensitive material which will release two or more electrons for each received. These in turn are attracted to another sensitive surface which emits, again, two or more electrons for each received and hence the signal is multiplied sometimes by a factor of more than a million. One example of a commonly used photomultiplier tube is the RCA IP-28 (Fig. 10-10). This tube is responsive over the spectral range of 200 to 700 mμ. Of course, the signal from the photomultiplier may be further amplified. These cells exhibit a very high sensitivity and low response time. Photoemissive cells are most commonly employed in ultraviolet and visible instruments.

Photoconductive Cells.   Certain materials upon exposure to the proper electromagnetic radiation release electrons in a solid which causes the material to be more conductive. The change in resistance may be measured in order to determine the intensity of the light beam striking the detector. Lead sulfide, deposited as a thin layer on the surface of glass or other substances, is often used. Lead sulfide cells are commonly found in near-infrared instruments, which systems show a very high sensitivity and moderate response time.

Thermocouples.   The thermocouple consists of two pieces of dissimilar metals in contact, the EMF of the junction is dependent upon the temperature. As infrared radiation strikes the thermocouple, the temperature of the junction changes, resulting in a change in the EMF of the junction. Obviously, the response and recovery times of these detectors are dependent upon the mass of at least one of the metals.

Thermistors.   Thermistors consist of materials, the resistance of which is dependent on the temperature of that material. Here again, the temperature of the receiver is dependent upon the intensity of the light impinging on the receiver surface. Obviously, a requirement would be that the material should have a comparatively high temperature coefficient of resistivity as well as a comparatively rapid response time. Other detectors are in use with infrared instruments but will not be discussed here.

AMPLIFIERS AND RECORDERS.   The signal from the detector is generally small and as a result amplification is necessary. Details of amplification and display devices are given in Chapter 15.

Several basic types of photometer designs are available. Many of these fall into the following basic classes of instruments:

1. Color comparators.
2. Single-beam electronic instruments with filters for the isolation of the required quality of light.
3. Single-beam electronic instruments using prisms or gratings for isolation of the required quality of light.
4. Double-beam electronic instruments using either a prism or grating or some combination of two of these for the isolation of monochromatic light.

EXAMPLES OF PHOTOMETERS

COLOR COMPARATORS.   A variety of devices, too numerous to mention *in toto,* is available for the direct comparison of quantities of materials. These comparators utilize the human eye as the detector, and a wide band of light, sunlight, and so forth as the source. The color of a standard material (dye, piece of glass) can be used to aid in identifying the amount of material in a colored solution. The assumption is made that Beer's law holds over the range of concentrations used. They have been widely used in the past for rapid measurements of pH using pH dye indicators, for soil testing, for swimming pool testing, and wherever rapid, convenient methods of measurement are required. Modifications of the color comparators were made by supplying a consistent light source, suitable dispersive device, and a suitable electronic detector. The modern colorimeters and spectrophotometers are outgrowths of these modifications. Today color comparators are still widely used for many purposes.

The use of a color comparator generally involves:

1. Preparation or purchase of a standard color substance. Frequently a dye is added to the liquid for the development of a color reaction, as in the measurement of pH with dye indicators. Many manufacturers have been able to prepare colored pieces of glass which resemble colored solutions and are more stable and more easily handled in the field. These are used as standard color pieces.

2. Addition of the dye to the unknown solution to be measured. Here, the amount of solution to be tested and the amount of dye added must be controlled.

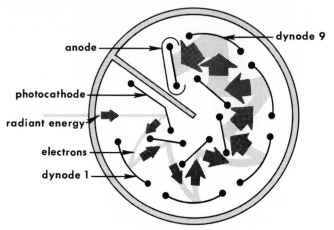

Fig. 10-10. Diagram of a commonly used photomultiplier tube (Courtesy, Beckman Instruments, Inc.).

3. Positioning the unknown solution by the standard for direct visual comparison in order to detect the concentration or amount of substance of interest in the unknown. Frequently, whenever slightly colored solutions, such as soil solution samples, exist prior to the addition of the color indicator a comparable thickness of this undyed solution must be placed in line with the standard in order that more nearly correct measurements may be made.

In order to describe more adequately the parts of a spectrophotometer and the function of these parts a brief description of the optical systems and components of three different spectrophotometers will be given. These include systems of the Bausch and Lomb Spectronic 20, a popular grating clinical spectrophotometer; the Beckman model DKZA prism ultraviolet, visible, and near infrared spectrophotometer; and the Cary model 14 prism-grating, ultraviolet, visible, and near infrared spectrophotometer.

BAUSCH AND LOMB SPECTRONIC 20 COLORIMETER-SPECTROPHOTOMETER. A schematic diagram of the optical components of this instrument is given in Fig. 10-11. The light source is a tungsten lamp. The source radiation is collimated with a lens (A) which focuses the source on an entrance slit. The light then passes through a collimating lens (B) and impinges upon the diffraction grating which disperses the light. The angle of the grating is controlled by rotating the cam to which are attached a wavelength scale and knob. Dispersed light from the grating then passes through a slit, the sample or blank, through a red filter (if measurements are made at wavelengths greater than 650mμ) and finally impinges upon the phototube.

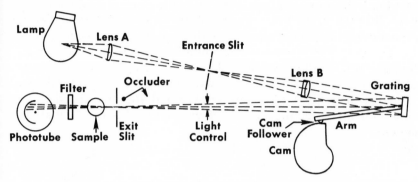

Fig. 10-11. Optical path and diagram of components of Bausch and Lomb spectronic 20 colorimeter-spectrophotometer (Courtesy, Bausch and Lomb).

The absorbance or per cent transmittance of a sample is measured by setting the dark current control such that the meter reads infinity absorbance or zero per cent transmittance without any sample positioned in the instrument. Without a sample in the instrument, an occluder falls into the light beam; as a result, the dark current should remain the same regardless of the wavelength selected. An appropriate blank is then positioned in the sample holder and the light control adjusted so that the meter reads 100 per cent transmittance or zero absorbance. The unknown sample is then positioned in the light beam and the absorbance of the sample is read directly from the scale on the meter. Concentrations are determined by use of a concentration with respect to absorbance graph which must be prepared using appropriate concentrations of the pure compound or by use of the formula $A = abc$, where (a), the absorptivity, must be determined by measuring, under like conditions, the absorbance of a known concentration of the chemical or mixture.

BECKMAN MODEL DK 2A SPECTROPHOTOMETER. Two different designs of the Beckman DK A series are available: DK 1A and 2A. The DK 1A is composed of two units, a monochromator and rack containing the other electronic components. The DK 2A is a bench-type model with a flat bed recorder, monochromator, and some of the electronic equipment housed in one unit. A diagram of the optical components of the DK 2A ratio-recording spectrophotometer is given in Fig. 10-12. Two light sources are used in the instrument: a hydrogen lamp as an ultraviolet source and a tungsten lamp as a visible and near infrared source. The source passes from mirrors through an entrance beam chopper. The light beam is then reflected from a collimating mirror to the prism. The back surface of the prism is aluminized and hence reflects the light beam back through the prism. The wavelength of light is selected by rotating the prism with respect to the collimating mirror. After having passed through the prism the light impinges upon the collimating mirror again and then passes through a slit into the double-beam optical system. Monochromatic light is passed alternately through the sample cell and the reference cell. Light energy transmitted by the sample cell or the reference cell is then received by one of two detectors—photomultiplier or lead sulfide cell. The photomultiplier is used for detecting energy of wavelengths between 170 and 700 mμ, and the lead sulfide cell for detecting energy of wavelengths between 400 and 3500 mμ.

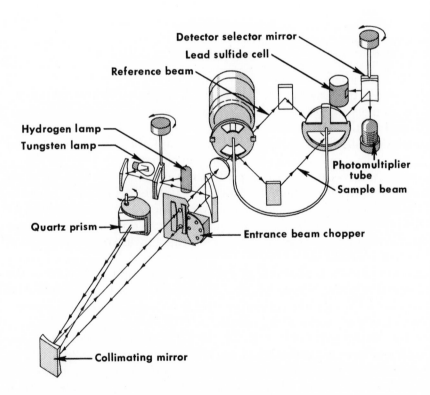

Fig. 10-12. Diagram of the optical components found in a Beckman model DK 2A spectrophotometer (Courtesy, Beckman Instruments, Inc.).

CARY MODEL 14. Figure 10-13 is a schematic diagram of the optical path of the Cary model 14 spectrophotometer. The effective measuring range of the Cary 14 is from 186 to 2600 mμ — ultraviolet, visible, and near infrared regions. The reported accuracy of this instrument is approximately ±0.002 absorbance unit at 0 to 1 absorbance and ±0.005 unit at or near an absorbance of 2. Frequently, the limiting factor with respect to accuracy is the recorder performance.

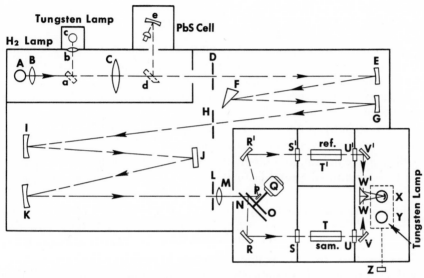

Fig. 10-13. Schematic diagram of the optical path of the Cary model 14 ultraviolet, visible, and near infrared spectrophotometer (Courtesy, Applied Physics Corp.).

The instrument employs three different light sources — a tungsten lamp *(c)* for measurements with visible light, another tungsten lamp *(y)* for measurements with near-infrared light, and a hydrogen lamp *(A)* for measurements with ultraviolet light. Light from either source is passed through a slit *(D)* and reflected from a collimating mirror *(E)* to a 30° fused silica prism *(F)*, to the collimating mirrors *(G)* and *(I)* onto a grating *(J)*. The grating is an echelette grating with 600 lines/mm. A double monochromator, therefore, is employed — a prism-grating combination. Monochromatic light is passed through another slit *(L)* and then either through to mirror *(P)* or is reflected by a rotating mirror at 30 cycles per second (cps) *(O)*. At this point the light is chopped producing alternating light and dark periods. The path of the monochromatic light is then alternated to *(R)* or *(R')* mirrors following which it is reflected to the sample and reference cells alternately. The light then passes to mirrors *(V')* or *(V)* and *(W')* or *(W)* and finally to *(X)* a photomultiplier. The photomultiplier, an IP28, receives light alternately from the reference side and the sample side of the compartment. The signals originating from the photomultiplier are stored in separate condensors and then compared by a 60 cps chopper. If the signals are unequal, a signal is generated which drives a servo mechanism in the recorder to bring the two signals into balance.

The optical path is reversed for measurements with near infrared radiations so that the photomultiplier is near the lamp housing used for the visible source.

EXAMPLES OF APPLICATIONS

A complete description of the many uses of spectrophotometers and colorimeters would require many volumes. It is intended here, then, to provide a small sample of some of the many uses for spectrophotometers and colorimeters in research, quality control, and routine clinical applications.

PHOSPHORUS ANALYSIS. Routinely, it is important to determine the quantity of phosphorus and other elements such as nitrogen, sulfur, and calcium, in biological materials as a basis for the estimation of the amount of protoplasm in general, or specific compounds in particular.

Often the convenient way to determine the quantity of phosphorus is to wet-digest the tissue with perchloric acid (0.9 ml 70 per cent per 10 μg of phosphorus). The digestion may be carried out in a hard glass test tube over a gas flame. To the digested, cooled material are added aqueous ammonium molybdate and aqueous aminonaphthol-sulfonic acid (0.5 ml of 2.5 per cent ammonium molybdate and 0.2 ml of aminonaphtholsulfonic acid prepared by adding 0.5 g of purified 1-amino-2 naphthol 4-sulfonic acid to 200 ml of 15 per cent sodium bisulfite (anhydrous) followed by 1.0 g of anhydrous sodium sulfite. The mixture is placed in a boiling water bath for exactly 7 minutes, cooled for 20 minutes at room temperature, and the absorbance read at 830 mμ wavelength. Of course appropriate blanks and standards must be treated in a similar manner [14].

ABSORPTION SPECTRA OF PROTOCHLOROPHYLL AND CHLOROPHYLL A. Protochlorophyll to chlorophyll a transformations may be observed by following the change in absorption spectrum of an etiolated leaf upon exposure to light. Bean plants are grown in the dark for a period of 10 days. A leaf is sandwiched between a piece of optical glass and a piece of opal glass and is then positioned in the well of a recording spectrophotometer [15-17]. A scan of the absorption spectrum of the etiolated leaf is made prior to exposure to light (Fig. 10-14). Protochlorophyll is converted to chlorophyll a after exposure to a tungsten lamp of 400 foot-candle (ft-c) light intensity for 1 minute following which the absorption spectrum of the leaf is determined again. In general, neutral filters must be placed in front of the reference beam of a recording spectro-photometer in order to more nearly balance the intensities of the beam, since the leaf is optically quite dense. It will be observed from the figure that upon exposure to light there is a shift in the absorption peak from the protochlorophyll peak to the chlorophyll 674 peak.

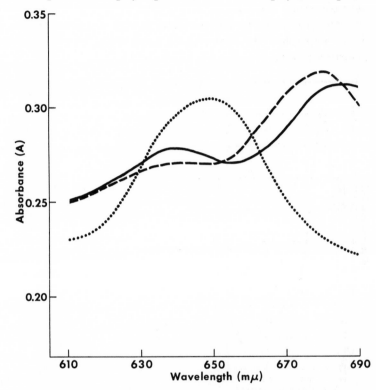

Fig. 10-14. Absorption spectra of protochlorophyll (dotted line) and two forms of chlorophyll a (dashed and solid lines).

QUANTITATIVE DETERMINATION OF SUGAR. Bath [18] and Bailey [19] have described a convenient method whereby simple sugars may be quantitated with ultraviolet spectrophotometry. The procedure involves the reaction of sugar, hexoses, pentoses, and suc-rose with 90 per cent sulfuric acid for 5 minutes at 100°C in a water bath, rapid cooling, and then measuring the absorption spectrum of the mixture. The absorption maxima (257 and 322 mμ) are similar for the hexoses — fructose, galactose, and glucose. Different absorption maxima are obtained for the pentoses arabinose and ribose (287 and 316 mμ) (Fig. 10-15). The relation of absorbance to concentration follows Beer's law.

In biological systems the sugars may be found free, in mixtures, or as moieties of larger molecules such as galactolipids. The sugars may be released from compounds such as the galactolipids by acid hydrolysis in sulfuric acid and then treated in the manner mentioned above. In general, a procedure such as the one mentioned would require a pure compound or be limited to no more than one hexose and one pentose, since the absorption maxima for many hexoses are alike as are those for many pentoses. Many sugars in a mixture may be effectively separated by paper chromatography, eluted, and measured colorimetrically.

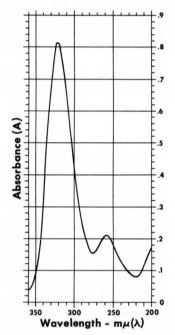

Fig. 10-15. Absorption spectrum of H_2SO_4 treated galactose — hydroyl — methyl furfural.

Densitometers

A variety of densitometric techniques is available for the quantitative estimation of material separated by paper chromatography, paper electrophoresis, thin-layer chromatography, gel electrophoresis, and other methods. The principles of densitometry are similar to those of spectrophotometry. That is, the light absorbed or reflected by a chemical of interest is measured with the chemical adsorbed on a paper or in a chromatographic medium. The components of a densitometer are somewhat similar to those in a spectrophotometer: light source, filters or monochromator, collimating device, sample compartment, photocell or photomultiplier, amplifier(s), and appropriate read-out device. Consider Fig. 10-16, which is a schematic diagram of the transmission density unit of Photovolt densitometer model 52. The amplification and read-out devices are found in another unit. Note the diagram of the tungsten light source. This instrument also is available with an ultraviolet source. Light from the source is collimated, passed through a heat-absorbing glass and then through a slit. The samples on filter paper or on other media are positioned over the slit between the slit and the photocell. A scanning mechanism is provided whereby the filter paper may be drawn continuously over the slit. The device is set at zero absorbance by positioning a piece of the paper used for chromatography over the slit. This paper must be stained and treated prior to this operation in the same manner as the sample paper. Light passing through the filter paper strikes the photocell and a signal is produced. The paper containing the absorbed material is passed at a slow, constant rate over the slit in front of the photocell. When an absorbing band passes over the slit the signal is reduced and so noted by observing the meter and/or the recorder trace.

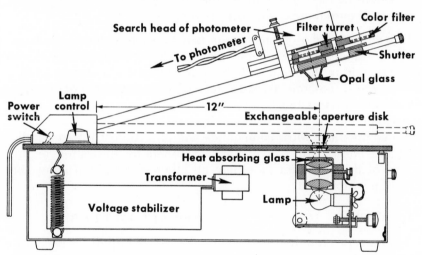

Fig. 10-16. Schematic diagram of the transmission density unit of a Photovolt densitometer (Courtesy, Photovolt Corporation).

Materials absorbing light energy of wavelengths in the ultraviolet, visible, and/or near-infrared may be detected.

Frequently a routine scanning of a chromatogram by this method will give a clear idea of the area of maximum density of the separated spot on the chromatogram and, as a result, should aid in the identification of R_f values. In addition, if the whole system is calibrated with a series of standards of the material of interest, an estimation of the amount of absorbed material may be made. It must be remembered, however, that often the size of the spot varies considerably and it is most difficult to relate light absorption of the spot to the amount of material found on the paper. Also, the relative response of the read-out device with respect to the amount of material on the support may not exhibit a linear relationship. A common practice in handling the data is to record the amplified signal from the photocell with respect to the distance the paper has moved under the slit. The integrated area under the curve is then taken as an estimate of the amount of the material only after reference to the standard determined in a similar manner. Integration of the area under the curve may be accomplished by:

1. Integrating the recorded area with a planimeter.
2. Automatic integration with an integrator built into the recorder.
3. Cutting the area out of the recorder paper, weighing the paper, and relating this weight to the weight per unit area of known sizes of recorder paper.
4. Counting the squares under the recorded area. Here, at best, an estimate of partial areas will have to be made.

Densitometry of a chromatogram may be used without prior treatment or staining of the compounds provided the compounds absorb radiation within the range of light emitted by the source, transmitted by the optical components, and detected by the detector. For example, conjugated unsaturated bond systems often absorb strongly in the ultraviolet and no prior treatment may be required for estimation of these compounds. Most compounds will absorb near infrared radiation and consequently may be determined by utilization of this region of the spectrum providing all other systems will allow this type of measurement.

EXAMPLE OF USE OF DENSITOMETER

Thin-layer techniques for separation of phospholipids are becoming widespread. For example, it is possible to separate a mixture of phospholipids with thin-layer techniques in some 60 to 70 minutes, whereas previously a similar separation on silicic acid-impregnated paper required some 16 to 18 hours. Possible breakdown of the compounds during long-term experiments may be avoided by this technique. In addition some nondiscriminatory methods for location of the spots may be used since paper is not employed. The crude mixture of phospholipids is spotted in one corner of the thin-layer plate covered with silica gel containing 5 per cent calcium sulfate used as a binder. The chromatogram is developed in a solvent system of 1:10:90 (v/v/v) acetic acid: diethyl ether: and petroleum ether (bp 30 to 60°C). Following development, the chromatogram is dried, sprayed with 50 per cent sulfuric acid, and the spots charred in an oven at a temperature above 180°C. The amount of charring is estimated by scanning the plate with a densitometer [20]. See Chapter 2.

Flame Photometers

Emission spectroscopic techniques, especially flame photometry, are widely used by analytical biologists. It is well known that active metals such as sodium, potassium, lithium, and calcium are easily activated by gas-oxygen flames. The light intensity emitted by these flame-excited metals is proportional to the quantity of metal excited per unit time. Flame photometers are used to measure the intensity of light and, in many cases, the wavelengths of light emitted by these excited metals. The measurements, in general, are rapidly and precisely made with slight modifications of spectroscopic systems mentioned previously.

Fluorometers

Fluorometers are instruments with which one may determine the quantity of materials which fluoresce. Fluorescence is the process whereby a chemical emits radiation as a result of a transition from a higher to a lower electronic state following excitation. The time interval between excitation and emission is from 10^{-8} to about 10^{-3} second. Processes involving longer intervals are included in the category of phosphorescence. The primary act consists of light absorption, usually ultraviolet, by a chromophore. Many aromatics, especially those which consist of several benzene rings, display fluorescence. Impurities and certain substituted groups may have a marked quenching effect on the fluorescence.

A diagram of the optical path of a common fluorometer is given in Fig. 16-2 B of Chapter 16. The light emitted by the sample at right angles to the ultraviolet source beam is detected by the photomultiplier. The fluorescent light intensity is compared with that of a known intensity (calibrated light beam). The intensity is adjusted by rotation of the fluorescence dial until the calibrated light beam intensity matches that from the sample (the null meter reads zero). The degree of fluorescence is read from the fluorescence dial. Accessories are available for adapting this and other fluorometers for continuous flow monitoring and for paper chromatogram scanning. An instrument used for detecting the wavelengths of fluorescence is called a *spectrofluorometer*. The fluorescence characteristics of some common biologicals are given in Table 10-2 [21, 22].

TABLE 10-2

ACTIVATION PEAKS AND FLUORESCENT PEAKS OF SOME COMMON
BIOLOGICAL COMPOUNDS

Compound	Activation Peak (mμ)	Fluorescent Peak (mμ)
Adenine	280	375
Adenosine	285	395
Adrenalin	295	335
Aureomycin	355	445
Adenosine Triphosphate	285	395
Diphosphopyridine		
Nucleotide (reduced)	340	435
Procaine	275	345
Quinine	250,350	450
Tocopherol	295	330
Vitamine A	325	470
Xanthine	315	435

Fluorescent characteristics of other important biologicals can be found in references [21] and [22].

References

1. R. P. Bauman, *Absorption Spectroscopy*, John Wiley & Sons, New York (1962).
2. A. Beer, *Ann. Physik. Chem.*, **2**, 78 (1852).
3. P. Bouguer, *Essai d' optique sur la gradation de la lumiere*, (1729).
4. W. R. Brode, *Chemical Spectroscopy*, John Wiley & Sons, New York (1950).
5. G. L. Clark, *The Encyclopedia of Spectroscopy*, Reinhold, New York (1960).
6. J. Glover, In *Modern Methods of Plant Analysis*, K. Paech and M. V. Tracey, eds., Springer-Verlag, Berlin (1956), p. 149.
7. R. F. Goddu, In *Advances in Analytical Chemistry and Instrumentation*, C. N. Reilley, ed., Interscience Publishers, New York (1960), p. 347.
8. C. F. Hiskey, In *Physical Techniques in Biological Research*, G. Oster and A. W. Pollister, eds., Academic Press, New York (1955), p. 74.
9. H. H. Jaffe and M. Orchin, *Theory and Applications of Ultraviolet Spectroscopy*, John Wiley & Sons, New York (1962).
10. G. F. Lothian, *Absorption Spectrophotometry*, Hilger and Watts, London, 2nd ed. (1958).
11. R. A. Sawyer, *Experimental Spectroscopy*, Prentice-Hall, Englewood Cliffs, N. J., 2nd ed. (1951).
12. J. F. Scott, In *Physical Techniques in Biological Research*, G. Oster and A. W. Pollister, eds., Academic Press, New York (1955), p. 131.
13. D. I. Arnon, *Plant Physiol.*, **24**, 1 (1949).
14. G. V. Marinetti, *J. Lipid Res.*, **3**, 1 (1962).
15. J. H. C. Smith, K. Shibata, and R. W. Hart, *Arch. Biochem. Biophys.*, **72**, 457 (1957).
16. V. M. Koski, C. S. French, and J. H. C. Smith, *Arch. Biochem. Biophys.*, **29**, 339 (1950).

17. I. B. McNulty and D. W. Newman, *Plant Physiol.*, **36**, 385 (1961).
18. I. H. Bath, *Analyst*, **83**, 451 (1958).
19. R. W. Bailey, *Anal. Biochem.*, **3**, 178 (1962).
20. O. S. Privett, M. L. Blank, and J. A. Schmit, *J. Food Res.*, **27**, 463 (1962).
21. S. Undenfriend, D. E. Duggan, B. M. Vasta, and B. B. Brodie, *J. Pharmacol. Exptl. Therap.*, **120**, 26 (1957).
22. D. E. Duggan, R. L. Bowman, B. B. Brodie, and S. Undenfriend, *Arch. Biochem. Biophys.*, **68**, 1 (1957).

Infrared Absorption Spectroscopy

Clara D. Smith

THE PRECEDING CHAPTER dealt with the basic principles of absorption spectroscopy and explained that these same principles apply throughout the ultraviolet, visible, and infrared regions of the electromagnetic spectrum. Despite this similarity, there are several reasons why infrared spectroscopy will be discussed separately. The instrumentation and optical materials required for making measurements in the infrared region are different from those required for the ultraviolet and visible portions of the spectrum. Much of the experimental work in infrared spectroscopy is done on solids and gases as well as on liquid solutions, and specialized sample-handling techniques are required. The energy of electromagnetic radiation of infrared frequencies corresponds to the energy of vibration of atomic groups in molecules and to rotational energies of entire molecules. From the many motions possible in polyatomic molecules there arises a complex pattern of absorption bands in the infrared region which constitutes the most definitive physical data known for a molecule or mixture of materials.

An infrared absorption spectrum in the commonly used wavelength region generally has about 10 to 50 principal absorption peaks and many of these absorption maxima exhibit side bands or shoulders that are distinctive for the particular compound or compound type being examined. Considering the absorptivity at each discrete wavelength measured, there are actually thousands of bits of information in an infrared spectrum. These bits of information describe the energies involved in the motions of the specific molecular structure of the absorbing molecule. The spectrum consists of a unique series of absorptivities. From these absorptivities the identity of the compound can be established; in this sense the infrared spectrum is like a fingerprint and can be used for qualitative analysis. Quantitative analyses can be made from infrared spectra because the amount of a given material in a mixture can be determined from the intensity of its absorption peaks. The frequency of an absorption peak is directly related to the energy of the motion observed and this relationship makes it possible for infrared spectra to be used in theoretical studies on the nature of the chemical bond.

The interpretation of the wealth of data available through infrared spectroscopy is a specialized field of science and is still being developed. It would require thousands of pages to assemble all of the known information on the infrared spectra of molecules. Hundreds of research articles are published annually on infrared theory and applications, and yet there is much to be learned about the significance of some of the best-recognized absorption characteristics in terms of molecular structure. There are many fields in which the application of infrared spectroscopy is still in its infancy. Biological research is an area where the powerful tool of infrared spectroscopic measurements undoubtedly has tremendous potential even beyond its present, widespread use. In most research programs where the molecular structure of materials is important, infrared spectroscopy can be one of the most valuable tools.

The aim of this chapter is to provide an introduction to the major theoretical principles of infrared spectroscopy, and guidance in laboratory technique and spectral interpretation.

Historical Background

The discovery that there is radiant energy beyond the red end of the visible spectrum was made by Sir William Herschel, an astronomer, in 1800. He measured the thermal energy of sunlight by placing a thermometer in the radiation dispersed by a glass prism, and found the highest temperature beyond the red portion of the spectrum.

Research in this region moved slowly for about eighty years. Progress was limited primarily by the necessity of using photographic plates for the detection of absorption bands. In 1882 Abney and Festing reported finding interesting relationships among atomic groups and absorption lines from an investigation of 52 compounds from 0.7 to 1.2 μ which was the limit of sensitivity of their photographic plates. They reported that some absorptions appeared characteristic of compounds with ethyl groups and others appeared characteristic of compounds with benzene rings.

Research interest increased as it became increasingly evident that such agreement could not be fortuitous.

By 1890 Ångstrom had extended investigation of some compounds to 8 μ, using a bolometer and a sodium chloride prism. He reported on absorption bands of carbon monoxide and carbon dioxide as well as simple hydrocarbons and carbon disulfide.

A more extensive work covering absorption spectra of twenty

organic compounds in the spectral region to 10 μ was reported by
Julius in 1892. He found that all compounds containing a—CH_3 group
had an absorption band at 3.45 μ and he reached the important conclusion that the absorption of heat waves is due to intramolecular
movements.

By 1898 absorption bands of water vapor had been observed as
far into the infrared as 20 μ. Water of crystallization, similarities and
differences between the isomeric xylenes, and the shift of bands by
solvents had all been observed by 1900.

The most comprehensive work among these early reports was the
publication entitled *Investigations of Infra-red Spectra* by William
W. Coblentz. His studies were started in 1903 while he was a graduate
student at Cornell University. By 1905, when his collected works
were published by the Carnegie Institution of Washington, they
filled 640 pages. The accuracy and research-mindedness he brought
to his investigations produced results that were not bettered for many
years thereafter. He firmly established that "... there is something, call
it 'particle,' 'groups of atoms,' 'ion,' or 'nucleus,' in common with
many of the compounds studied, which causes absorption bands that
are characteristic of the great groups of organic compounds ..."

Research investigations into infrared spectra of compounds gradually gained momentum as improved instrumentation became
available but as late as the 1930's and early 1940's most of the spectra
were plotted point-by-point from galvanometer readings. Nonetheless, researches such as those of H. W. Thompson and G. B. B. M.
Sutherland in England, and of J. Lecomte in France, rapidly extended
the foundation for applications of infrared spectra to the elucidation
of molecular structure.

Instrumentation reached the point where recording spectrometers
were feasible at the same time that research programs growing out of
the demands of World War II technology demanded them. Commercial spectrometers became available and a tremendous capability
in infrared spectroscopy was developed during the war years in the
laboratories of individual chemical and petroleum companies. The
decade following the war found a flood of analytical applications
reported in the scientific literature. Reviews published in *Analytical
Chemistry* [1] provide an excellent reference to the literature of the
post war years.

Theory

SPECTRAL REGION

The infrared region of the electromagnetic spectrum begins at the
red end of the visible spectrum and extends to the microwave region.

This is roughly from 0.78 μ wavelength to 400 μ. It is further divided for practical spectroscopy into at least three regions.

NEAR-INFRARED REGION. This is the region of shortest wavelengths, extending from the visible between 0.7 and 0.8 μ to about 2.5 or 3.0 μ. This corresponds in wavenumber units (waves per centimeter) to the range 13,000 to 4,000 cm^{-1}. This high frequency region is generally used for study of overtones and combinations of the fundamentals which occur at lower frequencies. Many of the near infrared spectrometers extend to 3 μ wavelength and permit examination of O—H and N—H stretching fundamentals.

CONVENTIONAL, ROCK SALT, FUNDAMENTAL REGION. Historically, the first commercial infrared spectrometers employed a sodium chloride prism and permitted measurement of the spectrum to wavelengths as long as 15 μ, where sodium chloride begins to absorb strongly. Thus, the "rock salt" region is an arbitrary portion of the spectrum whose limits have been dictated by the equipment available. It overlaps the overtone region, generally starting at 2 or 2.5 μ, and stops short of including many fundamental absorption bands which occur at wavelengths longer than 15 μ. It covers the fundamental triple-bond and double-bond stretching frequencies and many of the single-bond stretching frequencies of light elements including hydrogen, carbon, oxygen, nitrogen, fluorine, and chlorine.

There is no good descriptive term to denote this region of 2 to 15 μ because the "fundamental" region could very logically be considered as extending to at least 30 μ, perhaps 50 μ, for purposes of spectral interpretation. Many spectrometers cover the rock salt region and most of the known spectrum-structure correlations are in this range.

FAR-INFRARED REGION. This term will be found denoting observations at wavelengths longer than those observable in the rock salt region. Specific portions are designated by the prism used, such as potassium bromide for 15 to 26 μ and cesium bromide for 15 to 37 μ. Most spectroscopists prefer to think of far infrared as beginning at longer wavelengths, perhaps 40 or 50 μ. Other workers would use "medium far infrared" for the region around 40 μ and the term "very far infrared" in describing absorption beyond the lower frequency stretching fundamentals and wagging motions, essentially reserving the term "very far infrared" for low frequency rotational transitions or crystal lattice vibrations at wavelengths longer than 100 μ.

VIBRATIONAL FREQUENCIES

It will be recalled from the discussion of Planck's law in the last chapter that the higher the frequency of electromagnetic radiation, the greater the energy associated with it. Thus, at high frequencies (short wavelengths) we find the vibrational modes that require high energy in order for the absorption of light, or energy transitions, to occur.

This relationship of the frequency of the absorbed radiation to molecular vibrations can be readily visualized from consideration of the pertinent classical mechanics. In this comparison the motions of the internal groups within the molecule are depicted as being simple harmonic motions and the electromagnetic radiation that is absorbed by these motions is also periodic in nature. It is possible to calculate the absorption frequency for a particular pair of atoms to about 1 per cent accuracy simply by considering the atomic masses as small weights which are connected by springs (the bond strengths). If two masses, m_1 and m_2, are connected by a spring of strength k, the equation for the characteristic vibrational frequency, ν, of the system is given from Hooke's law as:

$$\nu = \frac{1}{2\pi}\sqrt{\frac{k}{\mu}} \tag{1}$$

where μ is the reduced mass and is given by the expression

$$\frac{1}{\mu} = \frac{1}{m_1} + \frac{1}{m_2} \tag{2}$$

A good discussion of the derivation of this relationship and its application to spectroscopy is given elsewhere [2].

It is very helpful in interpreting infrared spectra to have a sound grasp of what this equation shows in terms of the simple variables, bond strength and atomic mass. It says that to the degree a linked pair of atoms follows this simple harmonic motion, its vibrational frequency increases directly as the square root of the force constant. If force constants are taken to be 150 kcal/mole for a carbon-to-carbon double bond and 230 kcal/mole for a carbon-to-carbon triple bond, it would be predicted by the equation that the carbon-to-carbon double bond would absorb at lower frequencies than the carbon-to-carbon triple bond, and that the amount by which it would be lower could be calculated by the proportion $\sqrt{150}/\sqrt{230}$. By multiplying the known frequency of absorption of a C≡C group at 2100 wavenumbers by this ratio, one would calculate that C=C would absorb at about 1690 wavenumbers. In fact, C=C absorption generally falls between 1680 and 1630 cm^{-1}.

In practice this relationship is most often applied the other way around. The absorption frequencies are measured precisely and the force constants are calculated. Absorption spectra offer a fine probe into the forces between atoms in molecules by allowing comparisons of force constants as shown by frequency shifts which result when atomic groups are connected to other atoms which can influence the nature of the bond between them.

A useful example of the influence of masses of the atoms on the vibrational frequency of an atom pair is obtained by substitution of deuterium for hydrogen in a $-\overset{|}{\underset{|}{C}}-H$ group. The expected frequency shift would be calculated by first computing the reduced mass for each system:

for
$$C-H, \frac{1}{\mu} = \frac{1}{12} + \frac{1}{1} = 1.08; \mu = 0.93 \tag{3}$$

for
$$C-D, \frac{1}{\mu} = \frac{1}{12} + \frac{1}{2} = 0.58; \mu = 1.72 \tag{4}$$

and applying the proportional relationship,

$$\frac{\text{frequency C-D}}{\text{frequency C-H}} = \frac{\sqrt{\mu C-H}}{\sqrt{\mu C-D}} = \frac{\sqrt{0.93}}{\sqrt{1.72}} = 0.73 \tag{5}$$

Thus for a C—H band at 2900 cm^{-1} we would expect to find the corresponding C—D band at 0.73×2900 cm^{-1} or 2100 cm^{-1}. In practice this works out remarkably closely and considerable use has been made of the technique of substituting deuterium for hydrogen and looking for a shift in absorption frequency to prove whether or not a given band is attributable to hydrogen atom motions.

The terms *stretching, rocking, wagging, twisting,* and *rotation* appear repeatedly as we discuss molecular absorption of infrared radiation. These terms apply to motions of two atoms or groups of atoms relative to each other. The particular term applicable relates to the effect of that motion on the chemical bonds between those atoms. For example, reference to the OH stretching frequency of an alcohol means the vibrational motion in which the oxygen and hydrogen atoms move away from each other and then back closer together: —O—H, to O-----H, to —O—H. Another motion the OH group exhibits is the angular displacement of the hydrogen atom from the direction of the valence bond: $-O^{\nearrow H}$, to —O—H to $-O\overset{}{\underset{\searrow H}{}}$. This can be described as a wagging motion in the plane of this paper

$$-O\overset{\diagup H}{\underset{\diagdown H}{\,}}\downarrow, -O\overset{\diagup H}{\underset{\diagdown H}{\,}}\uparrow.$$

The motions of atoms or atomic groups in molecules are referred to normal coordinates (vectors perpendicular to each other) for mathematical description of the motions in space. Since there are three independent vectors, each atom has three degrees of freedom and a molecule of n atoms has $3n$ degrees of freedom. Three of these correspond to a motion of all atoms in the direction of each of three axes so they represent translations of the entire molecule. Rotation of the molecule about each of the three axes is described by another three degrees of freedom if the molecule is nonlinear, two degrees of freedom if the molecule is linear. After these degrees of freedom, which correspond to translation and rotation of the entire molecule, are subtracted the expression

$$3n\text{–}6, \ (3n\text{–}5 \text{ for linear molecules}) \tag{6}$$

is obtained to describe the number of vibrational modes of a molecule. For example, a nonlinear molecule of six atoms would have 3 (6)–6 or 12 fundamental vibrational modes.

The actual forms of motions in a complex molecule are dependent upon the masses, force constants, bond angles, and upon coupling between different modes. Very involved calculations are required to ascertain the vibrational modes of all but the simplest molecules. Because of this difficulty in calculating the vibrational frequencies for a molecule, it is common practice to rely upon empirical correlations between atomic groups and their observed absorption frequencies for interpreting spectra.

DIPOLE MOMENT

The mechanical picture of the vibrational modes of molecules and their correspondence to energy of infrared frequencies as described thus far has largely ignored the important term *electromagnetic* as it applies to light energy. It is the electromagnetic character of radiant energy that couples it with atomic vibrations.

The atoms of a molecule carry a positive or negative charge, and as the molecule vibrates these charges may move in such a way that there is a change in dipole moment. When an electromagnetic wave passes over a molecule the forces of an oscillating electromagnetic field tend to push positive charges in one direction and negative charges in the opposite direction, and these directions reverse as the field reverses. Since electromagnetic waves tend to change the dipole moment of a molecule by moving the charges, vibrational motions corresponding to a change in dipole moment will be excited when the electromagnetic wave is of a resonance frequency with the dipole moment change.

Electromagnetic radiation is *not* coupled with a vibrational frequency which does not produce a change in dipole moment of the molecule. An example of this selection rule can be represented by carbon dioxide. It is a linear, symmetrical molecule. An absorption band is observed for the frequency corresponding to the motion of the carbon atom toward one of the oxygen atoms, the asymmetric stretching mode,

$$
\overset{-\ +\ -}{O\ \ C\ \ O} \quad \text{to} \quad \overset{-\ \ +-}{O\ \ \ CO}
$$

but none is observed for the symmetric stretching mode in which both oxygen atoms move simultaneously toward, then away from, the carbon atom:

$$
\overset{-\ \ +\ \ -}{\leftarrow O \rightarrow C \leftarrow O \rightarrow}
$$

It is important in interpreting infrared spectra to keep in mind this necessity for a change in dipole moment to accompany a vibrational mode before the vibration is infrared active. For example, carbon-to-carbon double bond stretching bands will not be found in ethylene or other symmetrical olefins, and symmetrical diatomic molecules will not absorb at all under normal sampling conditions.

The intensity of an infrared band depends upon the rate of change of dipole moment, $\bar{p}$, along the vibrational coordinate Q. The greater the rate of change of dipole moment, the more intense the absorption band. Quantitatively, the intensity of the absorption as measured by the total area under the band (or integrated intensity) is proportional to $(d\bar{p}/dQ)^2$. It follows that polar atoms such as the halogens will exhibit intense absorption bands and that many hydrocarbon bands will be weak. This picture of polar atoms giving strong bands cannot be carried too far because it is the rate of change, or derivative, that establishes the intensity of the band; some hydrogen out-of-plane bending motions cause a high rate-of-change in dipole moment.

SYMBOLS

In following the literature of spectroscopy it is necessary to recognize the most commonly used symbols for describing the motions of atoms in molecules.

$$\nu - \text{stretching}$$
$$\delta - \text{bending}$$
$$\tau - \text{twisting}$$
$$\rho - \text{rocking}$$
$$\omega - \text{wagging}$$

Subscripts are used designating more detail: s or sym for symmetric, a or asym for asymmetric, ∥ for parallel, and ⊥ for perpendicular.

The language and symbols of group theory are carried into the mathematical description of vibrational modes. Exact treatment of molecular states begins with an analysis of the symmetry properties of the molecule. Designations for symmetry operations and point groups are lucidly described in reference [2].

Instrumentation

The equipment required for observing the infrared absorption spectrum of a material is basically similar to that used for observing absorption in other regions of the electromagnetic spectrum. Essential components are:

SOURCE OF LIGHT ENERGY.   A glowing object is a good source of infrared radiation and the sun is used as the energy source in some laboratories. The infrared source in most spectrometers is a small electrically heated rod made of silicon carbide (Globar) or of rare earth oxides (Nernst Glower).

SAMPLE HOLDER.   The specimen is mounted so that radiation passes through it and the transmitted radiation is then measured, or it is mounted so that the radiation is reflected from it and the reflected radiation is measured. The resulting data are called transmission spectra and reflection spectra, respectively.

MONOCHROMATOR.   Hot sources as described above yield radiant energy of all wavelengths, giving a continuous spectrum. The monochromator is the means of dispersing the radiant energy into separate wavelengths. Prisms and gratings discussed in the last chapter are commonly used to disperse the light and the degree to which consecutive wavelengths are separated is called the resolving power or resolution of the spectrometer. Light filters may also be used to isolate some particular wavelength interval, but this approach is not common for spectrometers used for general chemical application.

DETECTOR.   A device which is very sensitive to small changes in heat is needed to detect the amount of infrared light transmitted through the sample. The usefulness of a thermocouple is based on the principle that a voltage will be developed in a circuit formed of two different metals if one of their junctions is at a higher temperature than the other. In a bolometer there is a change in electrical resistivity of the detecting material with temperature. In a pneumatic detector there is an expansion of gas upon heating resulting in the movement of a flexible diaphragm.

These detectors are simple in principle but very elegant in their design and manufacture for use in infrared spectrometers. The temperature change in a thermocouple target is of the order of 0.01°C or less and control to only 1 per cent response accuracy demands that the design compensate for ambient temperature effects of 0.0001°C. The amount of gas expansion in a pneumatic detector is so small that in the most effective design, the Golay cell, the motion of the diaphragm is measured by changes in the reflected light from its mirrored surface.

AMPLIFIER AND RECORDER. The electrical signal from the detector is amplified and generally used to display a chart of the amount of energy reaching the detector at each consecutive wavelength. In most modern spectrometers the light beam is chopped and ac amplifiers are used to provide maximum signal-to-noise ratio.

Commercial spectrometers differ relatively little in the qualities of their source, detector, and amplifier components. The major differences in performance result from the optical design: single-beam or double-beam, single-monochromator or double-monochromator, prism or grating.

Double-beam spectrometers are more popular for general use than single-beam spectrometers. In a single-beam spectrometer the light is passed through the sample and the energy is dispersed and measured directly. In a double-beam spectrometer there are two light paths, one used for the sample, and one used as a reference. This arrangement provides compensation for environmental influences on the detector and simplifies some of the physical problems involved in spectrometer design.

One of these physical problems is the fact that the black body emission curve of the light source reaches peak intensity near $2\,\mu$ and diminishes rapidly to less than half of its peak intensity at $6\,\mu$, and is relatively very weak at $15\,\mu$. This means that a larger portion of the source energy must be introduced into the monochromator at long wavelengths than at short wavelengths. The adjustment of the amount of light entering the optical system is controlled by the adjustment of the width of the spectrometer slits. This control is normally achieved by a programed slit drive, but all sources are not identical, and one standard program can serve only to control the energy to approximately the same level throughout the spectrum. A double-beam allows for refinement of this control of energy level since the servo system responds to differences between the sample beam and the

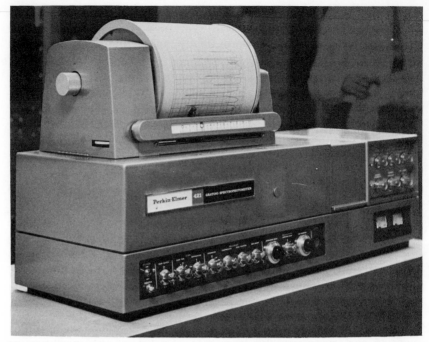

Fig. 11-1. Perkin-Elmer infrared spectrometer Model 421 (Courtesy, Perkin-Elmer Corporation).

reference beam. A double-beam spectrometer compensates for absorption by carbon dioxide and water vapor in the light path since they are present in both beams, and permits solvent compensation and differential spectra which are discussed in a later section.

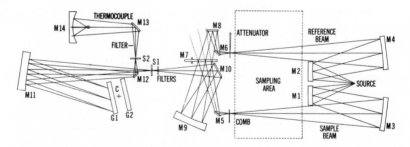

Fig. 11-2. Optical diagram of Perkin-Elmer infrared spectrometer Model 421 (Courtesy, Perkin-Elmer Corporation)

Another problem caused by the nonuniform distribution of energy from a black body radiator is the demand this energy variation places on the monochromator for high efficiency in eliminating "stray light." Stray light is radiation more different in wavelength from that being measured than resolution limits would allow. For example, the strong radiant energy output from 1 to 2 μ can equal 10 to 50 per cent of the light available over a small interval from 14 to 30 μ if only a small fraction of it is scattered in the spectrometer and reaches the detector. This could mean that a material absorbing all of the 15-μ light would record 20 per cent transmission at 15 μ if there were 20 per cent stray radiation. This large an error is avoided by baffles and by filters which eliminate short wavelengths while long wavelengths are being scanned. A double-monochromator provides a very effective means of eliminating stray radiation because the second monochromator admits only light already dispersed by the first monochromator.

Two excellent double-beam grating spectrometers for the infrared region are described in the following paragraphs.

The Perkin-Elmer Model 421 (Fig. 11-1) yields a continuous spectrum from 2.5 to 18 μ with grating resolution. The schematic diagram of its optical path is shown in Fig. 11-2.

Source energy from the Nernst glower is split into sample and reference beams by spherical mirrors M_1 and M_2. Mirror 3 focuses the sample beam onto a comb used for adjustment of the 100 per cent transmission line; mirror 4 focuses the reference beam onto a wedge-like beam attenuator, whose motions are used to record the spectrogram. Plane mirrors, M_5, M_6, and M_8 direct the sample and reference beams onto M_7. M_7 is a semicircular mirror which rotates and alternately reflects the sample beam and allows the reference beam to pass through to mirror 9.

Mirror 7 is the place in the light path where the two beams are combined into one beam pulsating alternately the sample beam light and the reference beam light. The pulse rate depends upon the rate of revolution of M_7 which is chosen to be 13 revolutions per second (rps). This pulsating rate permits fine discrimination in the electronic system against picking up other electrical signals.

Toroid mirror M_9 focuses this combined beam on entrance slit S_1 after it is reflected from M_{10} and has passed through filters to isolate first-order grating radiation. The diverging energy beam is collimated by the off-axis paraboloid M_{11} which directs it to the gratings. Gratings G_1 and G_2 are automatically placed into the beam at the proper time along with their corresponding filters. Dispersed radiation, whose wavelength is determined by the angle of rotation of the grating, is focused by mirror M_{11} on exit slit S_2 after reflection from plane mirror M_{12}. This monochromatic radiation is reflected by plane mirror M_{13} onto the ellipsoid mirror M_{14} which focuses it on the thermocouple target.

When energy in both sample and reference beams is equal, only a direct current is generated by the thermocouple. When the sample beam energy decreases or increases as a result of changes in sample absorption as the spectrum is scanned, the output from the thermo-couple is a pulsating direct current; an alternating current is generated, amplified, and made to drive the optical attenuator into or out of the reference beam in order to equalize the energy in both beams continuously. The motion of the attenuator which is driven until the beams balance (until an energy null is reached) is connected to the recorder pen. This motion then corresponds to any energy difference between the sample and reference beams.

The Beckman IR-9 spectrometer is shown in Fig. 11-3 and its optical path is shown in the diagram of Fig. 11-4. It combines double-beam, double-monochromator, and grating design features.

In the IR-9 a single area of the source is used and light from it is chopped by a rotating sector mirror and sent alternately through the sample and reference paths. A second sector mirror synchronized with the first recombines the two beams into a signal which is pulsating whenever there is an energy difference between the two beams. This combined beam is passed into the first monochromator which has a foreprism and serves as an order sorter. This dispersed radiation is passed into a second monochromator which uses gratings to give resolution of a few tenths of a wavenumber.

The advantage of grating resolution over prism resolution is generally not needed for qualitative analysis in which fingerprint matching is used. It can be very valuable for structural analysis, especially in the hydrogen stretching region, in separating olefinic C—H, aromatic C—H, methylene, and methyl groups. A comparison of the grating spectrum of indene in the C—H stretching region with the corresponding sodium chloride prism spectrum is given in Fig. 11-5.

It is very important in using an infrared spectrometer to understand the underlying physical principles of its operation so that the experimental limitations can be properly taken into account in planning the work, preparing the samples, recording the spectra, interpreting the spectra, and in evaluating the significance of quantitative data. This statement may seem obvious, but it requires vigilance in these days of automatic equipment to remember that research results do not come from a button pusher. Modern instrumentation is so advanced that the simplest spectrometers can be operated by a grade-school child. In practice, worthwhile spectra for research purposes are obtained only with considerable thought and care.

There are four scans of the spectrum of benzene from 6 to 8 μ in Fig. 11-6. All four scans were on the same sample with no difference in cell thickness. The only variations were amplifier gain, scanning speed, and slit widths. Curve A was obtained under normal operating conditions. For the run represented by curve B the spectrum was scanned too fast to allow full pen response. This rapid scanning time was combined with too low amplifier gain and the pen response was sluggish (curve C). Curves B and C would be very poor for any application at all. Curve D resulted from a run with good pen response and would reproduce well, but the slits were eight times as wide as the ones used to obtain curve A and resolution was low. These curves demonstrate that qualitative absorption differences between spectrograms can be created by variations in spectrometer settings, and that quantitative results can be greatly affected by the way in which a spectrum is obtained.

Instrument manufacturers publish excellent manuals describing the operating parameters of each spectrometer. It is important that the manual be studied carefully and that it be kept available for frequent reference by everyone who uses the spectrometer.

Fig. 11-3. Beckman Model IR-9 infrared spectrometer (Courtesy, Beckman Instruments, Inc.).

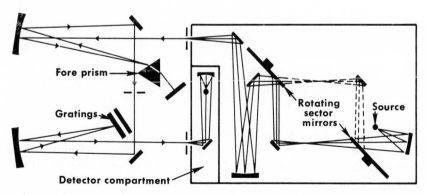

Fig. 11-4. Schematic diagram of optical path of Beckman model IR-9 infrared spectrometer (Courtesy, Beckman Instruments, Inc.).

Sample Preparation

Molecules placed in a spectrometer's light path in any physical state will absorb radiation at their characteristic frequencies. If there are too few molecules, the absorption may be such a small percentage of the total radiation that no absorption maximum will be observed,

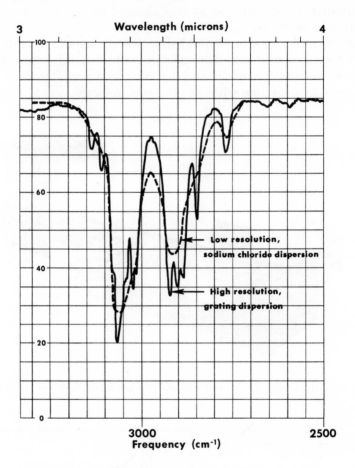

Fig. 11-5. Infrared absorption spectrum of the carbon-to-hydrogen stretching frequencies of indene.

and if there are too many molecules so much radiation may be absorbed that the sample will show few transmission windows. It is between these extremes of thickness, or of concentration per thickness used, that the ordinary sample must be prepared.

There is no single best way of preparing a sample for the determination of its infrared spectrum. Comparisons between spectra are most

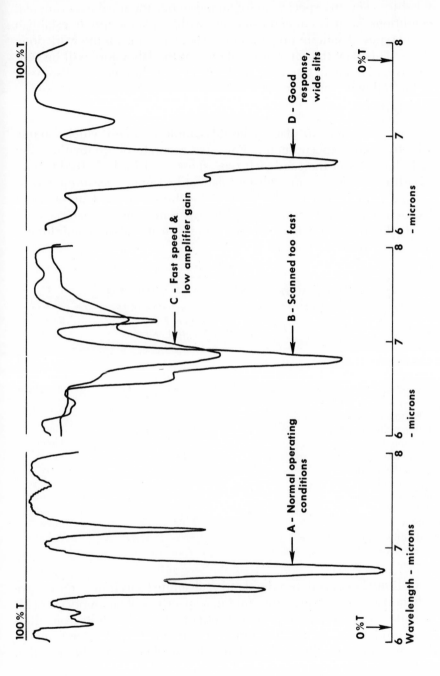

Fig. 11-6. Infrared absorption spectra of benzene scanned with varied instrument settings (cell thickness = 0.1 mm).

reliable when the spectra are obtained under identical experimental conditions, so it is common practice within a laboratory to establish a few types of sample preparation as standard runs for the work done there. This way the reference data file of the laboratory will be self-consistent. Some of the more generally used techniques are discussed in the following paragraphs.

LIQUIDS

It is convenient to place a liquid sample in a cell which mounts directly onto a spectrometer. For most accurate determinations the cell chosen is of the sandwich type shown in Fig. 11-7. In this type of cell the windows are polished flat, and accurate measurements of sample path length can be made. The thickness must be checked frequently because most infrared-transparent window materials are easily deteriorated. Some common window materials and their limitations are listed in Table 11-1.

TABLE 11-1

WINDOW MATERIALS FOR INFRARED SAMPLE CELLS

Material	Practical Long Wavelength Limit (μ)	Resistance to Water
Glass	3.3	Excellent
Quartz	3.3	Excellent
Irtran-2 (special glass made by Eastman Kodak Co.)	13.5	Excellent
Lithium fluoride	7	Good
Calcium fluoride	9.5	Good
Barium fluoride	12.5	Good
Sodium chloride	16	Very poor
Potassium bromide	25	Very poor
Cesium bromide	45	Very poor
Polyethylene	200+	Excellent
KRS-5 (thallium bromide iodide mixed crystal)	40	Good

Cell thickness is determined on an absolute basis from interference fringe patterns obtained by running a spectrum of an empty cell [3]. A pattern of maxima and minima is obtained which results from alternate reinforcement and diminution of radiation by reflection from the internal surfaces. The cell thickness is calculated from the equation

$$\text{Path length } (\mu) = \frac{n}{2} \frac{\lambda_1 \lambda_2}{(\lambda_1 - \lambda_2)} \qquad (8)$$

where n is the number of fringes between wavelengths λ_1 and λ_2.

Most pure compounds require very thin liquid cells for a qualitative spectrum. Only the most weak absorbers, such as saturated hydrocarbons, are generally run in cells as thick as 0.08 mm. Compounds with oxygen groups or halogens or even aromatic rings are apt to have such strong absorptions that they require thicknesses of 0.01 mm to 0.001 mm for a good qualitative spectrum. Cells that are this thin are difficult to fill and clean, and become prohibitively time-consuming for viscous materials. This is one of the reasons that solutions discussed in the next section are favored by some laboratories.

Good techniques for filling the liquid cells help extend both the applicability of the sampling method and the life of the cells. A Luer syringe fitted with a metal end is the most convenient cell-filling device. It fits snugly onto most standard sample cells and forms an air-tight seal. Good handling calls for holding the cell by the sides, avoiding placing the hand or fingers beneath the cell or near the windows, attaching the syringe firmly to one cell opening, and filling the cell from the bottom so that slow movement of the liquid forces all air out of the cell. When there is an abundance of sample both necks of the cell can be completely filled, allowing for a minute overflow when the sealing plugs are put in place. If each step is done with a steady firm motion and if the syringe plunger is moved slowly enough to allow a uniform front to the liquid ascending the space between the cells, no difficulty with air bubbles or with overflow contaminating the cell windows will be experienced. Viscous materials can be introduced if sufficient time is allowed for the sample flow between the plates.

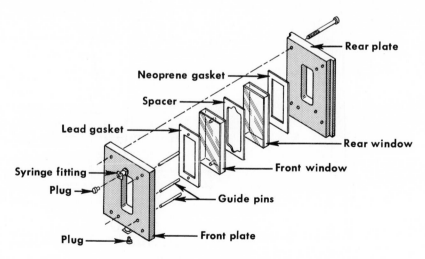

Fig. 11-7. Exploded drawing of sandwich-type fixed-thickness cell used for determining infrared spectra of liquids (Courtesy, Beckman Instruments, Inc.).

There must not be any air bubbles in the light path for the spectrum to be valid. When some of the light goes through the cell without passing through the sample a part of the light beam reaches the detector without any absorption having occurred. An example of this error can be seen in Fig. 11-8. The absorption bands of benzene near 6.8 and 9.7 μ are nearly "blacked out" at the cell thickness used for the normal curve A. During the scan of curve B the cell started leaking. The 6.8 μ absorption band is normal, but the bands beyond 7 μ are too weak. The series of small broad bands in curve B arise from interference fringe patterns from reflection at the internal surfaces of the cell windows where there was no sample. Curve C is a scan of the interference fringes of the empty cell. These symptoms of erroneously weak absorption bands and interference fringes are to be continuously watched for. It is good routine practice to examine the sample cell as soon as a spectrum has been scanned to ascertain the validity of the sampling.

In practice there is an occasional time that a sample cell with an air

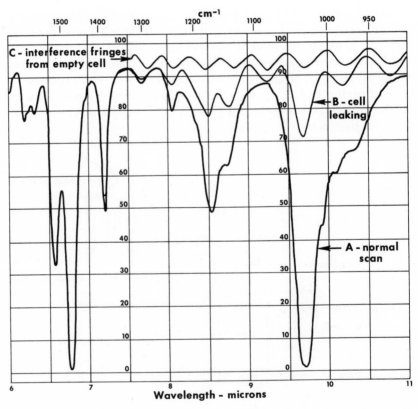

Fig. 11-8. Infrared spectra of benzene showing effects of air pockets in the sample cell (cell thickness = 1 mm).

pocket will need to be run. The combination of conditions that might result in this need in a laboratory would be insufficient sample to recover and refill the cell, no available micro-handling techniques to permit full use of a small sample, and impossible conditions for solution techniques such as interference by solvents at critical wavelengths. Rather than fail to obtain valuable spectral data under these circumstances, it is desirable to mask the bubble area carefully with cardboard or tape so that all of the light incident on it is blocked from the monochromator. The resulting spectrogram will be obtained with less than total light energy but will be a valid per cent transmission curve if instrument operating conditions are adjusted to give good spectrometer response.

Emptying the sample cell requires as careful attention to technique as filling it if cell life is to be of practical length and if contamination from sample to sample is to be avoided. Needs vary in individual laboratories and with specific samples, but for cells made with window materials such as sodium chloride, which is sensitive to moisture, the following steps are recommended.

After removal of the cell plugs a syringe filled with solvent is attached to one neck of the cell and an empty syringe is attached to the other cell opening. As the empty syringe is slowly opened to exhaust the sample from the cell the solvent is slowly introduced. The more viscous the sample is, the slower this flushing with solvent should be done. There is a tendency to force the liquid flow too rapidly and make a channel through the center of the cell. This channel will let the solvent move through the cell and leave sample clinging to the inside edges. If the cell has liquid at the edges after the solvent has been removed by air flushing, a step of allowing the solvent to soak in the cell will generally finish the cleaning.

The safest way to remove the solvent from the cell is to attach a drying tube to one neck and slowly exhaust with an empty syringe or a vacuum line at the other neck. Two warnings are in order here: if the connection to the drying tube is made with rubber tubing, care should be taken that any powder inside is flushed out to avoid its entering the cell; the air flow should be created by exhausting rather than by compressing the air into the cell by pumping, which can cause condensation on the cell windows.

If carbon tetrachloride or carbon disulfide is used as the cleaning solvent it is a simple matter to collect the waste from the cells beneath a layer of water in a beaker. This practice cuts down considerably on fumes either with or without a hood. Absorption bands of the solvents in spectra of samples, i.e., a sharp 6.6 μ peak from carbon disulfide or a 12.6 μ peak from carbon tetrachloride, warn that cell cleaning and drying have not been adequate.

It is desirable to run the cells empty routinely to check for contamination. This can be a rapid scan and does not need to delay laboratory work unduly. It is actually time-saving to obtain frequent blanks and cell calibrations so that sample cells can be used with confidence.

It is far easier to keep the outside windows of a sample cell clean by avoiding careless spilling and overflow during filling than it is to wash them in any way that avoids damage. Any spillage must be cleaned off, however, since absorption by sample on the outside of the cell window will show up in a spectrum just as clearly as absorption by sample inside the cell. Solvent flushed onto the cell windows cleans them with the least damage. Mechanical wiping generally leaves scratches, but is to be preferred to dirty windows. Soaking the entire cell in solvent can damage the gaskets and is not recommended.

Besides the fixed-thickness sandwich cell, similar cells are made demountable so that the plates can be separated for easy cleaning. The disadvantage of the demountable cells is that their thickness is not precisely known. There are calibrated, variable-thickness cells which prove particularly helpful in some applications such as use in a reference beam to match a sample cell thickness in a double-beam spectrometer.

Many liquids are mounted in the spectrometer between two transparent plates as a capillary layer, and some viscous liquids can be run as a smear of film on a single plate. In the latter case it is desirable, after the curve is completed, to rescan the part of the spectrum that was run first. This second scan permits detection of thickness change from sample flow during the determination. A capillary layer between salt plates is a quick preparative procedure for checking a material to see if it is important enough to warrant more exacting measurements.

Liquid cells made by hollowing out a block of window material are called cavity cells. These are produced commercially by Connecticut Instrument Corporation and are much less expensive than standard sandwich cells. Since the inner surfaces are not flat and polished, these cavity cells are not recommended for quantitative work. They are useful for qualitative spectra and are expecially helpful for unknown samples that might damage cell windows.

SOLUTIONS

Spectra of solutions have many features to recommend them and solution techniques should be given serious consideration as a standard procedure in most laboratories. They offer the only way that both solids and liquids can be put on a directly comparable basis and this versatility is an asset to a spectrum reference file. At 10 per cent concentration a large number of compounds give good spectra in 0.1-mm thick cells which are much easier to fill and clean than cells one tenth that thickness. Cell window attack is less by solutions in nondamaging solvents than by most polar compounds.

For quantitative and semiquantitative purposes there is an advantage in having standard compounds and mixtures all run in the same solvent. The solute molecules are surrounded by the solvent whether they are in the pure calibration standard or in a sample mixture, and the influence of solute-solvent interaction is relatively constant in comparison with the differences that can be introduced in the spectrum of a compound in going from pure, undiluted form to a mixture.

There is no good transparent solvent for the infrared region of the spectrum. For any specific problem any solvent may be chosen which has a window of transmission at the wavelengths to be measured. For most general use there are three favorites: carbon tetrachloride, carbon disulfide, and chloroform. The choice of chloroform is generally made by those laboratories which need its solvency power for the compounds of greatest interest to them.

A combination of carbon tetrachloride as a solvent for 2 to 7.5 μ and carbon disulfide for 7.5 to 24 μ works out very well. Spectra of these solvents from 2 to 15 μ are shown in Fig. 11-9. For spectra determined in cells about 0.1 mm thick the weak carbon tetrachloride band at 6.45 μ and the carbon disulfide band at 11.7 μ can be easily compensated by solvent in the reference beam, and a spectrum can be produced free of interference by solvent absorption bands.

Solvent compensation cannot be achieved if both beams are opaque. Under this circumstance there is no measurable energy reaching the detector and the pen is "dead." Bands such as the 6.5 to 6.8 μ absorption of carbon disulfide and the 12.5 to 13.4 μ absorption of carbon tetrachloride cannot be compensated for determination of the spectra of solutes.

SOLIDS

When a solid sample has low solubility in the more transparent solvents, it may be necessary to grind it to a fine powder to obtain its infrared spectrum. Very small powder particles can be spread or deposited on a sodium chloride window directly. Such powder layers normally scatter a large proportion of the incident radiation and special sample preparation techniques have been developed to minimize this scattering.

Light scattering from powders can be diminished in two ways: by grinding the particles smaller than the wavelength of light being used and by suspending the powder in a medium whose refractive index is close to that of the powder. For good quality spectra both of these steps are used in the two common techniques using solid-state, the oil mull and the pressed disc or pellet.

382   *Clara D. Smith*

OIL MULL PREPARATION. In oil mull preparation the sample grinding is usually done with a highly polished agate mortar and pestle. Best results are obtained if only a few milligrams of solid sample are evenly distributed over a large mortar and then vigorously ground until the sample becomes smooth and glossy, often glassy, in appearance. After this grinding step, which must be thorough for good results, a minimum of oil is added, a small drop at a time, and grinding is continued until the sample is carried into suspension and is diluted just enough to flow evenly and to cover the sample plates. A rubber policeman is used to transfer the viscous mull to the middle

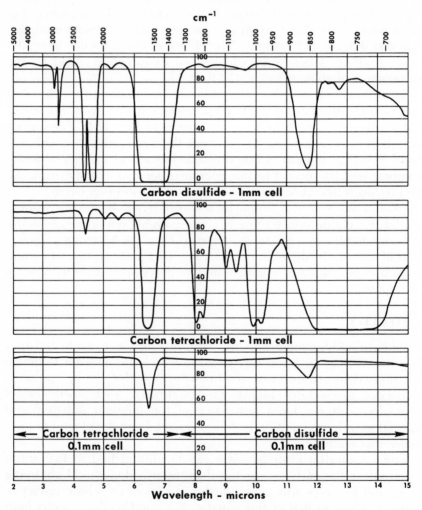

Fig. 11-9. Infrared absorption spectra of reagent grade solvents. Top curve: carbon disulfide in 1 mm cell; middle curve: carbon tetrachloride in 1 mm cell; bottom curve: carbon tetrachloride 2 to 7.5 μ, 0.1 mm, carbon disulfide 7.5 to 15 μ, 0.1 mm.

of a cell plate. Another plate is placed on top of the mull and the plates are gently squeezed together until the sample is uniformly spread to the desired thickness with no air bubbles present.

The most commonly used suspending oil is mineral oil which interferes with the determination at only the principal carbon-to-hydrogen frequencies. If the carbon-to-hydrogen bands are important in the work being done, then a split spectrum is run with a mull made with perfluorinated hydrocarbons, such as fluorolube, used as the mulling agent for the spectral range 2 to 7.5 μ, and a mineral oil mull used at wavelengths longer than 7.5 μ.

For many materials satisfactorily ground samples can be prepared by grinding in a tapered glass joint about 1 in. in diameter. Here again the powder should be uniformly distributed and ground until it becomes glossy before any oil is added.

Exact sample thicknesses are not known for oil mulls, and band ratios are relied upon for quantitative analyses. Internal standards which are generally useful are calcium carbonate and lead thiocyanate [4].

PRESSED DISC SAMPLE PREPARATION. In the pressed disc sample preparation technique a few milligrams or less of solid sample are ground thoroughly, then mixed with an inorganic salt transparent in the region to be studied. This mixture is pressed under high pressure until the salt sinters and the pellet becomes clear. For best results the pressing is done in an evacuated die with highly polished surfaces.

There are many ways of making pressed discs. A well-accepted procedure for each step is described below, along with some of the variations.

Grinding. About 2 mg of sample and a few stainless steel balls are placed in a stainless steel vial which is mounted in a mechanical vibrator grinder such as the Wig-L-Bug amalgamator (Crescent Dental Manufacturing Company). The sample is ground by vibrating from 30 seconds to 5 minutes, then about 200 mg of preground salt are added and mixing is continued for about a minute. Alternate techniques for this step include grinding with mortar and pestle, grinding in the presence of a solvent which is allowed to evaporate as grinding proceeds, and freeze drying a solution of the salt and sample. The solution techniques require the most time but give very small diameter particles, which yield the best spectra.

Matrix Selection. Potassium bromide is the most widely used salt and is available commercially in infrared quality. Some other matrices are potassium chloride, sodium chloride, and potassium iodide. The sintering properties, transparency, refractive index, and chemical stability are important considerations in the selection of a matrix.

The medium should be chemically inert to the sample to be studied. Many KBr pellet spectra are actually spectra of the reaction product between KBr and the sample. Since chemical reaction will increase with increased time of contact, and crystal forms may be varied with pressure, different spectra are obtained on some materials as mixing time or pressing conditions are changed and as pellets age.

Pelletizing. There are excellent evacuable dies commercially available designed for making KBr pellets. Pressing can be accomplished by any viselike arrangement which will permit pressures around 90,000 lb/in? on the pellet. The optimum rate of increasing the pressure, total pressure, and time of pressing, all vary with the sample, matrix, and grinding and mixing steps. A pressing time of 2 to 5 minutes at 85,000 lb/in? is common for KBr pellets, but a few tests on each type of sample are recommended to establish the conditions which give the best spectra.

Since most pellet matrices are hygroscopic, it is helpful to store the salts in an oven or over P_2O_5 *in vacuo* and to keep any equipment which will touch the samples in drying ovens. Samples should be predried and air exposure during pellet preparation should be kept to a minimum.

Both mull and pellet sample preparation techniques have special advantages and disadvantages. Mineral oil is more inert and less apt to distort the spectrum of a compound than ionic salts. Pellets are easier to manipulate in a semiquantitative fashion than mulls. The sample and matrix can be weighed so that the proportion is known and the finished pellet weight can be used to put any number of samples on a comparable basis. This technique is valid only to the extent that handling losses are equally distributed between matrix and sample.

Pellets are more adaptable than mulls to very small samples and this makes them especially valuable for biochemical research. It is not uncommon for a spectrum to be obtained on a scarcely visible sample. There are micro dies for pressing pellets smaller than 1 mm diameter, and beam condensing systems for focusing the sample beam of spectrometers on these small sample areas.

A major problem in semimicro and micro samples is the avoidance of contaminants which are easily introduced in quantities larger than the sample being studied. Sample losses and contamination during handling are minimized by various freeze-drying procedures. A special technique of introducing microgram quantities of sample into organic solvent, freezing it and placing it into a shell of frozen KBr and water slurry, and following this with solvent removal by freeze-drying results in fine spectra on one tenth the amount of sample used in more conventional semimicro procedures. Results showing that a good spectrum can be obtained in this way on only 2.7 μg of hydrocortisone acetate are given in Fig. 11-10.

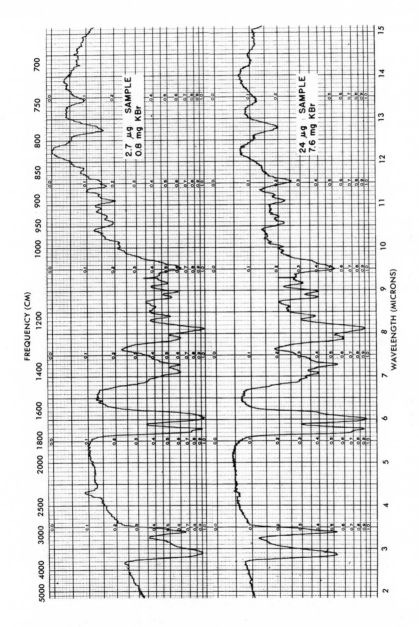

Fig. 11-10. Infrared spectra of hydrocostisone acetate showing similarity of spectra obtained from micro and semimicro samples (Courtesy, W. B. Mason, M.D., University of Rochester).

Quantitative work with pellets and mulls is a difficult process requiring careful testing with many standard blends. The use of an internal standard is generally suggested. The major problem encountered is that particle size variations have a large effect on measured absorptivity for a given weight per cent of a component. For the most accurate results it is essential that the particles be very small and of uniform size, shape, and distribution.

Two symptoms of inadequate reduction of particle size are easy to recognize. The most usual one is a steadily decreasing transmission measurement toward short wavelengths. Unless scattering is very bad this effect is noticed mostly between 2 and 5 μ. If a sample gives only 50 per cent as much transmission at 2 μ as at 5 μ, it should be ground again. It is usually possible to grind a sample to a small enough particle size to obtain 80 to 90 per cent as much transmission at 2 μ as at 5 μ, and this criterion should be met for precise quantitative work. The other symptom of bad light scattering from particles which are too large is known as the Christiansen effect. It results from a change in refractive index of a sample as it absorbs radiation. At some point during this change the refractive index of the sample approaches or matches the refractive index of the matrix and there is a decrease in the amount of radiant energy scattered. This lets an increased amount of radiation be transmitted and the spectrum has transmission peaks at the side of absorption bands, or, in extreme cases, gives transmission peaks instead of absorption peaks.

FILM-FORMING SOLIDS.   Solids which form films when evaporated from solution may be used while deposited on a salt window or as free films stripped from glass or metal surfaces. Trial and error are necessary to find the optimum thickness for these samples, and a comparison of band ratios must be used for semiquantitative work.

GASES.   The infrared spectra of gases are important to theoretical spectroscopists because molecules can be moved far apart or close together by changes in gas pressure, and this pressure variable permits investigation of forces between molecules and their effects on chemical bonding within a molecule. For practical gas analysis, mass spectrometry and gas chromatography are becoming more widely used than infrared spectroscopy. They offer advantages of greater sensitivity and fewer complications. Infrared spectra can be used for multicomponent gas analyses if very careful calibrations are made, and they are valuable for identifying unknown gases.

Regular gas sample cells are 2 to 10 cm long, sealed at the ends with windows of infrared-transparent material, and are equipped with stopcocks for evacuation and filling. Variations on these include tapered cells matching the shape of the sample beam so that no sample volume is wasted, and both micro and very large cells with mirrors for multiple reflection of the light within the cell to create long path lengths. Some of them are designed so that sample can flow through the cell during spectral determination.

ATTENUATED TOTAL REFLECTION

This is a relatively new sampling technique [5] and requires a special spectrometer attachment available from Barnes Engineering Co. or the Perkin-Elmer Corporation. It provides a way of obtaining a chart by reflection-like procedures that may be only slightly different from an absorption spectrum. This means that samples which are not readily prepared in thin layers or solutions can have spectra determined on them directly by examination of their surface. Living skin or surfaces of plant fibers are examples of the kind of substance that might be studied to advantage by attenuated total reflection.

DIFFERENCE SPECTRA

Difference spectra are run on double-beam spectrometers which record the difference in energy transmitted by the sample and reference beam paths. As was mentioned earlier, solvent bands can be compensated, or eliminated from the recorded spectrogram, by the use of solvent in the reference beam with a path length equivalent to that of the sample beam solvent. A 10 per cent solution in a 1-mm path length cell would have an equivalent solvent path of 0.9 mm, and compensation would be achieved with a 0.9-mm cell filled with solvent in the reference beam.

Although any double-beam spectrometer recording is, in fact, a difference spectrum, the term is normally used to refer to compensation other than that of solvent cancellation. It usually refers to cancellation of absorption bands of some component or components of a sample so that absorption bands of other components will be recorded more distinctly. This technique is invaluable when the absorption band which is to be observed overlaps a stronger band by so much that it appears in direct spectra as only a broadening of the strong band.

The small spectral variations which occur in complex mixtures such as blood or albumin are more readily detected by difference spectra than by direct spectra. Interesting recent articles have reported the application of difference spectra for comparison of red blood cells of vertebrates [6] and comparison of body fluids from diseased people with corresponding fluids from healthy people [7].

To obtain reliable difference spectra it is necessary to pay very close attention to instrument operating parameters. Usually the absorbance is increased by using path lengths several times greater than normal. The resulting energy loss is offset by increasing the spectrometer slits and scanning at a slower rate. It is essential that operating conditions be carefully tested to assure good pen response in any portion of the spectrum that is subsequently used for spectral interpretation.

Spectral Interpretation

The interpretation of an infrared absorption spectrum can be as simple as looking for the presence or absence of a known absorption band or identifying an unknown by searching a master file of data with an electronic sorter or a computer. It may be very complex and require considerable knowledge of reasons for small absorption frequency shifts or band shape variations. The discussion in this section concerns interpretation between these two extremes in difficulty. Information is presented to help the reader understand how to use known group frequency correlations and standard reference spectra to identify a compound from its infrared absorption spectrum.

It will be recalled that two main factors establish the absorption frequency for atomic groups: the masses of the atoms and the strength of the bonds joining them. The hydrogen atom is much lighter than any other atom so we expect to find hydrogen stretching bands at the highest frequencies (shortest wavelengths) of any of the elements. If we consider bond strength alone, we expect triple bonds to occur at a higher frequency than double bonds, and double bonds to be at higher frequencies than single bonds. These relationships are summarized in Fig. 11-11. There is some overlap in the ranges for each group, but essentially the sequence of stretching frequencies of atomic groups going from high to low frequencies is hydrogen stretching, triple-bond stretching, double-bond stretching, and single-bond stretching of all elements except hydrogen.

A few subgroups of these bond types are also shown in Fig. 11-11. There is only a little difference in the frequency range of carbon-to-oxygen double bonds and carbon-to-carbon double bonds. With this much overlap it is interesting to note that it is seldom difficult to distinguish between these two structures. It is an unusual olefinic group, for example, one highly substituted with fluorine atoms, which absorbs at frequencies as high as the common carbonyl compounds, around 1720 cm^{-1}. Carbonyl absorption bands are usually stronger than those from olefinic absorption and they are often broader, especially when under some influence which shifts them near the common olefinic C=C region of about 1630 cm^{-1}.

Compilations of these known group-frequency correlations are available in many chart forms. The most comprehensive book which has been written on the subject is *The Infra-red Spectra of Complex*

Molecules, by L. J. Bellamy, and it should be available for reference by anyone learning to interpret spectra.

Although it is easy to know the approximate spectral region for each type of bond stretching it is not equally easy to assign any particular absorption band to the structure causing it. This is because there are many more origins to absorption bands than stretching modes. For example, a scissors-like motion of the hydrogen atoms of an NH_2 group, or of the hydrogen atoms in water, absorbs near the same frequency, about 1640 cm^{-1}, 6.1 μ, at which many carbonyl (C=O) stretching bands absorb. The first harmonic of a carbonyl peak at 1700 cm^{-1} falls at 3400 cm^{-1} and may be mistaken for a hydrogen stretching absorption. Confusion of spectral interpretation by bands like these must be avoided by checking off all possible contributions throughout the spectrum of any structure whose presence is established by a unique characteristic.

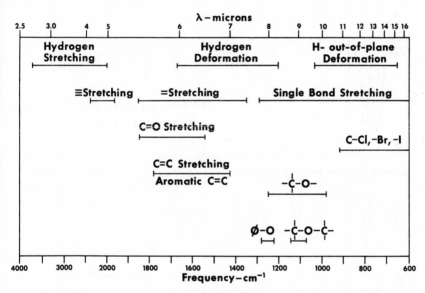

Fig. 11-11. Approximate regions of infrared absorption by atomic groups.

It is necessary to become accustomed to thinking of absorption bands in both wavelength units, microns, and wave-number units, cm^{-1}. There is some prospect that wavelength may eventually be abandoned in favor of the more useful wave-number designation. Nonetheless, both are now widely used and whenever spectra are recorded linearly in wavelength it is natual to designate a specific absorption in terms of its position in microns.

Examples of the absorption characteristics of some common organic structures are given by the pure compound spectra in Fig. 11-12.

The top spectrum is of a straight-chain paraffin, *n*-octane, which contains only methyl groups, —CH₃, and methylene groups, —CH₂—. Both of these structures contain carbon-to-hydrogen bonds. With the resolution of these curves the carbon-to-hydrogen stretching absorption of these two structures overlaps and is observed near 2900 cm⁻¹ or 3.4 μ. Deformation modes of CH₂ and CH₃ absorb at

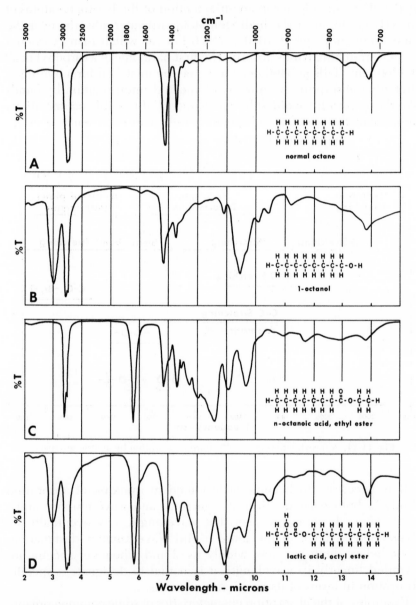

Fig. 11-12. Standard infrared absorption spectra of some C, H and C, H, O, compounds (Courtesy, Sadtler Research Laboratories, Philadelphia, Pa.).

1470 cm^{-1}, 6.8 μ, and the sharp band at about 1370 cm^{-1}, 7.3 μ, is caused by the hydrogen of the C—CH$_3$ groups. The band at 720 cm^{-1}, 13.9 μ, is caused by rocking motions of pairs of CH$_2$ groups in chains of four or more carbon atoms.

The second spectrum demonstrates the changes in infrared absorption which are introduced by the addition of a hydroxy group, —O—H, to the straight-chain paraffin, making the compound 1-octanol. The CH$_3$ and CH$_2$ structures described for n-octane are present, except that there is now only one methyl group. The hydrocarbon absorption bands at 3.4, 6.8, 7.3, and 13.9 μ are all present. In addition there is an oxygen-to-hydrogen stretching absorption band at 3.0 μ and a single-bonded carbon-to-oxygen absorption band at 9.5 μ. If one studies a series of straight-chain, primary aliphatic alcohols, these absorption bands are always found as the major spectral characteristics.

Two oxygen atoms are added to the straight-chain paraffin structure in the ester used for the third spectrum of Fig. 11-12. Once again the aliphatic carbon-to-hydrogen peaks are prominent. There is no OH structure, and there is no 3.0 μ absorption peak. The strong sharp peak between 5.7 and 5.8 μ is the double-bond stretching absorption of the C=O (carbonyl) group. The other oxygen is attached by single bonds to two different carbon atoms. There is considerable involvement of several atoms here in the single-bond stretching motion and the result is broad absorption in the 7.5 to 10 μ region. Interaction, or coupling, of vibrational modes is common in the skeleton of molecules and is the reason that band shape recognition is considered important for interpretation of bands from structures such as the carbon-to-oxygen single bond.

The bottom spectrum demonstrates the additive absorption from both hydroxy and ester groups on an aliphatic chain.

Functional group absorption characteristics similar to these for alcohols and esters can be recognized for olefinic structures, aromatics, carboxylic acids, aldehydes, amines, amides, nitriles, ketones, silanes, siloxanes, nitro groups, sulfone groups, phosphates, etc. The best way to learn to recognize them is to group together a few spectra of each class so that band shape and intensity can be observed at the same time that characteristic frequencies are studied from group frequency charts or Bellamy's book.

The summary data presented in Fig. 11-13 on carbonyl stretching frequencies demonstrate the type of information that can be used to derive detailed structural information from absorption bands. It is useful for each individual to assemble correlation charts especially meaningful to him with sketches of band shapes and notes of reasons for shifts in frequency of atomic groups from common absorption positions. This practice is especially helpful in a research program where more data may need to be assembled for some particular combination of structures than are otherwise available.

Applications

It has already been mentioned that compounds can be identified and their purity checked by using information from infrared absorption spectra. Thus, infrared spectroscopy is valuable in studying fractions of natural products isolated by chemical and physical means.

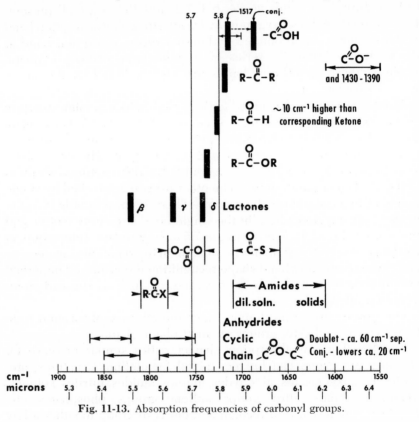

Fig. 11-13. Absorption frequencies of carbonyl groups.

It provides proof of composition of matter for purposes of patent claims. It can be used to identify trace amounts of insecticides in foods or halogenated solvents in blood or expired air. Research work on infrared spectra of steroids alone has been so extensive that major reference books [8, 9] have been written on the subject. Infrared analysis of renal and bladder calculi are used by physicians to plan medical programs for patients on the basis of the composition of the stones in question. Probes of the atmosphere of planets rely upon detection of water vapor, carbon dioxide, and hydrocarbon groups by infrared spectroscopy to suggest whether or not life as we know it might exist there.

Wherever a knowledge of the structure of molecules or comparison of the composition of complex mixtures can advance scientific knowledge, infrared spectroscopy can be invaluable.

References

1. R. Gore, *Anal. Chem.*, **21**, 7 (1949); **22**, 7 (1950); **23**, 7 (1951); **24**, 8 (1952); **26**, 11 (1954).
2. R. P. Bauman, *Absorption Spectroscopy*, John Wiley & Sons, New York (1962).
3. *Trans. Faraday Soc.*, **14**, 171 (1945).
4. L. B. Bradley and W. J. Potts, Jr., *Appl. Spectry.*, **12**, 77 (1958).
5. J. Fahrenfort, *Spectrochim. Acta*, **17**, 698 (1961); **18**, 1103 (1962).
6. R. D. Stewart and D. S. Erley, *Exptl. Cell Res.*, **23**, 460 (1961).
7. R. D. Stewart, D. S. Erley, N. E. Skelly, and N. Wright, *J. Lab. Clin. Med.*, **54**, 644 (1959).
8. K. Dobriner, E. R. Katzenellenbogen, and R. N. Jones, *Infrared Absorption Spectra of Steroids*, Vol. I, Interscience Publishers, New York (1953).
9. G. Roberts, B. S. Gallagher, and R. N. Jones, *Infrared Absorption Spectra of Steroids*, Vol. II, Interscience Publishers, New York (1958).

Manometric Devices

W. W. Umbreit

MANOMETRIC MEASUREMENTS are based upon the simple gas law $PV/T = P'V'/T'$ where P, V, and T represent the initial state of the gas and P', V', and T' its final state (P = pressure, V = volume, and T = absolute temperature). Suppose that, during a reaction, the *amount* of a given gas changes. Then if two of the variables (usually V and T) are held constant, P' must be different from P, and if the pressure difference is measured, the amount of gas used up (or given off) can readily be calculated. That is, the basic principle of the usual manometric systems is that at constant temperature and constant volume any changes in the amount of a gas can be accurately measured by determining changes in its pressure. Thus any reaction involving changes in the amount of a gas, or which can be converted into a gaseous change (as acid production releasing CO_2 from bicarbonate) can be measured both as to the rate and amount of reaction. It is remarkable how many reactions, otherwise difficult to measure, can be converted into a gaseous change, and thus are measurable by manometric methods.

There are, as one might expect, several methods for making such measurements, but one of these, the Warburg method, has been so widely used as to constitute the "standard" method and it will be described here. Details of other methods, and further details on the practical use of the Warburg method are described by Umbreit *et al.* [1]. This device (shown in Fig. 12-1) consists essentially of a reaction chamber attached to a simple manometer so arranged that the chamber, constituting by far the greater volume, can be held at constant temperature. It is this Warburg constant volume device which we shall describe further.

There are methods, appropriately called Van Slyke methods [2] that depend upon the release of gas by chemical means, and which are somewhat different from Warburg methods. In Van Slyke methods, the gas released may be measured by either its volume, or its pressure, and the latter method of measurement has been termed the manometric or micromanometric method. These are perfectly legitimate uses for these terms. However, we have here the situation where two distinct kinds of methods are described by the same title and we wish to make clear that this section concerns only the Warburg manometric system and not the Van Slyke manometric devices.

Apparatus

The apparatus is sketched in Fig. 12-1. It consists of a reaction flask which may be of any shape or size desired (but its volume must be known) attached to a manometer. The manometer is graduated generally in centimeters (numbered) and in millimeters. The manometer has a fluid reservoir and screw clamp which device is used to alter the level of fluid in the manometer. The manometer has a closed end (attached to the flask) and an open end. A reference point (usually

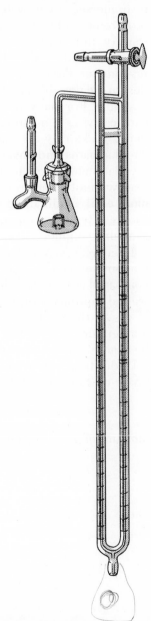

Fig. 12-1. A typical Warburg manometer. The center cup in the flask is normally used to hold KOH to absorb CO_2 which may be released. The closed arm of the manometer contains a three-way stopcock whereby gas mixtures may be run into the manometer through the flask and out the vent in the sidearm. The sidearm (there may be more than one) is for adding materials to start a reaction or for adding materials during the course of it. The flask and sidearm stoppers are held in place by springs (not shown). Also not shown are the rubber reservoir and screw clamp attached to the bottom of the manometer which serves to adjust the fluid level to a constant point in the closed arm of the manometer.

150 or 250 mm) on the closed side is chosen, and the liquid in the closed arm of the manometer is adjusted to this fixed point. The reading on the open arm is recorded and as gas is taken up or given off in the closed system, adjustment to a constant volume (achieved by forcing the fluid in the manometer to the reference point) will be reflected in proportional change in the height of the fluid in the open arm of the manometer. These matters will be clearer after a detailed description of the operation.

The manometer is mounted on a shaking device so that the flask is immersed in a water bath at constant temperature. The basic requirement of such a bath is that it is capable of maintaining a constant (within 0.5°C) and uniform temperature. The shaking is necessary to provide complete saturation of the fluids with the gas in the manometer flasks. Within these requirements wide differences in design are possible and two general types of systems are commercially available. For many years, the most common design was a rectangular bath carrying 7 manometers on each of two sides, the manometers being shaken by a rocking or reciprocating motion. More recently, circular baths and shaking devices have been available. These take less laboratory bench space; the manometers may be adjusted and read without interrupting the shaking and a uniform temperature is more easily maintained in a circular bath. The photograph (Fig. 12-2) shows a typical arrangement. Rectangular and circular models are available commercially.

In all cases, the flask is held at constant temperature and the manometer is not. The manometer gas volume is relatively small compared to that of the flask. Since the manometer is made from thick-walled capillary tubing, and since there are no changes in the amount of gas in the manometer, it is only necessary that it be at the same temperature during the run, but this temperature does not have to be exactly equal to the rest of the system.

Under the circumstances described, the amount of gas taken up or given off (and thus the amount of reaction) is measured as follows:

$$x = h \times k \quad (1)$$

(amount of gas exchanged) / (change in pressure measured on the open arm of the manometer) \ (flask constant)

where

$$k = \frac{V_g \frac{273}{T} + V_{fa}}{P_0} \quad (2)$$

where V_g = volume of gas in system, V_f = volume of fluid in system, T = absolute temperature of system, a = solubility of the gas involved in the fluid (when the gas is at 1 atm pressure), and P_0 = 760 mm of mercury expressed in terms of the fluid in the manometer. If the manometer is filled with Brodie's solution, which has a density of 1.033, P_0 = 10,000.

Derivation of this formula is given in detail in Umbreit et al.[1] and will not be repeated here.

As an illustration of the use of the Warburg manometric systems, we shall select an unusual application of manometry, i.e., that of quantitative hydrogenation of an organic compound. Pyridoxal (Fig. 12-3) may be reduced under alkaline conditions with H_2 and Pd to pyridoxine. Under acid conditions, it is reduced much further.

Fig. 12-2. Photograph of a typical Warburg apparatus. *(A)* manometer; *(B)* water bath (Courtesy, American Instrument Company).

398   W. W. Umbreit

Example I

We have a flask of 20.3 ml capacity and the empty volume of the flask and manometer, down to our constant point (150 mm), is 20.65 ml. In this flask we have placed 1 ml of a suspension (5 mg/ml) of Pd-black in the center space and 0.5 ml of a solution of pyridoxal (2.036 mg pyridoxal HCl/ml) in the sidearm. Both are in 0.1M phosphate buffer pH 8.0. We have filled the flask with H_2 gas and after equilibration at a temperature of 37°C we read the open arm of the manometer. Most commercially available manometers and flasks have an arrangement whereby any gas may be introduced through the manometer stopcock and discharged through a vent in the sidearm, which vent can be closed later to form a gas-tight system. When we see that the pressure is constant, we tip in the sidearm and continue readings as follows (we assume, for the moment, that the atmospheric pressure in the room is constant):

At Time	Open Arm Reads	Change (h)	Sum	μl H$_2$ (hk)
0	150	—		—
5'	148	−2		—
10'	148	0		—

—————————————Tip Sidearm—————————————

At Time	Open Arm Reads	Change (h)	Sum	μl H$_2$ (hk)
15'	122	−26	−26	43
20'	107	−15	−41	69
25'	83	−14	−55	93
30'	69	−14	−69	117
35'	69	0	−69	117

$$k = \frac{V_g \frac{273}{T} + V_{ta}}{P_0} \tag{3}$$

$V_g = 20.65$ ml $- 1.5$ ml of fluid $= 19.15$ ml $= 19,150$ μl; $T = 273 + 37 = 310$; $V_t = 1.5$ ml $= 1500$ μl; (solubility of hydrogen) a_{H_2} at 37°C $= 0.0165$ ml/ml; and (fluid of density 1.033 in manometer); $P_0 = 10,000$.

$$k = \frac{19,150 \times \frac{273}{310} + 1500 \times 0.0165}{10,000} = \frac{16,852 + 24.75}{10,000} = 1.69 \tag{4}$$

i.e., for each mm the manometer fluid drops, there will be 1.69 μl of H_2 taken up. Note that for a relatively insoluble gas like H_2 most of the hydrogen is in the gas space and only a little in the fluid. The data, calculated in terms of microliters of H_2 used, are plotted in Fig. 12-3.

In the case cited, 117 μl of H_2 were used up. This amount of gas is $117/22.4 = 5.2$ $\mu mole$. Since 1 g molecular weight (1 mole) at standard conditions occupies a volume of 22.4 liters, 1 mM of gas would occupy 22.4 ml, and 1 $\mu mole$ would occupy 22.4 μl. The amount of pyridoxal hydrochloride added is $2.036/2 = 1.018$ mg $= 1.018/203.6$ $\mu g = 5.0$ $\mu mole$, i.e., 1 H_2 per mole of pyridoxal.

The above illustration shows how the amount of gas exchange can be calculated. The data can be used in two ways: first, as above, to calculate the total amount, or second, as shown in Fig. 12-3, to calculate the rate of reduction.

The above calculations were made upon the assumption that the atmospheric pressure in the room remained constant. Since this is not always the case, one employs for each series of determinations a *thermobarometer*, which consists of a flask (its volume is immaterial and need not be known) and manometer, the flask containing some water. This system, in which no reaction takes place, will respond to change in atmospheric pressure and can be used to correct the observed changes on the manometers being used to measure a reaction.

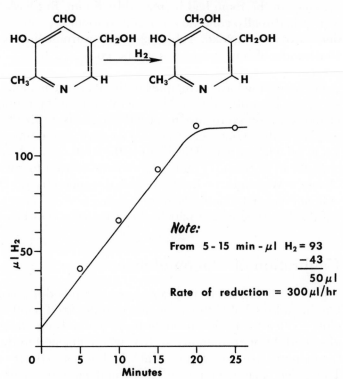

Fig. 12-3. Illustration of the reduction of pyridoxal to pyridoxine with H_2 under alkaline conditions.

Example II

For this illustration we shall use a biological example. In this case we place a suspension of bacteria into each of two Warburg flasks, as shown in Table 12-1. These flasks are similar to the one shown in Fig. 12-1, and in the center well we place 0.1 ml of 10 per cent KOH with a strip of filter paper folded accordion fashion, to provide a greater absorbing surface. In this case the bacteria use up oxygen but give off CO_2. The KOH is to absorb the CO_2 so that it will not influence the gas phase. Each flask has a sidearm, and into one we add buffer, in the other glucose. We set these in a bath at 37°C, together with a thermobarometer, (a flask containing KOH and buffer but no bacteria attached to a manometer), and after 10 minutes (to allow the contents to reach the temperature of the bath), we close the manometer taps and read all three manometers at intervals (Table 12-1). At 5 minutes the thermobarometer has gone up 7 mm so that all of the manometer fluids should have risen 7 mm. Flask 1 rose 3; therefore it had really gone down 4. From 10 to 15 minutes the thermobarometer dropped 5. All manometers should therefore have dropped 5 just because the pressure in the room had increased by 5 mm. But flask 1 went down 8 so it had really gone down 5 due to room pressure changes and 3 due to oxygen uptake. Table 12-1 will warrant further study as an illustration of how readings may be corrected for changes in room pressure.

These are the basic principles of the Warburg manometric method. First, the gas volume is held constant at a constant temperature and changes in pressure are recorded as gas is utilized or given off. Second, only a single gas can be measured at one time and one must know which gas it is. Third, since the system is subject to external changes in pressure, a thermobarometer is used to correct for these changes. Within these limits, Warburg manometry provides comfortable and accurate methods for measuring rate and amount of reaction within the range of 20 to 2000 μl of gas evolved or taken up.

Calibration of Manometer System

In essence one needs to determine accurately the volume of the system including that of the manometer, to the fixed point chosen on the closed sidearm. There are three basic methods employed. First, one fills the flask with mercury so that when attached to the manometer the mercury rises to a given point which is marked with a wax pencil. The empty manometer is inverted and mercury is provided to fill the capillaries from the wax mark to the fixed point on the closed arm, i.e., that space which would normally be gas. The weight of the

TABLE 12-1

DATA FROM A TYPICAL MANOMETRIC DETERMINATION

Thermobarometer		Flask 1					Flask 2				

Flask 1:
$V_g = 18.76$ ml ($= 18,760$ μl)
$V_f = 1.6$ ml
$t = 37°C$ in air ($a = 0.0239,0_2$)
$k_{0_2} = 1.65$

Flask 2:
$V_g = 22.70$ ml
$V_f = 1.6$ ml
$t = 37°C$ in air
$k_{0_2} = 2.00$

Center: 0.5 ml suspension of *Escherichia coli*
Compartment: 0.5 ml K_2HPO_4 buffer—pH 7.4
Center cup: 0.1 ml 10% KOH with paper

Time (min)	mm	Δ	Sidearm: 0.5 ml buffer					0.5 ml 0.01M glucose				
			mm	Δ	Cor-rected	μl	Sum	mm	Δ	Cor-rected	μl	Sum
0	150	—	150	—	—	—	—	149	—	—	—	—
5	150	0	147	−3	−3	5	5	146	−3	−3	6	6
10	157	+7	150	+3	−4	6	11	150	+4	−3	6	12
								glucose tip				
15	152	−5	142	−8	−3	5	16	135	−15	−10	20	32
20	147	−5	134	−8	−3	5	21	120	−15	−10	20	52
25	150	+3	134	0	−3	5	26	113	−7	−10	20	72
30	156	+6	137	+3	−3	5	31	109	−4	−10	20	92

mercury is used to determine the volume. A modification consists of using water in the flask and mercury in the manometer, inasmuch as a 20-ml flask will contain about 20 g of water but 260+ g of mercury; hence, the use of water permits one to use accurate balances more commonly available in the laboratory.

The second method involves the addition or withdrawal of a known quantity of gas from either the manometer, flask or the entire system. Calibration is achieved by displacing a fluid (mercury or water) from a micrometer plunger system; the amount of fluid added or subtracted is known from the change in micrometer reading while the change in pressure on the manometer can be recorded; thus the change in pressure can be related to the volume of gas added or subtracted. These methods are described in detail by Umbreit *et al.* [1] and by Lazarow [3].

The third method is to calibrate by actually releasing or absorbing a known quantity of gas within the system, i.e., if $x = hk$ and both x and h are measured, k is known. There are two basic methods for doing this. One involves the use of a primary weighed standard and is done as follows (1): 0.4 ml of 0.1M potassium ferricyanide will liberate 224 μl of N_2 under alkaline conditions according to the following equation.

$$4\ Fe^{+++}(CN)_6 + N_2H_4 \longrightarrow 4\ Fe^{++}(CN)_6 + 4H^+ + N_2$$

A typical arrangement employs:

Main compartment:
0.4 ml of 0.1M potassium ferricyanide (224 $\mu l\ N_2$)
0.4 ml of 4N NaOH
1.2 ml of water
Sidearm:
0.5 ml of hydrazine solution (saturated) (prepared by dissolving 5 g hydrazine sulfate in 100 ml hot water; on cooling, the excess separates and the saturated supernatant is used)
0.5 ml of 4N NaOH

The reaction is complete in about 30 minutes; $k_{N_2} = k_{O_2}$ since the solubilities of O_2 and N_2 are very close. This method has the advantage of starting with a weighed pure standard which may be standardized by titration, if necessary.

The other method is useful in calibrating a large number of flasks when the flask constant of one or two is known. To the main compartment is added 2.5 ml of approximately 0.005M $KHCO_3$ and to each sidearm 0.5 ml approximately 2N H_2SO_4. Upon tipping the acid, CO_2 is released. The flasks with known constants provide a measure of the amount of CO_2 released from which the constants of the unknown flasks may be calculated.

Uses of Warburg Manometry

Two illustrations, one of quantitative chemical hydrogenation, the other of a biological respiration, have already been given. It seems convenient to outline the variety of applications. These may be classified under four general groupings: measurement of chemical reactions; measurement of biological reactions (primarily respiration and fermentation of living cells); measurement of substances (by either enzymic or chemical methods); and measurement of reaction rates and the influence of substances thereon, for example, measurement of the effect of antiseptics by their effect on respiratory rates in tissues.

As an example of chemical measurements, we may cite catalytic hydrogenation, as described in Example I. So far the system is applicable to the measurement of hydrogen at atmospheric pressure only, but considering the small quantity of substance required and the relatively large amount of catalyst, it can provide very useful quantitative information. Similarly, oxygenation reactions may be measured. In fact, any reaction where the products or reactants are gaseous or can be converted into gases can be measured by a manometric system.

The largest use in measuring biological reactions is in the measurement of respiration, i.e., oxygen uptake, by living tissues: animal, plant, microbial. A typical system is that described in Example II. For the measurement of fermentation (or anaerobic glycolysis), that is, the production of acid and/or gas under anaerobic conditions, the system is modified so that oxygen is absent and the buffer is bicarbonate in equilibrium with CO_2 in the gas phases. Under these circumstances acid produced will release CO_2 from the bicarbonate and can thus be measured. By taking advantage of the markedly different solubilities of O_2 and CO_2, it is possible to set up a system in which both gases can be measured simultaneously. Respiratory quotients are thus easily obtained. Essentially any kind of substrate may be tested for its ability to be oxidized or fermented and both its rate and the amount of oxygen and/or acid per mole are determinable. This is accomplished by tipping in a known quantity from the sidearm and allowing the reaction to go to completion.

Frequently it is possible to distinguish several stages in a reaction pathway because of their differing rates. One may determine the sensitivity of a respiration or fermentation path to various inhibitors and thus frequently be able to define the nature of the metabolic pathway involved. One may compare organism, tissue, etc., as to ability to attack a given material and measure both the rate and the degree of reaction. This is especially useful in distinguishing between genetic mutants. One may measure the rate, extent, and quantitative relations in photosynthesis. Growth rates may be measured by observing the progressive increase in gas exchange per unit time as more cells are formed. One may determine the nature of an inhibition by a drug, i.e., whether it is competitive or noncompetitive, and thus obtain useful information on how such inhibitors act. Isotopes may, of course, be used with the manometric system.

Succinic acid, fumaric acid, malic acid, glutamic acid, lysine, and a wide array of other substances may be estimated by manometric method. These measurements may be made by using specific enzymes (for example, lysine decarboxylase will attack only lysine in an amino acid mixture and the CO_2 liberated is an accurate measure of the lysine present) or chemicals (for example, aniline citrate chemically reacts with β-keto acids and causes the release of CO_2; it thus serves as a manometric estimation of oxalacetic acid and acetoacetic acid).

The influence of drugs, inhibitors, and stimulants on tissues, on enzymes, and on chemical reactions is measurable by manometry. There is further a wide array of practical applications, for example, the measurement of the degree of sewage decomposition, the bio-chemical oxygen demand, etc.

It is evident from the above that the Warburg manometric methods have wide application and lend themselves not only to precise meas-urements of small quantities of substances, but also are expandable into convenient routine assay systems when required.

In addition to the principal reference work cited [1], details of the use, standardization, operating details, etc., are given in other pub-lications [4-10], which may be more convenient to consult than reference [1].

References

1. W. W. Umbreit, R. H. Burris, and J. F. Stauffer, *Manometric Techniques and Tissue Metabolism*, Burgess, Minneapolis, 4th ed. (1964).
2. J. P. Peters and D. D. Van Slyke, *Quantitative Clinical Chemistry*, Vol. II, "Methods," Williams and Wilkins, Baltimore (1932), reprinted (1943).
3. A. Lazarow, *J. Lab. Clin. Med.*, **38**, 767 (1951).
4. D. Burk and R. T. Milner, *Ind. Eng. Chem., Anal. Ed.*, **4**, 3 (1932).
5. M. Dixon, *Manometric Methods*, University Press, Cambridge, England, 3rd ed. (1951).
6. J. J. Perkins, *Ind. Eng. Chem., Anal. Ed.*, **15**, 61 (1943).
7. O. Warburg, *Biochem. Z.*, **142**, 317 (1923).
8. O. Warburg, *Biochem. Z.*, **152**, 51 (1924).
9. O. Warburg, *Uber den Stoffwechsel der Tumoren*, Springer, Berlin (1926); Translated by F. Dickens, Constable, London (1930).
10. H. H. Krebs, In *Die Fermente und ihrer Wirkungen*, Oppenheimer and Pincussen, eds., Vol. 3, Thieme, Leipzig, 5th ed., (1929), p.635.

Osmotic Pressure Measuring Devices

J. Levitt

THOUGH INTEREST in osmotic pressure has waned since the early work on the problem, the many new measuring devices described during the past few years demonstrate a renewed activity. It is, in fact, impossible to do justice to all of them. An earlier attempt to do so [1] resulted in a 400-page article, though several of the methods now in use were then undeveloped. Many of the unsolved problems of that era now seem to have been satisfactorily eliminated by the development of several commercial instruments capable of accurate, rapid, routine measurements on micro samples. The procedures described in this chapter will concentrate on some of the newer methods that have not been described in the earlier reviews [1-3] but will also include some of the older methods that are still irreplaceable. In most cases, no attempt will be made to give an exhaustive discussion of the details, and some equally useful techniques will not be described in any detail. The commercial instruments, of course, are supplied with full instructions and need not be described here. Several of the methods most recently published in scientific literature have apparently not been tried extensively outside the laboratories in which they have been developed. Consequently, it is difficult to compare them with each other and even to choose the most desirable one for each purpose. The reader may be aided in his choice by Table 13-1.

Direct Measurements

As in the case of all measurements, direct methods can be expected to yield the most dependable absolute values since they avoid the assumptions that must be made when the values are calculated from indirect measurements. Yet direct methods are almost never used nowadays for osmotic pressure determinations. There are several reasons for this: *(1)* the great difficulty in preparing perfectly semipermeable membranes, at least in the case of aqueous solutions; *(2)* the high pressures frequently involved; *(3)* the lesser accuracy and

TABLE 13-1

COMPARISON OF DIFFERENT METHODS OF MEASURING OSMOTIC POTENTIALS

Method	Time per determination	Amount of solution needed	Sensitivity and variability	Applications and advantages
a) Cryoscopic				
1. Classical	20 min	15 ml (Beckman) 0.5 to 1.0 ml (small thermometer or thermocouple)	0.1 atm	
2. Marr and Vaadia micromethod	5 to 10 min	1 drop		Concentrations up to 0.25 molal
3. Commercial osmometers	2 min	1 ml	0.001 osmolal	0-3 molal
b) Vapor pressure				
1. Barger-Halket	12 to 24 hr	few drops	0.01M	Simplicity
2. van den Honert	6 hr	few drops	0.1 atm	For values above 2 atm whole tissue pieces may be used, no strict temperature control needed
3. Thermoelectric (Baldes and Johnson)	15 min	0.01 ml	0.002 molar (deviation)	Strict temperature control needed (0.02°C)
4. Thermoelectric (Mechrolab)	5 min	0.01 to 0.2 ml	1-4%	
5. Weatherly's micro-osmometer	1 hr	0.06 ml or 0.001 ml	±0.06 atm (std. error)	No strict temperature control needed
6. Thermocouple psychrometer (Richards and Ogata)	1 to 3 hr		0.5% (coeff. of variability)	For soils, tissues etc.; for values near saturation; strict temperature control needed (0.001°C)
c) Membrane				
1. Hepp osmometer	2 to 3 hr			For colloidal dispersions
d) Refractometer	Few secs	0.02 ml	0.1 atm	Suitable for field work, and for large number of samples
e) Plasmolytic (incipient)	15-20 min	Single cell or tissue	Varies with the cell (±0.1 to 0.5 atm)	For living cells

sensitivity when relative values are more important than absolute values; *(4)* the slowness of the method; and *(5)* the large quantities of solution needed. The classical methods of Morse [4] and Berkeley and Hartley [5] can therefore still be considered standard.

In the case of colloidal dispersions, however, direct measurements are much simpler, since many membranes are semipermeable to them, and the pressures involved are small and therefore easily produced without damaging the membranes. A simple Hepp osmometer [6] consists of a Lucite chamber, at the bottom of which a membrane of cellophane or collodion separates the solution in the chamber from a tube to which a manometer may be attached. For gelatin solutions 2 to 3 hours are required before equilibrium can be attained. Even in this simple case, however, a completely satisfactory membrane had not been found.

The gap between colloidal dispersions and molecular solutions is, however, being bridged. A commercial osmometer now on the market manufactured by Mechrolab, Inc., can be used for dilute solutions of solutes with molecular weights from 20,000 to 1,000,000. Only small pressures are, therefore, required. However, this was developed mainly for determinations of molecular weights and for organic solvents and is not yet adaptable to aqueous solutions.

Indirect Measurements

Since osmotic pressure is only one of the colligative properties of solutions, all of which are related to each other, any of the others can be used for indirect measurements of osmotic pressure. From these other values the *osmotic potential* of the solution can be calculated, i.e., the osmotic pressure that the solution would be capable of producing if separated from the pure solute by a semipermeable and rigid membrane. Most modern methods eliminate the need for these calculations by comparing the measured value for the unknown with those of a series of dilutions of a solution whose osmotic potentials are known.

FREEZING POINT (OR CRYOSCOPIC) METHODS

The old classical method [2] is simple and accurate enough for some purposes. The osmotic potential of the solution can be calculated from the equation [7]:

$$P = 12.06\Delta - 0.021\Delta^2 \tag{1}$$

where Δ = the freezing point lowering of the solution. This equation is supposed to be exact to 0.1 per cent for values up to several hundred atmospheres. Conversion tables from 0 to 5.99°C may be found in Walter [2]. A correction for undercooling may be made from the following equation:

$$\Delta = \Delta' \, (1 - 0.025\mu) \tag{2}$$

where Δ' is the observed freezing point lowering and μ is the lowering due to undercooling below this. However, there are numerous sources of small errors, and it is safer to employ a correction factor from a curve of determinations on solutions of known freezing point lowerings [8]. One of the disadvantages of this classical method is its slowness — only 20 to 30 determinations may be completed in a whole day [2]. Another disadvantage is the large quantity of material needed (about 10 to 15 ml by the older method, less than 1.0 ml by the more recent (see Currier [8]). However, many modifications, such as the use of thermocouples or thermistors instead of thermometers, have been made to overcome these drawbacks.

The technique has been thoroughly and often described in standard texts of physics, physical chemistry, and physiology. The following procedure is especially adapted for work with plant saps [8].

The container (Fig. 13-1) is a half-gallon Thermos jug, with glass wool insulation (*h*) packed between an external metal covering and an inner vessel of earthenware. Replacing the lid and screw cap is a top (*d*) composed of Masonite, with holes drilled to receive a heavy wire stirrer (*a*), an ordinary thermometer (*b*) reading to −20°C to indicate bath temperature, a glass air jacket (*k*), and a small glass tube (*j*) in which a water-filled glass capillary (*g*) can be frozen. Within the air jacket a sample tube (*i*) is held in place by a cork fitted with holes to accommodate the freezing point thermometer (*c*), a fine wire stirrer (*e*) tipped with rubber, and a small hole (*f*) through which the glass capillary could be inserted into the test solution. The specially made freezing thermometer is calibrated in fiftieths of a degree and has a very small bulb (0.5 cm in diameter and 1.0 cm in length).

For the determination, the container is filled with an ice-salt mixture at approximately −10°C. A dropping pipette serves to introduce 0.7 ml of sap into the sample tube, after which the small thermometer is placed in position so that the bulb is completely immersed. The sample tube is then placed in an ice-water bath in a smaller double-walled vessel until the thermometer registers about +0.5°C. Then, after the excess water has been carefully removed, it is transferred to the air jacket of the cryoscope. This operation saves considerable time when a large number of determinations are being made. As the mercury nears −2°C., stirring of the solution is begun with an up and down motion of the left hand, repeated about three times per second. When the thermometer reads $-2°C.$, crystallization is induced by momentarily inserting the tip of the ice-filled glass capillary into the solution through the small hole (f). The mercury immediately rises to a maximum and remains there for a minute or so, then drops slowly. Stirring is continued until the plateau in the freezing curve is reached. The highest temperature is recorded as the observed depression. A small magnifier aids in reading the thermometer.

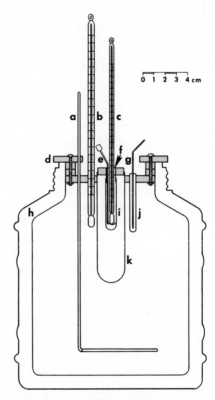

Fig. 13-1. Classical method for freezing point determinations, modified for small samples [8] (Courtesy, H. B. Currier and *Plant Physiology*).

Nowadays, it is no longer necessary to follow the above tedious, classical procedure, since so many simple and rapid push-button osmometers have been developed and are now available commercially (e.g., American Instrument Company, Industrial Instruments). These permit the routine determination of freezing points on 1-ml samples in a concentration range up to 3 osmoles to $0.001°C$ by use of thermistors and a thermoelectric or some other convenient method of cooling. Usually, no attempt is made to determine the actual freezing point, but the osmotic value is read directly in osmoles (the molarity of an ideal solution having the same freezing point). Each determination takes only 2 minutes and the accuracy depends on the series of known solutions used as standards. The exact procedures are fully described in the pamphlets issued by the individual companies.

A rapid cryoscopic technique for drop size samples has recently been published [9]. The problem of supercooling has been overcome by first freezing the sample and then determining the thawing temperature. The drawback is that it is limited to solutions not more than 0.25 osmolal (6 atm) because the ice must be in direct physical contact with the thermistor bead throughout the thawing period.

VAPOR   PRESSURE   METHODS

An amazingly large number of vapor pressure (vp) osmometers have been described in the literature of the past 2 to 3 decades. As a result, this instrument in one form or another seems to have displaced all others in popularity. The general trends in the evolution of the modern vp osmometer are shown in Figs. 13-2 to 13-6. The methods most commonly used are indirect. One major trend has been to do away with equilibrium measurements which are responsible for the major disadvantage of the earlier methods, namely, the great length of time the material must be left in the osmometer before a measurement can be made. This disadvantage has been overcome by allowing evaporation to take place for a brief but standard length of time and by comparing the rates. An empirically determined standard curve must, of course, first be prepared.

1. The Barger-Halket [10] osmometer (Fig. 13-2). The oldest and simplest vapor pressure method is the one originated by Barger for determining molecular weights and modified by Halket for use with plant saps. Capillary tubes about 3 inches in length are filled with a series of alternating drops of the unknown solution, separating them by means of a bubble of air. This is simply done by closing one end with the finger and touching the other end to the known solution, then allowing a bubble of air to enter before touching it in the same way to the unknown. In this way a series of about 5 to 7 drops is obtained in the capillary, the known being present at both ends. Both ends of the capillary are then sealed. A graded series of tubes, each containing the same unknown but a different known solution, is prepared in the same way; all the tubes are sealed successively to the same microscope slide by means of balsam or wax. The slides are kept in a Petri dish of water for ease of measurement and to maintain the temperature approximately constant. All the drops except the two terminal ones in each tube are then measured immediately by means of an ocular micrometer. The slides are then left overnight and the drops measured

again. The tube in which the drops fail to elongate or shorten contains the known solution with the same vapor pressure and therefore the same osmotic potential as the unknown. This may be obtained by extrapolation. Differences as small as 0.01M may be detected. The method has the advantage of using very small quantities of sap and not requiring elaborate apparatus. Its main disadvantages are the time required to reach equilibrium, and the care that must be taken to prevent appreciable mixing of the drops on filling the tubes.

Other simple modifications of the same procedure have been used, particularly by ecologists interested in determining values for soils. Ursprung [1] inverts a series of capillary tubes with different solutions in them over the unknown and by marking the meniscus at the beginning, determines which solutions take up water and which lose it. The solution that fails to gain or lose water will have the same osmotic value as that of the unknown solution (or soil, etc.). Other investigators suspend filter paper moistened with known solutions over the unknown and determine by weighing whether water is lost or gained by the filter paper [1].

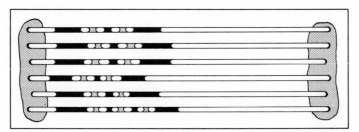

Fig. 13-2. Barger-Halket osmometer.

2. The van den Honert [12] osmometer (Fig. 13-3). A $CaCl_2$ solution of known value fills the capillary tube *(bcde)* up to about halfway in the graduated arm *(de)*, and soaks the porous, sintered glass vessel *(a)*. A piece of filter paper soaked with the unknown solution (or an unknown piece of tissue) is laid on a small glass pan which is placed on the sintered glass plate. The vessel is quickly closed, and the apparatus is immersed in a water bath up to *(h)*. The loss or gain of water vapor by the unknown to or from the $CaCl_2$ is detected by movement in the capillary arm *(de)*. A temperature fluctuation of 0.2 to 0.3°C introduces no significant error, but the instrument should be kept in the dark to prevent a temperature rise in the sample.

3. The Baldes and Johnson [11] thermoelectric osmometer [13] (Fig. 13-4). The moist chamber is kept at a constant temperature (±0.02°C) and the filter paper in it is wetted with distilled water or solution. A drop of distilled water (or known solution) is placed on one

loop of the thermocouple and a drop of the unknown on the other. The thermocouple is put into the moist chamber and left for 30 to 35 minutes before reading the galvanometer deflections. By this time an equilibrium has been established between the liberation of heat by condensation of water and the loss by radiation and conduction. The procedure is repeated with the drops reversed on the loops and the two readings are averaged. The thermocouple is always put into the

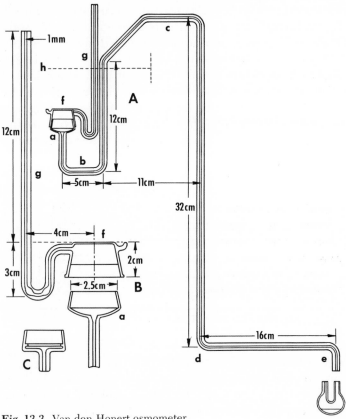

Fig. 13-3. Van den Honert osmometer.

chamber in the same position. Each thermocouple is calibrated with a series of concentrations, e.g., boric acid. The differences between the drops should not exceed 0.03M NaCl so that the known solutions must replace water (even for wetting the filter paper) when the unknowns have higher concentrations than this. A commercial thermoelectric osmometer is now available from Mechrolab, Inc.

The use of a thermocouple as a wet-bulb thermometer has been attempted by some investigators. Spanner [14] used the Peltier effect to cool a very fine thermocouple below the dew point. It then collects a minute amount of dew and can be used as an exceedingly fine wet-bulb thermometer. It is calibrated by means of salt solutions of known strength and is capable of determining differences of 0.1 atm. Thermal equilibrium is reached in 10 to 15 minutes and vapor pressure equilibrium is rapid at high vapor pressure.

4. The Richards and Ogata [15] thermocouple psychrometer [16] (Fig. 13-5). In the case of large leaves, the leaves are first frozen and thawed and a leaf section is placed around the inside wall of the sample container, with its undersurface toward the center of the container. In the case of small leaflets, soil, etc., a sufficient quantity is held in the above portion by means of a brass screen. The sample container is inserted in the water bath (25·000°C ± 0·001°), and the thermocouple, with a droplet of distilled water on the wet junction, is positioned in the sample container. Thermocouple output is followed until it reaches a steady state. Small leaks of water vapor from the sample chamber must be prevented. Calibration is obtained with KCl solutions, e.g., 5 solutions from 5 to 65 bars. One to three hours are required for equilibrium, and although the standard deviation was usually only 0·2 to 0·3 bars, Ehlig concluded that the determined

Fig. 13-4. Baldes and Johnson thermoelectric osmometer. (Courtesy, O. M. van Andel and Royal Netherlands Academy of Science.)

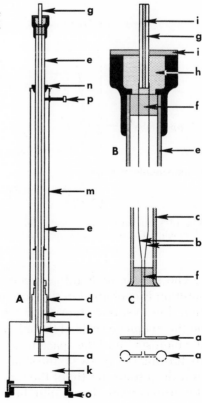

values may have been slightly high due to water loss from the container.

5. Weatherley's [17] micro-osmometer (Fig. 13-6) is intermediate between the simpler Barger-Halket method and the sophisticated thermoelectric osmometer. As in the latter cases, it measures the rate of distillation between an unknown solution and a known standard solution. As in the former method, it uses a simple capillary tube to measure the rate, and in this way avoids the need of thermoelectric measurements. Yet it duplicates the precision of the latter method by adopting its use of calibration curves with solutions of known osmotic potential. The method, in brief, is as follows:

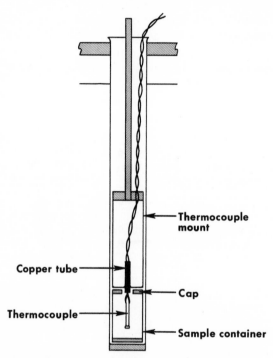

Fig. 13-5. Richards and Ogata thermocouple psychrometer. (Courtesy, Carl Ehlig and *Plant Physiology*)

The sample (0.06 ml) is placed in the capsule *(c)* and the standard solution is contained in the pipette *(p)*, where it is held at a fixed position due to surface tension at the jet. The upper meniscus is located on the eyepiece scale of the microscope *(m)*. The capillary tube above the meniscus and the space inside the screw plunger *(s)* are air-filled. By turning the screw *(s)* the standard solution can be extruded to hang as a drop from the tip of the jet. After a measured time (20 minutes) the drop is again drawn into the pipette to the fixed position at which it comes to rest automatically, and the change in volume, due to condensation or evaporation, is measured on the microscope scale.

If the sample has a surface tension not much lower than that of water, the osmometer can be used in the reverse way, the sample being drawn into the pipette and the standard into the capsule. Used in this way only 0.001 ml of the sample is needed.

A separate calibration curve is required for each standard and each standard has a range of about 9 atm ($\Delta = 0.75°C$). The standard deviation of single determinations is ± 0.06 atm ($\Delta = 0.005°C$). This is uniform over the range investigated (0 to 28 atm or $\Delta = 2.3°C$).

THE REFRACTOMETER METHOD

It has long been known that the concentration of pure solutions can be readily and quickly determined by means of a refractometer. If a plant sap contains mainly one solute, e.g., sucrose, the method may be applied with reasonable success for determinations of osmotic potentials [18]. But in order to obtain reliable results with saps, calibration curves must be drawn up from preliminary parallel determinations of freezing point lowerings and refractive indices [19]. This must be done not only for each plant but even for the same plant at different times of the year. Since one drop of the unknown is simply placed on the refractometer plate and a reading is made immediately, the refractometer method is, of course, unequalled in speed and simplicity by any other method, as far as the individual determinations are concerned, and is particularly suitable for field work. But the above requirement of calibration curves may completely obviate this advantage.

MEMBRANE METHODS. Although direct measurements of osmotic pressures are rarely made by these methods (see above), osmotic potentials are frequently determined by separating a known solution from an unknown by a semipermeable membrane and determining the direction of movement of the solvent.

NONLIVING SYSTEMS. A simple method has been used by Boiko and Boiko [20]. A graded series of solutions, e.g., sugar, is prepared in test tubes. An exact quantity of the unknown solution is measured into each of a series of collodion sacs. Each collodion sac is immersed in one of the tubes and left for 1 to 2 hours. The solution that fails to lead to a change in the volume of the unknown has an equivalent osmotic potential to that of the unknown. Since collodion is not by any means perfectly semipermeable, this method would seem to be useful only for approximate results.

Cellulose acetate membranes have recently been used for substances with molecular weights as small as 3800 [21], although membranes for such small molecules are admittedly difficult to make.

LIVING SYSTEMS.   There are many cases where extraction of sap for use in any of the above methods is impossible or at least undesirable. Direct measurements on living tissues must then be resorted to. The following are some examples: *(1)* where the osmotic potential of an individual cell or a single kind of cell in a mixed tissue is required; *(2)* in the case of aquatic plants whose surfaces cannot be dried adequately before expressing the sap; *(3)* in the case of fine roots, for the same reason; *(4)* where the surface is incrusted with salts or other substances, e.g., certain halophytes (in the latter two

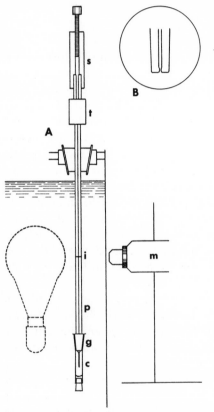

Fig. 13-6. Weatherley's micro-ocmo-meter. (Courtesy, P. E. Weatherley and *Journal of Experimental Botany.*)

cases surface washing may often introduce errors); *(5)* when the tissues are so dry that no representative sample of juice can be obtained, e.g., certain desert plants. In all other cases where the sap is obtainable from previously living cells, killing the cells and subsequently removing the juice for measurements may be expected to produce changes. Consequently, measurements on the living cells are always desirable, if this is possible, at least as a check on the above methods.

Yet in spite of their irreplaceability, methods using living cells have fallen into ill repute in recent years. Many investigators have, in fact, categorically denied the ability of such methods to determine osmotic potentials. This is because, as pointed out by Ursprung [1], although the methods are extraordinarily simple and have been described for decades in every practical manual, in no other case have so many errors in techniques been made and the literature is full of false values obtained by the methods. It is also partly due to the common error of mistaking precision and duplicability for accuracy. Whatever the reason, investigators have frequently preferred to build complicated and expensive equipment (see above) needing extremely careful checking and accurate temperature control even though the osmotic potential of the tissues could be more easily, more rapidly, and more accurately measured (sometimes even with greater precision) by the method of incipient plasmolysis described below.

Of the six following methods, 1 to 3 may be used for pieces of tissue or organs; 2, 4, 5, and 6 for individual cells.

1. The minimum weight method. Pieces of tissue are placed in a series of concentrations of a solution of known osmotic potentials containing a non-penetrating solute. The most dilute solution resulting in the maximum loss in weight will have the same osmotic potential as that of the cell sap.

2. The minimum volume method. This involves the same general technique as method 1, but long strips of tissue or individual cells are used, and length instead of weight is measured.

3. The tissue curvature method. Lockhart (22) has recently used a refinement of this method to determine the osmotic potential of pea stems. After incubation in hypertonic solutions of mannite, the mechanical deformability of the tissue under a standard, imposed load was found to be a linear function of the external osmotic potential over a considerable concentration range. Extrapolation of this relationship to zero deformation is assumed to yield the internal osmotic potential of the tissue at limiting plasmolysis. This method is, of course, only applicable to non-woody and non-leathery succulent tissues.

4. Höfler's plasmometric method. A solution causing plasmolysis of large vacuoled cells of rather regular shape, e.g., cylindrical cells, to about $\frac{3}{4}$ of the cell volume is used. From measurements of cell length (h), protoplast length (l), and cell diameter (d), and knowing the osmotic potential of the external solution (O_e), the osmotic potential of the unplasmolyzed cell can be calculated. The protoplast volume is proportional to

$$l - \frac{d}{3} \qquad (1)$$

cell volume to

$$h - \frac{d}{3} \qquad (2)$$

The osmotic potential of the unplasmolyzed cell (Fig. 13-7) will then be

$$\frac{l - \dfrac{d}{3}}{h - \dfrac{d}{3}} \times O_e \qquad (3)$$

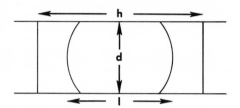

Fig. 13-7. Plasmometric method of determining osmotic potential.

5. The turgor method. If the turgor pressure can be measured in a cell in equilibrium with a solution of known osmotic potential, the osmotic potential of the cell is equal to the sum of the above two quantities. Tazawa [23] developed a technique for measuring the turgor pressure of the large cells of *Nitella* and was, therefore, able to calculate their osmotic potentials. But measurements of turgor pressure are difficult at best and can be used only in the case of such favorable material. In the case of higher plants, although a method of measuring turgor pressure has also been worked out [24], the other quantity would also have to be measured since the tissues are not immersed in a solution.

The above methods are, however, of limited applicability since (1) they can be used only on single cells (or strips of uniform tissue in methods 1 and 2), (2) the cells must be quite regular in shape when individual cells are used, (3) in the case of method 4 there must be no appreciable amount of nonsolvent space in the cell or else this must be taken into account, and (4) the length of time in the solutions may result in a significant change, sometimes even preventing the attainment of equilibrium.

6. The incipient plasmolysis method. (a) Objections and their elimination. For simplicity, accuracy, and general applicability to nearly all living plant cells, the method of incipient plasmolysis is the best of all methods. It can be used either for single cells or for

whole tissues. In the latter case, the usually small variations from cell to cell in a single tissue are taken into account by finding the solution that causes incipient (i.e., the beginnings of) plasmolysis in about 50 per cent of the cells. Many objections have been raised against this method, but if the technique is clearly understood and correctly used, few if any of these objections are valid. The following are some such objections: (1) The cell shrinks before plasmolysis can occur and therefore the cell sap becomes somewhat concentrated and the incipient plasmolysis method gives values which are too high. This objection is valid only if one is intent on finding the osmotic potential in fully turgid or nearly fully turgid cells. In the case of land plants, cells are seldom fully turgid (i.e., in equilibrium with 100 per cent relative humidity), and even in this state, the value will usually be only 10 to 15 per cent lower than at incipient plasmolysis. In the normal, partially turgid state, the value will be only 5 to 10 per cent lower than that obtained at incipient plasmolysis. If one is careful to determine the 50 per cent point mentioned above, the error may be still less. This amount of error is negligible in most biological problems, but if a refinement is desired, one can determine the solution that just fails to induce incipient plasmolysis or the correction factor can easily be determined by a few cell measurements. (2) The plasmolyte may penetrate the cell and give values which are too high. This objection is valid in some cases. Potassium nitrate was the plasmolyte used by many of the earlier investigators and this does penetrate. As a result, some of the published results are undoubtedly too high, e.g., values of 100 atm for guard cells of open stomata. To this day, some of the Japanese workers follow Molisch's example and use this solute. (3) Erroneous results may be obtained due to sticking of the protoplasm to the cell wall. (4) The cell may actively absorb the solute and, therefore, values which are too high may be obtained. (5) Some of the cell solutes may diffuse out, yielding values which are too low. This would certainly happen if plasmolysis injured the cells.

All the above objections can be eliminated by use of a suitable solute and the application of the correct technique. Sucrose penetrates the cell at a negligible rate, and has been used more commonly than any other solute. This popularity is undoubtedly due to its choice by Ursprung and Blum, whose monumental and classical researches have served as a model for all their successors. Yet Ursprung [1] himself fully recognized the tremendous advantages of $CaCl_2$, which make it an ideal plasmolyte for most cells. It decreases the permeability of the cell and therefore tends to eliminate objection (5). It does not penetrate at an appreciable rate, either passively or actively, and tends to eliminate objections (2) and (4). It diffuses much more rapidly than sucrose, and its solutions are no more viscous than water (in opposition to the highly viscous sucrose solutions) and for both reasons it leads to a far more rapid plasmolysis (5 to 10 times as rapid as in sucrose). In some cases where even sucrose is injurious, $CaCl_2$ is not [1]. This fact and the speed of determination of incipient plasmolysis effectively eliminate the last traces of objections (2), (4), and (5). Objection (3) is eliminated by the technique of plasmolyzing the cell first then deplasmolyzing it to determine the incipient point.

It must be emphasized that no one method is applicable to all cells, and special precautions are necessary in some cases. Some sections may require infiltration with the plasmolyte in order to remove the intercellular air which may otherwise interfere with visibility. According to Iljin [25], halophytes are permeable to Ca^{++}, and therefore before using it for plants of this group, the possibility of penetration into the cell should be checked. For these and any other cells that may be injured by $CaCl_2$, other solutions may be required, e.g., a balanced solution of 9 parts NaCl to 1 part $CaCl_2$. Concentrated sea water has been found necessary in the case of some cells whose habitat is the sea. The temperature at which plasmolysis is conducted may be important, e.g., certain algae are injured by plasmolysis at temperatures above 18°C [26]. Red algae and root hairs must be plasmolyzed slowly in order to prevent injury. Some animal cells and bacteria do not plasmolyze, but in some of these cases the beginnings of cell collapse or wrinkling of the surface (e.g., erythrocytes) may be used instead of incipient plasmolysis. Certain species of the blue-green algae are so permeable that even sucrose and $CaCl_2$ penetrate at rates rapid enough to lead to error [27]. But these very cells, with which the incipient plasmolysis method leads to difficulties, cannot have their osmotic potentials determined in any other way, and at least approximate values may be obtained plasmolytically.

For maximum sensitivity (±0.1 to 0.2 atm) the method should be used on long, narrow cells whose length is at least 3 to 4 times their width. Values can also be obtained with small, round cells, although one may have to be satisfied with a sensitivity of 1 to 2 atm. However, some of these very small isodiametric cells have high osmotic potentials, and the percentage error may still be small enough. In observing for incipient plasmolysis, the cells near the edges of the section should be ignored, since they may be injured, and because of an increased permeability may have lost some solutes. This is less pronounced when $CaCl_2$ is the solute used.

Time is of the essence in plasmolytic measurements. For though most cells of higher plants are uninjured by moderate plasmolysis for some hours, others are more sensitive. This is a major reason for selecting $CaCl_2$ as the plasmolyte. A determination may be completed in 15 to 20 minutes with practice and this may also eliminate injury as a factor even in the case of those cells that are sensitive to plasmolysis. For the same reasons, sections should be transferred immediately on cutting to the plasmolyzing solution. Since such hypertonic solutions may injure some sensitive cells, they are transferred to a weaker solution as soon as plasmolysis is distinct (2 to 3 minutes in most cases). When incipient plasmolysis is approached, the sections may be left for 5 minutes in order to permit equilibrium. When the solution that yields incipient plasmolysis is recognized, the cells should be checked again one or two times to be sure that equilibrium has been attained. Finally, to be certain that this is really the point of incipient plasmolysis, the sections should be transferred to a solution one step less concentrated. If all the cells deplasmolyze in this solution, then the one above was the correct one for incipient plasmolysis. It may sometimes be necessary to check the results with freshly cut sections, making use of the preliminary results in order to achieve maximum speed.

The advantages of going down the series instead of going up are several. It eliminates the possibility of erroneous results due to sticking of the protoplasm to the cell wall. It induces rapid rounding up of the protoplast during deplasmolysis. Due to the pronounced refraction line, incipient plasmolysis is much more readily detected in such rounded up cells than in those plasmolyzed concavely by going up the series. Finally, it is easy to judge how close one is to incipient plasmolysis and this speeds up the determination of the incipient point.

(b) Procedure. The step-by-step procedure is as follows: (1) Several freehand sections are made, about 1 cell thick at the edges, 2 to 3 cells thick at the middle, and transferred directly to a few drops of one and a half to twice isotonic $CaCl_2$ on a microscope slide. The solution to use is determined by preliminary rough trials. In some cases, of course, sections cannot be made and the procedure must be modified accordingly, e.g., filamentous algae, can be transferred directly, unicellular organisms may have to be centrifuged down and pipetted, etc. (2) After 2 to 3 minutes, the excess solution is drained off and the sections are covered with a cover glass and examined under the microscope. (3) As soon as plasmolysis is seen to be distinct, the two or three best sections are lifted from the slide by means of a glass hook, touched to a piece of filter paper to remove excess liquid, and transferred to a few drops of weaker $CaCl_2$ (e.g., 0.05M lower). The slide is allowed to stand 5 minutes in a covered Petri plate, and is then examined as in (2) for plasmolysis. Partial deplasmolysis and a consequent rounding up of the cells should have occurred. (4) If plasmolysis is still distinct, a considerably (e.g., 0.03 to 0.05M weaker solution is again tried as in (3). This is repeated by smaller steps until incipient plasmolysis occurs. (5) When about 50 per cent of the cells are found to show incipient plasmolysis and the rest no plasmolysis, the cover

glass is removed, fresh solution of the same concentration is added to
the slide, and it is allowed to stand another 5 minutes in a covered
Petri plate. (Of course, if the proper solution is overshot, one should
recommence with fresh sections). *(6)* If plasmolysis is still unchanged,
the cells have reached equilibrium. (If they have deplasmolyzed
completely, one must start again with fresh sections.) The sections
are then transferred to a slightly (e.g., 0.01 to 0.02M) weaker solution
and examined (after 5 minutes in the Petri plate). If all or nearly all
the cells are now deplasmolyzed, then the above solution that permitted incipient plasmolysis in 50 per cent of the cells, and in which
this degree of plasmolysis remained unchanged, yields the osmotic
potential of the cell, which can be read off from Table 13-2. Deplasmolysis in the slightly weaker solution proves that the protoplasts
are still osmotically normal and that the determination is valid. As
an added check, the cells may be transferred back to a hypertonic
solution to prove that they are still alive and able to plasmolyze
normally.

(c) Preparations. The transfer hooks are made by drawing out thin
glass rods (3 mm diameter) to needle diameter and forming a sloped,
slightly open hook (about 3 mm diameter) at the end of the needle.

The plasmolyzing solutions are made up as follows. A stock solution of M $CaCl_2$ should be prepared from an unopened bottle of anhydrous, reagent-grade $CaCl_2$, in order to be sure it is sufficiently free
from water. This should be checked by determining the freezing
points of some of the dilutions below and checking them against the
values in Table 13-2. It may even be necessary to adjust the pH, which
should be between 5 and 7.

TABLE 13-2

OSMOTIC POTENTIALS OF $CaCl_2$ SOLUTIONS*

Molality (wt molar)	Freezing pt (°C)	Osmotic Potential (atm at 20°C)
0.01	0.051	0.7
0.02		1.3
0.03		1.9
0.04		2.6
0.05	0.244	3.1
0.06		3.7
0.07		4.3
0.08		5.0
0.09		5.6
0.10	0.483	6.2

TABLE 13-2 *(Continued)*

OSMOTIC POTENTIALS OF· CaCl₂ SOLUTIONS°

Molality (wt molar)	Freezing pt (°C)	Osmotic Potential (atm at 20°C)
0.11		6.8
0.12		7.4
0.13		8.2
0.14		8.8
0.15	0.721	9.3
0.16		9.9
0.17		10.5
0.18		11.1
0.19		11.7
0.20	0.956	12.3
0.21		12.9
0.22		13.5
0.23		14.2
0.24		14.8
0.25		15.4
0.26		16.0
0.27		16.6
0.28		17.3
0.29		17.9
0.30	1.434	18.5
0.31		19.2
0.32		19.9
0.33		20.5
0.34		21.2
0.35		21.9
0.36		22.6
0.37		23.3
0.38		23.9
0.39		24.6
0.40		25.3
0.41		26.0
0.42		26.7
0.43		27.3
0.44		28.0
0.45		28.8
0.46		29.5
0.47		30.1
0.48		30.8
0.49		31.5
0.50	2.490	32.2

TABLE 13-2 (Continued)

OSMOTIC POTENTIALS OF CaCl$_2$ SOLUTIONS*

Molality (wt molar)	Freezing pt (°C)	Osmotic Potential (atm at 20°C)
0.55		35.7
0.60		39.2
0.65		43.2
0.70		47.2
0.75		51.7
0.80		56.2
0.85		60.7
0.90		65.4
0.95		70.1
1.00	5.85	75.0

* Calculated from freezing point depressions (International Critical Tables), using Lewis' formula and by extrapolation between them. The difference between weight molar and volume molar solutions in the biological range is not significant.

In order to cover the complete range of osmotic potentials likely to be found in most plant cells, the following dilutions are made and kept in dropper bottles:

0.01 to 0.30M (successive concentrations differing by 0.01M)
0.30 to 0.50M (successive concentrations differing by 0.02M)
0.50 to 0.70M (successive concentrations differing by 0.05M)
0.80, 0.90, 1.0.

Concentrations above 0.50M are seldom required. The higher the cell sap concentration, the smaller will be the effect of a specific change in concentration of plasmolyte on the degree of plasmolysis. For this reason, the solutions are spaced farther and farther apart at higher and higher concentrations.

It is convenient to make up 100 ml quantities of each dilution and to fill 35-ml screw-cap dropper bottles from these. The solutions last essentially indefinitely, although some fungus growth may eventually arise in the most dilute solutions if they are kept at room temperature.

Preparation of Sap Samples for Measurements and Interpretation of Results

In the case of large cells, such as the coenocytic cells of some algae (e.g., species of *Chara* and *Nitella*), it is possible to insert a micropipette into the vacuole and to extract enough cell sap to determine the osmotic potential by the above methods. Vessel sap can readily be obtained by centrifuging a stem piece in a centrifuge tube built with a shoulder above the bottom of the tube. If a wire screen is placed on the shoulder and the stem pieces placed on the wire screen, the vessel sap will collect in the bottom of the tube. Similarly, in the case of sieve tubes, it is possible to use the proboscis of aphids as a microcapillary which is inserted into the sieve tube by the aphid and after excision permits the cell sap to flow out and be collected in sufficient quantity for osmotic potential determinations. Even the exudate from a cut surface is often nearly pure sieve tube sap. In all other cases, the juice must be squeezed out of a whole organ or a piece of tissue; in the process the vacuole sap of living cells mixes with solutions or redissolves solutes from its own protoplasm and cell wall or from other cells, e.g., from the vessel or tracheid sap which usually has a much lower solute concentration than that of the living cells, or from the sieve tube sap which usually has a much higher solute concentration than that of the other living cells. An extreme case, now known to give totally incorrect values, is the genus *Atriplex* (salt bush), in some species of which the leaves excrete salt and accumulate it on their surface. It is obvious that when such leaves have their juice expressed this salt is redissolved and the osmotic values obtained from such samples are far higher than the actual osmotic potentials of the living cells. It is such determinations that have led to osmotic values of as high as 200 atm or higher. Recent investigations have indicated that the true values in the living cells may actually be only 1/5 to 1/10 of these published figures. In order to obtain the complete sap solution, the tissue must first be killed in some way, thus destroying the semipermeability of the cells. The best method is by freezing and thawing. This, of course, may introduce many errors, e.g., dilution by condensation of moisture on the cold tissue, autolysis, etc.

The usefulness of any osmotic pressure measurement will depend not only on the accuracy with which it is determined, but often on what information is available. In the absence of such additional information the measurement may be useless. If the plasmolytic method is used correctly, the measurement obtained may be directly interpreted without further information, since it gives the value at zero cell turgor. If, for instance, differences are found in the same organ and tissue at different times of the day, this must indicate a difference in the quantity of solute per cell. Differences by all methods using extracted sap, in the absence of further information, may, however, be interpreted as due to a difference either in solute content or in water content. If the tissues are turgid at the time of sampling, this information should always be given and it can then be assumed that variations in water content cannot, in most cases, account for more than a difference of about ±5 per cent. For more exact comparisons, or when the tissues are not turgid, control determinations should then be made on tissues that have been allowed to regain full turgor. Any such method, however, runs the risk of inducing a change in the solute content as well as in the water content. Perhaps the ideal method would be to measure the tissue turgor directly [24] before determining the osmotic potential, if methods other than the plasmolytic one are used. Unfortunately, however, this would greatly multiply the technical difficulties and the time needed and it cannot be done with all tissues.

It should be emphasized, in conclusion, that it is always advisable to check one method against another basically different one, at least as a preliminary test of the method to be used. When this is done correctly, the results should agree within the relatively broad biological limits of the methods used. Many investigators have used the methods correctly and obtained such agreement; others have failed to obtain agreement, usually because of incorrect use of the methods.

Table 13-1 compares the different methods described above. With regard to sensitivity and variability, Walter [2] has pointed out that the variability of biological material is so great that differences of 0.1 atm are already within the limits of error. Any greater sensitivity than this is therefore wasted.

References

1. A. Ursprung, *Handb. Biol. Arb.-Meth.*, 11, Teil 4, Heft 2, 1109 (1939).
2. H. Walter, *Handb. Biol. Arb.-Meth.*, 11, 353 (1939).
3. A. S. Crafts, H. B. Currier, and C. R. Stocking, *Water in the Physiology of Plants*, Cronica Botanica, Waltham (1949).
4. H. N. Morse, *Carnegie Inst. Wash. Publ.*, 198, 1 (1914).
5. Earl of Berkeley and E. G. J. Hartley, *Proc. Roy. Soc. (London)*, A92, 477 (1916).
6. W. S. Rehm, *Science*, 100, 346 (1944).
7. J. A. Harris and R. A. Gortner, *Am. J. Botan.*, 1, 75 (1914).
8. H. B. Currier, *Plant Physiol.*, 19, 544 (1944).
9. A. G. Marr and Y. Vaadia, *Plant Physiol.*, 36, 677 (1961).
10. A. C. Halket, *New Phytologist*, 12, 164 (1913).
11. E. J. Baldes and A. F. Johnson, *Biodynamica*, 47, 1 (1939).
12. T. H. van den Honert, *7th Ned.-Ind. Natuurw. Congr.*, 482 (1935).
13. O. M. van Andel, *Proc. Acad. Sci. Amsterdam*, 55, 40 (1952).
14. D. C. Spanner, *J. Exptl. Botan.*, 2, 145 (1951).
15. L. A. Richards and G. Ogata, *Science*, 128, 1089 (1958).
16. C. F. Ehlig, *Plant Physiol.*, 37, 288 (1962).
17. P. E. Weatherley, *J. Exptl. Botan.*, 11, 258 (1960).
18. R. A. Gortner, *Outlines of Biochemistry*, John Wiley & Sons, New York (1938).
19. B. Slavik, *Biol. Plant. Acad. Sci. Bohemoslov.*, 1, 48 (1959).
20. L. A. Boiko and L. A. Boiko, *Plant Physiol. (USSR)*, 6, 639 (1960).
21. M. F. Vaughan, *Nature*, 183, 43 (1959).

22. J. A. Lockhart, *Am. J. Botan.*, **46**, 704 (1959).
23. M. Tazawa, *Protoplasma*, **48**, 342 (1957).
24. S. Falk, C. H. Hertz, and H. I. Virgin, *Physiol. Plantarum*, **2**, 802 (1958).
25. W. S. Iljin, *Planta*, **16**, 352 (1932).
26. A. Diskus, *Protoplasma*, **49**, 187 (1958).
27. S. Pernauer, *Protoplasma*, **49**, 262 (1958).

Transducers

Grafton D. Chase and James N. Bierly

IN HIS PURSUIT of knowledge of the universe, it is expedient for the scientist to limit measurements and observations to an isolated and relatively simple *system*. He thereby reduces the number of parameters which must be known in order to understand the mechanism of the system.

Systems have been extensively described by Trimmer [1]. A system may consist of any part of the universe; its mechanism follows a specific law or set of laws. In general, it may be stated that the laws governing a system are determined by measuring the response of the system to a given stimulus — the stimulus being a force or energy of a given type and amplitude.

Each instrument used in the laboratory is itself a system — a system specifically designed to measure a particular phenomenon. Since the system (i.e., the instrument and its design), the laws governing the operation of the system, and the response of the system are known, the nature and intensity of the phenomenon being measured can be determined. Logically, the measuring instrument must be capable of sensing a force or energy related to the phenomenon being measured. The sensing element is called a *transducer*.

A transducer is a device which transforms one type of energy into another. An *input transducer* responds to a particular type of energy by producing a signal, capable of being transmitted or telemetered, and which is a known function of the measured phenomenon. Most of the transducers to be described here convert the energy of the system under investigation into electrical energy. The electrical signal thus produced is often very small and must be amplified. Occasionally it must be modified, as, for example, the conversion of an ac signal into a dc signal. Either before or after modification it may be transmitted, possibly by means of a cable, to another section of the instrument or even to a central control station, where an output transducer converts the electrical impulse into an observable phenomenon (see Chapter 15 for a discussion of output transducers). The output transducer may be a cathode-ray oscilloscope or simply a meter or a recorder.

Many transducers are basically the same in principle with variations on the input depending upon the phenomenon being measured. For example, a transducer designed to measure linear displacement can also be used to measure force if attached to a spring of known spring constant, or to measure temperature if attached to a bimetallic strip thermometer, or to measure stress if attached to a proving ring.

Prior to a description of specific transducers it might be helpful to list some physical effects and principles upon which most transducers are based. Some of these effects are laboratory curiosities at present but may be utilized in the future. Knowledge of these effects is also important because of their possible interference in the measurement of some other variable.

Physical Effects and Principles

EDISON OR RICHARDSON EFFECT

The thermionic emission of electrons from hot bodies at a rate which increases rapidly with temperature.

GALVANOMAGNETIC AND THERMOMAGNETIC EFFECTS

1. Hall effect. The development of a transverse electrical potential gradient in a current-carrying conductor upon the application of a magnetic field.
2. Ettingshausen effect. The development of a transverse temperature gradient in a current carrying conductor upon the application of a magnetic field.
3. Nernst effect. The development of a transverse electrical potential gradient in a heat carrying conductor upon the application of a magnetic field.
4. Righi-Leduc effect. The development of a transverse temperature gradient in a heat carrying conductor upon the application of a magnetic field.

THERMOELECTRIC EFFECTS

1. Seebeck effect. The electromotive force (emf) produced in a circuit containing two contacting conductors of different material having two junctions at different temperatures.
2. Peltier effect. The inverse of the Seebeck effect. When two unlike materials are joined and a current is passed through the circuit, heat is generated at one junction and absorbed at the other junction in addition to the I^2R losses in the circuit.
3. Thompson effect. A potential gradient is developed along a homogeneous conductor in which a thermal gradient exists. The inverse effect, the production of heat by the passage of a current, also exists.

GYROMAGNETIC EFFECTS

Change of magnetization by rotation (Barnet effect) and inversely, change of rotation by magnetization (Einstein-DeHaas effect).

PIEZOELECTRIC EFFECT

The interaction between electrical and mechanical stress-strain variables in certain materials. Thus, the compression of a quartz or Rochelle salt crystal generates an electrostatic voltage across it and, conversely, the application of an electric field may cause the crystal to expand or contract in certain directions. Piezoelectricity is only possible in crystals which do not possess a center of symmetry. Unlike electrostriction, piezoelectric deformations are directly proportional to the electric field and reverse their sign upon reversal of the field.

FERROELECTRIC EFFECT

Insofar as microscopic observations are concerned, a ferroelectric crystal (seignette-electric) may be defined as having a critical temperature (Curie point) on one side of which the dielectric properties exhibit nonlinearity and hysteresis (the ferroelectric region), while on the other side there is no hysteresis and the relation between polarization and field is nearly linear.

ELECTROSTRICTIVE EFFECT

All dielectrics, whether gaseous, liquid, or solid, when placed in an electric field, undergo a deformation which is independent of the direction of the field and proportional to the square of the field strength. Only in fields stronger than 20,000 v/cm is the deformation comparable with the effects of piezoelectricity.

MAGNETOSTRICTIVE EFFECTS

1. Joule effect. The change in length of a ferromagnetic material subjected to an increasing or decreasing longitudinal magnetic field.

2. Villari effect. A change of magnetic induction within a ferromagnetic material under longitudinal stress (inverse Joule effect).

3. Wertheim effect. The development of a transient voltage between the ends of a wire which is twisted in a longitudinal magnetic field.

4. Wiedemann effect. The twisting of a rod carrying an electric current when subjected to a longitudinal magnetic field. The inverse Wiedemann effect is the axial magnetization of a current-carrying wire subjected to twisting.

MAGNETORESISTIVE EFFECT

The change in electrical resistance of a metal or semiconductor by a magnetic field.

THERMORESISTIVE EFFECTS

The change in electrical resistivity of a metal or semiconductor as a function of temperature (in addition to changes in resistivity caused by dimensional changes).

MECHANORESISTIVE EFFECTS

1. The change in electrical resistivity of a semiconductor as a function of applied stress. (The material has a stress, or strain, coefficient of resistivity.)
2. The change in ohmic resistance of an electric element by movement of contacts (changing either effective area or length of resistance element). The movements of contacts can be produced by linear or rotary displacement, applied pressure, etc.
3. Variation of the transconductance or the plate resistance of a vacuum tube by movement of one or more of the elements.

ELECTRORESISTIVE EFFECTS

The change in resistance of a material as a result of a change in applied voltage. The Varistor (essentially silicon carbide with metallic contacts) is an electroresistive material with nonlinear resistance-voltage characteristics.

MECHANOCAPACITIVE EFFECTS

Variation of electrical capacitance of a capacitor by any of the following methods:

1. Change in separation of the plates.
2. Change in the effective area of the plates.
3. Change in the dielectric constant.

In the reverse effect, a change in the charge of a capacitor causes movement or distortion of the plates.

VARIABLE INDUCTANCE PRINCIPLE

The change in inductance of an inductor as a result of relative displacement of its elements (core position, armature position with respect to core, i.e., variable air gap) or the change in effective inductive reactance of a coil as the result of a change in mutual inductance between it and another circuit. The mutual inductance of a pair of coils can be changed by changing the distance between them or their relative orientation, or by altering the length, cross section, or magnetic permeability of an iron coil coupling the coils.

GENERATOR PRINCIPLE (MAGNETOELECTRIC EFFECT)

Development of an emf as the result of relative motion between a conductor and a magnetic field.

PROXIMITY EFFECT

The change in current distribution (with the relative changes in resistance and capacitance) in a conductor due to the field produced by an adjacent conductor.

PYROELECTRIC EFFECTS

1. The separation of electric charge in a crystal by heating.
2. The converse, or electrocaloric effect, is the change in temperature of a pyroelectric crystal caused by a change in the electric field.

TRIBOELECTRIC EFFECT

The separation of electric charges by friction between bodies.

VOLTA OR CONTACT-POTENTIAL EFFECT

The development of opposite electrical charges on two dissimilar uncharged metals when placed in contact.

LUMINESCENT EFFECT (OTHER THAN CAUSED BY HIGH TEMPERATURE)

1. Triboluminescence. Light emission due to rubbing or grinding certain solids.
2. Thermoluminescence. Light emission due to heating certain substances (such as diamond, lithium fluoride) at temperatures below a red heat.
3. Chemiluminescence. Light emission due to chemical action.
4. Cathodluminescence. Light emission due to excitation by fast electrons.
5. Electroluminescence. Light emission due to excitation by strong alternating electric fields.

6. Photoluminescence. Light emission due to excitation of certain crystals by optical radiation (UV, X-rays). If the time between the introduction of excitation energy and the emission of light is very short, e.g., 10^{-8} seconds, the phenomenon is usually called fluorescence; if the time is longer it is called phosphorescence.

PHOTOCONDUCTIVE EFFECT

The change in conductivity under the action of radiation.

PHOTOELECTRIC EFFECT

The liberation of electrons from a surface when radiation falls upon it.

PHOTOVOLTAIC EFFECT

The production of an electromotive force by incidence of radiant energy upon the junction of two dissimilar materials, such as a p-n junction.

ELECTRO-OPTIC EFFECT

The alteration of the refractive properties of an optical medium by the application of a strong electric field. In a liquid medium, the effect is designated as the Kerr effect and in a piezoelectric crystalline medium it is known as the Pockels effect.

FARADAY EFFECT

The rotation of the plane of polarization produced when plane polarized light or microwave energy is passed through a substance in a magnetic field (with the radiation traveling parallel to the field).

PHOTOELASTIC EFFECT

The change in the optical properties of isotropic, transparent dielectrics when subjected to stress.

PHOTOELECTROMAGNETIC (PHOTOMAGNETOELECTRIC) EFFECT

When a slab of a semiconductor, placed in a magnetic field, is illuminated in a direction at right angles to the field, a voltage is developed in a mutually perpendicular direction.

PHOTOTHERMOELECTRIC (THERMAL-PHOTOELECTRIC) EFFECT

The development of an electromotive force in a semiconductor carrying a thermal current when exposed to light.

ELECTROKINETIC EFFECTS

There are four phenomena involving electrical forces set up by the relative motion of solids and liquids and, conversely, such relative motions set up by electromotive forces.

1. Electroosmosis. An applied emf causes a liquid to move along the stationary walls of a tube.
2. Electrophoresis. An applied emf causes solid particles to move through stationary liquids.
3. Stream or flow potentials. The production of an emf by the motion of a liquid through stationary tubes.
4. Dorn effect. The production of an emf by the motion of solid particles through liquids.

GALVANIC (ELECTROCHEMICAL) EFFECTS

The production of electrical energy by chemical action (including changes in ion concentration at electrodes, i.e., changes in current flow as a function of concentration polarization) and conversely, the production of chemical change through electrolysis, i.e., the conversion of electrical energy into chemical energy by transfer of electrons and ions and recombinations of electrical charge.

PHOTOCHEMICAL EFFECT

The initiation of chemical changes by the absorption of light.

ADDITIONAL THERMAL EFFECTS

All materials and devices are affected by temperature in one way or another. In most measurements temperature must be controlled, compensated, or otherwise taken into consideration to minimize errors in measurement of the primary physical quantity. A number of effects which serve as bases for temperature measurement have been listed above. Additional effects which may be utilized for temperature measurements are given below:

1. The change in spectral radiation from a body as a function of temperature.

2. The displacements or change in size of a body as a function of temperature.

3. The change in pressure of a confined gas or vapor as a function of temperature (gas laws).

4. The melting, softening (e.g., pyrometric cones), or vaporizing of materials at fixed temperatures.

5. The relation between the amount of ionization in gases and temperature (above 4000°C).

6. The change in magnetic susceptibility of certain paramagnetic materials with temperature. This method can be used below 4°K.

7. The change in color of temperature-sensitive paints.

EFFECTS INVOLVING RADIATION FROM RADIOACTIVE SOURCES

MECHANICAL DISPLACEMENT AND STRAIN EFFECTS

In this category are included all displacements and dimensional changes of bodies (or devices) that occur in response to various mechanical quantities, e.g., pressure, torque, acceleration, velocity, momentum, or kinetic energy. The more important principles governing the operation of mechanical transducers are the following:

1. Newton's laws of motion and gravitational attraction.
2. The law of conservation of energy.
3. The law of conservation of linear and angular momentum. The operation of a gyroscope as an instrument for measuring and controlling displacement, velocity, direction, etc., is primarily based on the law of conservation of angular momentum.
4. Hooke's law (in an elastic medium, strain is proportional to stress).
5. The lever principle.
6. Static equilibrium principles.
7. Bernoulli's theorem.
8. Archimedes' principle.
9. Pascal's law.

Mechanical Transducers

POSITION AND DISPLACEMENT TRANSDUCERS

The measurements of position and displacement are two of the most common parameters of interest. For their measurement a variety of transducers is applicable. The choice of the instrument to be used is dependent upon a number of variables, such as the magnitude of the displacement, the accuracy desirable, and the electrical, magnetic, thermal, or atmospheric environment in which the transducer must operate. Certain transducers may have a maximum operating range of 0.1 inch, while others can operate over a distance of 10 ft. Some are extremely sensitive to vibration which could defeat their purpose, whereas others are insensitive to vibration. The final choice as to which transducer to use must be made with an understanding of all the possible interfering factors.

Displacement transducers are generally based on either resistance variation, capacitance variation, or inductance variation. By the use of suitable geometry, either linear or angular position or displacement can be measured. Possibly the simplest transducer for position is the microswitch to provide an on-off electrical signal at one or more positions. A variation of the microswitch is a series of fixed multiple contacts in a liquid level transducer as shown in Fig. 14-1 A. Such a system could be used to measure liquid level or pressure in a manometer. The disadvantage of these systems is that the measurement is not continuous but in steps.

RESISTIVE-DISPLACEMENT TRANSDUCERS. For the continuous measurement of position or displacement one of the simplest systems is a slide wire transducer shown schematically in Fig. 14-1 B. If R is a slide wire of uniform resistivity per unit length, then the resistance between terminals 1 and 2 should be proportional to the displacement. The accuracy of the measurement will depend upon the linearity of the wire and the length of wire. By utilizing circular potentiometers, angular displacements can also be measured. By using 10-turn potentiometers, one is not limited to only 360° of rotation. The multiturn potentiometers can also be utilized for linear measurements; they provide a more compact unit than a straight length of wire.

The main advantages of the potentiometer type of transducer are simplicity and accuracy, since for the basic circuit only a voltage source and a meter are needed for a readout. Their most useful application is for measuring relatively large displacements. One objection is the fairly large forces necessary to actuate them. This objection has been overcome for some applications by using a liquid column as the resistive element for small displacements (for details of such a transducer see reference [3]).

In general, the resistance changes produced by deformation of wires are too small to be useful for measuring displacement, although this effect is used to measure strain. Recently, semiconducting materials have been used as resistive elements. Lexington Instruments has produced a resistance-type transducer with great sensitivity, which results from the use of a filament of suitably oriented silicon as the strain sensitive element. Resistance changes are nominally 0.066 per cent/microinch with a full-scale deflection of 0.0003 inches.

CAPACITIVE-DISPLACEMENT TRANSDUCERS.   The capacitance of a parallel plate capacitor is given by the equation:

$$C = \frac{k}{4\pi\epsilon_0} \cdot \frac{A}{L} \tag{1}$$

where C is in farads, A is the area in meters squared, L is the plate
separation in meters, k is the dielectric constant and ϵ_0 is a constant.
In more useful units of centimeters

$$C\mu\mu f = 0.0885k\frac{A}{L} \tag{2}$$

From the equation it can be seen that the capacitance can be varied
in three ways to make three types of transducers:

1. Varying the plate separation.
2. Varying the effective area.
3. Varying the dielectric constant or the position of the dielectric.

Schematically these three methods are shown in Fig. 14-1 C.

VARIABLE SEPARATION CAPACITANCE TRANSDUCER.
The system utilizing the change in plate separation is the one most
frequently used. The sensitivity, defined as

$$S = \frac{\Delta C}{\Delta d} \tag{3}$$

is hyperbolic and therefore linear only over a small range. By decreasing the plate separation, the sensitivity can be increased but reaches
a limit dependent upon the dielectric breakdown (30 kv/cm in air).
The capacitive displacement transducer is extremely useful in situations where only small forces are available or where it is desirable to
isolate physically the quantity being measured. The force between the
parallel plates results in a change in energy density with separation
and can be expressed as

$$F = 4.4 \times 10^{-12} \frac{E^2 A}{d^2} \tag{4}$$

where E is the potential difference across the plates. With plates
2 cm² in area, separated by 1 mm and an applied voltage of 100 volts,
the force is about 1 dyne. The small force requirements, the extreme
sensitivity for small displacements (10^{-9} cm), and the good dynamic
response of the displacement transducer make it most useful for

measuring very small displacements [25]. Some disadvantages are the high output impedance and sensitivity to moisture and stray capacitance in the connecting cables.

VARIABLE AREA CAPACITANCE TRANSDUCERS. The change of area system is used to measure rotary motion. For the translation system, illustrated in Fig. 13-1 *C*, the sensitivity can be expressed by:

$$S = \frac{\Delta c}{\Delta x} \tag{5}$$

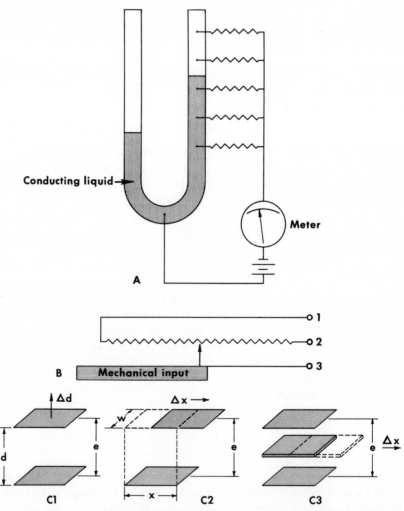

Fig. 14-1. *(A)* Liquid level transducer with multiple contacts. *(B)* Slide-wire transducer. *(C)* Variable capacitance transducers: C1–Variable plate separation, C2–Variable effective plate area, C3–Variable dielectric.

where x is the length of the overlapping area. In both cases, translation and rotation, the sensitivity can be increased by multiple parallel plates. Construction details for capacitative transducers are described in *Components Handbook* [4]. For other applications see references [5-7].

INDUCTIVE DISPLACEMENT TRANSDUCERS. Inductive transducers include inductance- and reluctance-variation transducers, variable differential transformers, eddy current displacement transformers, magnetoelastic and magnetoresistive transformers, and syncros. Of these the linear variable differential transformer is one of the most versatile and useful.

LINEAR VARIABLE DIFFERENTIAL TRANSFORMER (LVDT). The LVDT is an electromechanical transducer which produces an electrical output proportional to the displacement of a separate movable coil. As shown in Fig. 14-2 A, three coils are equally spaced on a cylindrical coil form. A rod-shaped magnetic core, positioned axially inside this coil assembly, provides a path for magnetic flux linking the coils.

When the primary or center coil is energized with alternating current, voltages are induced in the two outer coils. In the transformer installation the outer or secondary coils are connected in series opposition so that the two voltages are opposite in phase, the net output of the transformer being the difference of these voltages. For one central position of the core this output voltage will be zero. This is called the balance or null point. When the core is moved from this balance point, the voltage induced in the coil, toward which the core is moved, increases, while the voltage induced in the opposite coil decreases. This produces a differential voltage output from the transformer which, with proper design, varies linearly with changes in core position. If phase is always the same, the output appears as shown in Fig. 14-2 B.

Commercial models of LVDT have ranges of displacement from 0.0001 in. to several inches and can be used to measure displacements as small as 10^{-6} in. The transducer is extremely simple and rugged with a fairly simple control and read-out system. Such models are moderately insensitive to temperature but may be affected by a nearby magnetic field [8].

ELECTRONIC DISPLACEMENT TRANSDUCERS.

Moving Anode Transducers. The plate current in a space-charge-limited vacuum tube is a function of the electrode geometry. Small displacements can be measured with a triode system, illustrated in Fig. 14-3. A device of this type is the Mechano-Electronic Transducer, RCA Tube 5734. The cathode and grid assembly are held in a fixed position within a vacuum-tight envelope. The anode is supported by a rod which extends through the center of a thin metal diaphragm sealed to the tube envelope. Angular displacement of this rod leads to a variation of the plate current. The transfer characteristic is linear within about 2 per cent. The maximum permissible displacement of the rod is 0.5° about the zero position. For this displacement a torque of 13.3 g-cm is required. The frequency response is limited by the mechanical resonance of the plate shaft within the tube (about 12,000 cycles per second [cps]). The tube is generally operated in a bridge circuit. The maximum displacement of the anode rod by 0.5°

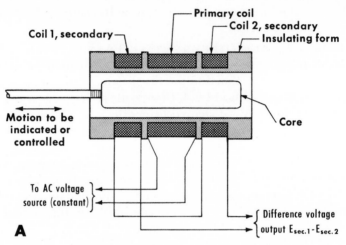

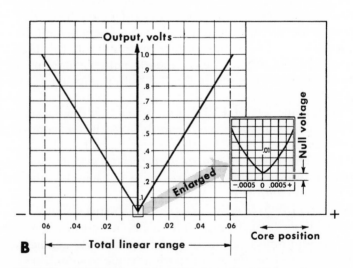

Fig. 14-2. *(A)* Operation of the Linear Variable Differential Transformer (LVDT). *(B)* "V" graph, absolute magnitude of LVDT output voltage as a function of core position; insert shows magnified view of null region (Courtesy, The Schaevitz Engineering Co.).

results in a variation of the output by 20 v. Mechanoelectronic transducers are extremely delicate both mechanically and electrically.

Ionization Transducers. A dc voltage of considerable magnitude arises between two electrodes in contact with a gas discharge caused by a radio-frequency (rf) field. This principle gives rise to a transducer system which permits conversion of mechanical displacements and capacitance changes into electrical signals.

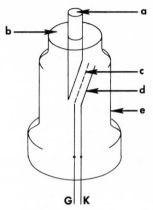

Fig. 14-3. Moving anode transducer, RCA Type 5734. *(a)* Operating shaft; *(b)* flexible metal diaphragm; *(c)* grid; *(d)* cathode; *(e)* metal shell.

A glass tube filled with gas at a pressure of about 10 mm Hg and containing two electrodes is brought into an electrical high-frequency field between the plates P_1 and P_2 of a capacitor, as shown in Fig. 14-4 A. If the field is sufficiently high, a glow discharge will arise in the tube. The two electrodes A and B act as probes in the discharge; their potential is determined by the space potential of the plasma surrounding each electrode and by the rf potential induced by their capacitive coupling to the plates P_1 and P_2. In the symmetry position the net charges of both electrodes are equal, so that their potential difference is zero. Outside of the symmetry position the charges are different for each electrode and give rise to a dc potential difference. The transfer characteristic, i.e., the output voltage E versus the displacement is shown in Fig. 14-4 B. Potential difference can reach values of more than 100 v and $\Delta E/\Delta X$ can reach values up to several volts per micron displacement. For technical reasons operation between 0.1 and 10 Mc is recommended.

With the ionization transducer, capacitance changes as low as 10^{-15} farads and displacements of 10^{-6} in. can be measured. Frequency dynamic response from zero to above 10,000 cps is claimed as is a resolution of 1 part in 10,000 with a linearity of 0.1 per cent.

A circuit for measurement of capacitance is shown in Fig. 14-5. The tube used here is somewhat different from that in Fig. 14-4 A. The internal probe electrodes are connected to one of the external electrodes through a differential capacitance. Every variation of this capacitor causes a corresponding change in the output voltage.

By capacitively coupling the appropriate probe to the sensor, configuration-in-question measurements of the following parameters can be made: capacitance, pressure, vibration, proximity, rotation, weight, liquid level, speed, temperature, thickness, strain, force, humidity, and displacement [9, 10].

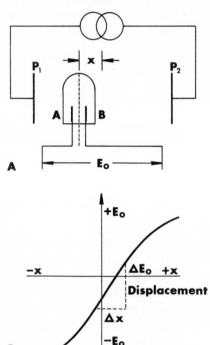

Fig. 14-4. *(A)* Ionization transducer schematic. *(B)* The behavior (Courtesy, The Decker Corporation).

TRANSDUCERS FOR FORCE, STRESS, AND STRAIN

Transducers designed to measure displacement can also be used to measure force, since all of the displacement transducers previously described require some force to actuate them. However, a modification of their input must be made. If the available force is large compared to the force necessary to actuate a transducer, then the transducer is essentially a displacement transducer. If the force required is large, then the deflection will be small and, if the force per unit displacement is known, then the transducer can be used to measure force. Another way of describing this is to say that a force-measuring transducer should have a large input impedance and a displacement transducer should have a low input impedance. Most E-M transducers have a low input impedance, but if connected to a stiff spring the impedance can be increased.

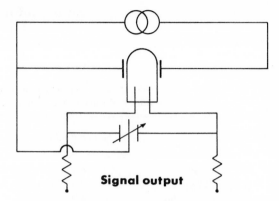

Signal output

Fig. 14-5. Capacitance-measuring circuit (Courtesy, The Decker Corporation).

Stress is defined as force per unit area. Thus, if the area of application is known and the force is measured, the stress can be calculated. For large stresses, such as might be encountered in tensile testing, a spring input would be awkward; consequently, a device known as a proving ring is often used. Proving rings can be constructed to measure stresses from grams up to 10,000 pounds.

STRAIN TRANSDUCERS. Strain is defined as elongation per unit length, so that the measurement of strain is essentially a problem of measuring displacement. A number of transducers designed specifically for the measurement of strain are commercially available. These are of two types—bonded and unbonded.

Bonded Strain Gauges. The bonded strain gauge is named thus because it usually is applied directly to a structure to be tested by means of adhesive. The strain gauge is elongation-sensitive, that is, its electrical properties change proportionately to the elongation of the gauge. The most common type consists of a small diameter wire (0.001 in.) of high electrical resistivity. To keep the gauge short the wire runs the length of the gauge several times. To simplify its mounting and to protect the wire, the wire is cemented between two thin pieces of paper, one of which has an adhesive coating by which to apply it to the object to be tested.

Strain in the test member is defined as

$$S = \Delta L/L \qquad (5)$$

The unit resistance change is $\Delta R/R$. The relation between the unit strain and the unit resistance change is known as the gauge factor, G (Table 14-1).

$$G = \frac{\Delta R/R}{S} = \frac{\Delta R/R}{\Delta L/L} \tag{6}$$

TABLE 14-1

TYPICAL GAUGE-FACTORS AND TEMPERATURE COEFFICIENTS OF
VARIOUS WIRES USED IN STRAIN GAUGES

Material	Gauge Factor	Temp. Coeff. of resistance (deg^{-1})
Advance	2.1	0.0001
Chromel	2.5	–
Constantan	2.0	0.00001
Manganin	0.47	0.00001
Nickel	−12.1	0.006
Platinum	6.0	0.0003

The simplest circuit for measuring strain gauges is a potentiometer arrangement.

There are many disadvantages to this arrangement for precision work, and instead a Wheatstone bridge method is favored. In the bridge, one or all of the arms of the bridge can be measuring elements or some can be dummy elements to provide temperature compensation. A simple example is shown in Fig. 14-6 A.

Unbonded Strain Gauges. A second type of strain gauge is the unbonded type illustrated in Fig. 14-6 B. The gauge is essentially a Wheatstone bridge with four active elements. As torque is applied to the free member, the resistance of two of the wires increases and that of the other two decreases to provide an unbalanced bridge. For gauges requiring a force of several grams, the maximum deflection is about 0.001 in. A wide range of gauges is available to measure forces up to 2,000,000 lb.

Semiconductor Strain Gauges. In place of the wire resistance, semiconducting materials have been used to produce ultrasensitive gauges. One such gauge manufactured by Lexington Instruments uses a filament of suitably oriented silicon as the strain-sensitive element. The transducer designed for biomedical work has a deflection factor of 2.4 microinches per gram and a maximum full-scale force of 125 g. The unit is extremely delicate but should be useful in cases where space is at a premium.

The main advantages of using strain gauges rather than other deflection transducers is their small size, flexibility, and stability. Disadvantages are the relatively high forces needed to actuate them compared to capacitance transducers, and their relatively low electrical output impedance.

TRANSDUCERS FOR VELOCITY AND ACCELERATION

Commercial transducers to measure acceleration, known as accelerometers, usually use a displacement-type transducer to measure the displacement of a known mass attached to a spring whose force-per cent-displacement is known. If a mass is accelerated there will be, according to Newton's third law, an equal and opposite reaction. This reaction will be in the form of the displaced spring. Thus if (m) is known, and the force (F) is measured by the spring displacement, acceleration (a) can be calculated

$$a = F/m \qquad\qquad (7)$$

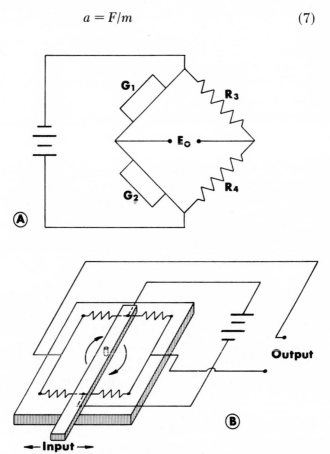

Fig. 14-6. (A) Circuit diagram incorporating a Wheatstone bridge for strain gauges. (B) Diagram of an unbonded strain gauge.

Let the core of a linear variable differential transformer (LVDT) be the known mass attached to a spring whose deflection-per-unit-displacement is known. If the whole unit is accelerated, the core will be displaced a distance x with a resultant electrical output from the transformer. The output can be related to the magnitude of the acceleration. In principle this unit could measure either acceleration or deceleration. However, some type of damping is necessary to prevent oscillations of the spring. This is often done with liquid or air damping.

LINEAR VELOCITY.   There are few physical phenomena, except for the motion of a current carrying conductor in a magnetic field, that are velocity sensitive. For rotary motion a variety of transducers are available utilizing the motor principle (for a description of many of these, see [11]).

For linear velocities, especially in cases where the total displacement is small, an indirect approach is often used, utilizing either differentiating or integrating circuits. Use is made of the relations

$$v = dS/dt \qquad (8)$$

and

$$a = d^2S/dt^2 \qquad (9)$$

for a differentiation and

$$v = \int a\,dt \qquad (10)$$

and

$$S = \int v\,dt \qquad (11)$$

for an integrating system. Schematically these two systems are indicated in Fig. 14-7. An application of this technique for measurements of ocular muscles is given by Lion [12]. He gives a circuit for obtaining velocity- and displacement-proportional signals from acceleration-proportional signals [12]. In general the integrating network is preferred to decrease noise in the electronic circuits.

Pressure Transducers

Pressure transducers can be divided into two categories — those for measuring pressures above atmospheric, and those for measuring pressures below atmospheric. The latter are called vacuum gauges.

HIGH-PRESSURE TRANSDUCERS

Many pressure transducers are indirect in action, using a force-summing system over a known area to measure pressure, and being coupled to a linear displacement transducer.

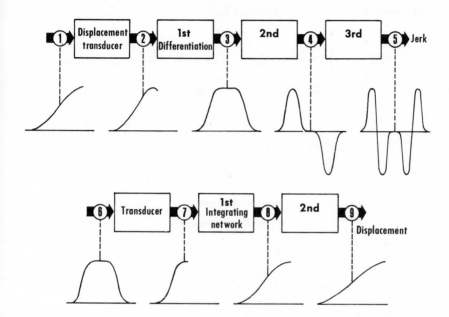

Fig. 14-7. Circuit for obtaining output signals proportional to velocity and acceleration from displacement transducer. *(1)* Mechanical displacement; *(2)* electrical signal proportional to displacement; *(3)* $v = ds/dt$; *(4)* $a = dv/dt = d^2s/dt^2$; *(5)* d^3s/dt^2. *(6)*Force or displacement proportional to acceleration; *(7)* electrical signal proportional to acceleration; *(8)* $v = \int a\,dt$; *(9)* $s = \int v\,dt$. (Adapted from Lions, *Instrumentation in Scientific Research, Electrical Input Transducers*, McGraw-Hill, p. 91 (1957) [25].)

There are four common force-summing devices:

1. Diaphragm
   a. Flat
   b. Corrugated
   c. Capsule
2. Bellows
3. Bourdon tube
   a. Circular
   b. Twisted
4. Straight tube

They are illustrated schematically in Fig. 14-8. An excellent description of these and other pressure devices is in reference [13].

The selection of a particular type of force-summing device depends upon the range of pressures to be measured. A variety of methods to detect the displacement are used, including potentiometric, variable resistance, variable reluctance, and capacitance methods. The variable capacitance method is useful for measuring very small pressures over a wide range of frequencies.

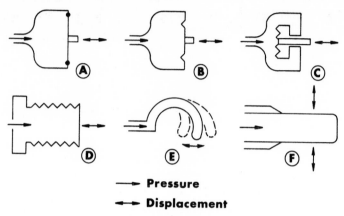

Fig. 14-8. Schematic diagram of force-summing devices (see text).

PIEZOELECTRIC PRESSURE TRANSDUCERS. Certain crystalline materials, when subjected to mechanical stress, develop surface electrical charges. The piezoelectric effect can be utilized as either an input or an output transducer. The materials most commonly utilized for piezoelectric transducers are quartz, Rochelle salt, ammonium dihydrogen phosphate, and barium titinate. The force F is applied to the face upon which a conductive coating is also applied. The two electrodes on opposite sides of the crystal, together with the crystal, form a capacitor with capacitance given by

$$C = Q/V = \frac{bA}{t} \tag{12}$$

When the force is applied, the induced charge on the plates is given by

$$Q = kF \tag{13}$$

where k is a constant of the crystal. Stress and strain are related by Young's modulus so that

$$Y = \frac{F/A}{\Delta t/t} = \frac{Ft}{A\Delta t} \tag{14}$$

so that

$$V = Q/C = \frac{KF}{kA/t} = (K/k)Pt = gPt \qquad (15)$$

g is a constant of the material, P is the pressure, and t the thickness.

The value of g depends upon the material and geometrical factors of how the crystal is cut, either X, Y, or Z. Details of these various orientations and properties are given in references [14-15]. Typical values of g are given in Table 14-2.

TABLE 14-2

VALUES OF g FOR VARIOUS TYPES OF MATERIAL[*]

Material	Cut	Voltage sensitivity g
		$\dfrac{\text{volts per meter}}{\text{Newtons per meter squared}}$
Quartz	X	0.055
	Y	0.108
Rochelle salt	X	0.098
	Y	−0.29
Barium titinate		0.0106

[*] See text for explanation of g.

By the proper choice of the various cuts, one can obtain transducers sensitive to compression, tension, shear, bending, or twisting.

Piezoelectric transducers are most useful for measuring extremely high and rapid pressure changes. Their frequency response is good at high frequencies up to the resonant frequency of the system but falls to zero under static conditions. Certain systems have been devised to measure static pressures utilizing a change in the resonant frequency of the crystal under load [16].

VACUUM TRANSDUCERS

There are three common systems for measuring vacuums. These depend upon either thermal conductivity, ionization, or the range of radioactive particles. These three are generally sufficient to cover the range of vacuum encountered in most laboratories. There are other systems to measure vacuums to 10^{-15} tore; however, the use of these instruments and the production of these vacuums is an art in itself.

Manometers and McLeod-type vacuum gauges are usually not capable of producing an electrical output unless some other system is added to read the level of the mercury. Such a system could be a multiple-contact resistance method described earlier or a liquid level detector. The McLeod gauge must be reset for every reading and is not convenient for continuous readings; however, it is an absolute standard for the calibration of other vacuum gauges. The range of manometers can be extended by the use of liquids lighter than Hg. The vapor pressure of the liquids and the physical size are, however, often a nuisance.

THERMAL GAUGES. Possibly the most common vacuum gauge in use is the thermal-type gauge. There are two common types: the thermocouple gauge and the Pirani gauge.

Thermocouple (TC) Gauge. The gauge consists of a thin wire (0.001 in.) mounted in either a metal or glass envelope which can be attached to the vacuum system of interest. Attached to the wire at its center is a thermocouple. The principle of operation is that the cooling or heat dissipation of the wire as it is heated by a constant current, will be dependent upon the density, pressure, and specific heat of the surrounding gas. In many respects it resembles the hot wire annemometer used to measure flow rates in fluids. Assuming that all variables except the pressure, and thus density, remain constant, the cooling rate due to convection will decrease with decreasing pressure and the temperature of the wire will increase. The rise in temperature will produce an emf in the thermocouple which can be related to the pressure. The instrument must be calibrated for different gases with which it might be used. In Fig. 14-9 *A* the TC gauge is shown.

The TC gauge is most useful in the range of 10 mm to 10^{-3} mm Hg. It is quite rugged and compact and the associated electronic circuit for reading is simple.

Pirani Gauge. The principle of operation of a Pirani gauge is much the same as for the TC gauge except for the method of reading the temperature of the heated wire. In the Pirani gauge the temperature is determined by measuring its resistance, usually in a Wheatstone bridge circuit. The current flowing in the arm serves to heat the wire. The unbalance of the bridge is a measure of the temperature and thus of the pressure.

IONIZATION GAUGES. The ionization gauge is essentially a triod vacuum tube in which the plate current is a function of the pressure within the system. Schematically the tube is illustrated in Fig. 14-9 *B*.

The grid is positive with respect to the plate. As electrons are emitted from the cathode and accelerated toward the grid, by collisions with the gas in the tube they form positive and negative ions. The negative ions are collected by the grid and the positive ions proceed through to the plate with a resultant plate current. The amount of ionization is dependent upon the gas pressure in the tube and thus upon the pressure, and upon the grid voltage which caused the ions. The pressure can then be expressed as some constant, k, times the ratio of the plate and grid currents.

$$P = \frac{kI_p}{I_g} \qquad (16)$$

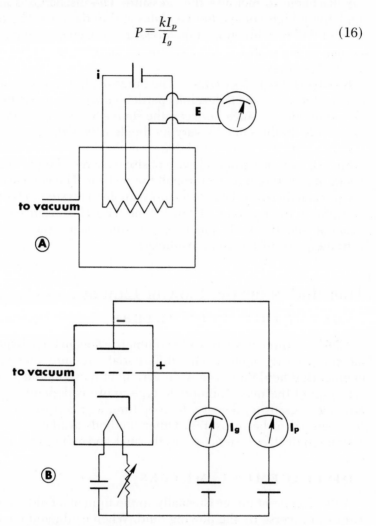

Fig. 14-9. (A) Schematic diagram of a TC gauge. (B) Schematic diagram of a triod vacuum tube used in an ionization gauge.

Similar to the thermal gauges, the ionization gauge must be calibrated against the gases which it will be used to measure.

The ionization gauge is most useful in the range of 10^{-4} to 10^{-8} mm Hg. Below 10^{-4} excessive currents will damage the tube and above 10^{-8} X-rays are generated which adversely affect the readings. By special arrangements of the grids and circuitry, the ionization gauge can be operated to much lower vacuums.

Philips-Pe ning Ionization Gauge. The Philips gauge utilizes a gas discharge to measure the pressure. The discharge is caused by applying a high voltage to two plates and to the grid. The discharge current will be a function of the pressure. A magnetic field is applied normal to the plates to increase the mean free path of the electrons at low pressures.

RADIOACTIVE GAUGES. The range of alpha particles in air has a characteristic shape if the alpha particles are monoenergetic. Instead of varying the distance between the source and the detector, one can effectively do the same by varying the density of the gas with a fixed distance between source and detector.

Since the alpha particles have a positive charge, their collection will result in a current flowing through the resistor. The voltage across the resistor can then be related to the pressure in the system. The alphatron is useful in the range of 10^{-3} to 10^3 mm Hg. The absence of a heated filament and the wide range of pressures make the alphatron an extremely useful vacuum transducer.

Transducers for the Flow of Liquids and Gases

VOLUMETRIC FLOWMETERS

There are three basic types of volumetric flowmeters: displacement meters, velocity meters, and differential pressure meters. In the engineering field there is a wide variety of these meters in use. The selection of the most appropriate type to use is dependent upon the flow rate, viscosity, density, temperature, and corrosive qualities of the material to be measured. Other methods available are resistive systems, inductive systems, sonic, thermal, and radioactive techniques.

DISPLACEMENT METERS

A displacement meter is usually in the form of a fluid pump which is run in reverse by the flowing fluid. When calibrated for a fluid of given density and viscosity, the meter rotation is directly proportional to the fluid flow rate and the sum of the number of revolutions is the total fluid volume.

VELOCITY METERS

Meters of this type obtain a measure of the velocity of flow; the rate of flow is then derived from the velocity and cross-sectional area of the pipe. The moving element is usually a helix, fan, or turbine rotor.

Minimum flow rates which can be measured are generally higher than those of the displacement meter. Lower pressure loss and the ability to handle a variety of corrosive fluids containing suspended matter are some advantages of the velocity meter. The meter must be calibrated for the specific fluids and operating conditions under which it will be used.

DIFFERENTIAL PRESSURE METERS

A third class of meters makes use of Bernoulli's theorem to measure flow rate and requires the measurement of a static and a dynamic pressure. Among these types of instruments are the Pitot tubes, Venturi tube, orifice meter, and Dall tube. More details of all of these methods are given in reference [13].

THERMAL FLOWMETERS

Flow meters have been developed which are based on the thermal properties of the fluid or gas in which the meter is placed. The method essentially involves the measurement of the cooling rate of a heated element due to the moving fluid. It is essential that the thermal conductivity, K, the specific heat, S, and the density, p, remain constant during the measurement. The "hot wire" method is one of the few methods for measuring the velocity of gases in a small volume in which there are large fluctuations in velocity and turbulent flow. The small cross section causes a minimum pertubation in the flow of the gas. Flow rates of fluids from hundreds of gallons per minute down to 10^{-3} cc per hour have been measured by means of thermal transducers. Additional information is available in reference [17].

INDUCTION-TYPE LIQUID FLOWMETERS

The flow of fluids which have a finite electrical conductivity (10^{-5} ohm^{-1} cm^{-1}) can be measured by an inductive system. The method is derived from the development of an emf in a current-carrying conductor moving perpendicular to a magnetic field. Instead of a wire, as one normally expects, the moving fluid is the moving conductor. Schematically this method is shown in Fig. 14-10.

The emf induced in a straight conductor of length l moving with a velocity v in a magnetic field B is given by

$$\vec{E} = \vec{lv} \times \vec{B} = lvB \sin \theta \tag{17}$$

The distance between the probes in the pipe is l. The average velocity of the fluid is related to the flow rate as

$$v = \frac{\text{total flow}}{\text{area}} = F/A \tag{18}$$

so that

$$E = \frac{lF}{\pi l^2/4} B = 4\frac{BF}{\pi l} \tag{19}$$

If l is in cm, B in gauss, F the flow rate in cc/sec

$$V = 4\frac{BF}{\pi l} \times 10^{-8} \text{ volts} \tag{20}$$

The advantages of the inductive flowmeter are the absence of any moving parts and the rugged construction. A disadvantage is the requirement that the liquid be conductive. This might be overcome by spiking the fluid in a method similar to the tracer techniques. References to the inductive method are given in references [2, 25].

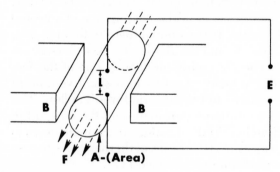

Fig. 14-10. Schematic diagram of an induction-type liquid flowmeter.

TRACER TECHNIQUES

In the tracer technique, material is introduced into the flow of fluid which will change its electrical conductivity or other physical properties in a fashion that can be detected downstream. The time between the detection of a change in the liquid properties between two fixed points enables one to calculate the average velocity of flow. Various materials, such as salt solutions to change the electrical conductivity, or short-lived radioisotopes have been used as the spiking materials. Generally this method is most useful for very large flow rates. The method is discontinuous and not adaptable to continuous measurement.

SONIC METHODS

The sonic method is also a "time-of-flight" method, in which the time for a sound pulse to travel between two piezoelectric sound transducers is measured, both up and downstream. This is illustrated in Fig. 14-11. If V is the velocity of the fluid and v is the velocity of sound in that fluid, the time for the sound pulse to travel a distance d in the direction of the flow is

$$t_1 = \frac{d}{(V-v)} \qquad (21)$$

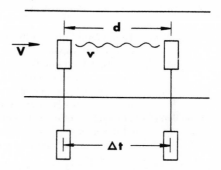

Fig. 14-11. Diagram illustrating the sonic method for measuring flow.

and the time to travel in the opposite direction

$$t_2 = \frac{d}{(V-v)} \qquad (22)$$

From these two values, the velocity can be calculated. The system approaches a continuous measurement, and linear velocities as small as 0.1 cm/second can be determined [25].

Transducers for Thermal Heat

Kinetic heat is attributed to the vibrational motion of molecules. As the temperature is lowered, this motion decreases. At absolute zero the motion of molecules ceases altogether.

Vibrating molecules act as minute radio transmitters since their vibration results in the emission of electromagnetic radiation in the infrared region of the spectrum. This radiated energy is often called radiant heat. Transducers for the detection and measurement of radiant heat are discussed in the section on light and radiant energy.

Recognizing the need for reliable temperature measurements, the International Temperature Scale was adopted in 1927. However, within twenty years of its adoption improvements in the accuracy of temperature measurement made revision of the scale desirable to improve its agreement with the thermodynamic (Kelvin) scale. The adjusted scale is known as the International Temperature Scale of 1948 (Table 14-3).

TABLE 14-3
FIXED POINTS OF THE INTERNATIONAL TEMPERATURE SCALE OF 1948

Fixed Point°	*Temperature,* °C†
Oxygen Point – Temperature of equilibrium between liquid oxygen and its vapor	−182.970
Ice Point – (fundamental fixed point) Temperature of equilibrium between ice and air-saturated water	0
Steam Point – (fundamental fixed point) Temperature of equilibrium between liquid water and its vapor	100
Sulfur Point – Temperature of equilibrium between liquid sulfur and its vapor	444.600
Silver Point – Temperature of equilibrium between solid and liquid silver	960.8
Gold Point – Temperature of equilibrium between solid and liquid gold	1063.0

° Measured at a pressure of 1 standard atmosphere.
† The word Celsius was adopted in 1948 by international agreement and should now be used instead of Centigrade.

EXPANSION THERMOMETERS

At constant pressure, the volume of a gas, liquid, or solid is a function of the temperature, and hence all three states of matter are applicable to the measurement of temperature or for the regulation of temperature as required for the operation of water baths, ovens, and other devices. A bimetallic strip, consisting of two dissimilar metals having different coefficients of expansion, and bonded together to form a single strip, will bend under the influence of a temperature change and this bending strip is useful for temperature control as a make-and-break element.

RESISTANCE THERMOMETERS

Any element designed to offer resistance to the flow of current may, in the general sense, be called a resistor. Although resistors used as components in electronic circuits are designed to minimize temperature-induced resistance changes, a resistance thermometer relies on such changes for its normal function. If a resistive element is to be useful as a temperature-measuring device, the resistance change must be reproducible and it must be substantial.

Over narrow ranges of temperature a linear relationship between resistance and temperature may be assumed and

$$R_2 = R_1[1 + \alpha(t_2-t_1)] = R_1(1+\alpha\Delta t) \qquad (23)$$

where R_1 is the resistance at temperature t_1, R_2 is the resistance at temperature t_2 and α is the temperature coefficient of resistivity. If temperature is to be measured over a wide range, then a more accurate relationship must be used.

$$R_2 = R_1(1+\alpha\Delta t+\beta\Delta t^2) \qquad (24)$$

A few selected values of the temperature coefficient of resistivity are given in Table 14-4.

TABLE 14-4

TEMPERATURE COEFFICIENTS OF RESISTIVITY

Material	$\alpha(deg.^{-1})$	Material	$\alpha(deg.^{-1})$
Aluminum	0.0039	Iron	0.0050
Carbon	−0.0005	Mercury	0.00089
Constantan	0.000008	Platinum	0.003
Copper	0.0039	Silver	0.0038

It will be noted that the values given for the metals are positive; they are said to have a positive temperature coefficient of resistivity. The temperature coefficient of resistivity for carbon, electrolytes, semiconductors, and insulators is negative since the resistance of these materials decreases with an increase in temperature. Resistive transducers may employ metallic wires, tubes of an electrolyte, or a semiconductor material as the resistive element.

METALLIC RESISTIVE TRANSDUCERS. In past years metals have been the most useful materials for resistive transducers because of the high degree of reproducibility possible. These elements take various forms, but in general consist of a fine wire wound into a spiral on an insulting support. The support for the wire should possess as little mass and bulk as possible in order to produce a minimum of disturbance to the system under investigation.

The temperature coefficient of resistivity is influenced by the purity of the wire used in the fabrication of the transducer. Values listed in Table 14-4 should only be considered as nominal. Either calibrated wire should be used or the value of α should be determined by experiment.

The resistance of the temperature-sensitive element is generally measured by means of a bridge circuit. A standard ohmmeter has neither sufficient stability nor sensitivity to be useful for this purpose. But all methods of resistance measurement require the passage of a current through the resistive temperature-sensing element. It is important that this current be kept to a minimum by use of a sensitive null detector to balance the bridge, otherwise the power dissipated in the resistive element will introduce a discrepancy into the measurement. Since power is given by

$$P = I^2/R \tag{25}$$

(assuming that the resistance of the transducer is essentially constant) it is seen that the power dissipated in the sensing element increases with the square of the current passing through it.

The effect of lead resistance must also be considered. Special bridge circuits have been designed to minimize this source of error. For example, the Calender-Griffiths bridge has compensating leads in the opposing arm of the bridge. These leads are made to be identical to the thermometer leads and are run parallel to them through the same sheath.

SEMICONDUCTOR RESISTIVE TRANSDUCERS.   Thermistors are temperature-sensitive semiconductors. They consist primarily of metallic oxides; oxides of nickel, iron, copper, as well as many others, are used. The oxides are mixed in various proportions to provide the desired properties. Binders are added to the mix and the thermistors are then cast in a variety of shapes, such as rods, discs, washers, and beads, prior to being baked. Thermistors are now available commercially in a variety of special forms also including, for example, a small type mounted within a hypodermic needle used for measuring subcutaneous or intramuscular temperature.

A thermistor is basically a resistive element. Its temperature coefficient of resistance is not only negative but its magnitude is of the order of 10 times that of ordinary resistors. It is this property which makes a thermistor so valuable as a temperature-sensing device.

There are three characteristics, or behavior patterns, which lead to all thermistor applications. These are:

1. Thermal characteristics (temperature-resistance behavior).
2. Electrical characteristics (voltage-current behavior).
3. Dynamic characteristics (voltage-time or current-time behavior).

1. Thermal Characteristics—The characteristic change in resistance with temperature variation is basic because the other characteristics derive from it. A typical temperature-resistance curve is shown in Fig. 14-12.

Here the negative-resistance characteristic is illustrated by the decrease in resistance with an increase in temperature. For many thermistors the resistance approximately halves for each 20°C increase in temperature.

One major disadvantage in the use of thermistors is the change of the temperature-resistance curve sometimes observed as the thermistor ages. The prolonged use of thermistors at elevated temperatures has been found to accelerate this aging process. The thermal characteristics of thermistors so treated are then less subject to further change.

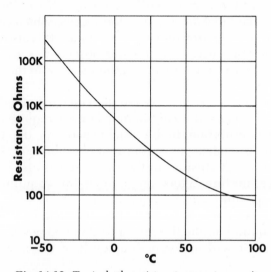

Fig. 14-12. Typical thermister temperature-resistance curve.

2. Electrical Characteristics — To demonstrate the electrical characteristics, a thermistor, T, is connected in series with a standard resistor, R, (Fig. 14-13 A and B) and a variable voltage power supply, E_{bb}. With E_{bb} equal to zero, the current, I, is also zero. Also the power,

$$P = I \, E_T \tag{26}$$

dissipated in the thermistor is zero so the thermistor is at room temperature. At very low values of E_{bb}, E_T is also small. Thus the power dissipated in the transistor is so small that the heat effect is negligible and the voltage-current relationship essentially obeys Ohm's law. As E_{bb} is further increased the power dissipation in the thermistor is not negligible. The increase in temperature causes a significant decrease in the resistance of the thermistor so that the current exceeds that predicted by Ohm's law for a given value of E^T. As E_{bb} is increased still further, a point is reached at which the voltage E_T across the thermistor actually begins to decrease with an increase in I. This is known as the *voltage breakdown point*.

The series resistor R is a current-limiting resistor. If it is omitted from the circuit the thermistor may be damaged. Without R in the circuit,

$$E_{bb} = E_T. \tag{27}$$

Thus when E_{bb} is made to exceed the value of E_T at the voltage-breakdown point the current will "run-away". It can be seen, then, that at the voltage-breakdown point, the voltage which can be developed safely across a thermistor is at a maximum. It is also evident that the nonlinear resistance characteristic observed is caused by the negative-resistance characteristic and the increase in the temperature of the thermistor.

3. Dynamic Characteristics—When the voltage applied to a thermistor is suddenly changed, a certain time lapse is required for temperature-current equilibrium to be established. As the temperature approaches the instantaneous or transient equilibrium value, current, and hence power, dissipation in the thermistor is also undergoing a change which in turn alters the temperature equilibrium point. Finally, a temperature-current equilibrium state is attained.

The dynamic response is indicated by the *time constant*, defined as the time required for the thermistor to attain 63 per cent of the rise in temperature it will undergo as a result of the new current (or voltage).

Resistance Ranges and Ratings.—Resistance values are available from about 500 ohms to 10 megohms, these values of resistance being measured at 25°C. Typical ratings for a thermistor (Type 51R2—Victory Engineering Corporation) are:

R_0 at 25°C	100,000 ohms
Dissipation constant	2.5 mw per °C
Time constant	20 seconds
R_0 at 0°C/R_0 at 50°C	9.1

The *nominal resistance* R_0 is the reference value of resistance measured at room temperature (25°C).

The *dissipation constant* is the power dissipated in the thermistor which will increase its temperature by 1°C in still air. Its ultility is illustrated by the following example: It is desired to use the type 51R2 thermistor to measure temperature with a maximum error of 0.5°C. Thus,

$$2.5 \times 0.5 = 1.25 \text{ mw} \tag{28}$$

Hence, the device used to measure resistance changes must not cause the dissipation of more than 1.25 mw of power in the thermistor.

The *time constant* is the time required for the thermistor to attain 63 per cent of the rise in temperature it will undergo as a result of a new current or voltage.

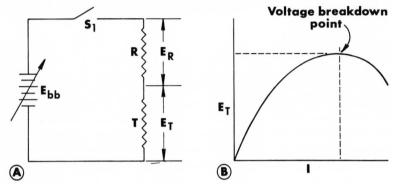

Fig. 14-13. *(A)* Circuit for measuring electrical characteristics. *(B)* A typical voltage-current characteristic curve.

The *temperature-resistance ratio* is an indication of the sensitivity of the thermistor to ambient temperature variations.

Modes of Operation. The usefulness of a thermistor rests with its resistance sensitivity to changes in temperature. Thus its utility is related to the methods by which temperature changes can be produced. On this basis there are three major modes of operation. These are based upon:

1. Ambient temperature changes.
2. Self-heating action.
3. Use with an independent heater.

In the first case, the temperature of the thermistor is assumed to be equal to the ambient temperature. Thus, the temperature of a liquid, for example, in which the thermistor is immersed can be measured, since the resistance of the thermistor will be a function of the temperature of the liquid. When operated in this manner the power dissipated in the thermistor by the resistance measuring device should be minimal.

In the second case, that involving a self-heating action, the thermistor is usually operated beyond the voltage breakdown point. Power dissipated in the thermistor by the current passing through it causes the temperature of the device to increase above that of the surroundings. If a constant current is maintained, the temperature, and hence the resistance, will depend upon the rate of heat loss to the surroundings. For example, if the thermistor is immersed in a liquid the rate of heat loss will increase, its temperature will decrease, and its resistance will increase. Applications involving this mode of action include liquid level control devices and differential thermal diffusion detectors for the analysis of gas mixtures.

The third method uses a separate heating unit. The temperature of the thermistor is thus a function of the heat generated, of the heat transfer to the thermistor, and of the heat lost to the surroundings.

THERMOELECTRIC TRANSDUCERS

If two wires consisting of dissimilar metals A and B are connected as shown in Fig. 14-14 A and B, and if the two junctions where the wires are connected are at different temperatures, a current will flow in the circuit. This effect was reported by T. J. Seebeck in 1823. This phenomenon is known as the Seebeck effect and the emf producing the current flow is called the Seebeck thermal emf.

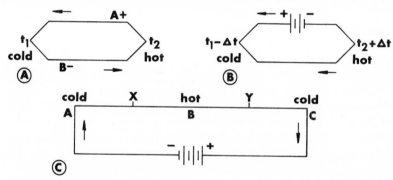

Fig. 14-14. *(A)* Seebeck effect. *(B)* Peltier effect (with battery opposing Seebeck thermal emf. *(C)* Thomson effect.

In 1834 M. Peltier reported that heat is liberated or absorbed when current flows across the junction of dissimilar metals. Heat is absorbed at the hot junction and liberated at the cold junction when current flows in the same direction as that produced by the Seebeck effect. If a battery is inserted into the circuit (see Fig. 14-14 B) so that current is made to flow in a direction opposite to that produced by the Seebeck effect, then heat will be absorbed at the cold junction and liberated at the hot junction. Thermoelectric refrigeration is based upon this effect.

If the only thermal effects prevailing in the thermocouple circuit were the Seebeck and Peltier effects, then the emf developed would be proportional to the temperature difference between the hot and cold junctions and would be independent of the absolute temperatures of the junctions. For example, the emf developed by a thermocouple with the cold junction at 0° and the hot junction at 50°C would be the same as the emf developed with the cold junction at 25°C and the hot junction at 75°C. This is contrary to the observed facts and led to the discovery of a third effect by Sir William Thompson (Lord Kelvin). If a temperature gradient exists along the length of a wire (see Fig. 14-14 C), heat will be absorbed from the surroundings by the wire (e.g., at point X) when the current is flowing in a direction opposite to the flow of heat—that is, from a cold area A to a hotter area B. If the current flows in the same direction as the flow of heat (e.g., from B to C) then heat will be lost from the wire (e.g., at point Y).

If the wire from A to B and from B to C were of the same composition the Thompson effect from A to B would be exactly equal and opposite to that from B to C if A and C are at the same temperature. If, on the other hand, the composition of the wire from A to B differs from that from B to C, the effects will not cancel.

Although the Thompson effect is smaller than the Seebeck and Peltier effects, it accounts for the need of the term in t^2 for the relation between thermoelectric potential and temperature given by Equation (30).

THERMOELECTRIC LAWS.   The intelligent application of thermocouples in practical circuits requires an understanding of certain principles. These can be expressed in the form of three thermoelectric laws:

1. Temperature differences along a homogeneous wire will not produce an emf and hence will not cause a current to flow in the wire. If, in the circuit illustrated in Fig. 14-15 A, a burner is used to heat the

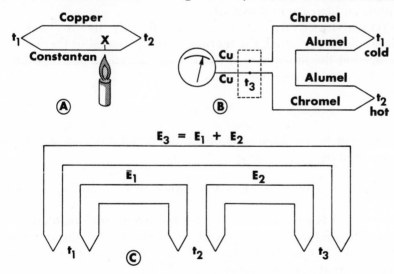

Fig. 14-15. (A) First thermoelectric law. (B) Second law. (C) Third law (see text).

wire at point X, no effect will be observed in the magnitude of the net emf of the system.

2. The emf produced by a thermocouple is unaffected by a third metal if the new junctions are at the same temperature. In Fig. 14-15 B, the chromel leads of the chromel-alumel thermocouple have been extended by means of copper wire. This is done for the sake of economy when the indicating meter is remote. No error is introduced by the copper-chromel junctions if they are maintained at the same temperature. A small, thermally insulated junction box serves to maintain these new junctions at the same temperature.

The sum of the emfs generated by a copper-alumel thermocouple and an iron-copper thermocouple is equal to that generated by an iron-alumel thermocouple. The practical application of this principle is shown by the circuits given in Fig. 14-16. The copper-chromel and copper-alumel junctions at temperature t_3 in Fig. 14-16 C are effectively an alumel-chromel junction at temperature t_3. That is, there is a Ch/Al junction at t_1. Proceeding in the same (clockwise) direction about the circuit, we find an Al/Cu junction at t_3 and a Cu/Ch junction also at t_3 which are equivalent to an Al/Ch junction at t_3.

3. If a thermocouple with its junctions at temperatures t_1 and t_2 produces an emf E_1 and an emf of E_2 when its junctions are at t_2 and t_3, then the emf produced when the junctions are at t_1 and t_3 will be $E_3 = E_1 + E_2$.

A *thermopile* consists of a number of thermocouples in series. The emf produced will be equal to the sum of the individual emfs. The result is an increase in sensitivity.

THERMOELECTRIC POTENTIAL. If only the Seebeck and Peltier effects prevailed, the thermoelectric potential or thermal emf produced at the junction of dissimilar metals would be proportional to the temperature difference, thus:

$$E = At \tag{29}$$

But because of the Thompson effect, the relation is more accurately represented by

$$E = At + \frac{1}{2}Bt^2 \tag{30}$$

Where A and B are constants, E is the thermoelectric potential, and t is the temperature. The observed potential, E_{obs}, is the difference between the hot junction potential E_2 at temperature t_2 and the cold junction potential E_1 at temperature t_1. Thus

$$E_{obs} = E_2 - E_1 = At_2 + \frac{1}{2}Bt_2^2 - [At_1 + 1/2\ Bt_1^2] \tag{31}$$

Because of the Thomson effect the observed emf depends not only upon the difference between t_2 and t_1 but also upon the exact values of t_2 and t_1.

Equation (30) describes a parobola, the vertex of which is called the *neutral temperature*, t_n. There are two temperatures at which the emf is zero. The higher of these is called the *inversion temperature*, t_i.

Thermoelectric power, Q, is the first derivative of the thermal emf with respect to temperature. Differentiating Equation (30) one obtains:

$$Q = dE/dt = A + Bt \qquad (32)$$

Since the derivative is the slope of the curve, then, at the neutral temperature

$$Q = 0 = A + Bt_n \qquad (33a)$$

$$t_n = -A/B \qquad (34)$$

Also, $E = 0$ at the inversion temperature, t_i, as well as at the reference temperature, t_0, taken as the ice point for convenience. Thus,

$$E = 0 = At + \frac{1}{2}Bt^2 \qquad (35)$$

$$0 = t(A + \frac{1}{2}Bt) \qquad (36)$$

The roots are:

$$t_0 = 0 \text{ (reference temperature)} \qquad (37)$$

$$t_i = -2A/B \text{ (inversion temperature)} \qquad (38)$$

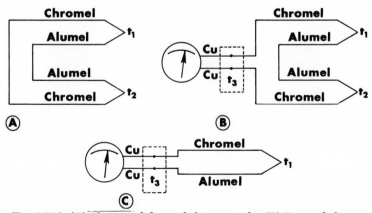

Fig. 14-16. (A) Theoretical form of thermocouple. (B) Practical thermocouple working between t_1 and t_2. (C) Practical thermocouple circuit working between t_1 and t_3.

From Equations (34) and (38) it is seen that

$$t_i = 2 \, t_n \tag{39}$$

Values are found in Table 14-5 for the constants A and B in the equation for thermoelectric power

$$Q = A + Bt \tag{33b}$$

where A is the thermoelectric power at 0°C, B the temperature coefficient, and t the temperature in °C. The values are given with respect to lead except where otherwise indicated. Values are regarded as positive if the current flows from the metal listed to the reference metal at the cold junction.

TABLE 14-5

SEEBECK COEFFICIENTS[*]

Metal	A ($\mu V/°C$)	B $\left(\mu V/°C^2 \times 10^{-2}\right)$
Aluminum, 99% pure	− 0.4717	+ 0.2718
commercial	− 0.38	− 0.01
Bismuth, commercial	− 43.688	−46.47
electrolytic	− 74.42	+ 3.2
Cadmium	+ 3.059	+ 2.856
Cobalt	− 10.7	− 5.70
Constantan, 60 Cu, 40 Ni	− 38.105	− 8.88
Copper, electrolytic	+ 2.705	+ 0.7866
pure, hard-drawn	+ 2.76	+ 1.22
Germanium	+302.5	+72.5
Gold	+ 2.90	+ 0.93
Iron	− 51.34	−20.4
transformer	+ 16.65	− 2.966
Manganin, 84 Cu, 12 Mn, 4 Ni	+ 1.366	+ 0.083
Mercury	− 8.8103	− 3.333
Nichrome, 58.5 Ni, 22.5 Fe, 16 Cr, 3 Mn (against Pt)	+ 25.0	. . .
Nickel	− 19.067	− 3.022
Platinum (Baker's platinum)	− 1.788	− 3.460
Platinum-iridium, 85 Pt, 15 Ir	+ 14.083	+ 1.06
90 Pt, 10 Ir	+ 13.208	+ 0.75
Silver, annealed	+ 2.50	+ 1.15
electrolytic	+ 2.947	+ 0.6782
Steel (piano wire)	+ 10.763	− 1.56
Tungsten	+ 1.594	+ 3.41
Zinc	+ 3.047	− 0.99

[*] Values in this table have been selected from a more complete list found in the *Handbook of Chemistry and Physics* 40th ed., Chemical Rubber Publishing Company, 1959, Cleveland, Ohio.

Use of the Table. If a thermocouple is made using 99 per cent pure aluminum and transformer iron, then

$$A = -0.47 - (+16.65) = -17.12 \ \mu V/°C \qquad (40)$$

and

$$B = +0.00272 - (-0.02966) = 0.03238 \ \mu V/°C^2 \qquad (41)$$

The thermoelectric power is then given by

$$Q = -17.12 + 0.03238 \ t \qquad (42)$$

Values of thermal emf can be calculated by the use of these constants in Equation (31).

Transducers for Radiant Energy (Infrared, Visible, and Ultraviolet)

Photocells can be classified on the basis of their mode of operation. Thus a photocell may be *photovoltaic, photoconductive,* or *photoemissive.*

PHOTOVOLTAIC CELLS

Photovoltaic cells, also called barrier-layer or self-generating cells, develop a potential when exposed to light. It might be said that a photovoltaic cell behaves as a battery, the potential of which is a function of the light intensity impinging upon the sensitive surface. If a microammeter is connected directly to a photovoltaic cell, the meter can be calibrated in terms of light intensity. No auxiliary potential source is required. Cells of this type are commonly used in photographic exposure meters. They are also utilized in various colorimeters (Klett-Summerson Photoelectric Colorimeter, Photovolt Colorimeter, etc.) as well as in some spectrophotometers (Coleman Jr. Spectrophotometer, etc.).

Selenium barrier-layer cells consist of a very thin layer of selenium coated on a supporting iron or aluminum disc. In turn, the selenium is covered with a layer of silver or platinum, sufficiently thin to allow the passage of light. This thin layer of metal acts as a collector of electrons. The construction of these cells is similar to that of the copper-copper oxide type which they have generally replaced, and resembles also the structure of the selenium or copper oxide rectifiers. It is of interest to note, however, that the electron flow when used as a photocell is in the opposite direction to that when used as a rectifier.

Because of the relatively large surfaces of the base plate, *b*, and collector, *c*, separated only by the thickness of the selenium layer, *s*, barrier-layer cells have a large inherent capacitance which limits the frequency response to about 10,000 cycles. The dc output of a barrier-layer cell will vary with constructional differences but may be expected to develop up to 0.1 v across 100 ohms. A typical simple circuit employing a selenium photocell is shown in Fig. 14-17. The advantage of such a circuit is the freedom from the need for batteries or power supplies.

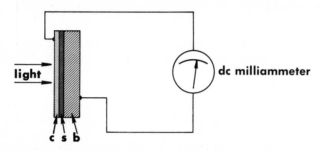

Fig. 14-17. Selenium photocell used as a basic light meter. (*b*) Base plate; (*c*) Collector film; (*s*) Selenium.

Selenium photocells are usually used as photoemissive cells although they also have *photoconductive* properties which may be utilized if a greater dc output is desired. The photocell is reverse-biased, the battery polarity being selected such that the photocell offers its high back resistance. When the cell is exposed to light, the bridge becomes unbalanced. The unbalance potential of the bridge may be as great as one half the battery voltage rather than a fraction of a volt obtained when it is used as a photovoltaic cell.

Silicon photocells are employed in the so-called solar battery. The high efficiency and ruggedness of this type of photovoltaic cell have made them useful as power sources for radio transmission from satellites.

PHOTOCONDUCTIVE CELLS

Photoconductive cells appear as variable resistors in electrical circuits. Among the photocells of this type is the *point-contact germanium photodiode* or *phototransistor*. Again, as with other semiconductors, both photovoltaic and photoconductive properties can be observed. In this case the photovoltaic effect is very small but the photoconductive property may be utilized effectively. Because the internal capacitance of a *point-contact photodiode* is generally less than 1 $\mu\mu$f, the frequency response is very good. Peak response is in the infrared region of the spectrum at about 1 or 2 mμ.

Junction-type photodiodes are also available. The internal capacitance is greater than for the point-contact type but the frequency response is good to about 10 kc. Peak response is again in the infrared region. Junction-type photodiodes also have both photovoltaic and photoconductive properties. The gold-on-germanium junction photocell consists of a thin circular piece of germanium upon which a thin film of gold is evaporated. Thus, a gold-on-germanium photocell requires no bias voltage or power supply for its operation. As a photoconductive element it is reverse-biased with the cathode positive.

Cadmium sulfide photocells are very sensitive. One type (Clairex CL-1) has a dark current as low as 0.05 μa with 100 v applied and a light current as high as 100 μa at the same applied voltage. With high light intensities the current may even be as great as 1 ma. Another type (Standard Piezo Company) is capable of carrying over an ampere.

Lead sulfide photocells consist of a deposit of PbS on glass. Although they respond throughout the visible region, they too have a response peak in the infrared region. This type of photocell is especially sensitive and will easily detect a lighted cigarette at a considerable distance.

PHOTOEMISSIVE TUBES

Photoemissive phototubes [22, 23] consist of two electrodes in an evacuated glass envelope. The cathode is a large curved metallic element, the surface of which is specially coated to increase sensitivity. When this sensitized surface is exposed to light, electrons are emitted and are attracted to the positively charged anode. The anode consists of a wire positioned at the center of curvature of the cathode. The surface area of the anode is minimal so that it will not interfere with the passage of light to the cathode.

Photoemissive tubes require an auxiliary source of potential. When connected in a basic circuit as illustrated in Fig. 14-18 the magnitude of the current flowing will be a function of the light intensity on the photoemissive cathode. Thus the potential developed across the load resistor R_L will likewise be a function of the light intensity.

Sensitivity may be expressed in several ways. The *radiant sensitivity* of a photocell is expressed as the ratio of the current flow through the tube to the light intensity (microamperes per microwatt of radiant flux). The *luminous sensitivity* (in terms of visible radiation only) is expressed as the ratio of the current flow to lumens of light flux (amperes per lumen). The sensitivity of a phototube depends upon the spectral distribution of the light and upon the properties of the sensitive coating on the cathode. The spectral response of photo-tubes is indicated by the so-called S-designations. Characteristics for S-1, S-3, and S-4 types of response are shown in Fig. 14-19. These curves are for equal radiant flux at all wavelengths and give the sensitivity in relative units; the peak is assigned an arbitrary value of 100. The S-3 response most closely approaches that of the human eye, while the S-1 surface has a peak in the red, and the S-4 surface a peak in the blue region of the spectrum.

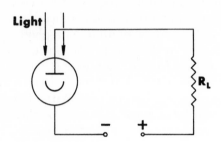

Fig. 14-18. Basic circuit for a photo-emissive phototube.

Phototubes are of two principal types, high-vacuum and gas. The *high-vacuum* type of phototube is especially useful for relay operation and in light-measuring equipment. High-vacuum phototubes have a fast response and are useful at relatively high frequencies. In the *gas type phototube* the presence of a small amount of inert gas increases the sensitivity. That is, the current produced by a given amount of illumination is increased over that obtained with a high-vacuum type phototube under similar conditions. Gas tubes are generally preferred for sound reproduction. They have a lower internal resistance than the corresponding high-vacuum type and are more likely to be damaged by operation at excessive potentials. Gas increases the current flow (*1*) by the formation of ions and (*2*) by increasing the emission of electrons from the cathode (secondary emission) produced as the positively charged ions strike the cathode.

The *static luminous sensitivity* of a phototube is the ratio of the direct anode current to the incident light flux when the tube is operating under a condition of steady illumination. However, when the light intensity fluctuates, as it does when used for sound reproduction, the sensitivity decreases. Thus, the *dynamic luminous sensitivity* is defined as the ratio of the change in anode current to the change in incident light flux. The cause of this decrease in sensitivity in gas-type phototubes is found with the lesser velocity of the gas ions as compared to the much greater velocities of the electrons in the high-vacuum type tubes.

MULTIPLIER PHOTOCELLS

In the case of the high-vacuum phototube previously discussed, photoelectrons emitted from the photosensitive cathode were simply collected by a positively charged anode. The gain of such a tube is in the order of magnitude of unity. In a multiplier photocell, the combined effects of photoelectron emission and secondary electron emission from auxiliary electrodes (dynodes) are utilized to produce a gain of 10^6 or better.

When light strikes the photosensitive cathode, electrons are emitted; the number of electrons emitted is a function of the light intensity. These free photoelectrons are attracted away from the cathode toward an electrode – the first dynode – having a more positive potential. Each electron striking the first dynode frees additional electrons which, in turn, are attracted to the second dynode. This is accomplished by holding the second dynode at a more positive potential than the first. The process of electron multiplication is repeated perhaps ten or more times through the use of additional dynodes, each held at a more positive potential than the previous one. Finally, the electrons emitted from the last dynode are collected at the anode from which the current passes to the associated electronic circuitry (see Fig. 10-10).

Photons impinge on one surface of the cathode and electrons are ejected from the opposite surface. Within the tube itself the dynodes assume various shapes. Several types of dynodes are available. These designs are based upon electron ballistics, electrostatic focusing, and other factors, since it is necessary to control the path of the electrons to assure their striking the next dynode.

Dynodes are coated with various surfaces in order to promote the production of secondary electrons. Silver-magnesium and cesium-antimony coatings have been used for this purpose.

An external voltage-dividing resistor network is normally used to supply the appropriate potentials to the dynodes of the photomultiplier.

Transducers for Nuclear Radiation

The operation of all transducers for the detection of nuclear radiation depends upon the formation of ions, either directly or indirectly, by the incident radiation. In most instances these ions are collected on electrodes by the application of a potential from an external source. Radiation detectors which require the collection of ions include the electrometer type of ionization chamber, proportional counters, Geiger-Müller counters, and solid-state detectors. Scintillation counters and Čerenkov counters, on the other hand, do not require the collection of ions. Electroscopes, photographic emulsions, cloud chambers, and bubble chambers, although useful for the detection of nuclear radiation, do not fall within the strict definition of transducers.

ION PRODUCTION BY RADIATION

The common types of nuclear radiation are alpha, beta, gamma and X-rays, neutrons, and protons. These radiations differ widely in their properties and in their ability to produce ions. When charged particles collide with atoms, these atoms are ionized through the coulombic interactions of the field about the incident alpha particle, beta particle, or proton, and the field about the atomic orbital electron.

Because neutrons have no charge they are incapable of coulombic interactions such as those mentioned above. For a neutron to be detected it is necessary that it participate in a reaction with a nucleus —a reaction capable of producing a charged particle. It will be seen that neutron detectors do indeed depend upon such a reaction and that the particle ultimately detected may be an alpha particle or a proton produced by the neutron.

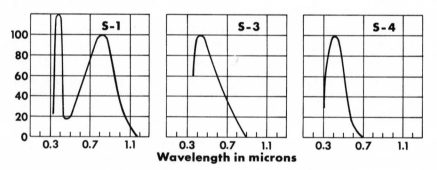

Fig. 14-19. Spectral sensitivity curves.

X-rays and gamma rays are electromagnetic, rather than particulate, radiation. X-rays are generally considered to be of extranuclear origin, while gamma rays are of intranuclear origin. This is the only real difference since they are physically the same. While most but not all X-rays have an energy below 100 kev, most but not all gamma rays have an energy in excess of 100 kev. In general, the probability of interaction of electromagnetic radiation with matter is less than for particulate radiation. Although "soft" X-rays (up to about 10 kev) are readily absorbed by matter, "hard" X-rays (from about 50 to 100 kev) are much more penetrating and a 1 Mev beam of gamma rays requires more than a centimeter thickness of lead to reduce its intensity by one half.

Electromagnetic radiation is discontinuous. The unit of electro-magnetic energy is the photon. Photon energy is given by

$$E = h\nu \tag{43}$$

where ν is the frequency. Since wavelength is related to frequency by

$$\lambda = c/\nu \tag{44}$$

(see Chapter 10), it can be seen that the energy of a photon is inversely proportional to the wavelength of the radiation.

Low energy radiation interacts with matter primarily by the photo-electric effect; gamma rays with an energy of about 500 kev will most probably interact by the Compton effect, and as the gamma energy increases above 1.02 Mev the probability of interaction by pair pro-duction becomes greater. In each of these interactions energy is trans-ferred from the photon to an electron. The resulting high-energy electrons then dissipate their kinetic energy through the formation of ions.

Specific ionization is a measure of the ability of radiation to produce ions. It is defined as the number of ion pairs produced per unit length of path (usually per mm) of the ionizing radiation. Specific ionization is energy dependent as illustrated by the Bragg curve (Fig. 14-20) for

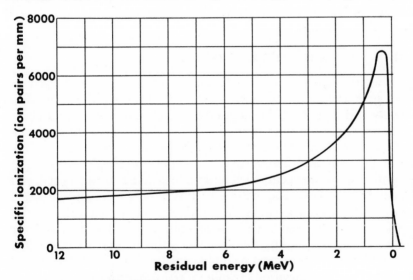

Fig. 14-20. Bragg curve for alpha particles.

the alpha particle. Although specific ionization is energy-dependent, and further depends upon the nature of the absorbing material, an approximation of the ratios of specific ionization for alpha, beta, and gamma radiation might be 2000, 100, and 1, respectively.

THE QUANTITY MEASURED

All radiation is discontinuous. Thus, ion production by radiation is also discontinuous, each particle or photon producing a burst of ions which results in the production of a pulse of current flow. Each pulse may last from less than a microsecond to more than 300 microseconds, depending upon the nature of the transducer.

If the radiation detection device is used with a *differentiating circuit*, the instrument will record individual pulses. The result is a measure of *decay rate*, since the quantity registered is the number of discrete pulses caused by incident particles or photons.

If the radiation detection device is used with an *integrating circuit*, the instrument will record a quantity which is proportional to the average current flow in the transducer. The result is a measure of *exposure rate*, since the average current flow is proportional to the energy dissipated by ionizing radiation in the transducer.

For electromagnetic radiation, the relationship between exposure rate and decay is given by

$$\frac{\Delta X}{\Delta t} = \frac{\Gamma A}{l^2} \tag{45}$$

where $\Delta X/\Delta t$ is the exposure rate in roentgens per hour, A is the activity in curies, l is the distance in meters, and Γ is the specific gamma-ray constant $(R\ m^2\ h^{-1}\ c^{-1})$.

GAS-FILLED DETECTORS

Charged particles and, to a lesser extent, gamma and X-rays, produce ions and electrons as they interact with the gas in a gas-filled chamber. If no potential is applied to the chamber, the ions and electrons recombine to form neutral atoms and no current flows through the chamber. But if a potential is applied across the chamber, some or all of the ions and electrons will migrate to the electrodes before recombination can occur, each ionizing particle causing a small pulse of current to flow. The nature of this process depends upon the applied potential, the shape of the electrodes and chamber, and the composition of the gas within the chamber, as well as the parameters of the electronic circuitry. An important phenomenon is *gas amplification* and it is with respect to this factor that gas-filled detectors are classified as (*a*) ionization chambers, (*b*) proportional counters, and (*c*) Geiger counters. The operating conditions for these detectors are illustrated in Fig. 14-21.

Region of Sample Ionization. If the chamber is filled with air, and if the chamber is subjected to radiation of constant intensity, ions and electrons will be produced within the chamber at a constant rate. Without the application of a potential, the ions and electrons simply recombine, but if a potential of increasing magnitude is applied to the chamber a greater and greater percentage of the ions and electrons will migrate to the electrodes and fewer will recombine. Finally, a potential is reached at which essentially all of the ions and electrons reach the electrodes and none recombines. At this point, further increases in potential result in no increase in current flow; the current is regulated now by the number of ion pairs produced by the incident radiation. This is known as the region of saturation current.

Although rarely used as a pulse counter, i.e., to measure rate of decay, it can be used as such, and the amplitude of the discrete pulse produced by an incident alpha or beta particle is given approximately by

$$dV = dq/C = 1.60 \times 10^{-19} \, n/C \tag{46}$$

where dV is the pulse height, dq the magnitude of the charge migrated to the cathode, and C is the capacitance of the chamber in farads. Since the electronic charge is 1.60×10^{-19} coulombs, the rise in potential can also be given in terms of n, the number of electrons migrating to the center wire. This relationship neglects the effect to the positive charges.

The integrated current flow is expressed by

$$I = Q/t = 1.60 \times 10^{-19} \, n/t \tag{47}$$

and is simply the product of the electronic charge and the number of electrons migrating to the center wire per second. Current amplitude is normally in the range of from 10^{-15} to 10^{-12} amp. Since n is proportional to the energy expended within the chamber by the incident radiation, operation of the instrument in this fashion measures exposure dose.

PROPORTIONAL REGION. If the potential is further increased beyond that characterized by simple ionization, the ions and electrons produced by the incident radiation are accelerated toward the electrodes with sufficient energy to cause the formation of additional ion pairs (secondary ion pairs). This process is called *gas amplification*. If conditions are carefully regulated, the total number of ion pairs produced by an incident alpha or beta particle is proportional to the energy dissipated by the particle within the chamber and the gas amplification A is equal to the total number of ion pairs produced per primary ion pair formed by the incident particle. The pulse height can be estimated by

$$dV = dq/C = 1.60 \times 10^{-19} \, An/C \tag{48}$$

For practical purposes, the upper limit for the value of A is about 10^5.

One of the most important features of the proportional region is the ability to differentiate between alpha and beta particle, since n is larger for alpha particles by a factor of about 20 — the ratio of specific ionization for the alpha particle to specific ionization for the beta particle.

GEIGER REGION.   At still higher potentials, the value of A does not increase proportionately. At potentials in the Geiger region, all initiating events cause a flood of ion pairs to be produced. This avalanche results in the formation of output pulses of essentially equal amplitude regardless of the energy dissipated by the incident particle. Although the advantage of being able to differentiate between alpha and beta particles has been lost, the increase in the output pulse height eliminates the need for electronic preamplification of the pulse at the detector.

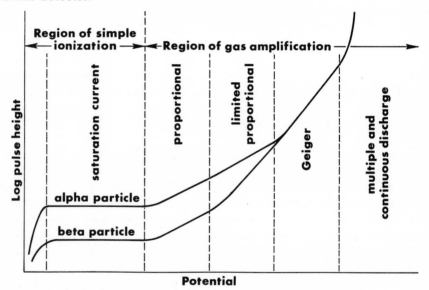

Fig. 14-21. Composite characteristic curve for gas-filled detectors.

IONIZATION CHAMBERS

Ionization chambers, operating in the region of simple ionization, are almost always used to measure exposure rate of X- or gamma radiation or the total energy expended in the sensitive volume of the chamber by alpha or beta radiation. Thus the chamber is used in conjunction with an integrating circuit in which the current flow through the ion chamber is caused either (1) to charge a capacitor or (2) to produce a potential across a resistor (Fig. 14-22). These modifications of the integrating circuit are known as the *rate-of-charge* circuit and the *high-resistance-leak* circuit, respectively. In both instances a sensitive electrometer is used to measure potential, across the capacitor or across the resistor.

Fig. 14-22. Cary-Tolbert ion chamber (Courtesy, Applied Physics Corporation).

RATE-OF-CHARGE CIRCUIT. This circuit, in simplified form, is illustrated in Fig. 14-23 A. When the switch Sw is opened, current flowing from the battery through the ion chamber will charge the capacitor C (Fig. 14-23 A). For reasons previously discussed, the current flow is a function of the radiation intensity passing through the chamber and is independent of the battery voltage, providing that the potential of the chamber is in excess of the minimum required to produce saturation current. The potential E developed across C is given by

$$E = Q/C = 1.60 \times 10^{-19} \, n/C \tag{49}$$

where Q is the charge in coulombs and n is the number of electrons reaching the anode of the ion chamber. The potential E is measured by means of a vacuum-tube electrometer or vibrating-reed electrometer. The *rate* of potential increase (or *rate* of charge of the capacitor) is a measure of the radiation intensity.

HIGH-RESISTANCE-LEAK CIRCUIT. A simplified version of the high-resistance-leak circuit is illustrated in Fig. 14-23 B. The operation of the ion chamber itself is the same as when used with the rate-of-charge circuit, and irradiation of the chamber causes a charge to accumulate on capacitor C. In this case, however, the charge does not build up monotonously but leaks off through resistor R. In a short time an equilibrium is established with the charge leaking off through

R at a rate equal to that at which the capacitor is charged through the ion chamber. Current flow through resistor R is given by

$$I = E/R = 1.60 \times 10^{-19}\, n/t \qquad (50)$$

If the strength of the radioactive source changes, n/t and consequently I and E will change proportionately as a new equilibrium condition is established. Because the high-resistance-leak circuit enables the radiation level to be recorded in time, it is useful for kinetic studies.

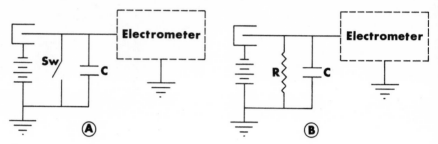

Fig. 14-23. *(A)* Simplified rate-of-charge circuit. *(B)* simplified high-resistance-leak circuit.

PROPORTIONAL COUNTERS

Operating in the proportional region of gas amplification, the proportional counter is especially useful because it can be used to distinguish between alpha and beta radiation while at the same time being insensitive to gamma radiation. Operation in the proportional region is not accomplished simply by increasing the potential on an ionization chamber, but requires the utilization of a specially designed chamber, the use of an extremely fine center wire, and often the use of a special gas mixture.

Proportional counters take a variety of shapes and perform various functions. The sensitive volume may be filled with air, with a simple gas such as methane or with a gas mixture such as P-10, a mixture of 90 per cent argon and 10 per cent methane. The gas may be permanently sealed into the counter, as in the case of the end-window types, or gas from a cylinder may be passed through the detector, a type known as a gas-flow counter which utilizes no window at all or a window so thin that a certain degree of gas leakage occurs. The Bernstein-Ballentine and other internal counters require gaseous samples and special filling with counting gas at each use. Specially designed proportional counters are used for the detection of neutrons.

Successful operation of a proportional counter relies upon controlled gas amplification. That is, the formation of secondary ion pairs must be promoted but must, at the same time, be held in check. One approach to avalanche control is through the use of an extremely fine anode wire to alter the potential gradient. If the electrodes are parallel plates, an essentially uniform field results except at their periphery, but if the anode is a wire mounted concentrically within a cylindrical cathode, a high potential gradient (volts/cm) exists near the anode while a relatively low gradient exists near the cathode. The smaller the wire the greater this effect. Electrons, being attracted to the center wire, do not accumulate sufficient energy to cause an appreciable avalanche until very close to the wire. Because the atoms with which the electron can interact are restricted to the small volume about the wire, they are relatively few in number and the avalanche is thereby controlled. In addition, the composition of the gas is important, since some types of gas molecules tend to quench the gas discharge by absorbing electron energy.

If the potential applied to a proportional counter is incrementally increased, pulses resulting from alpha particles will be detected first. At high potentials, the value of gas amplification A increases and beta pulses will be detected as well. For a mixed alpha-beta source, a characteristic curve similar to that of Fig. 14-24 should be obtained.

A detector for thermal neutrons represents a unique application of a modified proportional counter. Since operation of the counter depends upon the production of ions by the incident radiation, either directly or indirectly, the neutrons must undergo a reaction resulting in a charged particle. This can be accomplished by a reaction with boron-10.

$$_5B^{10} + _0n^1 \rightarrow _3Li^7 + _2He^4$$

Boron-10 is in the filling gas of the tube as BF_3. The alpha particles and recoiling lithium ions produced in the nuclear reaction bring about the ionization necessary for detection. Proportional operation allows detection of the alpha pulses and discrimination against gamma radiation. Since alpha and beta particles from external sources cannot pass through the thick walls of the detector, the result is a high specificity for slow neutrons since little if anything else is detected.

GEIGER COUNTERS

The Geiger counter (or Geiger-Müller counter) is available in many shapes and sizes, the two most common being the end-window and side-window types. Flow counters may also be operated in the Geiger region by use of the appropriate gas composition, (e.g., 99.05 per cent helium and 0.95 per cent isobutane), use of the proper type center wire, and adjustment of the applied potential.

When a Geiger tube detects a particle, the avalanche is not restricted as it is with the proportional counter. Once initiated, the discharge continues unless quenched, either externally by electronic means or internally by polyatomic gas molecules. Most tubes today use a quenching gas. This gas may be organic (isobutane, alcohol, etc.) or the gas may be a halogen. Organic-quenched tubes usually have a life of about 10^8 counts while the life of a halogen-quenched tube is considerably longer.

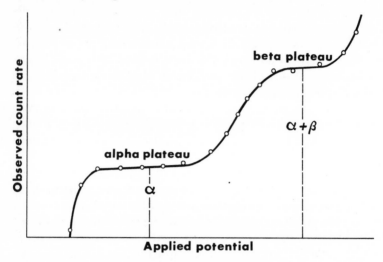

Fig. 14-24. Typical characteristic curve for a proportional counter using a mixed alpha-beta source.

Once ionization is initiated, a Geiger tube becomes insensitive to subsequent incident radiation for a period of from 100 to 400 microseconds. This is known as the resolving time. Because the tube is insensitive for a given fraction of the counting time, the observed activity r will be less than the true activity R. If the resolving time τ is known, the true activity can be calculated.

$$R = \frac{r}{1 - r\tau} \qquad (51)$$

The condition of a Geiger tube can be determined by plotting a characteristic curve. As the tube ages the length of the plateau decreases and the slope increases. The slope is often used as a figure of merit and is usually expressed as the per cent change in count rate per 100 volts increase in the applied voltage.

$$\%/100 \text{ volts} = \frac{100 \ \Delta R/R}{\Delta V} \times 100 \qquad (52)$$

A good tube should have a slope of less than 10 per cent, and usually of as little as 3 per cent. Occasionally a tube with a slope of less than 1 per cent is found.

SOLID-STATE DETECTORS

Most recent of the nuclear radiation detectors to be developed, solid-state detectors, are rapidly replacing ionization chambers, proportional, and Geiger counters because of their higher efficiency and smaller bulk. In mode of operation, solid-state detectors are similar to ionization chambers.

CRYSTAL COUNTERS.   Crystal counters consist of a thin slice of diamond, silver chloride, or other nonconducting crystal, on the faces of which are deposited thin metallic electrodes. In diamond, for example, the crystal lattice of the lattice of the carbon atoms is such that all orbital electrons are bound and therefore unavailable to conduct an electric current. When radiation strikes the crystal, the structure is disrupted as electrons are forcibly dislodged from the lattice. These electrons, and the positive "holes" left behind, are capable of conducting a current. If a potential is applied to the metallic electrodes of the crystal detector, a pulse of current results as the electrons and holes are swept out of the structure.

Crystal detectors suffer from two disadvantages – polarization and dark current. In some crystals the holes are immobile or become immobile, and polarization occurs as the positive holes form a barrier or space charge in the vicinity of the negative electrode. Immobilized electrons can also form a similar space charge in the vicinity of the positive electrode. Reversing the polarity and/or warming can often resensitize a polarized crystal. Dark current refers to the current flowing through a crystal even in the absence of ionizing radiation. Although insignificant in the case of diamond, it can be a serious problem with silicon and germanium since the valence electrons of the latter two elements are less firmly bound than are those of carbon. One way to decrease the dark current is to dope the crystals with carefully controlled amounts of elements of the third or fifth periodic groups, as required, to produce trapping centers which capture mobile electrons. It will be recalled that carbon, silicon, and germanium are members of the fourth periodic group.

SURFACE-JUNCTION DETECTORS.   If a silicon crystal is doped with boron (three valence electrons) the result is a p-type (positive-type) crystal, since each boron atom is capable of trapping an electron which then leaves a positive hole. If one surface of the p-type crystal is now doped with phosphorus (five valence electrons) this region becomes an n-type (negative-type) crystal because of the excess electrons available from each phosphorus atom. Some of these electrons will fill positive acceptor sites and a region called the depletion region is formed between the p-type and n-type regions. Application of an external potential will increase the depth of the depletion region. Passage of ionizing radiation through the depletion region creates mobile electrons and holes which are quickly swept out by the applied potential. The result is an electronic pulse.

SURFACE-BARRIER DETECTORS.   In some respects the operation of the surface-barrier detector is similar to that of the surface-junction detector. Silicon or germanium is doped with phosphorus to produce an n-type crystal. The surplus valence electrons from the phosphorus tend to migrate to the surface of the crystal leaving a depletion region just beneath the surface. If metallic-film electrodes are evaporated onto the faces of the crystal, a potential can be applied to increase the width of the depletion region – the radiation-sensitive volume. The width D of this depletion region is a function of both the applied potential (bias voltage) E and the resistivity ρ of the silicon.

$$D = 0.5\,(\rho E)^{1/2} \tag{53}$$

LITHIUM-ION-DRIFT DETECTORS.   This detector was developed in an effort to increase the width of the depletion layer to enable quantitative energy measurements of high energy particles to be made. It may be considered as a combination of a crystal counter and an n-p junction counter. Lithium is diffused into one face of a boron-doped (p-type) silicon crystal. Lithium acts as an electron donor (n-type) but it is an interstitial impurity rather than a substitutional impurity (e.g., phosphorus). That is, lithium does not become a part of the crystal lattice but, at elevated temperatures, is capable of diffusing through holes and tunnels in the crystal structure. Upon application of a potential, at a temperature of 125° to 150°C, positively-charged lithium ions migrate through the p-type silicon until they encounter negative boron acceptors which they neutralize, thereby producing a layer having the properties of intrinsic silicon of very high resistivity. The resulting detector has three distinct regions: *(1)* a lithium diffused layer, *(2)* a lithium compensated region which is the sensitive volume of the detector, and *(3)* an uncompensated region (Fig. 14-25).

The lithium diffused layer is an n-type region containing an excess of mobile electrons and immobile lithium ions (lithium is immobile at room temperature). The uncompensated region is rich in positive holes. Application of a reverse bias sweeps the depletion layer free of electrons and holes and causes it to be sensitive to ionizing radiation. An incident ionizing particle now passing through the depletion layer produces a plasma of electrons and holes which are swept out of the region by the applied potential – this process producing a pulse with an amplitude proportional to the energy dissipated in the depletion region by the incident particle. Associated with the detector mentioned here in radiation detection instruments are scalers, rate meters, automatic changers, scanners, and/or other electronic devices, most of which have received some mention in other parts of this book. The fundamental aspect of these sometimes expensive and elaborate instruments is the detection system.

Illustration of the uses of radiation detection instrumentation are found in the other chapters.

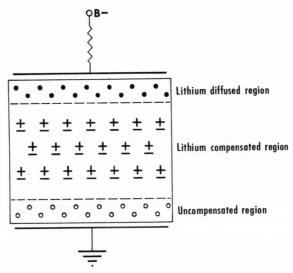

Fig. 14-25. Lithium-ion-drift detector.

● Excess Electrons
± Neutralized Boron Acceptor Sites
○ Positive Holes

Auxiliary Instrumentation for Nuclear Radiation Detection

A variety of complete systems, from input transducer to recorder, are available for the detection and measurement of nuclear radiation. These systems differ principally in the manner in which they modify and utilize the output of the transducer.

Radiation is discontinuous. It follows, therefore, that the current flow produced in a nuclear radiation transducer must be discontinuous also, since the current consists of surges or pulses rather than of a smooth or continuous flow of electrons. These pulses can be modified in one of two ways: (1) They can be smoothed out to produce a dc potential by use of an integrating circuit or, (2) they can be accentuated by use of a differentiating circuit to produce sharper pulses.

An integrating circuit is employed with ion chamber detectors and the resulting dc potential is measured with a sensitive electrometer. The vibrating-reed electrometer is one of the most sensitive and widely used for this purpose. It is simply a very sensitive dc amplifier. It has essentially infinite input impedance and is carefully designed for linearity. The output of the amplifier is displayed by a meter or, if desired, by a recorder. When such a circuit is used, the output potential is a function of the energy dissipated in the sensitive volume of the transducer. That is, the instrument measures *dose rate* and not *radioactivity*.

Not all transducers are useful for the direct measurement of dose rate. Electroscopes and ion chambers operating in the region of simple ionization are useful for this purpose; Geiger counters are not. Radioactivity can be calculated from the gamma dose rate by use of equation (45). In the proportional- and Geiger-counting systems the pulses are differentiated and, except for the gross difference in pulse height obtained between alpha and beta particles in proportional counting, the exact pulse amplitude is not utilized for measurement. Each ionizing event in the detector results in the formation of a discrete pulse. These pulses are first amplified, then passed through a discriminator to sort them from the usually much smaller noise pulses and, finally, each pulse is caused to trigger a scaling circuit which registers and keeps a tally of such events. Alternatively, the pulses can be made to trigger a ratemeter which will indicate the average time-rate of pulse production in the transducer. If a permanent record is desired, the output of a ratemeter can be fed into a chart recorder. Proportional and Geiger systems measure radioactivity. Many commercial radiation-survey meters have a G. M. detector yet indicate radiation dose in mr/hour. This is misleading since such instruments can be accurate only when used to measure radiation from the particular nuclide used for calibration. The meter scale should only indicate counts per minute.

SCALERS

Scalers were named for the scaling circuits which are the principle component. Scaling circuits accumulate and register the number of pulses. Electronically, they are multivibrator or flip-flop circuits connected in series so each will transmit an impulse to the next on every other pulse. In addition to scaling circuits, most commercial scalers also have a differentiating circuit at the input, followed by a stage of amplification, a discriminator, and a high voltage supply for the operation of the detector. The discriminator is usually factory adjusted to reject any pulse of less than 0.25 v amplitude. On many of the newer scalers a front panel control allows the operator to adjust the discriminator at will. This adjustment is sometimes called the *sensitivity control*. Since it is necessary to know the time during which the pulses have been recorded, a timer is often included as a part of the scaler.

Early scalers used the binary system of numbers. From the standpoint of circuit design it was only natural that this be so since a vacuum tube may be in either of two states — conducting or non-conducting. These states correspond to the numbers 0 and 1. At the cost of slightly more complex circuitry, decade type scalers soon became available. Their single advantage over binary scalers is in the ease of read-out for the operator.

RATEMETERS

Ratemeters are similar to scalers in that they have a differentiating circuit at the input, followed by a stage of amplification and discrimination. Many ratemeters also include a high voltage supply for operation of the detector. They differ from scalers in that the scaling circuits are replaced by a pulse shaping circuit and an integrating circuit. Together these two circuits produce a dc potential, the amplitude of which is proportional to the rate at which pulses are received. This dc potential is displayed on a meter mounted on the front panel.

A chart recorder can be connected to most ratemeters by means of a jack or terminals provided for the purpose. If the recorder is potentiometric, its input can be connected in parallel with a resistor of appropriate value in the meter circuit of the ratemeter. Such a recorder can be connected without modification of the ratemeter circuit since it places no additional load on the system.

Another widely used chart recorder has a resistance of 1500 ohms and requires a current of one milliampere for full-scale deflection. In this case the ratemeter must be designed so that attachment of the recorder replaces a 1500 ohm resistor in the circuit. Replacement of the resistor with a recorder of equal resistance causes no functional change in the circuit and no error is introduced by the modification. In all cases where recorders are used, it is important that the recorder input be matched to the ratemeter output.

Acoustic Transducers

Sound is sometimes defined as a phenomenon capable of stimulating the sense of hearing, but, in the broader aspect, sound includes vibrational motion from a few cycles per second to many thousands of cycles per second. If the frequency of sound is greater than that which can be perceived by the ear it is said to be ultrasonic.

While sound transmission through the atmosphere is most frequently experienced, any medium will do; the transmission of an acoustic event can take place through gaseous, liquid, or solid media.

The energy content of ordinary sounds is exceedingly small, normal speech representing considerably less than a milliwatt of energy. Therefore transducers for the detection of acoustic energy must usually be extremely sensitive. Since sound is a form of mechanical energy, it is not surprising that acoustic transducers would bear a resemblance to certain mechanical transducers, being based on the same fundamental principles. But with acoustics we are interested in the measurement of a vibrational or oscillatory displacement rather than a fixed displacement, and constructional details must therefore be modified by reducing inertia, for example, to allow moving members of the transducer to follow the rapid change in motion.

MECHANORESISTIVE TRANSDUCERS

The carbon microphone, the first type of microphone to be used, operates on the mechanoresistive or variable resistance principle. A diaphragm, mechanically coupled to a volume of closely packed carbon granules, compresses the granules in proportion to the sound pressure on the diaphragm. If connected to a battery and transformer as shown in Fig. 14-26 A, resistance changes of the carbon granules result in fluctuation of the current. This signal (the fluctuation) is then coupled to an electronic amplifier through the transformer.

MECHANOCAPACITIVE TRANSDUCERS

The principle of operation involves a change in capacitance brought about by a change in the separation of the plates. In the capacitor microphone, frequently called a condenser microphone, the diaphragm constitutes one plate of a capacitor. When a polarizing potential E of about 100 to 200 v is applied to the microphone (see Fig. 14-26 B), the capacitor (microphone) assumes a charge Q where

$$Q = CE \tag{54}$$

If the diaphragm is displaced, a change $-\Delta C$ causes a corresponding potential change $-\Delta E$. This potential increment causes a current to flow through the primary of the transformer. The changes in current flow, corresponding to changes in acoustic pressure on the diaphragm, are transmitted through the transformer to the amplifier.

A condenser microphone is capable of giving the least distortion of any and has, in addition, the greatest frequency range of any of the available transducers. The principle disadvantage of the variable capacitance transducer is its extremely high impedance. The load into which it works must therefore be of very high impedance, especially for the reproduction of low frequencies.

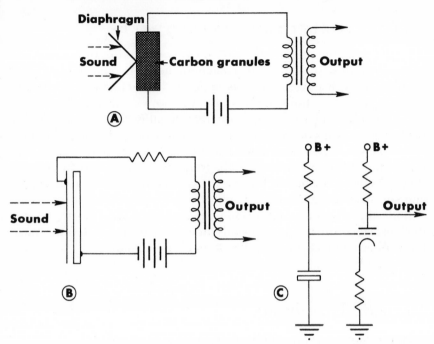

Fig. 14-26. *(A)* Mechano-resistive transducer. *(B)* Mechano-capacitive transducer, transformer coupled. *(C)* Mechano-capacitive transducer, directly coupled.

PIEZOELECTRIC   TRANSDUCERS

Rochelle salt ($NaKC_4H_4O_6{\cdot}4H_2O$), quartz (SiO_2), and other crystals develop an electric potential between their faces when distorted. The potential varies in proportion to the degree of distortion produced by the acoustic energy.

The impedance of piezoelectric transducers, although less than that of mechanocapacitive transducers, is still very high—0.5 to 5 megohms. Consequently, the load resistance must be very high in order to preserve the low-frequency response. At the high end, the frequency response of a piezoelectric transducer drops off at about 7000 to 9000 cycles per second.

Extremes of temperature and humidity may damage the crystal if made of Rochelle salt and other unstable crystals. To meet this problem, ceramic elements possessing piezoelectric properties have been developed. These ceramics are made from such materials as barium titanate ($BaTiO_3$). The individual crystals are originally oriented in a random fashion, but the application of a polarizing potential causes the crystals to become oriented and the ceramic becomes piezoelectric.

MAGNETOELECTRIC TRANSDUCERS

In the dynamic microphone, sound waves striking the diaphragm cause a coil of wire to move in a magnetic field. As the conductors cut through lines of force, an emf is generated. Fluctuations in the emf correspond to variations in the sound pressure on the diaphragm.

In the ribbon microphone, a very thin metallic ribbon is suspended between the poles of a magnet. The principle of operation is the same as for the dynamic microphone except that there is but a single conductor to cut the lines of force. The frequency response is from about 30 to 15,000 cps or better, but the ribbon microphone is rather fragile and sensitive to mechanical shock.

Both the dynamic and ribbon microphones are low-impedance devices. Accordingly, it is usually necessary to use a step-up transformer before electronic amplification of the signal.

Magnetic Transducers

In the laboratory, magnetic fields with a range of from 10^{-6} to 10^6 oersteds may be encountered. For their measurement a wide variety of magnetic transducers is available. Some of these transducers, such as a Hall probe, are fairly simple and compact instruments, while others using nuclear magnetic resonance are extremely complex.

Below are listed some of the techniques and the range of magnetic fields in which the method is most applicable.

Method	Range in gauss
Induction	
A. Dc fields	$10^{-3} - 10^5$
B. Ac fields	$10^{-5} - 10^5$
Moving coils	
A. Translation	$10^{-2} - 10^5$
B. Rotation	$10^{-1} - 10^5$
C. Oscillation	$10 \quad - 10^5$
Induction in moving liquids	$1 \quad - 10^5$
Magnetron tubes	$10 \quad - 10^3$
Electron-beam magnetometer	$10^{-6} - 10^2$
Hall effect	$10^{-1} - 10^3$
Magnetoresistance	$10^2 \quad - 10^5$
Induction variation	$1 \quad - 10^5$

Permeability variation	$10^{-5} - 10$
Even harmonic method	$10^{-5} - 10$
Peaking strips	$10^{-1} - 10^3$
Nuclear resonance	$10^{-1} - 10^5$
Moving coil	$10 \;\; - 10^5$
Wire loop deflection	$10^3 \;\; - 10^5$
Single-wire mechanical deflection	$1 \;\; - 10^3$
Thermal method	$10^{-5} - 10$
Faraday effect	$10^{-5} - \; 1$

An excellent summary of all of these methods is given in Lion's book on *Electrical Input Transducers* [25].

Many of the magnetic transducers are based on a flip or search coil method.

If the magnetic flux-intercepting coil of area A is varied by any of a number of methods, such as rotating the coil, translating, or by varying the magnetic field with the coil stationary, an emf will be induced in the coil. The emf will be proportional to the rate of change of the flux according to the expression:

$$E \approx \frac{\Delta\phi}{\Delta t} \quad \text{or} \quad E = k\frac{d\phi}{dt} \tag{55}$$

For a coil of area A having n turns in a medium of permeability u, the flux normal to the coil is given by:

$$\phi = nAB = nAuH \tag{56}$$

In the electromagnetic system of units, H is measured in oersteds, B, the magnetic field intensity, is measured in gausses. The relationship of B to H is $B = uH$, where u is the magnetic permeability (1 for air). The total magnetic flux ϕ is measured in maxwells. Thus a gauss is one maxwell per square centimeter.

If ϕ is in maxwells and t in seconds, then V is in volts and the constant k has a value of 10^{-8}.

$$E(\text{volts}) = nA \; dB/dt \times 10^{-8} \quad \text{or} \quad B = \frac{k}{nA}\int_{t_0}^{t} E dt \tag{57}$$

With the search or flip coil, either a meter capable of reading instantaneous values of the voltage or an integrating circuit, such as a ballistic galvanometer or fluxmeter, is necessary. Usually the coil is rotated through 180° in a time which is short compared to the period of the galvanometer.

The continuous conversion of magnetic fields into electric signals can be accomplished by driving a coil with a motor and forming, essentially, a motor-generator. Depending upon the take-off, either a dc or an ac signal is produced.

In some circumstances it is desired to measure a magnetic field which may vary considerably over the dimensions of the usual coil size, or where the available gap is too small to introduce a flip coil. In the expression $E = kd\phi/dt$, E can be increased by making dt small rather than $d\phi$ large. Chapin [24] has devised a very interesting magnetic transducer utilizing this fact. A single loop of wire is driven by a piezoelectric bimorphic crystal at 872 cps so that the total motion of the detector is only 0.15 mm, a d it has a sensitivity of 3×10^{-8} volts per gauss.

HALL EFFECT MAGNETIC TRANSDUCERS

Magnetic transducers based on the Hall effect in many instances have advantages over the moving coil type. They are solid-state devices with no moving parts and can be made extremely compact and rugged. With suitable geometry they can be used to measure axial as well as transverse magnetic fields.

Schematically the Hall transducer is illustrated in Fig. 14-27. If

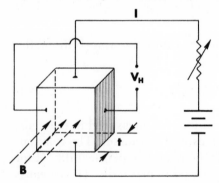

Fig. 14-27. Schematic diagram of a Hall transducer.

I is the control current in amperes, t is the thickness in centimeters, and B is in gauss, the Hall voltage in volts is given by:

$$V_H = \frac{R_H I B}{t} \times 10^{-8} \tag{58}$$

R_H is the Hall constant, usually expressed in cm³/coulomb. For the measurement of the output voltage, a potentiometer can be used.

The Hall effect can also be used in a Wattmeter. The Hall transducer can be employed for steady magnetic fields as well as for rapidly varying fields up to a megacycle. New intermetallic compounds, such as indium antimonide and gallium arsenide, have greatly increased their sensitivity. The temperature dependency of the Hall constant can be compensated for by incorporating a temperature-sensitive resistor in the control current circuit.

In addition to the specific references given in the text of this chapter, other general references include [25-32].

References

1. J. D. Trimmer, *Sci. Monthly*, **69**, 328 (1949).
2. *Telemeter Transducer Handbook*, Vol. 1, WAAD Technical Report, ASTIA, Arlington, Va., (1961).
3. P. E. K. Donaldson, *Electronic Apparatus for Biological Research*, Butterworths, London (1958).
4. *Components Handbook*, M.I.T. Radiation Laboratory Series, McGraw-Hill Book Co., New York (1949).
5. W. Sucksmith, *Phil. Mag.*, **43**, 223 (1922).
6. F. A. Long, *Phil. Mag.*, **43**, 113 (1925).
7. H. Mills, *J. Sci. Instr.*, **25**, 151 (1948).
8. "Bulletin AA-1A," Schaevitz Engineering, Camden, N. J.
9. "Decker Technical Bulletin No. 01," The Decker Corp., Bala-Cynwyd, Pa.
10. K. S. Lion, *Rev. Sci. Instr.*, **27**, 222 (1956).
11. V. Z. Viskanta, *A Study of Rotary Speed Measuring Techniques*, Armour Research Foundation, WAAD TR 60 to 210 (1960).
12. K. S. Lion, *J. Appl. Physiol.*, **4**, 276 (1951).
13. *Pressure Transducing and Instrumentation Handbook*, Vol. 1, Book 1, WAAD Technical Report, 59 to 743.
14. W. G. Cady, *Piezoelectricity*, McGraw-Hill, New York (1946).
15. W. P. Mason, *Piezoelectric Crystals and Their Application to Ultrasonics*, D. Van Nostrand, Princeton, N. J. (1954).
16. T. Perls and C. W. Kissinger, *Nat'l. Bur. Std. (U.S.) Rept.*, **2300-a** (1955).
17. A. Linford, In *The Instrument Manual*, United Trade Press LPD, London, 3rd ed. (1960).
18. C. C. Miesse, "Study of Mass Flowmeters," Armour Research Foundation, Final Report, **ARF D**, 173 (1959).
19. J. M. Prausnitz and R. H. Wilhelm, *Rev. Sci. Instr.*, **27**, 941 (1956).
20. W. G. James, *Rev. Sci. Instr.*, **22**, 989 (1951).
21. H. P. Kalmus, *Natl. Bur. Std. (U.S.) Tech. News Bull.*, **37**, 30 (1953).
22. A. Sommer, *Photoelectric Tubes*, Methuen and Co., London, and John Wiley & Sons, New York (1951).
23. V. K. Zworykin and E. G. Ramberg, *Photoelectricity and Its Applications*, John Wiley & Sons, New York (1949).
24. D. M. Chapin, *Rev. Sci. Instr.*, **20**, 945 (1949).
25. K. S. Lion, *Instrumentation in Scientific Research. Electrical Input Transducers*, McGraw-Hill Book Co., New York (1957).
26. C. F. Hix and R. P. Alley, *Physical Laws and Effects*, John Wiley & Sons, New York (1958).

27. J. Pearlstein, *Searching the Literature for Transducer Information. Part 1. A Guide to the Literature*, Diamond Ordinance Fuse Labs., Washington, D. C.
28. *Notes on LinearVariable Differential Transformers*, Schaevitz Engineering Co., Camden, N. J.
29. W. G. Cady, *Piezoelectricity*, McGraw-Hill, New York (1946).
30. W. P. Mason, *Piezoelectric Crystals and Their Application to Ultrasonics*, D. Van Nostrand, Princeton, N. J. (1956).
31. J. Strong, *Modern Physical Laboratory Practice*, Blackieston, London (1938).
32. E. H. Putley, *The Hall Effect and Related Phenomena*, Butterworths, London (1960).

Read-out Devices

Gabor B. Levy

Scope of the Chapter

In all measuring techniques, the final step is the *read-out*—the visual presentation of the measured quantity. This is not a trivial matter. The accuracy and the precision of the entire measurement can be, and often are, limited by that of the final read-out. This is particularly true when the indicator or recorder is an independent piece of equipment which is attached to the apparatus. It is less true when the read-out is part of a commercial instrument, integrated into the over-all design. In all cases, however, a thorough understanding of the function and the limitations of the read-out is essential to the efficient operation of instruments. This is universally valid. However, the examples that follow are taken mainly from photometry and spectrophotometry. This field offers a great variety and complexity of read-out devices because usually two parameters are recorded (wavelength and absorbance), and the difficulties introduced by unlinearity are often substantial. Occasional references are made to unusual recording requirements in other techniques but, in the main, spectrophotometry will serve to illustrate all the usual methods of data presentation.

There is a curious discrepancy between the great number of read-out devices and the sparsity of comprehensive amount of literature. To illustrate the former fact, a recent survey of recorders [1] lists 155 manufacturers of 253 models. In this brief chapter, minor details cannot be considered, but only the general characteristics of the three main groups—meters, recorders, and digital read-out devices—are given. The interested reader is referred to the few general texts [2], and to the references given below.

The scope of the chapter is limited in that mainly direct current measuring devices are considered. This is justified because the overwhelming majority of laboratory instruments employ dc transducers and signals. Even when the signal is ac (e.g., due to chopping) and ac amplifiers are employed, the electrical output is usually demodulated or rectified so that ultimately dc devices present the data. In other cases the frequency is quite low, and what may be considered typically ac meters are rarely of interest. This is certainly true in electrochemical and photoelectric devices whose indicating methods are considered here.

In all cases the final indication has a rational (as well as physical) connection with the measuring device. As the examples deal mainly with photometry, the general character of these devices is sketched in the following pages. Moreover, recording spectrophotometers contain servo mechanisms which balance or adjust the optical system and record incidentally, as it were. These are discussed in a separate section following that on servo recorders.

Photoelectric Measuring Instruments

Reduced to essentials, a colorimeter or spectrophotometer consists of a light source, a monochromator (or filter), and a photometer. The sample is usually placed between the last two elements, and it attenuates the beam. The read-out device indicates the degree of attenuation, i.e., light absorption. The result then serves for qualitative or quantitative analysis of the sample. Simple commercial colorimeters are, in fact, built essentially along these lines. Usually, a barrier-layer photocell is employed as a photoreceptor (for which no amplifier is needed), and this is connected to a microammeter.

The major consideration in this read-out system is that photocells become increasingly unlinear with load, i.e., they will furnish current proportional to illumination only when almost short-circuited. For linear operation, the meter should have as low an internal resistance as practicable. Double-beam variants of photocell colorimeters offer the advantage of automatically compensating the fluctuations of the light source, since one beam serves as reference and the other has a sample interposed in it. The photocells in the respective beams then work in opposition. In this scheme, the optical or electrical balancing null system is usually employed (as it is also in some single-beam instruments). In these cases, the read-out is actually the position of a manually adjusted slide wire, shutter, etc. The meter merely indicates the restoration of the same electrical current in the photometer circuit after the sample is inserted into the beam. The linearity of the indicating meter is then not at issue, but only its sensitivity and damping characteristics.

When the measurements are extended to the ultraviolet, photocells cannot serve, and phototubes or photomultiplier tubes are employed. The four schemes—single- or double-beam, direct-reading, or null-balancing—are applicable here, too. However, the phototubes will not function if an appreciable current is drawn (in contradistinction to photocells), and for this reason, an amplifier is virtually always part of the phototube circuit. This allows considerable flexibility as far as the read-out meter is concerned. However, the proper matching to the amplifier with respect to sensitivity and damping characteristics is essential.

The simplicity of these instruments is only in the read-out requirements – straightforward dc current indication. The optical and electrical design may be quite elaborate; for instance, the high quality single beam spectrophotometers fall into this group. The Beckman DU is typical of a null-balancing instrument, while the Zeiss PMQ II and the Perkin-Elmer Model 139 are direct indicating, the former employing a galvanometer, and the latter a microammeter (Fig. 15-1). The Rudolph model 200 photoelectric polarimeter is an interesting example of a complex manual null-system (Fig. 15-2 A). In this instrument, an auxiliary polarizer is automatically flipped into two extreme positions at 2.5 cycles per minute (cpm). The analyzer is then rotated manually until the multiplier photometer indicates minimum deflection. This sensitive photometer contains a stabilized power supply and a dc amplifier, which is typical of this type of device. The circuitry is quite complex, but a simple microammeter serves. It is furnished with off-set scales for null-balance indication in this application, and with a linear scale in general photometric use.

In infrared spectrophotometers, the light beam is usually interrupted by a mechanical chopper. In this manner, the infrared receptor responds only to the sample and reference beams, and is made independent of outside infrared stray radiation and the fluctuations of the light source. This scheme also permits the use of ac amplification which makes for long-term stability. The output can conveniently serve to actuate a balancing servo-mechanism of a recorder, as will be discussed below. However, it can also be demodulated and displayed on a meter for direct reading or as an indication of null balance. This approach is not limited to infrared instruments. Fig. 15-2 B shows the scheme of the Turner fluorescence meter in which three beams are chopped – the sample beam, and two reference beams. It is a null instrument containing manually adjusted shutter and a cam. The shutter is used for blank adjustment comparing the two reference beams, and the cam to balance the sample beam. The small meter indicates zero, and the reading is taken off the cam dial.

These schemes, and their combinations, encompass all photometric devices. Details, together with references, were given in preceding chapters. Pertinent here is that phototubes, photocells, etc., have different characteristics, that the dc amplifiers lend themselves to simple meter read-out, and that ac systems are preferred in more complex servo-balancing instruments.

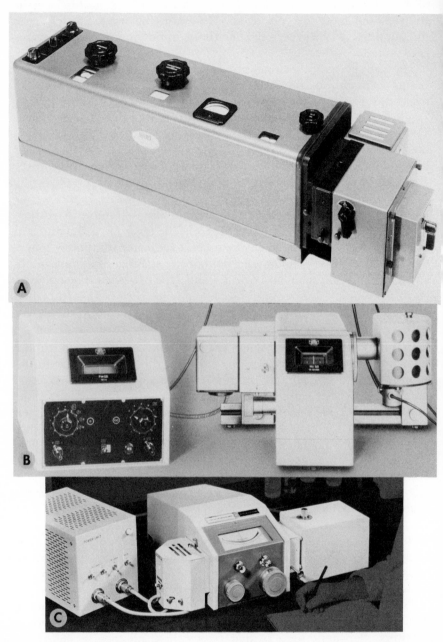

Fig. 15-1. Single beam spectrophotometer. *(A)* With manual null-balancing and meter (Courtesy, Beckman Instruments, Inc.). *(B)* Direct reading with galvanometer (Courtesy, Carl Zeiss, Inc.). *(C)* Direct reading with microammeter (Courtesy, Perkin-Elmer Corporation).

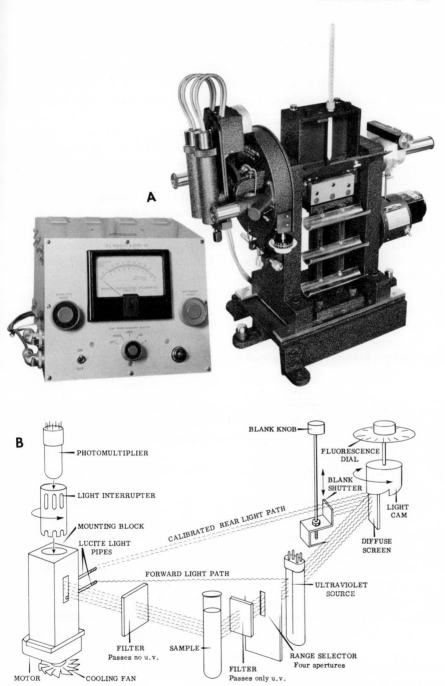

Fig. 15-2. Balancing systems. *(A)* Photometer as null indicator in Rudolph model 200 photoelectric polarimeter attachment (Courtesy, O. C. Rudolph & Sons, Inc). *(B)* Chopped triple-beam system of Turner fluorometer (Courtesy, G. K. Turner Associates).

Direct Reading Meters

GALVANOMETERS

GENERAL PRINCIPLES. The galvanometer is a remarkable instrument on two counts. It had its origin shortly after the discovery of electric currents, and had reached close to theoretical perfection some 50 years ago [3]. Its operating principle is quite straightforward. When current flows through a conductor, it induces a magnetic field at a right angle to the flow. When another, permanent magnetic field is present (and the earth's magnetic field is sufficient), the fields will tend to line up, with a force proportional to the current.

To construct the instrument, it is only necessary to suspend either the magnet or the conductor and restrain it in some manner. The angular rotation will then indicate the magnitude of the current. Moving magnet galvanometers are of historical interest only, as today moving coils are invariably used. A coil, rather than a single conductor loop, is employed because, for a given current, the force is proportional to the number of turns. The suspension of the coil is a wire or ribbon which is twisted as the coil turns in the field of the permanent magnet. It provides the suspension, the restoring torque, and usually serves also as an electrical conductor to the coil.

Thus galvanometers are inherently current-measuring devices. However, they can equally serve to measure small voltages. In either service, they are potentially very sensitive. Inertia is small, as the coils are made very light despite many turns; friction is negligible due to air resistance and the very small molecular friction within the suspension wire. The ultimate limit is the Brownian movement which tends to "wash out" the deflecting force. This limit can be reached with careful construction.

MIRROR GALVANOMETERS. In order to keep the inertial mass of the moving system at a minimum, the indication of the rotation is made by a light beam rather than a pointer. A mirror is attached to the coil suspension to reflect the beam, but its weight can be as small as a milligram. Light from a small bulb is projected onto this mirror which reflects it to a scale. A reticle (a thin wire) in front of the lens results in a hairline image on the scale, and the position of the coil can be read off with ease and precision. Alternatively, the image of an illuminated scale can be reflected by the mirror onto a translucent window.

Obviously, the further the read-out position is from the mirror, the larger the deflection. The simple geometry of a triangle is involved here, since the scale spread increases linearly with distance. This is an "optical lever," but with increasing length the instrument becomes unwieldy. By using several mirrors, the beam can be folded and the over-all dimensions of the galvanometer kept within bounds (Fig. 15-3). Multiple-reflection galvanometers are more precise because, and to the extent, of the optical leverage. Inherently there is no difference between single and multiple-reflection instruments. Commercially, however, there is a division because the added cost of the optical system is only justified when sensitivity is to be pushed to its limits. Consequently, multiple-reflection galvanometers are equipped

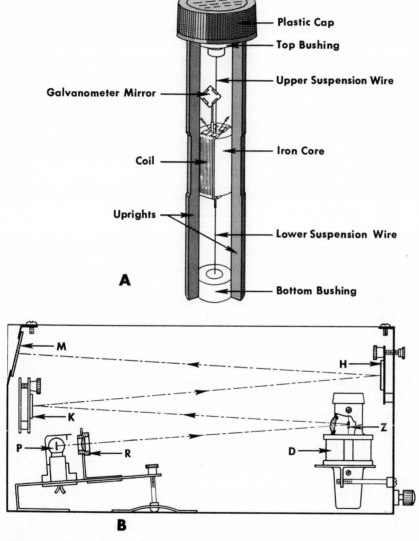

Fig. 15-3. Galvanometer. *(A)* Moving system of a mirror galvanometer. *(B)* Optical arrangement of a multiple-reflection galvanometer (Courtesy, Photovolt Corporation).

with extremely sensitive moving systems, while less sensitive instruments employ the single-reflection design.

POINTER GALVANOMETERS.   When sensitivity and linearity are not at a premium, simple pointer galvanometers can be used. Their design is similar, except that a pointer sweeping a small scale is directly attached to the moving coil. The leverage is small and the angle of rotation necessary for indication relatively large. Moreover, the weight of the moving elements is greater. This makes pointer galvanometers less suitable for direct-reading instruments. They are more sensitive than moving coil microammeters, but the latter are more convenient and rugged. For this reason, pointer galvanometers are not often seen in laboratory equipment except, perhaps, as null devices built into potentiometer bridges and the like.

SENSITIVITY.   Whether used as null current indicators or as microampere- or microvolt-measuring instruments, the sensitivity of the galvanometers is of prime concern. The sensitivity depends on the following factors: strength of the permanent magnetic field, the length of the beam, the number of turns in the coil, and the stiffness of the suspension.

The strength of the field is rather circumscribed by the nature of magnet materials, and is fixed within a design. Similarly, the optical system is fixed in a given model. The coil design is flexible within limits, and exchangeable moving systems are often available for a galvanometer. However, there are conflicting factors which result in limiting conditions. As the number of turns increases, the length of the wire in the coil increases, too. If the same gauge wire is used, the resistance of the coil increases in the same proportion, so that at fixed voltage input there is no net gain. If the signal comes from a constant current source, there is a real gain, of course. In actual practice, at the low power levels usual in measurements requiring a galvanometer, this is not the case. Rather, there is an in-between situation which requires quantitative evaluation (page 501 and Fig. 15-4).

The stiffness of the suspension can be varied, too, but this also results in conflicting conditions. The weaker the restoring force, the larger the deflection, i.e., sensitivity. However, the response time increases quite rapidly. The sensitivity varies approximately as the inverse square of the natural frequency of a galvanometer, and it, in turn, is determined by the stiffness of the suspension and the inertia of the rotating parts.

These conflicting and incompatible requirements tax the ingenuity of the designer. The number of turns that can be squeezed into a coil, the smallness of the gauge to reduce size and mass, and yet not to increase electrical resistance, the stiffness of the suspension, the time constant, and the damping characteristics – all these are interrelated. For each application the factors are optimized, and the choice of galvanometer and moving system is made according to intended use. It is noted that not only do the sensitivity and the cost of the instrument run parallel (which is quite usual in instruments) but so also do the sensitivity and slower response and the difficulties in proper damping.

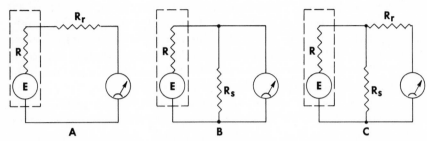

Fig. 15-4. Galvanometer connection. *(E)* external circuit voltage; *(R)* external circuit resistance; *(R_r)* series resistance; *(R_s)* shunt resistance.

DAMPING. In a low-friction system represented by a galvanometer, the damping is of major importance. When current is applied, the moving system tends to overshoot; the excessive torsion then forces the movement back toward the starting point, and so forth, in the well-known pattern of undamped oscillation. In moving coil galvanometers, damping is automatically provided by induced electricity counteracting the applied signal. This electromagnetic damping (and no additional damping is usually provided, other than natural air friction) comes about by the motion of the coil in the field of the permanent magnet.

As the wires of the coil cross the magnetic lines of force, current is generated. This current, if allowed to flow unimpeded, would tend to turn the movement back. However, if high resistance is inserted into the circuit the effect is reduced. Inherently, electromagnetic damping is smooth and automatic; the larger the signal, the more rapid is the movement and the larger is the damping force. This damping is perfect, *provided* the external electrical resistance matches the damping requirements, i.e., the sum of the resistance of the coil and that of the external circuit equals a critical value. However, if the external resistance is too high, the galvanometer is underdamped. It will overshoot and oscillate. With too low an external resistance, the galvanometer is overdamped, and will "creep" to the final indication. The damping characteristics depend on fixed construction details, as does the sensitivity, viz., the strength of the permanent magnet, the stiffness of the suspension, and the internal electrical resistance. So in choosing a galvanometer, the sensitivity and critical external damping resistance require equal consideration, and are always listed by the manufacturer.

THE CHOICE OF GALVANOMETER.   The first step in choosing a galvanometer is the consideration of resistance tolerance of the device to which it is to be connected. A typical example already mentioned is that of photocells which should work against a resistance not exceeding, say, 1000 ohms. Phototube circuits require high resistance, as do electrodes, etc. The next consideration is that of the critical external damping resistance of the galvanometer which is intimately tied up with the former. Generally, the output resistance of the device to which the galvanometer is connected should be slightly above the critical external damping resistance (i.e., the galvanometer should be slightly underdamped), but the leeway is small.

If the match is not perfect, and the output resistance of the device is too small, a resistor is inserted in series with the galvanometer without loss of current sensitivity. However, the total resistance of the galvanometer and series resistor should not exceed the output tolerance (1000 ohms in the example cited). If the output resistance is higher than the critical external damping resistance, a shunt resistance across the input of the galvanometer can be used. However, in this case the sensitivity is reduced since part of the current flows through the shunt, and only part through the galvanometer.

If the output resistance of the device to which the galvanometer is connected is less than the critical damping resistance, this can be simply corrected by using a series resistor, as shown in Fig. 15-4 A (symbolized by R_r). In Fig. 15-4 the device is represented by an output potential E and resistance R. The nominal sensitivity of the galvanometer in millimeters per microvolt (S) is the basis of calculating deflections. In Fig. 15-4 A the value of the series resistor and of the deflection is simply:

$$\text{Defl.} = ES \tag{1}$$

$$R_r = R_{\text{critical}} - R \tag{2}$$

If a shunt is needed because R is larger than R (critical), a shunt (R_s) should be provided for proper damping (Fig. 15-4 B). In this case the calculations are:

$$\text{Defl.} = \left[\frac{ES}{\left(1+\dfrac{R}{R_s}\right)} \right] \tag{3}$$

$$R_s = \frac{R \times R_{\text{critical}}}{R - R_{\text{critical}}} \tag{4}$$

A series resistor may be added (Fig. 15-4 C). The sensitivity is the same, of course, and the value of the series resistor should be:

$$R_r = R_{\text{critical}} - \frac{R_s \times R}{R_s + R} \tag{5}$$

Altogether it is advisable to select a galvanometer of an internal resistance and external critical damping resistance as closely matched to the circuit requirements as possible. The remaining factor is then the sensitivity. In this connection, attention is called to the variation in units in which sensitivity is listed by manufacturers. Sensitivity is often expressed as $\frac{\text{mm/m}}{\mu\text{a}}$ or $\frac{\text{mm/m}}{\mu\text{v}}$, i.e., the deflection in millimeters on a scale at one meter distance produced by 1 μa current or 1 μv potential. This is the proper expression for intercomparison, but what actually counts is millimeter deflection at the actual scale distance (which may be more or less) of the instrument. Even less revealing is the expression deflection per scale division (which is usually of the order of 1 mm but may be more or less). After a decision is made on the desired least detectable quantity (e.g., 0.01 μa) to represent a noticeable deflection, the required sensitivity of the galvanometer is readily chosen. The result of these estimates will disclose that a less sensitive single-reflection instrument will suffice (in the price range of $100.00), or that a multiple-reflection galvanometer is required (range $200.00 to $400.00).

The period of response time is the final parameter to be considered. It ranges between 1 and 10 seconds, and is usually listed by the manufacturer, and therefore, for a given application, the choice of the proper galvanometer is easily made. If the galvanometer is to serve several functions, the most exacting requirement should be guiding. It is always possible to make adjustments for the uses requiring lesser sensitivity by shunt and series resistors, as shown in Fig. 15-4.

PRECAUTIONS IN USE. Galvanometers are remarkably rugged and trouble-free. Delicate as the construction may seem, it has a built-in safety device — the simple short-circuiting of the input. The larger the critical damping resistance (and it usually rises with sensitivity) the more the instrument is overdamped by short-circuiting. In moving the galvanometer (or when it is not in use), a piece of bare wire should be put across the input terminals, and the coil is then virtually immobilized by its own electromagnetic damping.

It really takes substantial overloads to destroy a galvanometer. However, tremendous overvoltage can be supplied quite handily, by connecting the 6-v lamp supply to the input terminals (this is possible in some models). Short of this mistake, there is very little that can go wrong.

The factors which affect the ultimate precision and accuracy are largely academic. Inhomogeneity of the magnetic field, magnetic contaminants, thermoelectric effects, etc., are rarely limiting in laboratory practice. As far as long-term accuracy is concerned, which is of interest when the galvanometer is used as a direct reading instrument, the loss of strength of the permanent magnet is not entirely negligible. It becomes acute when the magnet is disassembled even momentarily. In this case, recalibration is a necessary precaution.

As to other cautions, they are quite simple: the galvanometer should be level, it should be protected against large temperature fluctuations, and external vibration for the sake of precision and convenience of read-out. Altogether, a galvanometer is trouble-free and requires no maintenance whatever. It would seem that this is the main reason for the continued popularity of this venerable instrument.

MICROAMMETERS

CONSTRUCTION AND USE. [4] The essential difference between galvanometers and microammeters is the greater ruggedness, simpler construction, lower sensitivity, and lower cost of the latter. When using electronic amplification, the high sensitivity and low impedance of the galvanometer are not required (typically 10^{-6} amp full-scale and 100 ohms) and a microammeter of, say, 10^{-4} amp full-scale sensitivity and 1000 ohms is more than adequate. This permits compact, inexpensive, and relatively simple construction.

The basic principle is the same, involving two magnetic fields, one permanent and the other induced by the current flowing through the instrument. In meters, fixed coils and rotating magnets are quite usual. However, moving magnet or soft-iron types are not particularly accurate, though cheap and rugged. They are extensively used, particularly in ac indication, but in electrical rather than scientific instruments. In the present context, the moving coil meters only are considered.

The moving coil microammeter (or millivoltmeter) in its traditional form contains a coil rotating on steel pivots in jewel bearings. The restoring force is provided by coiled springs, and a pointer, connected with the moving systems, sweeps over a circular scale (Fig. 15-5 A). A recent improvement eliminates the only substantial defect of this microammeter design, viz., the wear of the jewels and consequent friction. This came with the introduction of a taut-band suspension shown in Fig. 15-5 B. Here the restoring force is the elasticity of the alloy band. This construction resembles that of the galvanometer, except for the short, stiff, suspension. The basic sensitivity is also several orders of magnitude less than that of the typical galvanometer. The meters are faster acting, they tolerate large overloads, and the damping considerations are not as critical.

Special meter configurations which permit a sweep of the pointer of 270° are also offered. They usually utilize dish-shaped magnets, rather than the usual horseshoe shape. These minutiae are of small importance. In general, when sufficient power is available, and the requirements are not unusual with respect to precision, etc., a simple, moving coil meter will always be preferred over more complex readout devices. A well-constructed meter is almost indestructible, and the taut-band type will show no wear. Jewel types will wear out and they are not quite as immune to mechanical shock, but damaged meters can be simply replaced in view of their modest price.

LIMITATIONS. In contradistinction to a projected hairline or scale, a pointer indication is subject to parallax. In other words, different readings are obtained at different viewing angles. Inexpensive meters are subject to this error. However, a mirror placed behind the sweep of the pointer will permit exact viewing alignment (when the pointer and its reflected image overlap). For this reason, better-class instruments are equipped with an antiparallax mirror. The thickness of the pointer should not exceed 1/10 the distance between scale divisions, and then the average observer can estimate the reading to within 1/10 scale division.

However, such a precision is largely illusory. First of all, few commercial instruments claim such precision, and the actual accuracy of the graduations usually falls short even of the claims [5]. Realistically, a precision of a few tenths should be accepted for highest class instruments, and closer to 1 per cent for good quality meters.

At this point, some general observations on precision may be in order. Precision is always expressed as *per cent of full scale*. The actual error of a single measurement may rise to an alarming percentage if the reading falls to a low value. This is true in most devices, as the error tends to be constant over the full range. In meters, the situation is often aggravated because the ends of the scale tend to be less accurate than the center. The most sweeping solution is the use of a balanced or bridge circuit already touched on in the introduction. In this manner, an inaccurate (but sensitive) meter can serve, and precision as high as 0.02 per cent can be obtained provided the slide wires (or other balancing means) are sufficiently linear and accurate. Against this approach speaks the need of a more complex design and the fact that balancing does slow down the taking of data and it is cumbersome. A fair compromise can be had in a partial solution. If shunt resistors are provided in the read-out device, the meter readings can be brought into the favorable middle-to-upper range where the relative error is minimized.

To return to more typical meter limitations, the sensitivity and internal resistance need consideration. When used as voltage measuring devices, meters are provided with a resistance of 1,000 to 20,000 ohms/volt. However, as the voltage decreases, the resistance drops drastically since the current to drive the movement needs to be maintained. In the more usual operation when used as microammeters, the lower limit is of the order of 5 μa full scale.

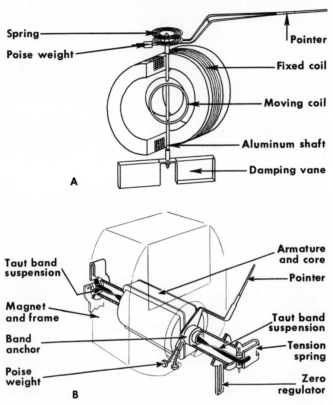

Fig. 15-5. Microammeters. *(A)* With jewel bearings (Courtesy, Weston Instruments Div., Daystrom Inc.). *(B)* With taut-band suspension (Courtesy, The Hickok Electrical Instrument Co.).

In such high sensitivity meters, the external critical damping resistance is just as important as it is with galvanometers. Resistance matching, according to Fig. 15-4, applies here, too. However, as the sensitivity decreases, the matter becomes less critical. Besides, at medium sensitivity, available meters of many designs cover a wide range of external damping resistances. Finally, in the milliampere ranges, the external resistance becomes rather unimportant as the meters will come to proper rest virtually at open circuit.

NONLINEAR PRESENTATION. In colorimetry and spectrophotometry, as well as in other applications, it is of substantial advantage to have a logarithmic display proportional to absorbance
rather than to per cent T (cf. spectrophotometry chapters). One
solution is based on the quasi-logarithmic characteristics of photomultiplier tubes when the photometer itself has a logarithmic response
as in the Sweet circuit [6]. In these tubes, if means are provided to
maintain the current constant, the voltage at the anode will change
roughly logarithmically with illumination. Final correction to the
logarithmic can then be done with diodes and the approximation can
be good over a wide dynamic range. It is well suited for photographic
and dark room applications where the requirements for absolute
precision are moderate but the required range extends over several
orders of magnitude. A commercial instrument utilizing this principle,
with a logarithmic response and linear display, is shown in Fig. 15-6.

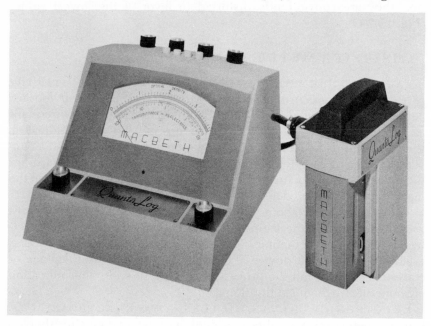

Fig. 15-6. Photometer with linear optical density scale (Courtesy, Macbeth Instrument
Corporation).

The requirements in other photometric applications are different,
with a single decade of logarithm being of prime interest. Moreover,
inexpensive photocell and phototube instruments employ simple
linear amplifiers or none at all. In these cases, a linear microammeter
is used, with a log scale just marked off (Fig. 15-7 A). This system
has obvious disadvantages in that the graduations at high concentrations (high optical density or absorbance) are extremely crowded.

This crowding can be counteracted by using a shaded-pole meter whose response is roughly logarithmic. In these meters the pole pieces of the permanent magnet are shaped in such a way as to give an inhomogeneous magnetic field so that the sensitivity of the meter has different values at different angles of rotation. The scale is empirical, but it can be quite accurate, as long as the pointer is not bent. Figure 15-7 *B* shows such a scale with almost even divisions in the most interesting middle range (incidentally, by range switching, successive logarithmic decades can be displayed if the sensitivity ratios are 1:10).

An interesting extension of this system is found in the Photovolt radiation densitometer. In this case, the very low absorbances are of special interest. The upper decades of density are displayed roughly logarithmized by a shaded-pole meter, as before. However, the lowest densities are fed into the meter with reversed polarity. In this manner, they are conveniently distorted in favor of the lowest values (Fig. 15-7 *C*).

AMPLIFIER-METER COMBINATION

VACUUM TUBE VOLTMETERS (VTVM). When the sensitivity of a simple meter is insufficient, and particularly if the circuit does not permit current drain in measuring potentials, or when higher frequencies (rather than dc) are involved, the use of a VTVM is indicated. It consists, in its usual form, of a single dc amplifier stage and a conventional microammeter in the plate circuit. Such a simple amplifier is neither particularly linear nor drift-free. This, superimposed on the inaccuracy of meters, does not make for high precision.

The inexpensive (about $100.00) and ubiquitous VTVM is most useful in checking electronic circuitry and similar tasks. However, besides serving in temporary or exploratory work, it is rarely used as a laboratory read-out device. The exception is when the voltage or current reading is not the prime datum, e.g., in end-point indication of some electrochemical titrations.

ELECTRONIC GALVANOMETERS AND ELECTROMETERS. Galvanometers are not vibration-proof, and even when sturdily constructed, they do not offer the ease of operation of the less sensitive meters. These advantages are combined with high sensitivity in "electronic galvanometers." By chopping, the dc signal is conveniently converted into ac, and then the superior qualities and ease of ac amplification become available. The limits of amplification are extremely wide so that null indicating and direct indicating electronic galvanometers can be constructed with sensitivity equaling or exceeding the best moving coil galvanometers. The input resistance is usually only moderately low (1000 ohms or more), but this can be made up by extra sensitivity permitting the use of shunts. At the other extreme, electrometers are commercially available which may have input impedance exceeding 10^{14} ohms. Such instruments can be connected directly to ionization chambers, glass electrodes, etc., and they are unique in this respect.

Fig. 15-7. Nonlinear meter presentation. (A) Linear meter with added logarithmic scale. (B) Shaded pole meter with approximate linearization of optical density (absorbance). (C) Special scale spreading of the logarithm by reversed use of this meter (Courtesy, Photovolt Corporation).

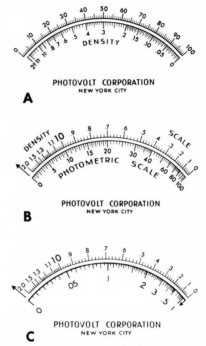

Detailed description of these amplifiers exceeds the scope of this chapter. However, electronic galvanometers are substitutes for the older, conventional types and offer substantial advantages. They are extremely fast acting (1 second or better), and their simple meter presentation is easily read. They are immune to vibration, need no leveling, and usually tolerate extremely large overloads. Best of all, the meter damping is optimum, is set by the integral amplifier, and is independent of the impedance of the external signal source.

Their initial price is, however, rather high, and they are subject to maintenance, as are all electronic devices. For these reasons, they have been slow to replace conventional galvanometers in general laboratory use.

OSCILLOSCOPES

The main field of application of oscilloscopes is in the observation of transient phenomena and signals of high frequency. Inertia, which limits the response time of meters, is all but eliminated. This is accomplished by using an electron beam as a pointer which is deflected by an electrostatic (or electromagnetic) field.

The beam of electrons is furnished by an electron gun in which the electrons are boiled off a filament and focused on a fluorescent screen. The "stiffness" of the electronic beam pointer is provided by high voltage which accelerates the electrons moving toward the screen. To provide a bright image and fast action, the voltage is high (typically 700 v); for this reason considerable voltage is also required to deflect the beam. Amplification of the signal is necessary. The beam is deflected in two dimensions, with separate circuits provided for horizontal and vertical deflection of the beam. The beam is observed on the screen, which is provided with a two-dimensional grid.

The horizontal deflection is, conventionally, the time base and the dependent variable is plotted vertically. The electron beam is moved across and snapped back, similar to television, by a saw tooth voltage (a voltage uniformly increasing with time in each cycle deflects the beam to the right, and suddenly drops back to the starting point — snapping the spot back to the left). To observe and measure 60-cycle phenomena, the timing is simply synchronized to the electrical line. Oscilloscopes are also provided with more or less elaborate internal oscillators, so that setting a scanning frequency means simply turning a dial. In addition, it is possible to trigger a scanning cycle by the input signal. This is the mode of operation which permits the "freezing" on the screen of extremely fleeting transients (Fig. 15-8).

It is in these very rapid and high-frequency applications that the oscilloscope comes into its own. It has phenomenal "writing speeds" of 10,000 miles per second and over, or a frequency response which reaches into the megacycle (10^6 cycles per second) range [7]. The fact that the oscilloscope is not particularly precise as a read-out device and that it is costly ($500.00 to $2000.00) has little weight. There is just no substitute for oscilloscopes when extremely rapid response is required. They can also serve to display two variables (other than the usual time base). For this reason, oscilloscopic read-out is used in some polarographs (current vs. applied voltage), the Aminco scanning spectro-fluorimeter (emission vs. wavelength), and other similar applications (cf. Fig. 15-28).

Recorders

GENERAL

An observer watching the face of a meter and equipped with paper, pencil, and a watch, is a recorder in the literal sense of the word.

There is much to recommend this mode of recording—adaptability, flexibility, and (sometimes) judgment. However, the speed of response is limited at about one second and only one observation can be made at one time. Fast-acting and multichannel automatic recorders outperform the human by a fantastic margin and they have taken over whole areas of instrumentation. Moreover, an experimenter jotting down data gives a digital presentation. The points are discontinuous, taken at the judgment of the individual, and there is always the danger of missing an important transient event. So, even low-frequency, single-channel recording is a field for automatic recorders.

Fig. 15-8. Oscilloscope read-out. x-axis, 200 to 800 mμ; y-axis, relative fluorescence intensity (Courtesy, American Instrument Co., Inc.).

The fact is that some techniques are only possible because of the availability of recorders. For instance, polarography was based on automatic recording from its very beginning [8]. Even traditionally manual techniques, such as polarimetry, become most cumbersome in kinetic studies, and recording becomes a virtual necessity [9]. When dynamics are involved, the laboratory strip chart recorder has a secure place. However, even in simpler measurements, recorders are often used as a matter of economics. A recorder costs no more than a few weeks' salary of a trained laboratory worker. It can operate on a 24-hour basis, it is free from fatigue and bias, and it is simple and inexpensive to maintain. Little adverse criticism can be offered, and when difficulties are encountered in the use of recorders, they are mostly due to a lack of understanding of their individual design characteristics and to consequent misuse. To this, the following section is mainly directed.

CLASSIFICATION

Recorders are so diverse [1, 10, 11] that their classification is mandatory, arbitrary as this may be. A sensible separation is that of industrial from laboratory recorders. The former are more numerous and can be found in plants and factories where they serve as indicators and controllers, as well as recorders. Those which are potentiometric servo-recorders are essentially identical to their laboratory counterparts (except for hardware, casing, etc.); but a discussion of industrial recorders is not pertinent and is omitted.

Another distinction often made refers to the mode of chart presentation. Circular, rather than strip charts, are frequently used in industrial recorders. Laboratory recorders sometimes employ single sheets rather than a continuous strip of paper. The method of writing (whether ink; pressure, heat, or light-sensitive paper is used) distinguishes the instruments. However, it seems more logical to classify recorders by basic operating principles, and this also roughly delineates their field of application. Such is the scheme followed here.

The first and most important group is that of electronic recorders, potentiometric servo-recorders in particular. Nonlinear servo-recorders and servos built into spectrophotometers are discussed as separate classes because of their special features. Also important are galvanometer recorders, which may be equipped with preamplifiers, and they are described next. In addition, there are a great number of special recorder types which have unusual characteristics. They are briefly reviewed last.

POTENTIOMETRIC SERVO-RECORDERS

PRINCIPLE OF OPERATION.   The outstanding merit of servo-recorders is that they are inherently precise. They employ the principle of the potentiometer, i.e., the comparison of the signal with a known (reference) voltage. This is analogous to a potentiometer bridge in which the voltages are adjusted manually until the null-galvanometer indicates no flow of current, i.e., balance. In the recorder, this adjustment is made automatically by a servo-motor which moves the slide wire contact to the balance point.

In its most popular form, the variable element is a wire-wound resistive slide wire, with a stable reference voltage across its terminals (Fig. 15-9). The sliding contact brings into opposition to the signal voltage a portion of the reference voltage. The voltage difference (the "error signal") is amplified and then drives the servo-motor which moves the slider to balance. A pen linked to the mechanism draws on the chart a time-curve of the balancing movement which is a faithful reproduction of the signal changes.

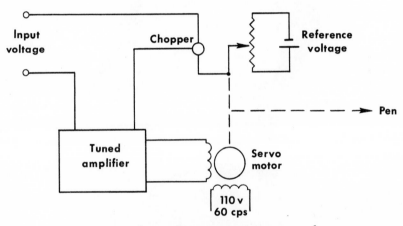

Fig. 15-9. Scheme of potentiometric servo-recorders.

An important feature of this system is that it is a *null-system*. In other words, the linearity does not depend on the amplifier or mechanical elements but solely on the slide wire. The latter can be wound to a precision of a fractional per cent without undue difficulty or cost. Another important advantage is that a potentiometric recorder draws essentially *no current* at balance; it is basically a high impedance device. The response time, on the other hand, is limited to the order of 1 second and recorders of this class are definitely dc devices, or very low frequency ac (less than 1 cycle).

CONSTRUCTION DETAILS.   The most important detail of servo-systems of this type is the conversion of the error signal to ac. Using powerful alternating current circuitry, the reliable detection of a very small unbalance is possible and very sensitive recorders can be constructed commercially. Figure 15-10 A shows a 10-in. recorder of 1/2

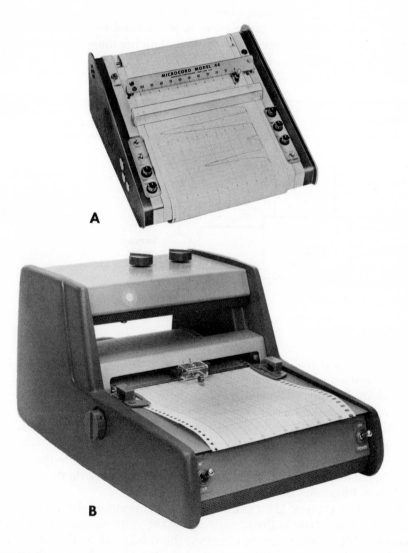

Fig. 15-10. Laboratory strip chart recorders. *(A)* High-sensitivity 10-in. recorder (Courtesy, Photovolt Corporation). *(B)* 5-in. recorder (Courtesy, Varian Associates).

mv full-scale sensitivity, viz., 50 μv per inch. Several methods are used for the conversion of dc to ac, all amounting to chopping. Generally, a mechanical device is used which is an oscillating relay, or a photoelectric chopper. In the latter, a small gas discharge tube is made to flash at a fixed frequency and the light is directed on a photoresistor. In any of the methods, the signal is interrupted and converted to an alternating wave form suitable for ac amplification.

Another important factor is the reference voltage. Obviously, it needs to be stable since any change in its value will simulate a signal change. It used to be necessary to employ a standard cell and use it for periodic standardization of a battery which provided the working reference voltage. Since the advent of mercury batteries this has become unnecessary, and they are used directly to provide the reference voltage, as they are stable and long-lived. Alternatively, the voltage is provided by a network based on Zener diodes. This has the substantial advantage of permanence, and Zener supplies are incorporated into the majority of servo-recorders.

The mechanical construction of laboratory recorders is essentially similar. The chart is perforated and is moved by a sprocket mechanism driven by a synchronous motor. The pen rides on a rod and is pulled by a loop of string or cable which runs over pulleys and is wound around a pulley on the servo-motor shaft. Potentiometric servo-recorders have generally either 5 in. or 10 in. chart width. Figure 15-10 B shows a typical example of the former and Fig. 15-10 A of the latter. This difference is not as superficial as it may seem, because the doubling of the chart width exactly doubles the nominal sensitivity (a 10 in. recorder of a full-scale sensitivity of 10 mv, has a sensitivity of 5 mv over 5 in. width, etc.). The pen speed, at corresponding values is doubled, too. In addition, the difficulties of damping, chart transport, etc., are substantially greater. The result is that the 10-in. recorders are about twice as expensive at corresponding specifications.

Two-pen recorders are also available. These are essentially two independent recorders with their own servo system, sharing only the chart drive and outer case. They are of definite advantage when two interrelated variables are to be plotted (e.g., a signal and its time integral). However, they offer little economy and their use in general laboratory practice would be wasteful. The situation is somewhat different with respect to x-y recorders. These recorders also contain two servo systems but acting on a single pen. They are designed to plot a dependent vs. an independent variable. They furnish a record in the form of a single sheet (e.g., $8\frac{1}{2} \times 11$ in.), a graph, and in this sense they are uniquely useful (cf. recording spectrophotometers). Their cost is relatively high and their use is rationally limited to the recording of such things as transmittance vs. wavelength,

current vs. voltage, stress vs. strain, etc. A less expensive variant of
these flat-bed recorders are the so-called T-Y recorders, which record
a variable vs. time. However, these differ from regular strip chart
recorders only in that their time axis is limited by the chart size, and
for this very reason they are less convenient.

Many variations in construction details exist. Most of these are
apparent and obvious—the configuration of the chart bed, the chart
paper positioning, chart speed variations, etc. Some are not visible;
the slide wire may be circular (single or multiturn) or linear. A new
variable resistance element based on strain gauges, rather than a slide
wire, can be found in some Honeywell industrial recorders. All of
these differences are quite easily spotted in the manufacturers'
descriptions which are customarily rather detailed.

OPERATING CHARACTERISTICS. The theory of servo-mechanisms is a highly developed specialty requiring considerable mathematical skill. Here, only a few major features are considered as they
relate to recorders, viz., gain, damping, impedance, and noise rejection. (A condensed exposition on servo-mechanisms can be found
in reference [12]).

In servos, as already outlined, the error signal sets the servo-motor
in motion. Due to static friction, a threshold voltage has to be reached
before the motor starts at all (breakaway). By increasing the gain of
the amplifier, the magnitude of the original signal necessary to initiate
the motion can be reduced at will, i.e., the responsiveness of the
recorder is increased. As the voltage at the motor input is increased,
the speed of rotation increases linearly, too, but the inertial forces rise
with the square. This increases the tendency to overshoot, and eventually a point is reached where the balancing mechanism cannot come
to rest at all. At the least applied signal it will break into oscillations.
Then the gain has to be reduced. Commercial laboratory recorders
usually have a manual gain control, which may be labeled *gain* or
damping. For best utilization of the inherent sensitivity, the gain
should be set just short of oscillation. The recorder is then tight and
has a minimum dead-zone.

Damping, proper, is related but distinct. Static friction is higher
than dynamic friction, i.e., more power is needed to start the mechanism than to keep it in motion. Once in motion, appreciable force is
required again to stop the action and overcome the inertia of the
mechanism. The proper damping keeps overshoot within bounds.
There are several ways to account for these changing requirements
which become crucial in fast-acting recorders. Some higher priced
industrial recorders employ tachometers which generate voltages
proportional to the pen speed. They can serve to vary the amplifier
gain. Alternatively, thyratron circuits can supply the extra energy

required for rapid starting and stopping. In most laboratory recorders the damping problem is simply taken care of by the time constant of the instrument which is regulated by a resistance-capacitance network. This can be easily adjusted manually by means of a potentiometer control.

The input impedance (internal electrical resistance) of a potentiometric recorder is essentially infinite, i.e., it draws no current. This is desirable in most practical cases because the output potential of an instrument can be recorded without interfering with it. However, this is only strictly true *at balance*. Obviously, the recorder will be somewhat off-balance in any dynamic situation and then the recorder impedance will drop to measurable values of, say, 30,000 ohms. Usually this is tolerable, particularly as it is transient in fast acting recorders.

However, in less expensive multirange recorders only the basic (most sensitive) range may be potentiometric and the additional ranges are furnished by a voltage divider. In these, current is then drawn at all times whose magnitude depends on the value of the divider. Of course, all recorders draw current when they are used as current (micro- or milliampere) recorders, since they actually measure the voltage drop across a standard resistor. If this resistor is built into the recorder, its value should be known for proper connection with the external device whose current is to be measured, to make sure that it is a negligible addition to its output resistance. Similarly, all potentiometer recorders can be converted into current recorders by putting a fixed resistor across the input. Ohm's law applies, and the value of the resistor is simply calculated from the basic sensitivity of the recorder divided by the desired current sensitivity.

The input in all cases is dc, and the rejection of ac is an important feature. Inexpensive recorders usually have no provisions, while better quality recorders employ filtering networks which ground out ac noise. A few recorders incorporate isolation transformers in the chopper circuit (usually described as floating input) and these are most effective in eliminating ground loop voltages, too. At high sensitivity recording ground loops may falsify the record appreciably. They arise when the recorder and the instrument to which it is connected are on different grounds and so a small voltage is fed into the system. It is sometimes possible to minimize the effect by reversing the line plugs and by making different ground connections. Some recorders have provisions to change grounding conditions by simple switching.

Alternating current interference can manifest itself in various ways. Transients are easy to spot by the erratic pen movement, but they are difficult to eliminate short of redesigning the recorder. Steady ac inputs (and many instruments, e.g., spectrophotometers, put out appreciable ac noise superimposed on the dc signal) are likely to cause sluggish recorder action. Ultimately, the recorder may be swamped by ac and its amplifier blocks. Then the recorder goes dead without any functional defect, but it will act properly as soon as the ac signal is eliminated. The remedy must come from the instrument whose output is recorded.

CHOOSING AND TESTING THE RECORDER.   When choosing a potentiometric recorder, it is understood that it is a high impedance device of high precision which records dc (if high frequency response is required, oscillographs or oscilloscopes must be selected). The first choice then is that of sensitivity. For general utility a multiple-range instrument is preferable, provided all ranges are potentiometric and that the maximum sensitivity is sufficient for the application at hand.

The next choice is then that of chart width. The point of view is readability. If a precision of, say, 1 per cent is adequate, a 5 in. recorder will suffice. However, if 0.5 per cent limit is considered, the corresponding pen displacement will be only a little over $\frac{1}{2}$ mm, and a 10 in. recorder is indicated.

The precision claimed by the manufacturer is usually correct based on the precision of the slide wire. However, this will not take into account the readability or the dead-zone, and the latter can only be tested by actual trial.

A good test is simply to move the pen by hand and see how tight the servo action is. The dead-zone can be determined precisely by approaching a fixed value alternately from a higher and lower value. The resulting gap between the pen positions is the true limit of sensitivity and precision. Incidentally, a system of superimposed pen vibration essentially overcomes dead-zone. This is provided by an auxiliary circuit which is optional in some recorders and standard in others (e.g., Photovolt recorders). When testing such recorders, the vibrator should be set to its normal operating amplitude.

The speed of response is usually given by the manufacturer in terms of five time constants (approximately 98 per cent of final value). But here, again, value may be optimum rather than actual. It will be found in some multirange instruments that the gain is insufficient in the highest sensitivity setting; if the ac rejection is also inadequate, very sluggish action results. It is desirable to connect a signal to the recorder and alternately shut it off and observe the pen action. It is noted that the output impedance of the signal source should be in the range which is compatible with the time constant of the recorder. Either the recorder should be adjusted (if it has provisions for it) or the instrument to which it is connected so that the total resistance gives the proper R-C value.

Alternating current signal rejection cannot be tested easily, and the printed claims may be accepted. Usually, if no such claims are made, no provisions are incorporated into the recorder. Noise rejection can be tested by plugging a spark generator into the line, next to the recorder. An electric drill can serve, but this represents a rather drastic test.

Besides these important characteristics, recorders differ in convenience features. Experience has shown that there are no surprising bargains in this competitive field. Quite generally, the higher price indicates added features which result in better performance. With the guide lines given, a rational choice should be possible.

The bugaboo of all recorders is, surprisingly, the pen. There is no single pen on the market that is entirely satisfactory. Some manufacturers offer two or more pen options for the same recorder. At this writing, capillary-type pens seem to be the least objectionable. However, the pen, the recording paper, and the ink should be considered as a package. Results are better if brands are not interchanged, but used as furnished by one manufacturer.

It is fair to state that potentiometric servo-recorders are trouble-free and easy in operation, as compared to other laboratory instruments. They are almost impossible to destroy by overloading (the string moving the pen is likely to break first). When improperly matched to the signal source, they may perform at less than their best, but the indication will still be largely accurate. Besides, defective performance will be clearly visible on the recording.

GALVANOMETER NULL-BALANCE RECORDERS. While the majority of null-balance recorders use the principle outlined previously, a few other successful designs are worthy of mention. Of great historical interest is the Leeds and Northrup Micromax recorder which is primarily an industrial recorder but which has been standard laboratory equipment for many years. In this recorder, the unbalance is sensed by a pointer galvanometer. The pointer, after coming to rest, is clamped down and serves as a stop to the motor-driven slide wire contact. Ruggedness and trouble-free operation are advantages of this system. The drawback is that balancing is periodic (rather than truly continuous) and quite slow.

Several null-balance recorders have been designed which employ a mirror galvanometer for sensing unbalance. The light beam is directed by the mirror to either of two phototubes which set the balancing mechanism into motion until the light beam is centered, i.e., when balance is reached. It is noted that in all these schemes, a galvanometer is involved and the considerations given on page 498 apply. The inherent current sensitivity of the galvanometer is combined here with the precision of the null-system. However, the high impedance and absolute ruggedness of the modern potentiometric system are not realized.

NONLINEAR RECORDING

LOGARITHMIC RECORDING.   Recording in terms of the logarithm of the signal, rather than in linear proportion to the signal, offers advantages. It may be desirable when a large dynamic range is to be covered (tenfold increase in signal is only one unit increase in log). However, it becomes really important when a physical property changes in logarithmic fashion. Then only the logarithmic presentation reflects the data properly. This is the case in some chemical, electrochemical, and biochemical processes — whenever first-order reaction rates are involved. The logarithmic presentation results in a straight line whose slope is the rate constant. Important as these applications are, the overwhelming majority of logarithmic recording is done in spectrophotometry. The importance of data presentation in terms of absorbance (proportional to $\log 1/T$) has already been discussed. An interesting refinement is the recording of the log of absorbance (log-log) which offers great advantage in studying dye mixtures, as well as in studies of reaction kinetics [13].

In recording spectrophotometry, linear potentiometric recorders can be used provided that the output of the photometer is already logarithmized. In automatic recording spectrophotometers this is usually the case, but it is not so in the nonrecording types to which external recorders are to be attached. One solution is to substitute a logarithmic photometer [6]. This accessory is commercially available (Guilford). However, this is an expensive solution of the problem and it is more usual to employ a logarithmic recorder.

There are several distinct principles employed in logarithmizing servo-recorders. A popular scheme is to employ slide wires which are logarithmically wound so that their resistance changes with the logarithm of the linear or angular displacement of the slide contact. An alternative scheme is to tap a linear slide wire with a large number of auxiliary resistors of logarithmically increasing value, so that the resultant slide wire resistance is a close approximation of the log. This latter scheme is more adaptable to a large dynamic range. Figure 15-11 shows a tapped linear slide wire system extending over two absorbance units and the display of an industrial-type logarithmic recorder, using a tapped circular slide wire which extends over three absorbance units.

A less expensive solution of the logarithmizing problem can be had by purely mechanical means. While using a linear slide wire, the motion imparted to the recording pen can be made logarithmic by a pair of gears as shown in Fig. 15-12. The objection that the backlash error is constant, while the value undergoes large changes, is rather academic, and several successful commercial instruments employ this simple system (Bausch & Lomb, Sargent). It may be added that logarithmic recording is never really simple, because the input changes at least one order of magnitude across the span. This necessitates careful gain control of the servo-amplifier which has to vary smoothly and automatically. A drawback of both systems mentioned above is that the logarithmic recorder has a definite span, while the absorbance function runs to infinity. On two or three cycle recorders this is no serious limitation, but with a single cycle (0 to 1 absorbance) this can be an annoying operational feature. It is true that the useful range of quantitation in spectrophotometry does not exceed 1.0. However, absorption peaks can unexpectedly exceed this value and then the pen simply goes off the chart with no indication by how much the limit was exceeded, and no hint of what dilution should be tried next to get into range.

Fig. 15-11. The use of logarithmic slide wires. (A) Tapped linear slide wire of Cary Model 14 recording spectrophotometer (Courtesy, Applied Physics Corporation). (B) Industrial recorder with a range of 3 absorbance units (Courtesy, The Bristol Co.).

This difficulty is eliminated by a different logarithmizing principle used in the Varicord recorders (Photovolt)(Fig. 15-13) [14]. In these instruments, an auxiliary linear slide wire is coupled with the servo-motor and main slide wire. As the recorder goes upscale, the value of the resistance of the auxiliary slide wire changes too, and it is used to attenuate the reference voltage. In an alternative scheme, the auxiliary slide wire is used as a voltage divider, and it attenuates the signal directly, as shown in Fig. 15-14. In either case, the input is weighted in a logarithmic fashion. This is the electrical analogue to a cam or gear arrangment with the significant exception that the signal can be registered down to zero. The signal is logarithmized over 90 per cent

Fig. 15-12. Logarithmizing gears (Courtesy, Bausch & Lomb, Inc.).

of its value and then the rest is made to converge to zero by utilizing a tap on the slide wire to introduce the necessary curvature. The recorder will display 0 to 1 absorbance (or any other decade) in a linear fashion, with the balance to infinity added in a compressed form (Fig. 15-13).

VARIABLE RECORDING. This system of logarithmizing is particularly valuable when the curvature of the transfer function (signal-to-pen excursion) is to be varied. In spectrophotometry and densitometry, the logarithm is only useful as long as Beer's law holds (cf. Chapter 10). When the deviations from this law are severe, (and this is the case in electrophoresis materials), curvatures much steeper than the logarithm are required to obtain quantitative recording in terms of concentration. The "Varicord" principle can then be expanded by combining fixed resistors with the auxiliary slide wire, as shown in Fig. 15-14. The result is an array of transfer functions shown in Fig. 15-15 A. Curve 1 is regular linear recording and curve 5 corresponds to log (absorbance). Curves of higher number represent increasing curvatures beyond the logarithm. The practical importance is demonstrated in Fig. 15-15 *B* which shows the corresponding densitometric tracings of a normal human serum sample. Curve 1 is linear, and the albumin fraction which should be about 60 per cent of the area under the curve, is patently too low. Even the absorbance curve 5 represents only 45 per cent. Curve 9 gives exactly 60 per cent which is therefore the proper function to use; while curve 12 is over-compensated yielding 65 per cent of the area under the curve.

An array of mechanical cams can yield similar compensation, and there are commercial recording densitometers which use such mechanical means for variable transfer functions (Spinco, Joyce). Electrical switching is a newer solution. It appears to be simpler in operation and offers greater flexibility.

LINEAR/LOG   VARICORD   MODEL   43
PHOTOVOLT CORPORATION - NEW YORK CITY
∞ 2.1.5 1.2 1.1 1.0 .9 .8 .7 .6 .5 .4 .3 .2 .1 0

Fig. 15-13. Absorbance display (zero to infinity), with the first cycle linearized (Courtesy, Photovolt Corporation).

RECORDING SPECTROPHOTOMETERS

Spectrophotometers comprehensively illustrate the trends in read-out techniques of laboratory instruments. In their earliest and simplest forms, meters or galvanometers served. Null-balancing instruments were then introduced for better precision, utilizing the same type of read-out (Fig. 15-1 A). Concurrently, spectrophotometers were also developed which had more convenient direct-reading presentation but employed precise and sophisticated electronic amplifiers (Fig. 15-2 B and C). Since one of the major tasks of spectrophotometers is to determine absorbance with respect to wavelength, the point-by-point operation proved too cumbersome. This led to automatic wave-length-scanning instruments briefly reviewed below. Even these instruments offer only partial help in the complex task of evaluating and correlating spectra, and the trend is toward more extensive auto-mation. These developments are treated later.

At present, however, recording spectrophotometers dominate their field. Single-beam instruments have only limited utility. In wave-length-scanning a curve is obtained, but in it the absorbance of the sample and the variable spectral sensitivity of the instrument itself are lumped together. Recording with this type of instrument is, there-fore, practical only at fixed wavelength. This is an important function in enzyme studies and similar work on kinetics, but it is too limited to justify the construction of integrated recording instruments of this type. Instead, single-beam instruments are equipped with recorder outlets carrying a dc potential, proportionate to per cent T. An external laboratory recorder, preferably of the logarithmizing type, then furnishes an absorbance vs. time record.

When the more general task of wavelength-scanning is involved, the record must be in terms of the ratio of the intensities of two beams, one containing a sample, the other the blank (solvent). This cancels out the spectral sensitivity of the instrument, both beams being affected in the same ratio. Decreasing sensitivity may reduce precision, but it has no effect at all on the absolute value of absorbance as recorded. For this reason, then, it is imperative to operate with two beams. Universally, a single light source is used, and the light beam

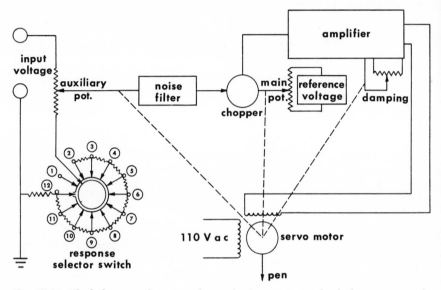

Fig. 15-14. Block diagram of a Varicord recorder (Courtesy, Medical Electronic News).

split into two pathways by a mirror structure. Usually the beams are reunited, permitting the use of the same photoreceptor. This involves time-sharing of the two beams in the photometer since their signals have to be brought into a ratio relation to each other. The signal separation can be accomplished by a rotating shutter which alternately opens and closes the light paths. An interesting variant is the electro-magnetically driven vibrating mirror system employed in the Beckman DB model (Fig. 15-16).

All of these systems furnish chopped (i.e., ac) signals which are inherently suitable for amplification and which can actuate a servo-system. In less expensive instruments, the output is converted to dc, and indicated on a meter. However, in the majority of instruments, the availability of a suitable signal is utilized directly, and a recorder forms part of the spectrophotometer. This recorder is intimately connected with the instrument and, ordinarily, cannot serve any other purpose. This is usually no hardship, as these relatively expensive instruments ($5,000 to $30,000) are only acquired if they can be put to constant use.

The recording section of spectrophotometers is part of the system on many counts. First of all, it does not receive a dc signal proper, but rather an ac signal of the light chopper frequency, and the phasing (viz., electrical labeling of the two photosignals) must come from the chopper. Moreover, it records not a voltage as the ratio of a standard reference voltage, but rather the ratio of two photocurrents, both of which are constantly subject to change. Even more intimate is the connection when the recorder actually serves to balance the spectrophotometer (and moves the recorder pen as a secondary function).

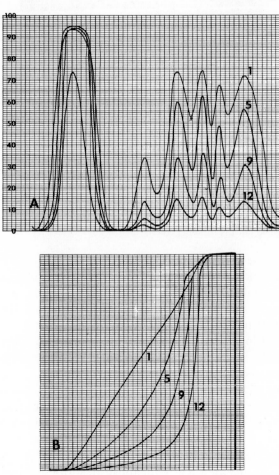

Fig. 15-15. Variable recording. (A) Transfer curves in four responses. (B) Corresponding scans of an electrophoresis strip (Courtesy, Medical Electronic News).

This is the case in the Perkin-Elmer Model 202 which is optically null-balanced by an ingenious, logarithmically cut comb. In this instrument, the servo-motor establishes equal intensity of the two beams and the recorder pen traces the corresponding absorbance value.

Fig. 15-16. Vibrating mirror beam splitter (Courtesy, Beckman Instruments, Inc.).

This brings up the question of logarithmic recording, which is desirable in recording spectrophotometers. It is not quite as essential as in the case of single-beam instruments, because in double-beam instruments the recorder yields per cent T (rather than just energy) and logarithmic chart paper can save the effort of computation. However, the log (absorbance) record is extremely convenient as the pen excursions are then in linear relationship to concentration. Furthermore, the logarithmic response extends the range of best precision of the instrument to high absorbance values, whereas in photometers based on per cent T the maximum precision is in the neighborhood of 40 per cent (0.4 absorbance) [15]. When the logarithmizing is done in the recorder section, which is the usual approach, the methods used are identical with those described above (Figs. 15-11 A, 15-12, and 15-14 are actually taken from recording instruments).

The independent variable, i.e., the wavelength-drive, may introduce linearity problems, too. The wavelength obtained through a prism monochromator is a complicated function of the angle of rotation of the prism, and elaborate cams are required to linearize the system. With grating instruments this problem does not arise, as the wavelength is in linear relation to the angle of rotation. However, filters may have to be placed into the beam at predetermined wavelength positions. Frequently, various orders of the grating are used in different wavelength regions and this, too, requires cam drives in automatic operation. The most complex systems are those with prism-grating combinations, as illustrated by the well-known Cary-White Infrared Spectrophotometer Model 90 in Fig. 15-17. By such means, the wavelength falls in even increments on the x-axis of the chart paper. Usually, several scanning speeds are provided (for quick survey or more precise work) and the chart speed and wavelength drive are rigidly linked. An interesting and eminently practical system is part of the Bausch & Lomb Model 505. In this instrument, the speed of

Fig. 15-17. Wavelength mechanism of a prism-grating spectrophotometer (Courtesy, Applied Physics Corporation).

wavelength scan is governed by slope of the y-axis (absorbance with respect to wavelength). When the pen moves rapidly up-or-down-scale, the drive is slowed down by a tachometer-controlled brake, giving the recorder time to track the information completely. At flat sections of the absorbance curve, the scan proceeds at high speed. This is analogous to the burette drives in titrators with automatic end-point anticipation.

The actual chart presentation is usually in the form of an x-y graph, but some instruments employ regular strip charts which are more convenient for extended scans and also permit time studies at fixed wavelengths. The former may be in the configuration of a flat-bed recorder, but in recording spectrophotometers, a chart-drum shown in Fig. 15-18 is more common. An integral strip chart recorder is illustrated in Fig. 11-4.

Fig. 15-18. Recording spectrophotometer. Drum-type, x-y recorder (Courtesy, Perkin-Elmer Corporation). Strip-chart presentation may be seen in Fig. 11-4 (Courtesy, Beckman Instruments, Inc.).

The complex mechanical and electrical design of recording spectrophotometers is matched by the engineering effort which goes into their construction. They are remarkably trouble-free and require only occasional recalibration. They are always furnished with extensive operating instructions, and further discussion here is superfluous.

GALVANOMETER RECORDERS

Although servo-recorders are typical of general laboratory practice, as outlined, direct indicating recorders using galvanometer movements have a place in the laboratory, too. Actually, there are two separate and distinct types in which galvanometers are used to advantage: very fast-acting and very slow [10]. The former are used when high frequency signals are to be charted, the latter when recording is to extend to hours or days and rapid changes are not anticipated, e.g., temperature or humidity monitoring.

OSCILLOGRAPHS. As discussed previously, galvanometers are capable of registering minute signals and they can be made to respond very rapidly. These are conflicting requirements, and fast-acting galvanometers have only moderate sensitivity. This is the type used in oscillographs, which are fast recording instruments, as the name indicates. To get around the sensitivity limitation, preamplifiers are virtually always part of the system. This also improves flexibility with respect to input impedance and permits the use of additional damping. The price of the equipment rises commensurately, and it can reach $5,000 to $10,000 for an extensive multichannel complex, limiting the use to applications in which the high frequency response is essential.

At higher pen speeds, the method of writing becomes a problem. Very light pen structures with free ink flow are adequate up to a point. Pressure sensitive papers or carbon-transfer systems (analogous to typewriter carbon paper) can be used to around 100 cycles per second, and they reduce maintenance problems. So does the use of heat—or electro-sensitive chart papers. At yet higher frequencies, the use of mirror galvanometers is mandatory, and light-sensitive chart paper furnishes a permanent record. The sweep of a galvanometer is an arc, which is somewhat inconvenient as the record has a curvilinear grid. The linearizing can be accomplished with direct-writing recorders by means of linkages, tangential writing, etc., and in mirror galvanometers by proper optical layout. In multichannel instruments with narrow individual chart widths this is of lesser importance, but the trend is towards rectilinear presentation.

The range of oscillographic equipment is extremely wide [1] and a detailed survey is not possible here. An example is the electro-cardiograph. It has a typical sensitivity of 1 mv full-scale over a 2 in. chart. This sensitivity is obtained through a built-in preamplifier, and the frequency response extends from 0.1 to about 100 cps. This is a rather specialized single-channel instrument. A general-purpose multichannel instrument is shown in Fig. 15-19 A. It is a direct rectilinear writing instrument of 0 to 110 cycle response, carrying up to 8 channels. The sensitivity varies with the exchangeable preamplifier complement but can be as high as 100 μv full-chart width with an input impedance of 1 megohm. Figure 15-19 B shows an optical oscillograph capable of 2000 cps response over an 8 in. chart and up to 8 channels can be incorporated into the unit. A somewhat different concept is that of a laboratory recorder based on a direct-writing galvanometer with wide (5 or 10 in.) chart. The sensitivity and speed of response are in the medium range (typically 10 mv up to 250 cycles). The input impedance is typically that of a galvanometer but the recorder uses convenient rectilinear presentation (Fig. 15-20 A).

MONITORING GALVANOMETER RECORDERS. Instruments of this class employ the same galvanometer principle but differ in construction details. Since the aims are long-term stability, unattended operation, and general ruggedness, these features of the galvanometer are used advantageously, rather than the potential high-frequency response. Because of the sturdy construction, this

A   B

Fig. 15-19. Oscillographic recorders. *(A)* Direct-writing, 8-channel recorder (Courtesy, American Optical Co.). *(B)* Optical high-frequency instrument (Courtesy, Sanborn Co.).

type of recorder is particularly well suited for industrial applications. The widespread industrial use brought about a high degree of perfection and relatively low price, and they spilled over to laboratory practice. Figure 15-20 *B* shows a portable galvanometer recorder with

Fig. 15-20. Laboratory galvanometer recorders. *(A)* With 10-in. rectilinear chart (Courtesy, Texas Instruments, Inc.). *(B)* Portable, with curvilinear chart (Courtesy, The Esterline-Angus Co.). *(C)* Striker-bar type with preamplifier (Courtesy, Yellow Springs Instrument Co., Inc.).

curvilinear presentation which is suitable for long-term monitoring of line voltage.

Recently, very compact and inexpensive recorders have become available which employ a pointer galvanometer movement. The pointer rides over a pressure-sensitive chart, and is periodically

pressed down by a striker bar. In this manner, the galvanometer movement is freed of pen friction. At the usual slow speeds, the individual
points on the chart coalesce into a curve. The presentation is rectilinear but the chart width is only about 2 in. This is appropriate
for the task of long-term monitoring with moderate precision. In its
basic form, the recorder is rather insensitive and has a relatively low
input impedance (typically 1 ma, 5000 ohms), but it costs less than
$100. Combined with a preamplifier and range switches, this recorder
can serve as a general-purpose laboratory instrument. The input
impedance can then be of the order of 1 megohm and the sensitivity
from 1μa or 10 mv upward (Fig. 15-20 C). The precision and readability are still modest but this type of instrument represents a good
economical compromise.

SPECIAL-PURPOSE RECORDERS

MECHANICAL RECORDERS.   The oldest, the simplest, and still
useful recorders are entirely mechanical. In these, the signal (usually
a linear displacement) acts on a pen through linkages. The pen rides
on a chart which is usually fixed to a rotating drum. Kymographs,
rheological instruments, humidity recorders, etc., use this system.
The recorders can be fast-acting and rather precise, but they require
appreciable force at the signal source. Moreover, they are mechanically connected to the apparatus and are definitely single-purpose
instruments.

PNEUMATIC AND HYDRAULIC RECORDERS.   The greater
part of industrial controllers and recorders employ pneumatic, rather
than electrical, transmission. This technology is extremely well
developed, but it merits only passing mention in the present context.
Recorders based on this principle are hardly ever found in the laboratory; exceptions are when the transducer itself originates a pneumatic
or hydraulic signal (pressure or temperature sensors).

OSCILLOSCOPE-CAMERA RECORDERS.   The inherent advantages of oscilloscope read-out have been discussed earlier. The
more or less fleeting indication on the face of the cathode ray tube
can be preserved as a permanent record by photography. Cameras
which are attached to the oscilloscope are usually offered by their
manufacturers. These ordinarily employ either 35 mm film or larger
Polaroid films, which offer instant development. Another variety of
camera equipment permits fuller utilization of the extreme speed
of the oscilloscope. These are streak cameras where the film is not
exposed in frames but rather in continuous fashion up to 400 feet per
second. Equipment of this type is far too expensive to serve in general
laboratory practice.

Oscilloscope-camera combinations are employed in special cases only, whenever the oscillograph proves too slow to record fleeting transients or high-frequency phenomena from 5 kc upward.

TAPE RECORDERS. Tape recorders have become a familiar piece of equipment in sound recording. Actually, they were employed for engineering purposes from the very beginning, and they were used in flight testing as early as 1936 [16]. A tape recorder is not a recorder in the same sense as those discussed above, in that it does not present a record. It is rather an instrument for the collection and storage of data.

The frequency response of tape recorders is in the kilocycle range and they can be used to advantage to store an extremely large amount of digital data. This application dates back about 15 years, and it is rapidly expanding with the general use of digital computers. When a computer is used, the tape recorder really offers an excellent method of data collection. General-purpose portable models have become commercially available (Fig. 15-21).

Digital Read-out

GENERAL

Digital read-out promotes precision, in contrast to pointer indication. The latter assures rapid recognition of the general level of a datum and reduces the chances of gross error, but the presentation of the actual number in a read-out device enhances precision in observation and transcription. These facts have been firmly established in aircraft instrumentation, where the proper recognition of data is literally a vital concern [17]. In laboratory instrumentation, such considerations are not so pressing, and digital read-out was limited, in the past, essentially to those instruments in which the data are collected in digits, as it were. For instance, in radioactivity counting devices the measured quantity consists of electrical pulses. The flip-flop circuits which serve to add these pulses can be conveniently equipped with indicating lights and so yield direct digital read-out. When counting tubes are used for this purpose, the figures can be read off their face directly.

This attitude is undergoing a change and today laboratory equipment is often furnished with digital read-out indication. Small mechanical counters are inexpensive, and they can be attached to rotating shafts, provided that the force is sufficient to actuate them (in./oz. range). Microburettes, both manually and electrically driven, now come equipped with counters. (Fig. 15-22. A). Analytical balances and electric stop watches are other typical examples. In some instances, the measurement of elapsed time is the basis of an analytical procedure, and then this type of read-out is logical and convenient. For example, commercial chloride analyzers using a coulometric method [18] are constructed in this manner (Fig. 15-22 *B*).

Fig. 15-21. Portable tape recorder (Courtesy, Minneapolis-Honeywell Regulator Co.).

Because of the increasing use of digital read-out, this type of indication gives instruments a modern appearance. Actually, any device which contains a servo-mechanism can drive a counter rather than a pen. Alternatively, electrically switched read-out devices can be used and they furnish attractive, large, and readable numbers, e.g., Nixie tubes. This is the usual presentation in digital volt meters and in several laboratory instruments, such as the Bendix photoelectric polarimeter (Fig. 15-22 *C*). A somewhat unusual example of a servo-driven counter is the Polarad pH meter (Fig. 15-22 *D*). In these instances, the read-out mechanism contributes appreciably to the cost of the instrument.

The guiding point of view, however, should be neither cost nor sales appeal but, rather, the utility of this type of data presentation. When the datum is an isolated set of figures, digital read-out is definitely preferable. Consequently, balances, stop watches, burettes, and the like, so equipped, promote quick and precise read-out. In these cases, the mechanism comes to a dead stop, and the final result is picked up in an unambiguous manner. This is not so true in devices which contain servos continuously seeking balance. If there are no special precautions taken, digital read-out in such cases is most distracting, as the electrical noise keeps the last digit in constant flux.

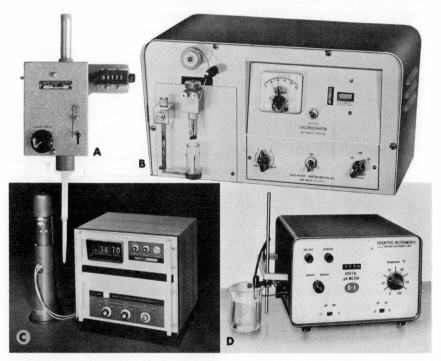

Fig. 15-22. Digital data presentation. *(A)* A burette (Courtesy, American Instrument Co., Inc.). *(B)* Electrometric chloride analyzer (Courtesy, Buchler Instruments, Inc.). *(C)* Photoelectric polarimeter (Courtesy, The Bendix Corporation). *(D)* Digital pH meter (Courtesy, Polarad Electronics Corp.).

The effect of noise can be eliminated by damping or lock-in arrangements, and this brings psychological relief. However, if the measured variable itself is apt to fluctuate or change with time, digital indication is not at all desirable. A moving pointer which can be read at a glance, even though not with the utmost precision, is the method of choice in such cases.

As it turns out, however, the most significant contribution of digital read-out in modern laboratory instrumentation is in the area of rapidly changing variables. However, in these cases digital recording or print-out is used. This, naturally, eliminates the preceding objections. At this writing, the most widespread success of this type of data presentation is in integrators. These important devices are discussed in the following, including types which do not yield digital records in the strict sense.

INTEGRATORS

In many analytical procedures, the area under the recorded curve is the significant datum, rather than the curve itself. Since recorders usually operate on a time basis, the integral is obtained through a point-by-point summation of the pen excursions with time. Similarly, the chart and pen movements can be multiplied point-by-point, if the former is not based on time. Finally, intergration can be based on a nonlinear function of the pen excursion, by using cams or other non-linear linkage to the integrator mechanism.

MECHANICAL INTEGRATORS.   An early noteworthy commercial integrator is of this type. It is an attachment to the G. E. Spectrophotometer which is a widely used instrument for the determination of surface color. Human color vision can be described in terms of three functions of spectral reflectance (or transmittance), and any color is accurately described by three figures, representing the integrals according to these three functions. The spectrophotometer proper is a double-beam, null-balance servo-instrument, conveniently arranged for reflection measurement. The spectrum is scanned synchronously and the pen recorder traces the reflectance curve through the visible spectrum. Three cam linkages act on three synchronously driven mechanical counters. The counters accumulate figures weighted according to the three functions due to the shaping of the cams. The use of counters is fully justified because the figures are only meaningful after the completion of the scan, i.e., they represent stationary, discrete figures.

Other, more common integrators must correlate the area under all curve segments, not just under the entire curve. This is true in gas chromatography and electrophoresis — at present the most important fields for integrators. In these cases, an ever-changing counter indication is neither convenient nor does it promote precision. Therefore, such integrators should, and usually do, print or record the areas under the curve continuously as the curve is recorded. Mechanically linked disc-and-ball integrators can be attached to strip chart recorders to accomplish this. A disc is driven by a synchronous motor (in synchronism with the chart), and a movable ball transmits the rotation by friction to a roller. The radial position of the ball is regulated by the pen excursion, and thus the rotation of the roller is proportional to the area under the recorded curve at all times (Fig. 15-23). A second pen, linked to the roller-shaft, records the integral on the edge of the chart, in alignment with the curve to which it refers. The excursion of this pen is made to repeat (oscillate) as shown in Fig. 15-25 C.

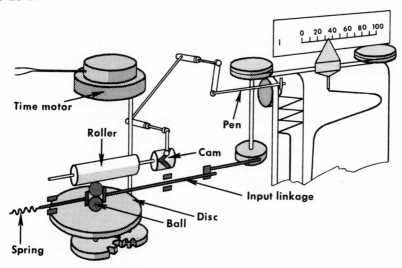

Fig. 15-23. Disc and ball integrator (Courtesy, Disc Instruments, Inc.).

ELECTROMECHANICAL INTEGRATORS. Although mechanical integrators have been brought to a high degree of perfection, mechanical parts are subject to friction and inertia, which limit precision. For this reason, electrical linkage between recorder and integrator has been an alternative approach. There is an additional advantage, perhaps, in the simplified attachment of the integrator which need not be located inside the recorder case. Strip chart recorders can be equipped with an auxiliary slide wire mounted on the same shaft with the balancing slide wire. This transmitting potentiometer, when connected to a stabilized voltage supply, puts out a potential proportional to the recorder pen position. This voltage serves as a signal for the integrator.

The electromechanical integrator can utilize a low inertia motor whose speed of rotation is proportional to the applied voltage. A mechanical counter is used to sum the shaft rotation with respect to time. However, the power output in this simple scheme is limited because the integrating motor, which is the heart of the instrument, cannot sustain loads. To drive a printing device, or the like, a velocity servo loop is introduced. In this system, a servo-motor drives a tachometer generator whose voltage output is compared to the input voltage. The error voltage is fed through an amplifier and serves to drive the servo-motor. A counter, printer, etc., can be attached to the common shaft. There is ample power to drive these read-out accessories, but the complexity and cost of the integrator are substantially increased.

ELECTRONIC INTEGRATORS.   To eliminate drawbacks associated with mechanical and electromechanical devices, purely electronic integrators are often preferred. The gain is freedom from inertia and friction, but the penalties are potential defects associated with electronic circuitry (particularly drift). Electronic design is flexible and prolific, and provides a great variety of purely electronic integrators. The details are of little interest to the user of the device, but, for the sake of completeness, the scheme of a commercial instrument (Photovolt Model 49) is given in the following.

The transmitting potentiometer of the recorder feeds a voltage (proportional to the pen excursion) to the integrator. This voltage regulates an oscillator whose frequency changes with applied voltage. The integrator also contains an oscillator of fixed frequency, against which the variable frequency oscillator beats. The beat frequency thus reflects the product of pen position and time, viz., the integral. This scheme yields a manageably low frequency of considerable (and easily adjustable) dynamic range. The frequency pulses are fed into a trigger circuit which actuates a decade counting tube. As a result, distinct pulses are available for both single counts and tens. In this model, a double-acting solenoid pen is used which lays down "pips" at the edge of the chart, in two digits, as it were (Fig. 15-25 B).

In all electronic integrators, mechanical parts play no role since the final recording is tacked on the system. However, most integrators of all three types draw their input signal from recorders (either by mechanical linkage or through a transmitting slide wire). Should the recorder itself not be fast enough to follow the original signal, then the frictional and inertial characteristics of the recorder mechanism will be reflected in the integral even if the integrator is fast-acting. This is particularly noticed in gas chromatography with capillary columns which is characterized by extremely sharp and rapidly passing fractions. In these cases, direct integration is the solution, with the recorder (if used) serving only as an auxiliary visual monitor.

DIRECT ELECTRONIC INTEGRATORS.   This class of device is characterized by the fact that the signal is drawn directly from the transducer, usually the gas chromatograph detector. The equipment is, naturally, all electronic, for extremely fast action and high resolution. It contains an operational amplifier, viz., an integrating circuit. Because the ultimate print-out is bound to slower mechanical devices, the integrator contains simple memory circuitry so that fast integration proceeds even while the slower print-out takes place. Figure 15-24 *B* shows the block diagram of the Infotronics CRS-1 gas chromatography integrator (Fig. 15-24 *A*); both an auxiliary recording, and the print-out, are shown in Fig. 15-24 *C*.

DATA PRESENTATION. Figure 15-25 shows various other methods of presentation of the integrals under the curve. The most direct digital presentation (Fig. 15-25 *A*) is rare because the use of printing counters introduces difficulties. The reason is that the printing itself requires time, short as it may be. In conventional gas chromatography, the situation is most favorable, because the signal returns essentially to zero between fractions, and then integration ceases. At this point, the integral of the fraction just recorded needs printing and there is time for it. In faster recording, or if the signal is more or less continuous, this technique will not do. Then the use of direct electronic integrators is recommended, but they are costly (ranging to $4000). For these reasons, the continuous recording of the integral is more common. Figure 15-25 *B* is a digital presentation of this type. It contains two digits (units and tens), and the track is laid down on the edge of the recording paper in juxtaposition with the record to which the integral refers. The area under any curve segment is proportional to the number of counts opposite the segment.

Similar to this presentation is the method resulting in a record at the edge of the chart shown in Fig. 15-25 *C*. This mode of presentation is not strictly digital in that the area under the curve segments is proportional to the number of cycles plus the fraction of a cycle, which has to be estimated. This estimation can be done more precisely when the entire chart width is used. Integrating recorders are available (Texas Instruments, Fisher Scientific Co.) which use two independent pens writing simultaneously, one recording the curve and the other the integral.

In an alternative scheme, the recorder pen is used for both purposes on a time-sharing basis. In this case, the integrator output is a voltage of suitable range for the recorder. Whenever the integral is to be recorded, a push button interrupts recording momentarily, and impresses the voltage proportional to the integral of the section just recorded. A bar graph results, and the integral is read off the scale divisions of the chart paper.

CHOICE OF INTEGRATORS. Integrators are usually accessory equipment and so the question of choice is pertinent. The most important criterion is precision or resolution. But since excessive resolution may cause unnecessary expense, this question should be carefully weighed.

For instance, if 2 per cent is set as the minimum precision and the smallest fraction is expected to cause a 2 per cent pen excursion of at least 1 minute's duration, the necessary maximum count rate should be

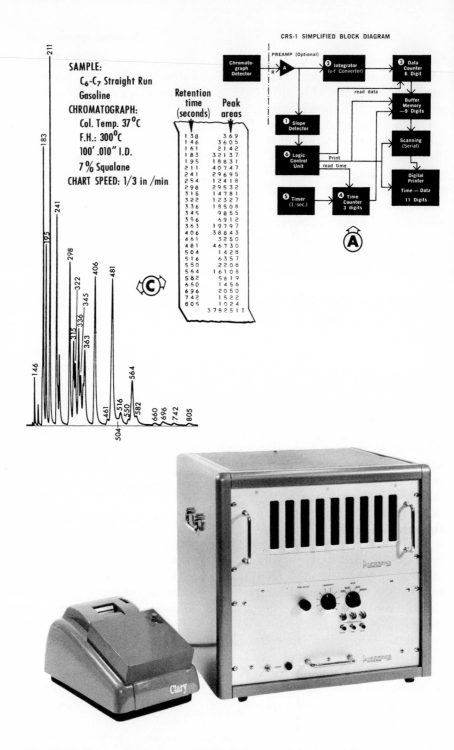

Fig. 15-24. Electronic integrator. *(A)* Block diagram. *(B)* View of the instrument. *(C)* Data presentation and corresponding chromatogram (Courtesy, Infotronics Corp.).

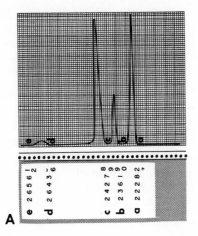

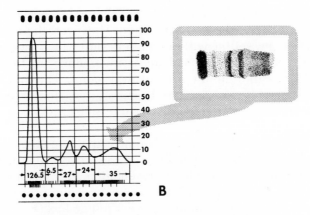

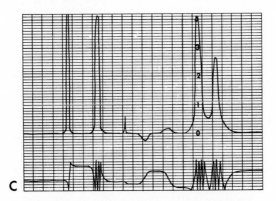

Fig. 15-25. Various presentations of integrals. *(A)* Printed figures (Courtesy, Perkin-Elmer Corporation). *(B)* Unit and decade pips (Courtesy, Photovolt Corporation). *(C)* Digital analog trace (Courtesy, Disc Instruments, Inc.).

(50×50) 2500 counts per minute. In this example the lowest limit will still correspond to at least 1 count. In truly digital presentation, the limit can be predicted without ambiguity. However, in mixed digital-analog presentation (Fig. 15-25 C) caution is necessary. It is customary in the manufacturers' literature to cite one oscillation as equivalent to 100 or even 500 counts. On a 10 in. chart, the figure 500 corresponds to 1/50 in. and a count of 100 on a 1 in. track to only 1/100 in. The user is cautioned not to be carried away by the manufacturer's enthusiasm, but to make his own judgment as to the minimum discrimination he can conveniently make.

Drift is the next consideration in choosing an integrator. It is of lesser importance in work of short duration, but in integration extending over hours, lack of drift will turn out to be more important than maximum count rate. Expensive electronic integrators are stabilized to a remarkable degree, and actual performance data are usually given by the manufacturers. In less expensive instruments, this may not be the case, and their drift characteristics should be checked. Mechanical integrators are inherently drift-free. However, the relaxation of the delicate screw setting will cause a zero shift which is equivalent to an electrical drift. Electromechanical integrators are beset by yet another defect—the minimum breakaway point. This has the effect of an indeterminate zero point and causes errors similar to drift.

The performance of integrators is quite satisfactory in each class. They reduce the labor of determining the area under the curve tremendously, compared to manual planimetering. Even the least expensive and least accurate integrator is more precise than the manual method, and the digital mode of presentation adds much to the convenience. The trend is toward the most convenient print-out models as illustrated by the gas chromatography integrators (Fig. 15-24) and the carbon-hydrogen-nitrogen analyzer (Fig. 15-26).

Computer Techniques

A description of read-out techniques would be incomplete without considering data handling methods used in computer technology. Electronic computers are so superior in their capacity to arrange, correlate, and evaluate data that their utility needs no further discussion. Actually, the integrators are modest single-purpose computers, but computer capabilities extend far beyond this function. General understanding of this technology, particularly of digital computers, has become a necessity for the laboratory worker, as pointed out by Savitzky [19]. The reader is referred to one of the general texts (e.g., references [20] and [21]; for programing, reference [22]; or for the more detailed works, references [23] and [24]).

Three distinct approaches may be taken in using computers. The first, and most expensive, consists of feeding raw data into a large computer. The labor of converting the conventionally gathered data and of setting up a program is then necessary. This involves the minutiae of the technique, and is not described here. The second approach to the collection of data in a suitable form for direct use in computers is more attractive. Equipment for this type of operation is gradually becoming available and it is briefly discussed. Finally, it is possible to connect the experimental apparatus with a computer which furnishes results promptly and directly. This approach opened up exciting new applications, some of which are reviewed in the conclusion of this chapter.

Fig. 15-26. Automatic gas chromatographic C,H,N analyzer, with print-out integrator (Courtesy, Fisher Scientific Co.).

Laboratory data are virtually always obtained in analog form (electrical voltage or current, shaft rotation, etc.). They require conversion into digital form, as their processing with precision implies the use of digital computers. This is an easy task because analog-to-digital converters are an item of commerce [21]. In a spectrophotometer, for instance, both the output (absorbance) and wavelength position can be continuously put into punched paper tape during the scan at a rate of 10 readings a second [19]. The tape is encoded in a form suitable for the type of computer which may be available to the laboratory. This opens up an extremely wide range of possible computative operations — rational smoothing of curves, statistical studies, analysis of underlying structure, correlation with other analytical data, etc. A digitized instrument system is shown in Fig. 15-27 A.

The result of a typical computer analysis of a spectrum is shown in Fig. 15-27 B. The main features of the spectrum are recognized by the computer through the first and second derivatives of the absorption curve. The corresponding wave numbers and transmittance figures are also printed-out. Additional computations, e.g., extinction coefficients, can be carried out just as well. Nor is this approach limited to spectrophotometry, and any laboratory instrument is potentially suitable for this type of data collection and data handling.

The ultimate in automation is when a computer programs the experiment itself, then collects and processes the data. This is by all means possible and practical. A demonstration of this approach in biophysics is the recent compact and elegant work on the human eye tracking movement [25]. In these experiments, the movement of the target, an illuminated spot, was controlled by a small general-purpose digital computer. The eye movements of the experimental subject were picked up by a pair of photoresistors, and this information was fed back into the computer. The on-line computer then performed all the calculations, including a Fourier analysis of the eye movement response to a random continuous input. A mathematical model and a complete theory of this important biological servo-mechanism was the end result.

Such extensive use of computers is not always possible for economic reasons, nor is it necessary for simpler tasks. Small, special-purpose computers can be used to advantage, and they fit the budget of modest programs. An interesting example is the CAT (Computer of Average Transients) which has found use in biological investigations [26]. It is a small, portable, digital computer which is used on-line, with up to four electrical signals fed directly into it. It serves to peel out the significant data which are buried in background noise in repetitive signals. It can do several tasks, including the summing and averaging in cardiograms, electroencephalograms, etc. The actual readout device can be the built-in 3 in. cathode ray tube (Fig. 15-28) or an accessory x-y recorder. The data can also be taken in digital form which is particularly valuable if they are to be processed further. This output is also usable for an automatic typewriter. This method of data presentation is the clearest, and it is gaining in popularity with the widespread use of automatic data handling devices.

At the other extreme are massive and imposing computers. They are used if there is a sufficient economic leverage which justifies the expense, and when high performance is required. It is also an economic

BANDFINDER II c

go from +9900 to +9100
go from +8800 to +7000
go from +0

9900	861	START	1
9760	672	Inflection - left	
9670	563	Shoulder - left	
9600	474	Inflection - left	
9570	439	PEAK	
9520	559	Inflection - right	
9440	654	VALLEY	
9390	616	Inflection - left	
9350	598	PEAK	
9290	660	Inflection - right	
9100	778	FINAL	1
8800	571	START	2
8630	228	Inflection - left	
8520	23	Strong	
8270	32	PEAK	
8160	255	Inflection - right	

B

end
8040   515

Fig. 15-27. Digitized spectrophotometer system. *(A)* View of the instrument. *(B)* Typical printed record of spectrogram (Courtesy, Perkin-Elmer Corporation).

question whether large single-purpose computers are to be preferred or whether general-purpose installations should be employed. When data are accumulated at a slow rate, the very fast general-purpose computers may not be fully utilized. At the extremely high initial cost, such waste may be prohibitive. One solution was already outlined, viz., the accumulation of the data on tape recorders (Fig. 15-21) or punched tape (Fig. 15-27 A). In other instances, special-purpose recorders, or a combination instrument (Fig. 15-29 A) may offer the better compromise.

Fig. 15-28. Portable digital computer (Courtesy, Mnemotron Corporation).

Expensive computer installations are fully justified in many activities. This is the case in the metal industry where prompt and precise analysis of alloys is a prerequisite of successful multimillion dollar operations. This industry has a distinguished tradition in analytical techniques. In many installations (notably Alcoa) the big spectrographs were replaced by even bigger and more expensive direct-reading spectrophotometers a long time ago. In these, the emitted light of the individual spectral lines is collected by photomultiplier tubes and electrically processed in individual channels, bypassing the photographic process. The analytical task is still formidable because, among other things, the individual line strength depends on the over-all composition of the sample.

This is the proper field for computers, and equipment of this type is being introduced. A very complete on-line digital computer is

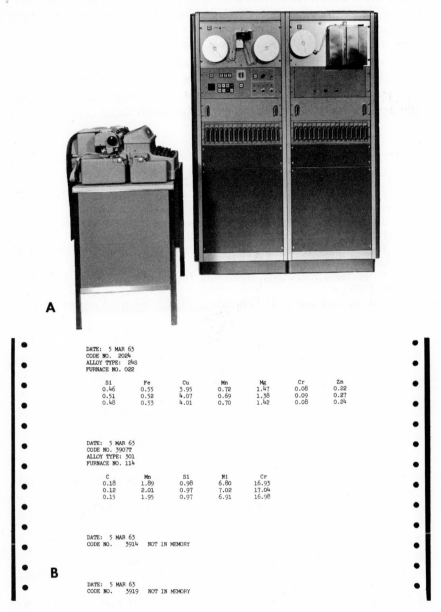

A

B

DATE: 5 MAR 63
CODE NO. 2024
ALLOY TYPE: 24S
FURNACE NO. 022

Si	Fe	Cu	Mn	Mg	Cr	Zn
0.46	0.55	3.95	0.72	1.47	0.08	0.22
0.51	0.52	4.07	0.69	1.38	0.09	0.27
0.48	0.53	4.01	0.70	1.42	0.08	0.24

DATE: 5 MAR 63
CODE NO. 3907T
ALLOY TYPE: 301
FURNACE NO. 114

C	Mn	Si	Ni	Cr
0.18	1.89	0.98	6.80	16.93
0.12	2.01	0.97	7.02	17.04
0.15	1.95	0.97	6.91	16.98

DATE: 5 MAR 63
CODE NO.   3914   NOT IN MEMORY

DATE: 5 MAR 63
CODE NO.   3919   NOT IN MEMORY

Fig. 15-29. Spectrometer-computer. *(A)* Console. *(B)* Results of complete spectrographic analysis, typed by the machine (Courtesy, Applied Research Laboratories, Inc.).

now commercially available which connects directly to optical and X-ray spectrometers. It stores calibration factors and corrections for interelement interference, and a library can be built up in the memory circuits of the computer in short order. The computer will retrieve this information on command and evaluate the samples in the proper calibration mode.

The physical appearance of such a computer console is impressive (Fig. 15-29 *A*), but even more impressive is the resultant type-written report (Fig. 15-29 *B*). At present, this mode of data handling and presentation is the ultimate in routine analysis.

References

1. R. C. Nelson, *Instru. Control Systems*, **35**, No. 7, 75 (1962).
2. E. J. Bair, *Introduction to Chemical Instrumentation*, McGraw-Hill, New York (1962).
   E. W. Golding, *Electrical Measurements and Measuring Instruments*, Sir Isaac Pitman & Sons, London (1961).
   G. R. Partridge, *Principles of Electronic Instruments*, Prentice-Hall, Englewood Cliffs, N. J. (1958).
   H. E. Soisson, *Electronic Measuring Instruments*, McGraw-Hill, New York (1961).
3. E. G. Schlosser and K. H. Winterling, *Galvanometer*, Verlag G. Braun, Karlsruhe (1960) (In German).
   E. Meyer and C. Moerder, *Spiegelgalvanometer and Lichtzeigerinstrumente*, Akademische, Verlagsgesellschaft, Leipzig (1952) (In German).
4. C. Moerder, *Grundlagen der Drehspulinstrumente und Verwandter Systeme*, Verlag G. Braun, Karlsruhe (1960) (In German).
5. F. D. Weaver, *Instr. Automation*, **27**, 1812 (1954).
6. M. H. Sweet, *J. Soc. Motion Picture Eng.*, **54**, 35 (1950).
7. W. Wilson, *The Cathode Ray Oscillograph in Industry*, Chapman & Hall, London (1953).
8. J. Heyrovsky and M. Shikita, *Rec. Trav. Chim.*, **44**, 496 (1925).
9. G. B. Levy, *Anal. Chem.*, **23**, 1089 (1951).
   G. B. Levy and E. S. Cook, *Biochem. J.*, **57**, 50 (1954).
10. A. Palm, *Registrierinstrumente*, Springer Verlag, Berlin, 2nd ed. (1959) (In German).
11. S. R. Gilford, *Elec. Mfg.*, **52**, No. 11, 114, and No. 12, 120 (1953).
12. I. Ritow, *Elec. Mfg.*, **57**, No. 2, 98; No. 3, 82; No. 4, 114; No. 5, 107; No. 6, (1956).
13. T. J. Porro and H. T. Morse, *Instr. News*, **14**, No. 1, 10 (1962).
14. G. B. Levy, *Med. Electron. News*, **3**, No. 2, 12 (1963).
15. T. J. Porro, W. Slavin, and H. T. Morse, *Pittsburgh Conf. Anal. Chem. Appl. Spectry.*, Paper No. 150 (1963).
16. G. L. Davies, *Magnetic Tape Instrumentation*, McGraw-Hill, New York (1961).
17. R. A. McFarland, *Human Factors in Air Transport Design*, McGraw-Hill, New York (1946).
18. E. Cotlove, H. V. Trantham, and R. L. Bowman, *J. Lab. Clin. Med.*, **50**, 358 (1958).

19. A. Savitsky, *Anal. Chem.*, **33**, 25A (1961).
20. P. Siegel, *Understanding Digital Computers,* John Wiley & Sons, New York (1961).
21. M. L. Klein, H. C. Morgan, and M. H. Aronson, *Digital Techniques for Computation and Control,* Instruments Publishing Co., Pittsburgh (1958).
22. D. D. McCracken, *A Guide to Fortran Programming,* John Wiley & Sons, New York (1961).
23. N. R. Scott, *Analog and Digital Computer Technology,* McGraw-Hill, New York (1960).
24. H. D. Huskey and G. A. Korn, *Computer Handbook,* McGraw-Hill, New York (1962).
25. L. Stark, G. Vossius, and L. R. Young, *IRE Trans. Human Factors Electr.,* **3**, 52 (1962).
26. M. Clynes, *Instr. Control Systems,* **35**, No. 8, 87 (1962).

Index

Acceleration, transducers for, 445-446
Accuracy, 9
Acids
buffer systems for, 315-317
column chromatography for, 126-131
electrophoresis for, zone, 110-111
paper chromatography for, 53-54
thin-layer chromatography for, 68
Acoustic transducers, 485-488
Adsorption chromatography, 58, 113, 116
Alcohols, chromatography for, 49,69
Aldehydes, 69
Alkaloids, chromatography for, 49,69
Alumina, 64, 116
Amino acids
in column chromatography, 127-128
in paper chromatography, 13, 18, 30, 44-46, 49-50, 108-109
in thin-layer chromatography, 69-70
Amplification, 347
drift, 320
gas, 474,475
-meter combination, 508-509
Anions, thin-layer chromatography for, 70
Anode, moving, transducers, 439-441
Anthocyanins
column chromatography for, 131-132
paper chromatography for, 53
Antoine equation, 174
Apiezon M, 187
Archibald method, 253-255
Area, variable, capacitance transducers, 438-439
Argon
chromatography of, 184
detectors, 163, 167, 182

Artifacts, chromatographic, 17-18
Ascending chromatography, 24-26
Ascorbic acid chromatography, 55,77
Attenuated total reflection, 387
Autoradiogram, 31
Autoscanner, 47

Balances. *See* Weighing.
Baldes-Johnson osmometer, 411-413
Barger-Halket osmometer, 410-411
Barrier-layer cells, 467-468
Beer's law, 332-334
Benzene spectrum, 372-373
Blanks, 4
Bouguer-Beer law, 332-334
Boundary locator method, 272-273
Bragg curve, 473
Brownian motion, 231-234
Buffer systems, 315-317
Buoyancy in sedimentation equilibrium, 261
Buoyant effect in weighing, 310

Calcium chloride in plasmolysis, 419, 422-424
Calibrations, 4
in gas chromatography, 181-183
Capacitive-displacement transducers, 437-438
Capillary column chromatography, 141-142, 158
Carbohydrates, electrophoresis for, 109-110
Carbon dioxide, chromatography, 184
Carbon disulfide and carbon tetrachloride spectra, 379, 381, 382
Carbon-hydrogen-nitrogen analyzer, 542, 543
Carbonyl
absorption frequencies, 391
gas chromatography, 185

551